Penny Press is the publisher of a fine family of puzzle magazines and books renowned for their editorial excellence.

This delightful collection has been carefully selected by the editors of Penny Press for your special enjoyment and entertainment.

PENNY PRESS, INC.
6 Prowitt Street, Norwalk, Connecticut 06855-1220

Printed in Canada

PENNY PRESS PUZZLE PUBLICATIONS

✦ PUZZLE MAGAZINES ✦

All-Star Variety Puzzles
All-Star Word Seek Puzzles
Approved Crossword Puzzles
Approved Crosswords Special
Approved Variety Puzzles Plus Crosswords
Classic Variety Puzzles Plus Crosswords
Easy & Fun Word Seek Puzzles
England's Finest Logic Problems
Family Variety Puzzles & Crosswords Plus
Family Variety Puzzles & Games
Fast & Easy Crosswords
Favorite Easy Crosswords
Favorite Fill-In Puzzles
Favorite Variety Puzzles & Games
Favorite Word Seek Puzzles
Fill-In Puzzles
Good Time Crossword Puzzles
Good Time Variety Puzzles
Good Time Word Seek Puzzles
Master's Variety Puzzles Plus
Merit Variety Puzzles & Games
Nice & Easy Crosswords
Number Fill-In Puzzles
Original Logic Problems
Penny's Famous Fill-In Puzzles
Quick & Easy Crosswords
Super Word Seek Puzzles
Tournament Variety Puzzles Plus
Variety Puzzles & Games
Variety Puzzles Special Issue Plus
Word Seek Puzzles
World-Class Logic Problems
World's Finest Variety Puzzles

✦ SPECIAL COLLECTIONS ✦

Selected Anagram Magic Square
Selected Brick by Brick
Selected Codewords
Selected Crostics
Selected Crypto-Families
Selected Cryptograms
Selected Diagramless
Selected Double Trouble
Selected Flower Power
Selected Frameworks
Selected Jigsaw Squares
Selected Letterboxes
Selected Masterwords
Selected Missing Vowels
Selected Places, Please
Selected Quotagrams
Selected Quotefalls
Selected Scoremaster
Selected Syllacrostics
Selected Word Math

✦ PUZZLES FOR PUZZLE LOVERS ✦

Crossword Puzzles
Special Editions
Word Games
Word Seek Puzzles

✦ PUZZLER'S CHOICE SERIES ✦

Large-Print Crosswords
Logic Problems

Word Games for Puzzle Lovers, July 1999, No. 83. Puzzles for Puzzle Lovers are published seven times a year (February, April, May, July, August, September, November) by Penny Press, Inc., 6 Prowitt Street, Norwalk, CT 06855-1220. Penny Press is a trademark registered in the U.S. Patent Office.

ISBN: 1-55956-423-7

Printed in Canada

MAZE

Find your way through this maze from the arrow at the top to the one at the bottom.

Solution on page 327

FLOWER POWER

The answers to this petaled puzzle will go in a curve from the number on the outside to the center of the flower. Each number in the flower will have two 5-letter answers. One goes in a clockwise direction and the second in a counterclockwise direction. We have entered two answers to help you begin.

Solution on page 327

CLOCKWISE

1. Jazz-trumpeter Gillespie
2. Labyrinths
3. Sword handles
4. Greenhouse item
5. Zodiac Ram
6. Skeleton parts
7. John Paul ____
8. Partners
9. Military-school student
10. Christmas song
11. Tokyo's country
12. Started
13. Wooden duck
14. Takes five
15. Actress Duke
16. Dungarees
17. "The ____ of the Nile"
18. "M*A*S*H" setting

COUNTERCLOCKWISE

1. Fluffy
2. Bogs
3. Eye color
4. Type of pie
5. Place for bowling
6. Spoiled children
7. Puts together
8. French painter
9. Walking sticks
10. Actress Phoebe ____
11. Some green minerals
12. Exposes
13. Train terminal
14. Majestic
15. Praline ingredient
16. Actor Alexander of "Seinfeld"
17. Pier
18. Romantic poet

PICTURE SLEUTH

Each of these four boxes contains many different designs, but there are only three designs that are in all four boxes. Can you find which ones they are? **Solution on page 327**

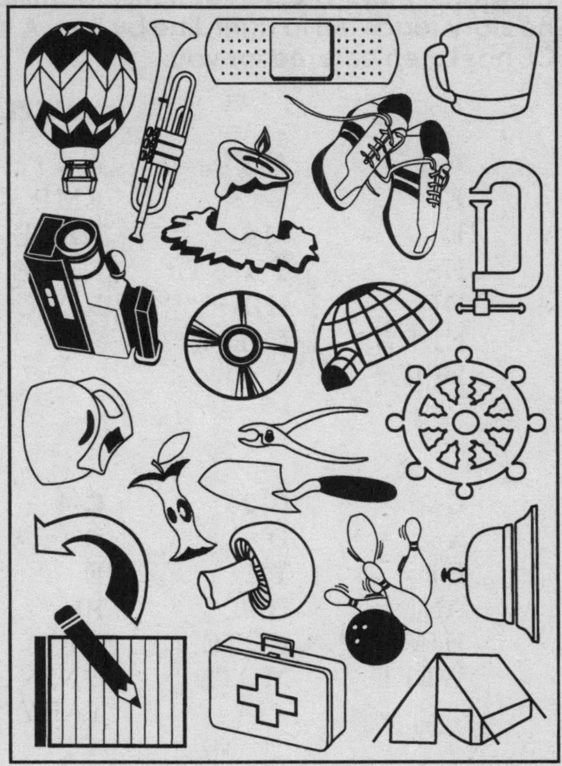

JIGSAW SQUARES

Your goal is to fit the **PUZZLE PIECES** into their proper places in the diagram to reveal a humorous story. Fill the diagram by placing the **PUZZLE PIECES** horizontally into their corresponding sections of the diagram. There are 16 sections, identified by letter-number combinations (A-1, A-2, A-3, etc.). The story reads left to right, line by line. A black square indicates the end of a word. One PUZZLE PIECE has been entered for you.

Solution on page 327

PUZZLE PIECES

A-1	A-2	A-3	A-4	B-1	B-2	B-3	B-4
H	E	E	EMP	IN	HIS	SEC	E
O	E	MA	HERE	IN	HIS	BUIL	Y
R	ES	TO	NAGE	ACC	THE	HAST	DI
AN ✓	OF	HIS	REAC	ALED	IDEN	TALL	HE
NE	EDED	LSEW					DING
ON	FFIC						RETA
LOYE							

C-1	C-2	C-3	C-4	D-1	D-2	D-3	D-4
G	S	D	D	IT	C	H	E
T	HE	TH	E	KED	Y	IS	R
RY	AND	HEL	PH	THE	IT	ME	AS
TO	HIM	ECRE	UP	REPL	NO	AME	IS
ANS	WERE	MOTI	ONIN		FOR	EIVE	THE
ONE			TARY		REC		YOU

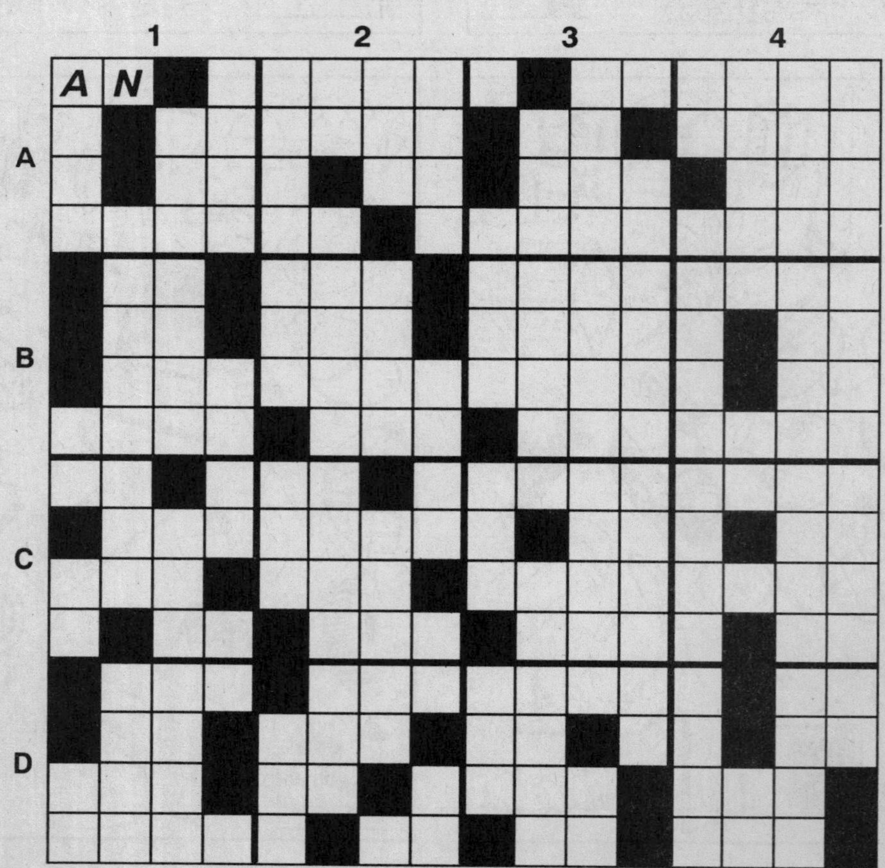

ALPHABET SOUP

Insert a different letter of the alphabet into each of the 26 empty boxes to form words of five or more letters reading across. The letter you insert may be at the beginning, the end, or in the middle of the word. Each letter of the alphabet will be used only once. Cross off each letter in the list as you use it. All the letters in each row are not necessarily used in forming the word.

Our solution on page 327

Example: In the first row across we have inserted the letter E to form the word EMERALD.

A B C D E F G H I J K L M N O P Q R S T U V W X Y Z

M	I	L	D	E	M	E	R	A	L	D	E	W
M	A	N	D	O	L		N	T	R	I	A	N
G	L	E	C	R	S		U	A	S	H	M	N
R	T	U	R	N	I		A	U	N	I	F	P
R	M	A	B	F	A		R	I	C	J	S	N
T	N	U	R	N	O		S	T	E	R	U	R
E	P	I	P	L	A		T	I	C	G	E	O
M	U	S	H	R	O		M	N	A	C	R	O
B	A	T	O	X	P		R	A	S	E	B	T
P	A	T	I	E	N		E	M	U	S	E	A
V	O	C	P	O	W		E	R	A	D	O	S
M	A	N	D	O	A		O	C	A	D	O	L
I	N	E	M	E	E		C	U	S	E	M	A
L	A	C	R	O	B		T	D	P	H	E	A
S	A	V	I	S	I		O	R	N	T	T	U
R	N	I	P	P	I		E	O	N	F	A	B
R	S	H	R	I	E		I	C	P	A	T	I
E	N	C	C	H	A		L	E	N	G	E	W
D	E	R	A	C	N		R	T	U	R	E	M
O	B	A	T	E	N		O	Y	E	A	V	O
C	A	A	B	S	E		T	D	O	O	Y	S
T	E	R	C	R	A		O	R	H	A	L	E
T	M	A	U	N	I		O	R	M	N	D	O
L	I	N	V	C	A		E	R	A	I	S	I
T	O	R	P	O	T		I	A	N	G	L	E
W	M	I	L	R	O		B	O	A	T	B	S

MATCH-UP

Can you find the two pictures that are identical?

Solution on page 327

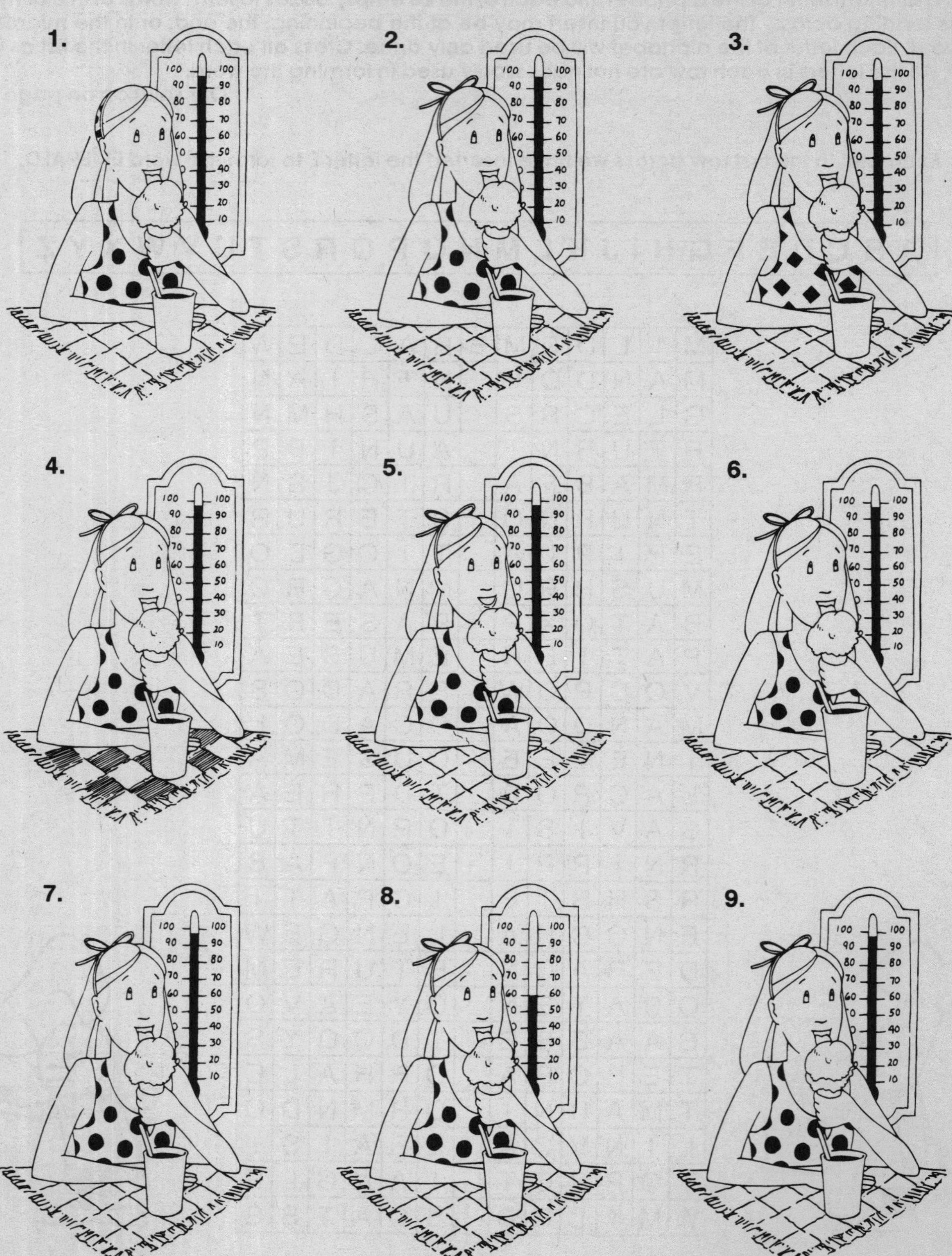

AROUND THE BLOCK

Find your way from START to FINISH by passing through all the white squares one time only. You may move up, down, and across, but not diagonally.

Solution on page 327

WHEELS

Answer the clues for the 6-letter words, which go clockwise around the inner Wheels starting at the heavy lines. Three letters of each are given. Then place the three letters you added in the adjoining spaces in the outer Wheel so that a message can be read starting at the arrow and proceeding clockwise.

Solution on page 327

A. CLUES

1. Type of piano
2. Harsh
3. E.T. and ALF
4. Least number
5. Kind of hound
6. Taper
7. Occult
8. List of things to do

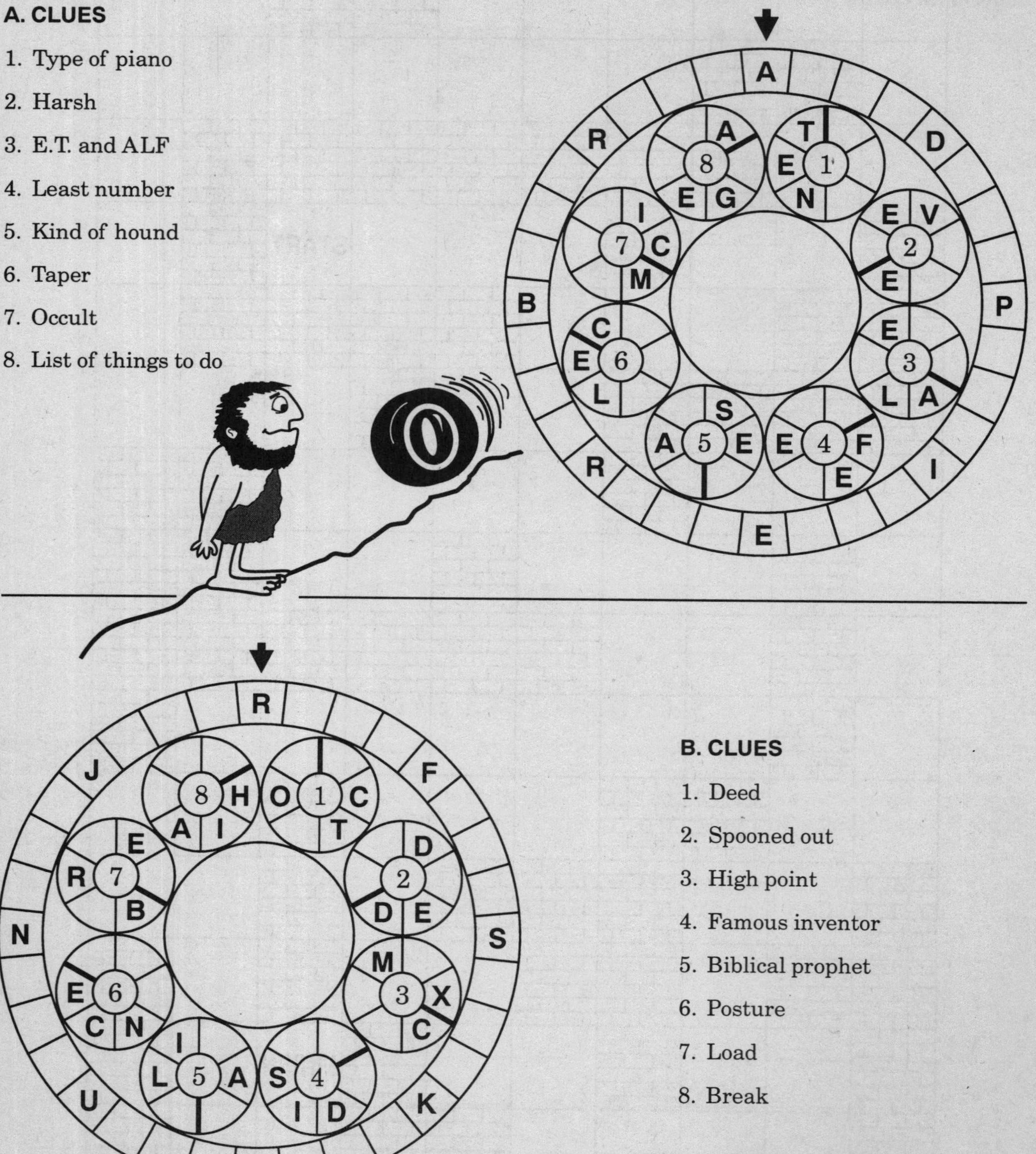

B. CLUES

1. Deed
2. Spooned out
3. High point
4. Famous inventor
5. Biblical prophet
6. Posture
7. Load
8. Break

SUM TOTALS

Place one digit (1 to 9, no zeros) in each square so that the sum of the numbers in each group of squares across or down is the number given. The number below a diagonal is the sum of the numbers below it. The number to the right of a diagonal is the sum of the numbers to the right of it. IMPORTANT: No digit is used more than once in any group of squares leading to a sum. One group of digits has been given for you.

Solution on page 327

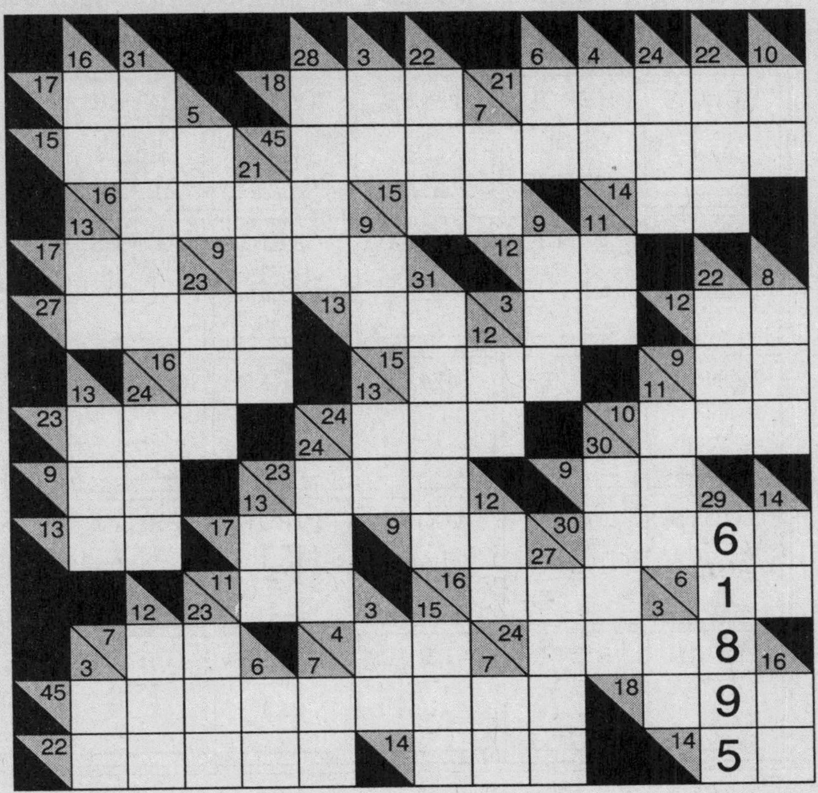

Classified Adds

Fill in the spaces with answers that begin and end with the given letters and fit the categories shown. Answers may be any length. For example, in number 1 below, you must think of a seafood item beginning with the letter S and ending with the letter N, a computer term beginning with the letter N and ending with the letter K, and so on. There are many possible solutions.

Our solutions on page 327

	SEAFOOD ITEMS	COMPUTER TERMS	WORLD NATIONS	ACTORS	FLOWERS	
1.	S	N	K	T	A	A
2.	M	L	P	L	N	S
3.	S	P	M	O	R	E
4.	C	B	E	R	D	L
5.	H	K	D	K	F	A
6.	S	I	T	D	O	D

ANAGRAM MAGIC SQUARE

Rearrange the 5-letter word in each box to form another word. The anagrammed word will answer one of the clues. Put the number of that clue into the small square and write the anagram on the dash. The numbers in each row and column will add up to 65. Write the first letter of each anagram on the correspondingly numbered dash at the bottom of the page; and, presto!, the saying will appear. We have put in one anagram and its clue number and set its first letter on the proper dash.

Solution on page 327

BELOW ☐ ___	HEROD 1 *HORDE*	TINES ☐ ___	LEASE ☐ ___	LAYER ☐ ___	= 65
TAPED ☐ ___	FIBER ☐ ___	OGLED ☐ ___	CARES ☐ ___	RUNES ☐ ___	= 65
RANGE ☐ ___	ROUTE ☐ ___	SHARE ☐ ___	HIKES ☐ ___	STONE ☐ ___	= 65
LOUTS ☐ ___	STATE ☐ ___	ALOFT ☐ ___	DIRGE ☐ ___	BRUTE ☐ ___	= 65
THORN ☐ ___	BITER ☐ ___	NERVE ☐ ___	FATES ☐ ___	GLEAN ☐ ___	= 65
= 65	= 65	= 65	= 65	= 65	

1. Throng
2. Intersection of lines
3. Hunting residence
4. Banquet
5. Wrath
6. Water lily
7. Commencement
8. Land measures
9. Parade vehicle
10. Map within a map
11. Arab ruler
12. Short
13. Arm joint
14. Navajo or Sioux
15. Sample
16. Ahead of time
17. Chain of hills
18. Potato, e.g.
19. Listens to
20. Skillful
21. Compass direction
22. Hospital worker
23. Exterior
24. At no time
25. Artist's stand

H																								
1	2	3	4	5	6	7	8	9	10	11	12	13	14	15	16	17	18	19	20	21	22	23	24	25

CRYPTO-FAMILIES

Each Crypto-Family is a list of related words in code. Each Family has its own code. When you have identified a word, use the known letters to help decode the other words in the Family.

Solutions on page 328

1. SHAPE UP!
Example: Hexagon

OMRJKGCFM
XLKWTGX
JOLKGCFM
MFFLQYM
QMGJKCTG
QBOKWLX
RBFLGXMO
RLORFM
RTGM
TPKF

2. IN THE MAIL
Example: Magazine

HBVJBMA
FSQFXBXFZS
SANOHBHAL
VFLVWPBL
HZOXVBLU
PABYPAX
VBXBPZM
PAXXAL
VIAVJ
TFPP

3. SHOW ____
Example: Man

ITEULREE
VLB QRYY
JULBCJ
OYVXR
EQCOORG
ICVQ
XVER
OURXR
QTLR
BCJL

4. GET BETTER
Example: Upgrade

TLOKP
JMGFMOHH
MOXQHO
OKUTKAO
QLJMGXO
AGMMOAN
POXOYGJ
TPXTKAO
MOWGML
OKMQAU

5. COMIC RELIEF
Example: Garfield

BQ FWR JDQZ
SPPEJP SFQJPA
EBP OFX ZQRP
SJDWRQP
FWRA UFII
JQ'J FSWPX
WFWUA
IPFWGEZ
RDDWPZSGXA
UFEBA

6. WATCH YOUR DIET
Example: Vitamins

LDFCZTR
MUQFDTZI
MKFQZICZDFQ
MUQMTEH
ATNZD
RTUMTR
LFCUIITEH
AUC
UHTRF UMTJ
TFJTRZ

THE SHADOW

Can you find the picture that matches the silhouette shown?
Solution on page 328

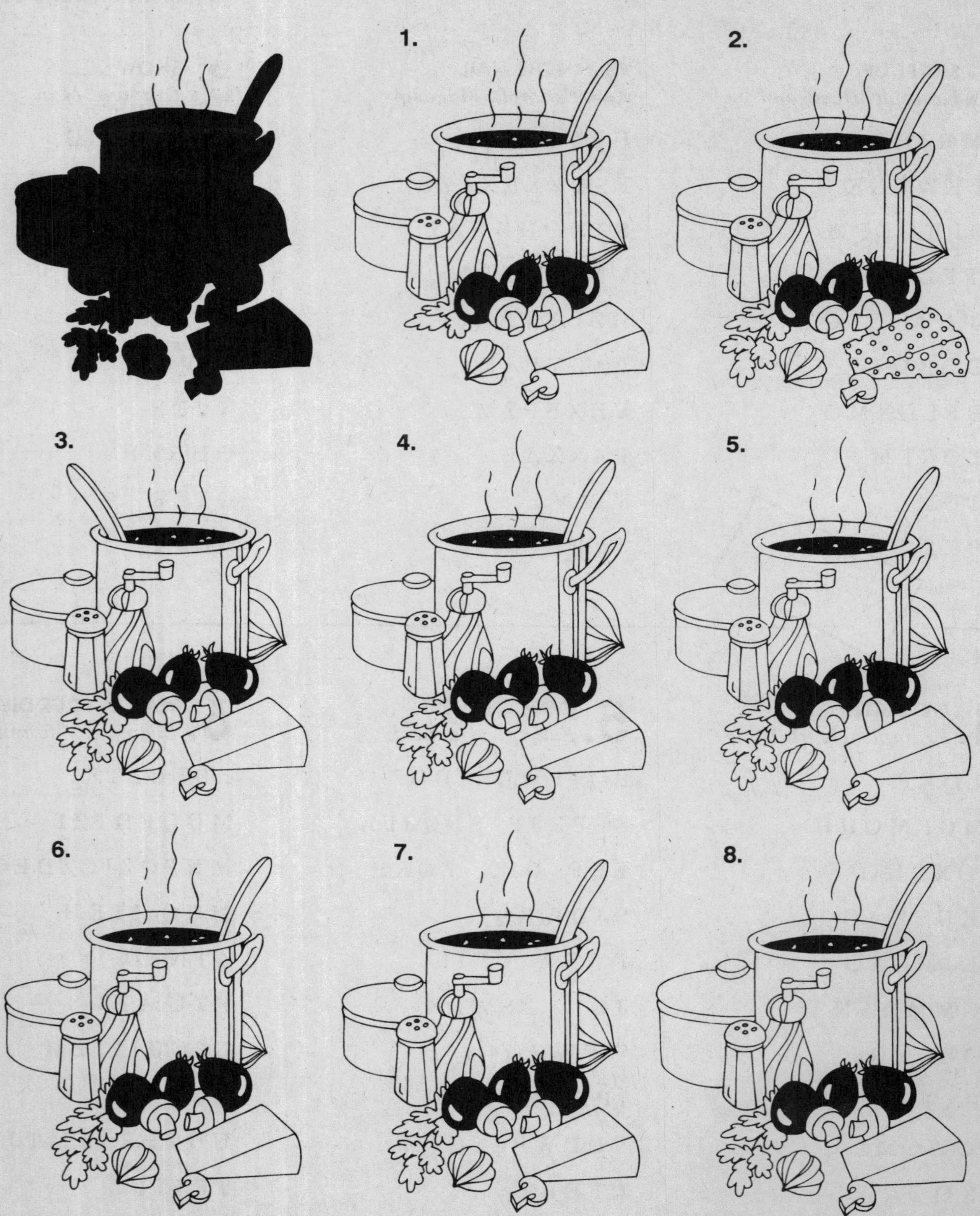

SIMON SAYS

Start with PLUMBER and follow the directions carefully to discover a phrase that is apropos.

Solution on page 328

1. Write the word PLUMBER. — 1. PLUMBER
2. Replace PLUM with RAIN. — 2. RAINBER
3. Reverse the order of the first 4 letters. — 3. NIARBER
4. Reverse the order of the last 3 letters. — 4. NIARREB
5. Replace REB with SURE. — 5. NIARSURE
6. Add ON to the beginning. — 6. ONNIARSURE
7. Insert a G before the last vowel. — 7. ONNIARSURGE
8. Delete all vowels. — 8. NNRSRG
9. Place an A after every letter. — 9. NANARASARAGA
10. Replace the third A with a D. — 10. NANARDSARAGA
11. Delete the first 2 letters. — 11. NARDSARAGA
12. Insert an I between the N and A. — 12. NIARDSARAGA
13. Add ON to the end. — 13. NIARDSARAGAON
14. Delete the 4th vowel. — 14. NIARDSARGAON
15. Insert an E before the O. — 15. NIARDSARGAEON
16. Delete the 4th vowel. — 16. NIARDSARGEON
17. Reverse the order of the first 5 letters. — 17. DRAINSARGEON
18. Change the third vowel to a U. — 18. DRAINSURGEON

HOW TO SOLVE: Fill in as many boxes as you can to form eleven words starting with the given letters. No letter may be repeated in the word itself, in the word above, or in the word below. For each word the number of letters needed to earn the maximum score is indicated by the number of boxes.

HOW TO SCORE: Each letter used is worth one point. If you use all 26 letters of the alphabet, give yourself a bonus of ten points. Include the given letters in all scoring.

Our solutions on page 328

Sample:

							Score
S	A	M	P	L	E		6
R	I	N	G				4
C	L	O	U	D	Y		6

In this sample the word RING cannot be RINGER because the letter R would be repeated in that word and because the letter E appears above in SAMPLE. It cannot be RUNG because U is below in CLOUDY.

1.

WORDS | **SCORE**

							SCORE
T	O						
C							
J							
B							
M	O						
S							
D							
K							
F							
C							
T	O						

TOTAL ☐☐

2.

WORDS | **SCORE**

							SCORE
C	A						
D							
S							
H	E						
F							
T							
J	O						
S							
B							
S							
L	U						

TOTAL ☐☐

SHARE-A-LETTER

Fill in the diagram with answers to the clues. Letters to be filled into the larger areas will be shared by more than one word. All answers read across only. Two clues are given for rows containing two answers. If you can't get an answer, solve the words above and below to discover more letters in the word. We have entered one answer and two other letters to get you started.

Solution on page 328

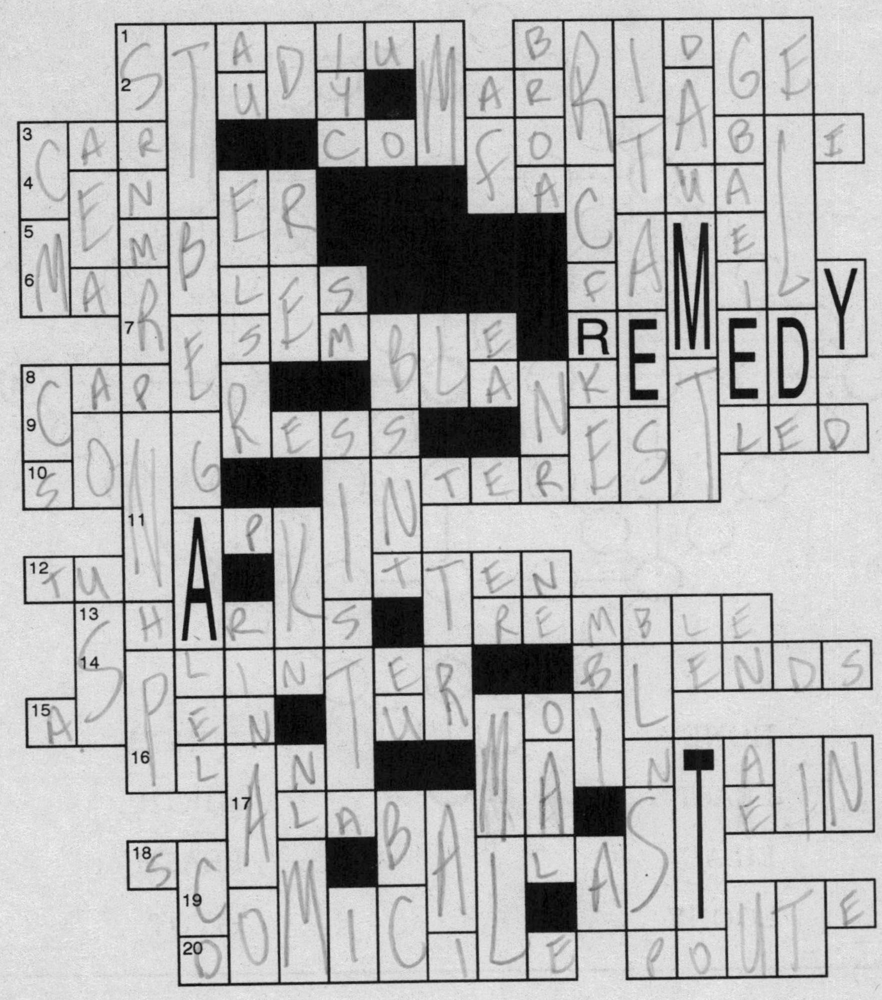

1. Sports arena • Border
2. Scrutinize • Wedlock
3. Wagon • At ease
4. Core • Based on what is known
5. Part of a group • Desert animal
6. Agates • "All in the ____"
7. Look like • Cure
8. Escapade • Covered
9. National legislature • Snuggled
10. Tune • Bank's payment
11. Table linen item
12. Food fish • Young cat
13. Hammerheads, e.g. • Quiver
14. Sliver • Mixes together
15. Colorado resort • Uproar
16. Factory • Hold onto
17. Montgomery's state • Beer mug
18. Swindle • Stabilizing weight
19. Funny • Perceptive
20. Abode • Sulk

CIRCLES IN THE SQUARE

The twenty 5-letter words all fit in the diagram. All words begin and end in a dark circle. Horizontal words read from left to right; all other words read from top to bottom. We have placed one letter in the diagram.

Solution on page 328

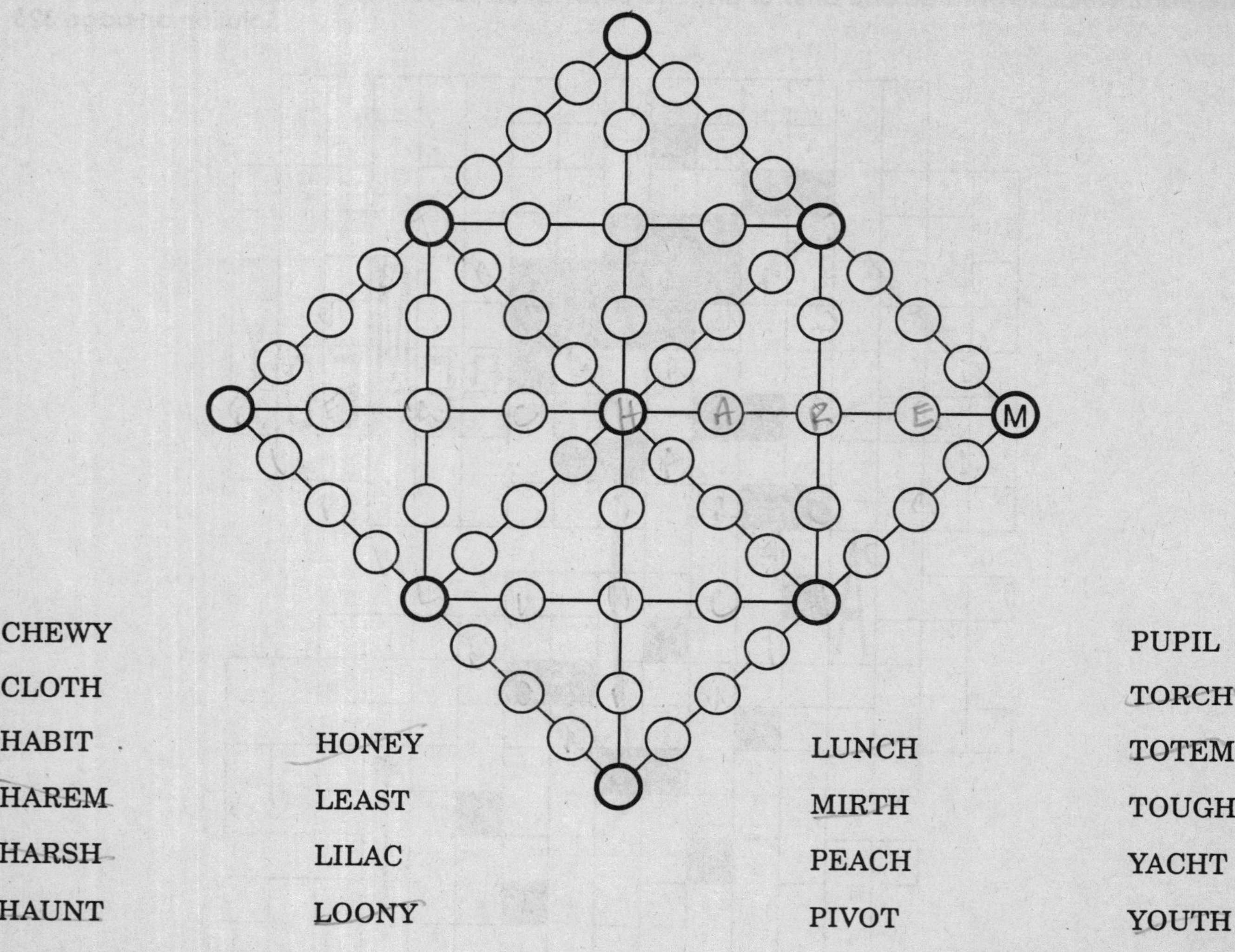

CHEWY
CLOTH
HABIT
HAREM
HARSH
HAUNT
HONEY
LEAST
LILAC
LOONY
LUNCH
MIRTH
PEACH
PIVOT
PUPIL
TORCH
TOTEM
TOUGH
YACHT
YOUTH

Across and Down

Place the answers to the clues into their correct places in the diagrams so that the same words read both Across and Down.

Solutions on page 329

A

1. Squander
2. Thespian
3. Boulder
4. Healthy drink
5. Build

1	2	3	4	5
2				
3				
4				
5				

B

1. Evident
2. Depart
3. Overhangs
4. Prevent
5. Takes five

1	2	3	4	5
2				
3				
4				
5				

Window Boxes

There is a common 4-letter word hidden in each strip of letters in Column I. Think of the strips in Column II as open and closed windows. Then match each letter strip with its correct Window Box so that the 4-letter word will show. There are different possibilities, but there is only one way in which each letter strip and each window strip are used once.

Solution on page 328

Example: | P | L | O | D | E | N | T | → | P | ■ | O | ■ | E | ■ | T |

COLUMN I		COLUMN II
1. T C S L U H B		a. □ ■ □ ■ ■ □ □
2. M I W O T R K		b. □ □ ■ □ □ ■ ■
3. P Q U G L I Y		c. □ ■ ■ ■ □ □ □
4. K T B N I L T		d. ■ □ ■ □ □ ■ □
5. D E R A S W P		e. □ ■ □ □ ■ □ ■
6. W S T E O P T		f. ■ ■ □ □ □ ■ □
7. V W I O C N E		g. □ ■ □ ■ □ □ ■
8. A O B E L E V		h. ■ □ □ ■ ■ □ □
9. K T E O L X T		i. ■ □ □ ■ □ □ ■
10. J O B I N L P		j. ■ ■ □ □ ■ □ □

A Few Choice Words

Find the 6-letter answers by choosing one letter from each of the letter groups to the right of each clue. For example, the answer to number 1 is FLOWER.

Solutions on page 327

1. Blossom	oaf	alb	ore	low	met	ril
2. Amazement	awm	oar	rin	doe	erg	lnr
3. Interfere	mis	bne	odt	eod	lpr	ten
4. Attractive	lap	rom	eva	mat	sit	yol
5. Clamor	ruh	apu	mir	oat	bac	try
6. Muslim ruler	mos	hup	lmb	art	cpa	ian
7. Reddish brown	ace	unc	bit	lou	rmw	anl
8. Milk product	bcy	ouh	tag	cut	fir	tac

JIGSAW PUZZLE

When you have put the pieces of the Jigsaw Puzzle into their correct places in the diagram, they will form a crossword puzzle with words reading across and down. Do not turn the pieces. The heavy lines in the diagram will help you locate their proper places. We have set one piece to start you off.

Solution on page 327

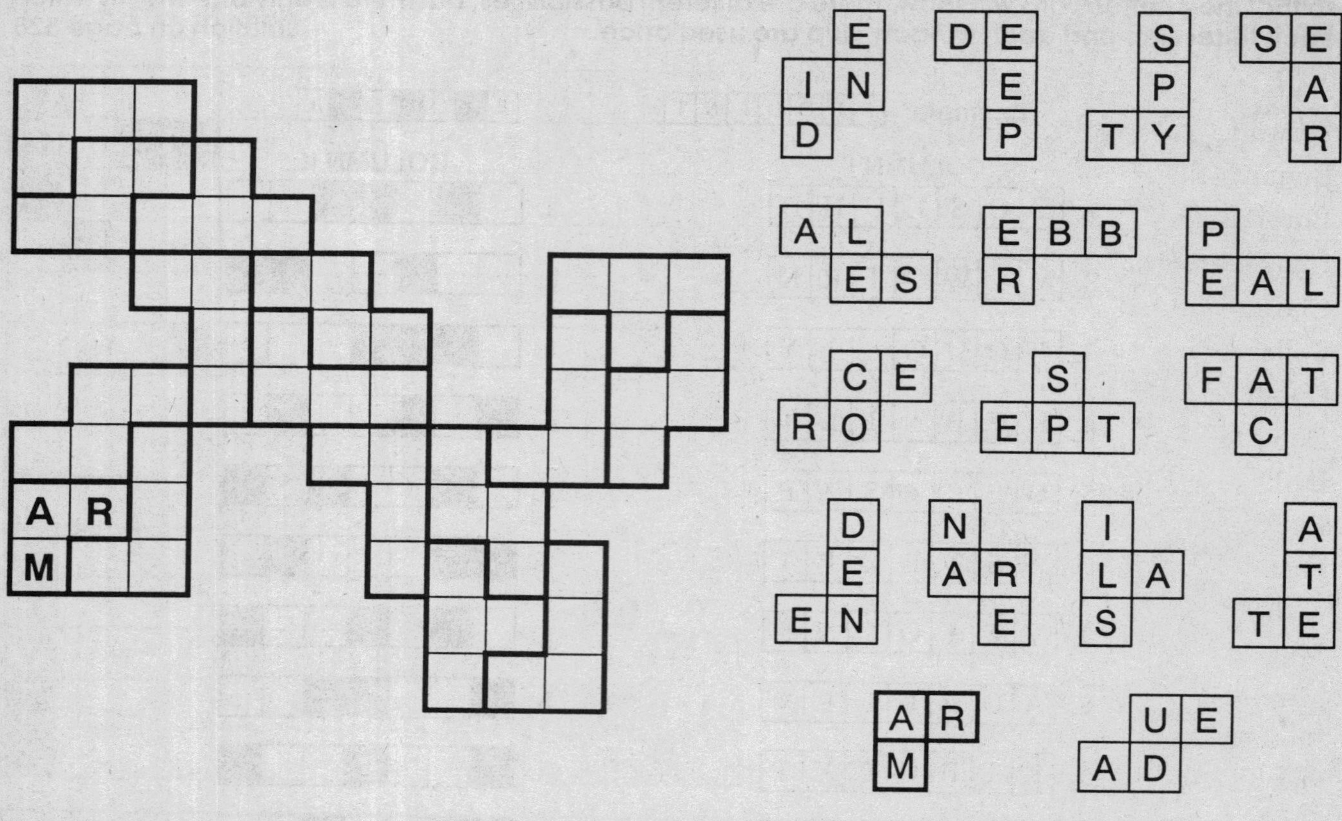

Plus One

Add one letter, a vowel or consonant as indicated, to the letters given and rearrange all the letters to form a word. The vowels and consonants you've added, reading down, will spell a bonus word.

Solution on page 328

1. L + H + E + Y + C + I *plus one* consonant = __ __ __ __ __ __ __
2. P + X + N + I + A + E *plus one* consonant = __ __ __ __ __ __ __
3. U + R + Q + T *plus one* vowel = __ __ __ __ __
4. I + I + C + C *plus one* consonant = __ __ __ __ __
5. H + U + T + H + G *plus one* vowel = __ __ __ __ __ __
6. B + N + O + C + A *plus one* consonant = __ __ __ __ __ __

BONUS WORD: ________________

LETTERBOXES

Can you find the correct places for the words related to mining in the word list? The starting letters for all the words are given in the circled squares. These letters may also be used as parts of other words because of overlapping or crossing. The words read in a straight line and in all directions — forward, backward, up, down, and diagonally. Do not pass over a black square as you are solving. When the puzzle is completely solved, there will be a letter in every space. We have filled in one word to start you off.

Solution on page 327

Adit
Airway
Bonanza
Borehole
Chokedamp
Claim
Collar
Cupel
Deposit
Drill
Excavation
Face
Ledge
Matrix
Mine
Mother lode
Ore
Pay dirt
Pillar
Pit
Pocket
Prospector
Reef
Riddle
Seam
Shaft
Shoot
Smelt
Stope
Strike ✓
Trepan
Trommel
Tunnel
Vein

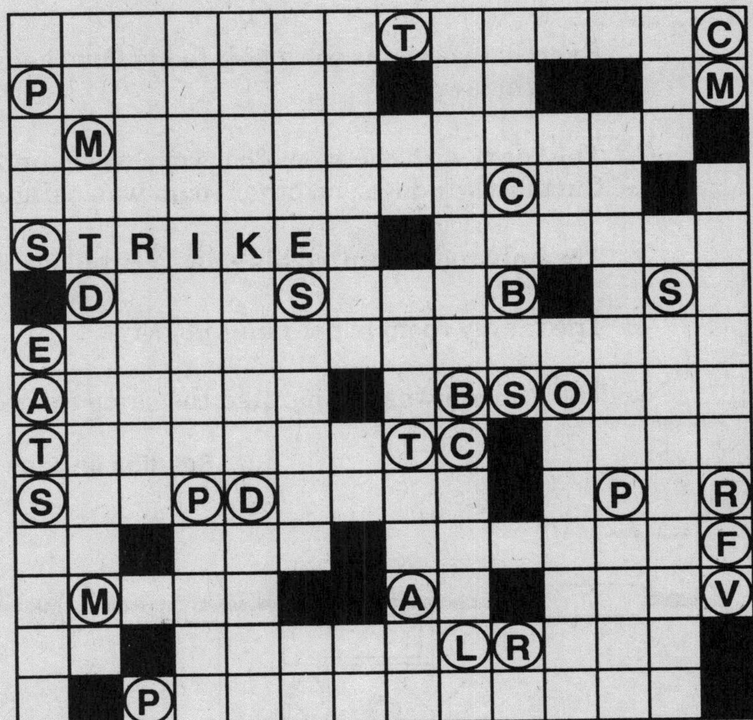

A Perfect Ten

Enter the 5-letter answer to each clue into the circle starting at the corresponding number. The last letter of the first word will be the first letter of the second, and so on around the ring. When you have filled in the circle, transfer the letters from the outlined boxes in clockwise order into the column to find the name of a television character.

Solution on page 328

1. Triangle, e.g.
2. Eat away
3. Mistake
4. Verse
5. Artist's stand
6. Yearns

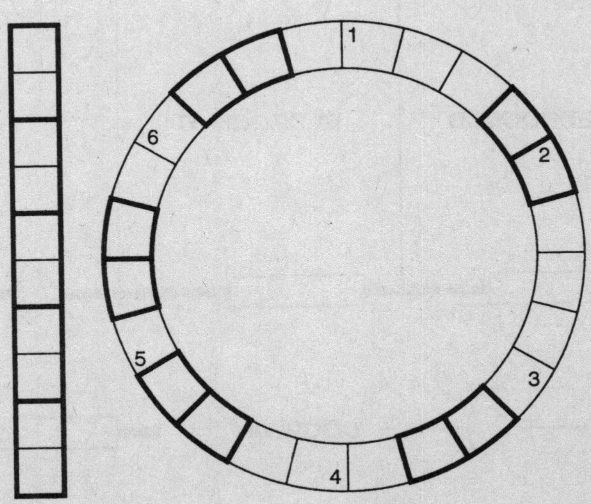

DEDUCTION PROBLEM

RAINBOW ROOMS

The Ferris family recently repainted seven rooms of their house (kitchen, dining room, living room, family room, and three bedrooms). They painted each room one of four colors (yellow, blue, gray, or white). The floor plan (illustrated below) shows that each room has at least one window and one doorway; some of the doorways are shared by two rooms. Two rooms have fireplaces. Using the information given, can you tell which color each room was painted?

1. Exactly two rooms were painted yellow: bedroom B and a room with one window.
2. The room with the most doorways was painted the same color as the room with the most windows; no other room was painted this color.
3. The only room painted blue has a fireplace.
4. The family room is not painted gray.
5. The kitchen was not painted the same color as the dining room.

Solution on page 328

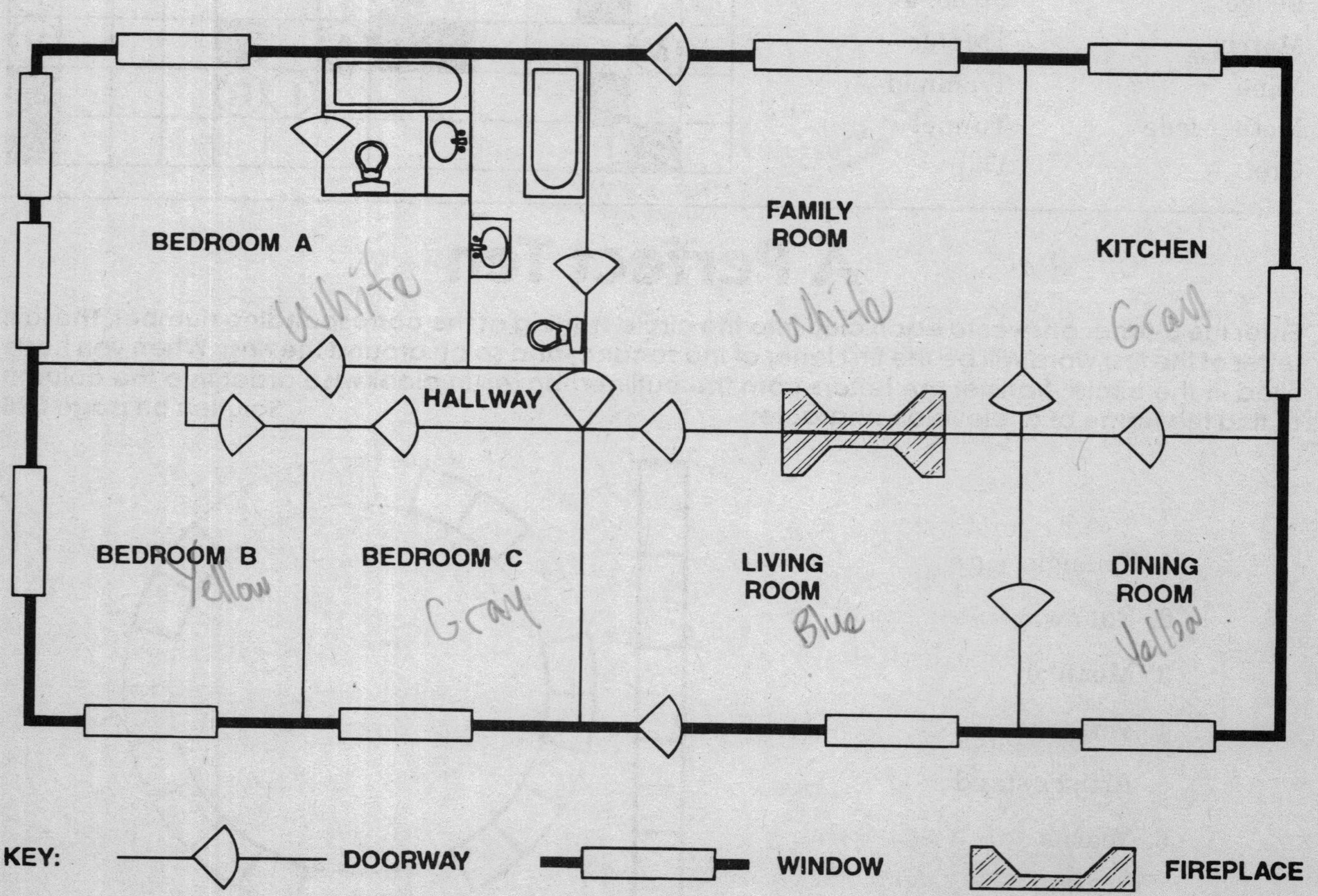

BULL'S-EYE SPIRAL

This is a new target for those who can think in circles. The game works two ways, outward and inward. If you're outward bound, guess the word that fits clue 1-3. Then go on to clue 4-7 and so on. If you're stuck with an outward-bound word, try the inward clues. Work both ways to hit the Bull's-Eye.

Solution on page 328

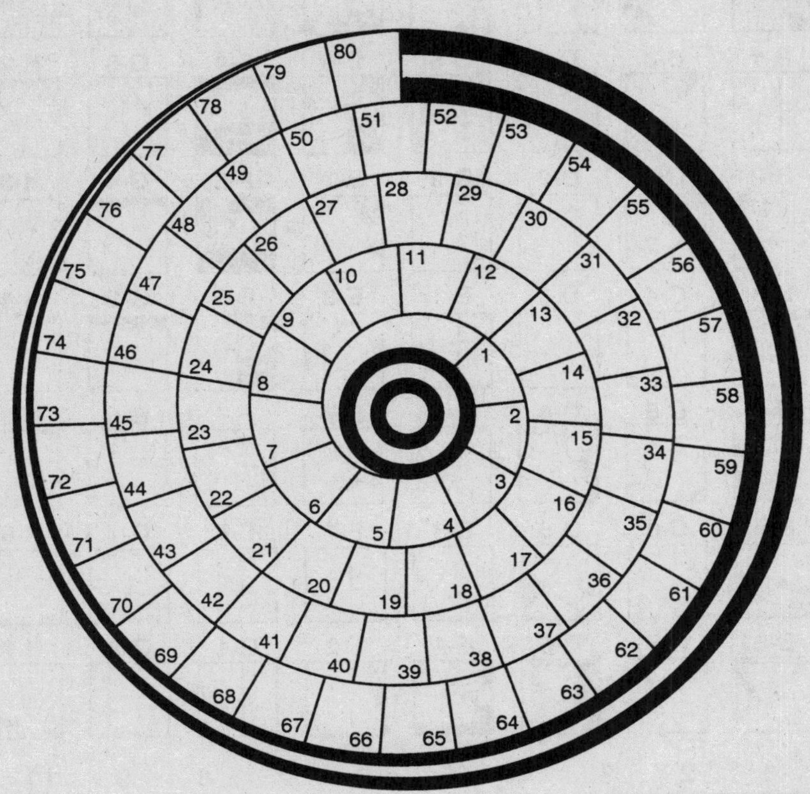

OUTWARD

1-3. Young boy
4-7. Fencing blade
8-13. Seabird
14-20. Sings
21-26. Harsh
27-32. Occurring in spring
33-38. Attic room
39-43. Spanish mark
44-49. Fireplace shelf
50-54. Slip-up
55-60. Not level
61-65. Licoricelike flavoring
66-69. Gambling cubes
70-74. Jeans fabric
75-80. Consideration

INWARD

80-77. Pull behind
76-71. White fur
70-64. Makes a choice
63-59. Senseless
58-53. Areas of activity
52-47. Straw bed
46-42. Dubbed
41-36. Trash
35-30. Type of sleeve
29-24. Admire greatly
23-18. Ship
17-11. Street fighter
10-6. Indian tent
5-1. Foot lever

PICTURE THIS

You do not need any special art training to produce a picture in the empty grid. Use the letter-number guide above each square and carefully draw what is shown into the corresponding square in the grid.

Solution on page 327

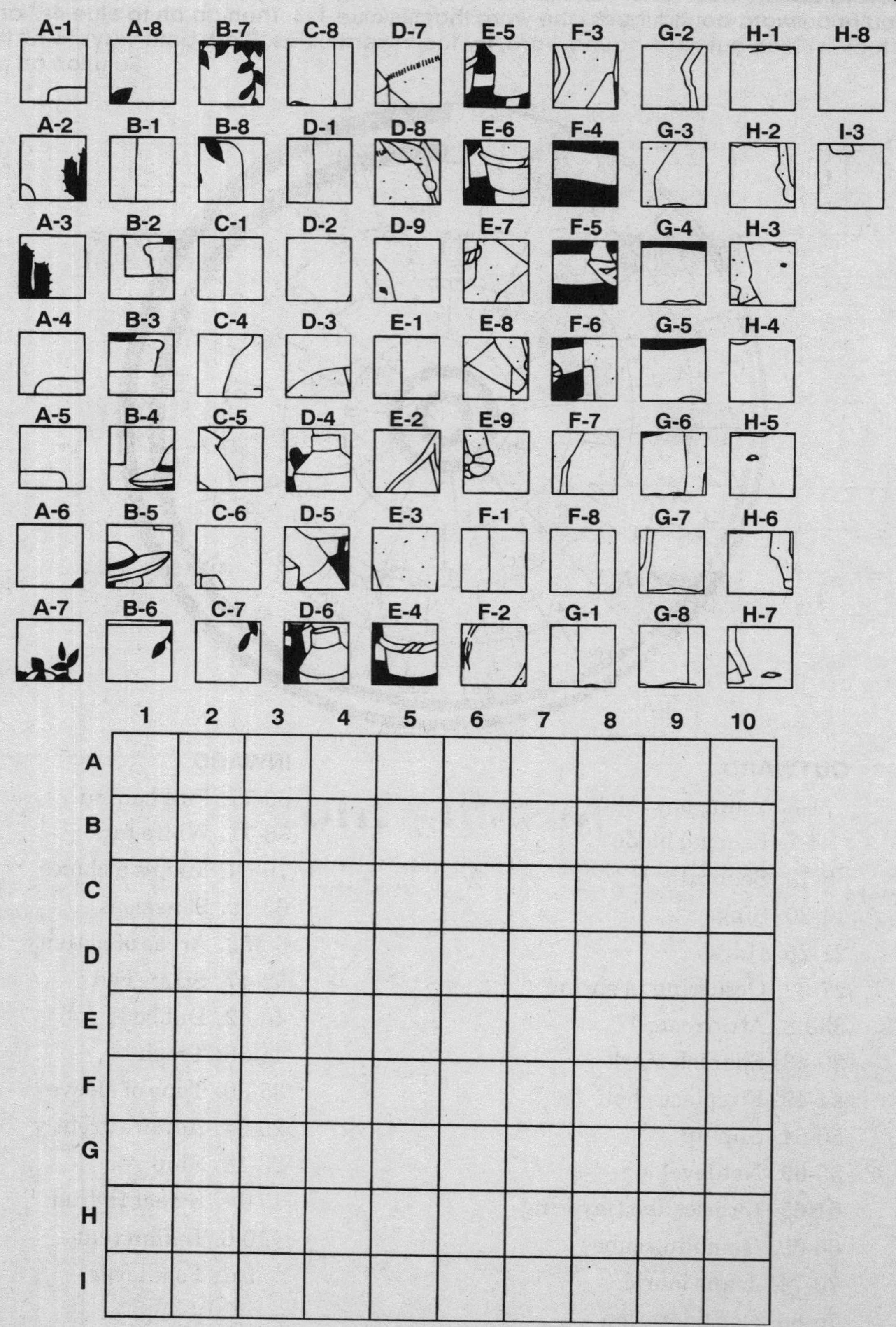

CODEWORD

Codeword is a special crossword puzzle in which conventional clues are omitted. Instead, answer words in the diagram are represented by numbers. Each number represents a different letter of the alphabet, and all of the letters of the alphabet are used. When you are sure of a letter, put it in the code key chart and cross it off in the alphabet box. A group of letters has been inserted to start you off.

Solution on page 328

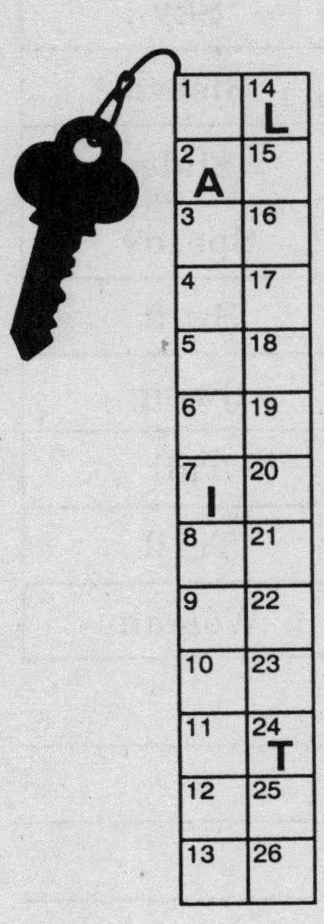

1	14 L
2 A	15
3	16
4	17
5	18
6	19
7 I	20
8	21
9	22
10	23
11	24 T
12	25
13	26

5	18	13	24	■	2	14	23	5	■	5	9	8	2	26
2	8	7	2	■	9	23	1	24	■	24	7	2	8	2
12	23	6	24	23	8	7	24 T	3	■	22	24	24	23	8
■	■	■	24	23	23	■	2 A	14	7	15	7	■	■	■
5	25	22	14	14	■	24	7 I	23	8	■	16	7	26	5
26	7	1	23	■	26	22	14 L	5	23	■	23	17	7	24
2	12	23	■	20	2	15	5	■	■	22	1	7	24	3
■	■	21	22	18	24	23	■	19	18	8	5	24	■	■
23	8	22	26	24	■	■	15	23	2	1	■	2	26	23
15	18	2	5	■	2	12	2	26	24	■	5	24	22	1
15	23	14	24	■	19	23	1	24	■	5	26	23	1	12
■	■	■	2	10	23	2	12	■	14	7	23	■	■	■
8	2	12	7	18	■	13	2	11	18	8	2	15	14	23
2	9	18	8	1	■	23	4	18	5	■	25	23	23	14
4	23	23	5	23	■	1	23	19	5	■	5	23	2	14

~~A~~	N
B	O
C	P
D	Q
E	R
F	S
G	~~T~~
H	U
~~I~~	V
J	W
K	X
~~L~~	Y
M	Z

Missing Trios

For each numbered group fill in the same three missing letters (not necessarily in the same order) to complete a 7-letter, 6-letter, 5-letter, 4-letter, and 3-letter word. The Missing Trio is different for each group.

Our solutions on page 329

1. LE___ ___ ___LE   ___OX___N___   ___ ___N___O   ___L___ ___   ___ ___ ___
2. ___E___RA___N   ___N___O___M   ___A___ ___Y   ___ ___ ___T   ___ ___ ___
3. ___ ___TTER___   N___ ___KI___   ___ ___I___T   ___L___ ___   ___ ___ ___
4. F___ ___ ___ING   YE___L___ ___   BE___ ___ ___   ___ ___ ___F   ___ ___ ___
5. ___EFE___S___   E___ ___UR___   ___ ___ ___IM   ___U___ ___   ___ ___ ___
6. H___ ___EFU___   ___ATR___ ___   S___ ___O___   ___ ___O___   ___ ___ ___
7. ___V___RA___E   ___LL___ ___E   ___R___P___   ___ ___ ___R   ___ ___ ___
8. T___EAT___ ___   ___AT___ ___R   S___O___ ___   ___I___ ___   ___ ___ ___

THREE'S COMPANY

This alphabetical list of seemingly unrelated words actually contains 15 groups of three related items. Your job is to sort them out into those 15 groups using each item only once. The trick is that some of the items could be used in more than one list, but only one arrangement of all the items will work. Remember, use each item only once and have exactly three items in each group.

Solution on page 329

Army	Girl	Joist	Pursue	Sky
Azure	Gleam	Lady	Quick	Sleeve
Bacon	Glow	Locked	Rafter	Slide
Beam	Grandstander	Marines	Regal	Speedy
Collar	Ham	Mark	Royal	Swift
Crane	Hardy	Navy	Sausage	Swing
Derrick	Hasty	Noble	Seesaw	Tail
Exhibitionist	Hoist	Princely	Shadow	Trail
Fall	Hotshot	Pulley	Shimmer	Woman

1. Show-off — Grandstander — Exhibitionist — Hotshot
2. Follow — Trail — Pursue — Shadow
3. Shades of blue — Sky — Royal — Azure
4. Shine — Shimmer — Gleam — Glow
5. Land followers — Locked — Fall — Mark
6. Lifting devices — Hoist — Pulley — Derrick
7. Rapid — Quick — Hasty — Speedy
8. Pork products — Bacon — Sausage — Ham
9. Females — Woman — Girl — Lady
10. Authors — Hardy — Swift — Crane
11. Parts of a shirt — Sleeve — Tail — Collar
12. Supporting pieces — Joist — Beam — Rafter
13. Majestic — Regal — Princely — Noble
14. Military branches — Army — Navy — Marines
15. At the playground — Slide — Swing — Seesaw

PLACES, PLEASE

Fill the diagram with all the words in the word list. The words from each group start on their matching number, and they will read in all directions—forward, backward, up, down, and diagonally. Words from different groups sometimes overlap; therefore, some letters will be used more than once. We have started the puzzle for you by entering the starting letters and the words from number 8 and number 15. When the puzzle is completed, all the squares will be filled.

Solution on page 329

1. THIRTEEN
   TIC
   TINTLESS
   TREK
2. HAL
   HARMONIOUS
   HASTE
   HAYMAKER
   HOARD
3. EAR
   EGO
   ENSNARE
   ETE
4. CAVERNOUS
   CEMENT
   CHARLATAN
   CIAO
   CLAY
   CONTEXT
   COOK
   CREATURES
5. SARI
   SLUE
   SOMEONE
   STALK
6. ACANTHUS
   AMOS
   ARMY
7. KENYA
   KEYPAD
   KIMONO
   KNEES
   KRYPTONITE
8. TEAL ✓
   TOAD ✓
   TRY ✓
   TUTELARY ✓
9. YEASTY
   YEOMANRY
   YESTERDAY
   YOGURT
10. SEA
    SERMONS
    SIR
    SKI
    SURMISE
11. POI
    PRO
    PSALM
    PUN
12. CAKE
    CATS
    CLOUD
    COHO
    COLA
    CONY
    CORD
    COSMOS
13. TAM
    TARP
    THEN
    TRANSOCEANIC
    TRUE
    TURN
    TYPO
14. PHI
    PITHY
    POT
    PSI
15. ERROR ✓
    ESPRESSO ✓
    EXTRA ✓
16. AIRS
    AKIMBO
    ALTERNATORS
    AMID

		[1]T								[2]H				
													[3]E	
				L				[4]C						
	[5]S				[6]A									
						E								[7]K
				D	A	O	[8]T							
						U		R						
[9]Y					T				Y			[10]S		
				E					A				R	
			L			[11]P				R			O	
		A	[12]C								[13]T		R	
	R						[14]P					X	R	
Y						O	S	S	E	R	P	S	[15]E	
			[16]A											

COMMON COMBOS

Listed below are groups of four unrelated words. Find a word that either precedes all the words in each group or follows all the words in each group.
Solutions on page 327

1. DRUM	BANK	JELLY	PAY	______
2. KNOT	DANCE	DEAL	ROOT	______
3. MAST	OVER	EGG	BULK	______
4. RAIN	EAVES	GUM	BACK	______
5. BATH	CAGE	BRAIN	HOUSE	______
6. MASTER	TIME	MANTEL	CROSS	______
7. PEN	MATE	GROUND	BOY	______
8. BEFORE	STAGE	SECOND	OFF	______
9. LOOSE	BALL	LOCKER	NOTE	______
10. SAW	SHELL	WAGON	BOX	______

Ringmaster

Place the letter groups in the diagram to form 24 five-letter words as indicated by arrows. The two-letter groups go in the circles in the outer ring, the three-letter groups in the inner ring. Two words have been given to start you off.
Solution on page 329

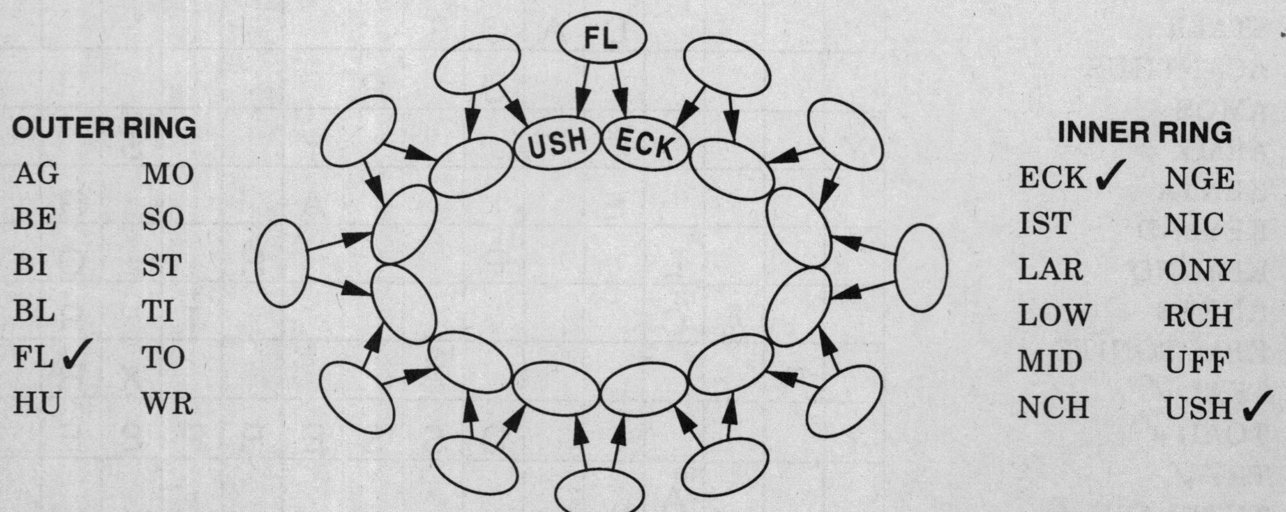

FANCY FIVES

Each answer in this puzzle is a 5-letter word! Place the answers to the Lettered Clues into the protruding outside squares of the diagram. The answers to the Across and Down Clues are placed in only those boxes which contain numbers (1-21 Down is entered into the squares numbered 1, 6, 11, 16, 21). The answers to the Cube Words are entered in scrambled order into the squares containing the corresponding numbers and the four squares surrounding those squares.

Solution on page 328

LETTERED CLUES

a-b. Rose's barb

c-d. Relish

f-e. Plentiful

h-g. Chop small

ACROSS CLUES

1-5. Behaved

6-10. Anxiety

11-15. "Home ____"

16-20. Wanderer

21-25. Frock

DOWN CLUES

1-21. Medal

2-22. Hue

3-23. Treasure-____

4-24. Sea eagles

5-25. Tinters

CUBE WORDS

1. Signified
2. Educate
3. Maestro's stick
4. Renegade
5. Thick
6. Turn on a hinge
7. Mexican dishes
8. Derrick
9. Sign up
10. Long
11. Cart
12. Yards
13. Arctic or Atlantic
14. Identical copy
15. Poetry
16. Statement of belief
17. Large deer
18. Poison
19. Singer John
20. Disdain
21. Fear
22. Knight's wear
23. Smoothing tool
24. Delay
25. Frighten

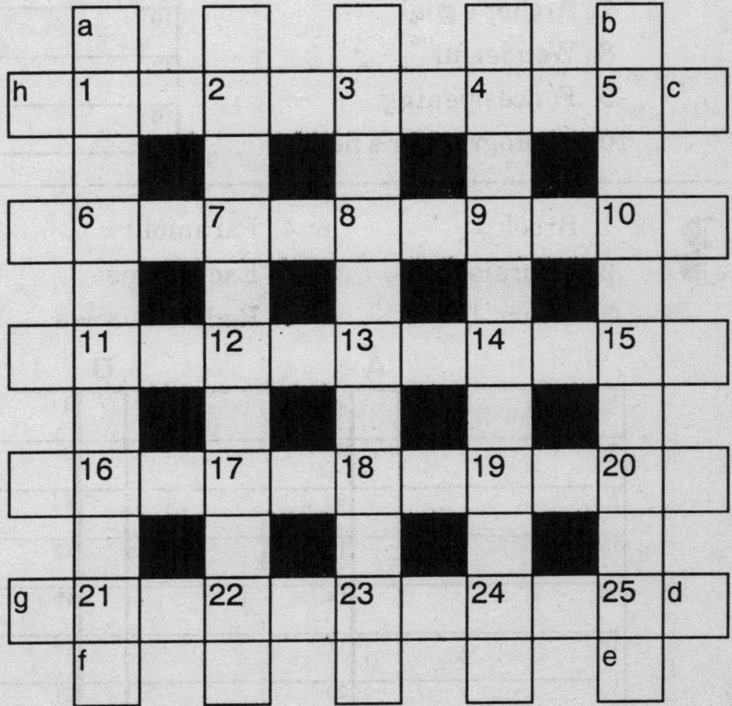

ESCALATORS

Write the 6-letter answer to clue 1 in the first space. Drop one letter and rearrange the remaining letters to answer clue 2. Put the dropped letter into Column A. Drop another letter and rearrange the remaining letters to answer clue 3. Put the dropped letter into Column B. Follow this pattern for each row in the diagram. When completed, the letters in Column A and Column B, reading down, will spell related words or a phrase.

Solutions on page 329

1

1. Suave
2. Owls' cries
3. Scat!
4. Musical composition
5. Yuletide visitor
6. Colony insects
7. Ordinary
8. Large tooth
9. Wander
10. Loud commotion
11. Race site
12. Wagon
13. Longs
14. Trap
15. Close by

	A		B	
1		2		3
4		5		6
7		8		9
10		11		12
13		14		15

2

1. Steal
2. Pilot
3. Irritate
4. Give
5. Made an initial bet
6. Look after
7. Archer's goal
8. Wonderful
9. Fence opening
10. Photographer's need
11. Best part
12. Land measure
13. Floor covering
14. Summary
15. Find fault
16. Golf-course sections
17. Show indifference
18. Embraces

	A		B	
1		2		3
4		5		6
7		8		9
10		11		12
13		14		15
16		17		18

3

1. Brook
2. Appraises
3. Char
4. Paramour
5. Excursions
6. Reddish brown
7. State firmly
8. Fixed gaze
9. Satisfy
10. Slipped
11. Beg
12. Agreement
13. Hope
14. Harvests
15. Mast
16. Stuffed
17. Meadow
18. Folder
19. Gives a speech
20. Cook in an oven
21. Leading actor

	A		B	
1		2		3
4		5		6
7		8		9
10		11		12
13		14		15
16		17		18
19		20		21

STRETCH LETTERS

These words, listed alphabetically by length, are to be entered in the diagram across only. Words do not read down. When writing in a blank taller than a square, stretch the letter to the full height of the blank. The stretched letters are part of more than one entry.

Solution on page 329

• MONOPOLY GAME •

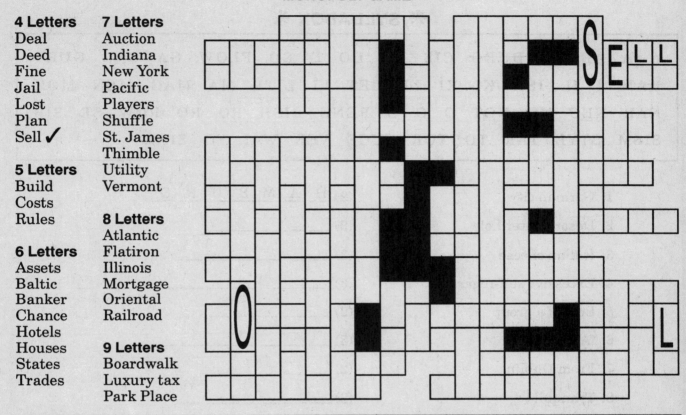

4 Letters
Deal
Deed
Fine
Jail
Lost
Plan
Sell ✓

5 Letters
Build
Costs
Rules

6 Letters
Assets
Baltic
Banker
Chance
Hotels
Houses
States
Trades

7 Letters
Auction
Indiana
New York
Pacific
Players
Shuffle
St. James
Thimble
Utility
Vermont

8 Letters
Atlantic
Flatiron
Illinois
Mortgage
Oriental
Railroad

9 Letters
Boardwalk
Luxury tax
Park Place

Circle Sums

Each circle, lettered A through I, has its own number value from 1 to 9. No two circles have the same value. The numbers shown in the diagram are the sums of the circles that overlap at those points. For example, 16 is the sum of circles A and D. Can you find the value of each circle?

Solution on page 328

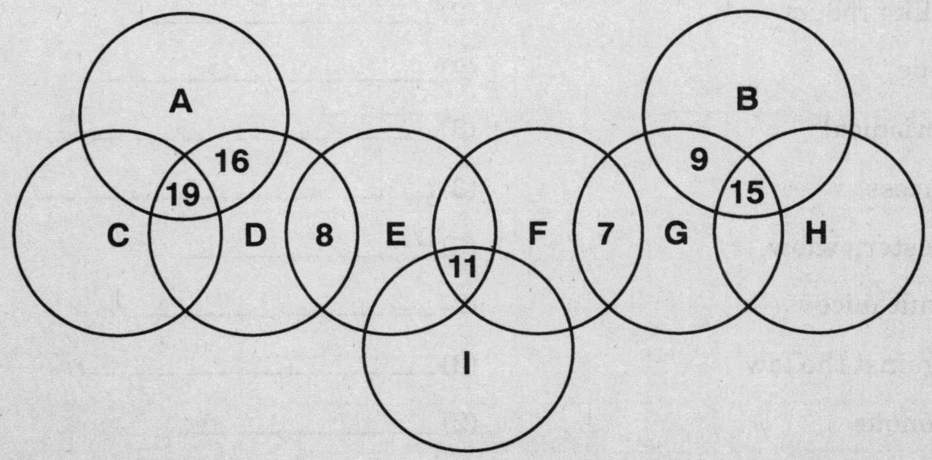

SYL´´LA-CROS´TIC

Fill in the answers to the clues by using all the syllables in the Syllabox. The number of syllables to be used in each answer is shown in parentheses. The number of letters in each answer is indicated by the dashes. Each syllable will be used once. When the words are correctly filled in, their first and last letters, reading down, will reveal an epigram preceded by its author's name.

Solution on page 329

✱ SYLLABOX ✱

A A AB AL ~~BURG~~ CIS DE DO E ED FLOW GA GAL GURT
~~HAM~~ I IL ISH KI KÌ LE LET LI LITE MA MAG MEN MOR
NAR NEC NO NOT O O O RENE RISH RO RO ROW SE SIS
SISM STYL TAR TO TOR TUCE VER WAI YO ZINE

1. German city (2) H A M B U R G
2. Desert water hole (3) _ _ _ _ _
3. Italian cheese (3) _ _ _ _ _ _
4. Excessive self-regard (3) _ _ _ _ _ _ _ _ _ _
5. Best of a group (2) _ _ _ _ _
6. "Annie" song (3) _ _ _ _ _ _ _ _
7. From Dublin (2) _ _ _ _ _
8. Tranquil (2) _ _ _ _ _ _
9. Large reptile (4) _ _ _ _ _ _ _ _ _
10. Salad green (2) _ _ _ _ _ _ _
11. Honolulu beach (3) _ _ _ _ _ _ _
12. Stomach (3) _ _ _ _ _ _ _
13. Milk product (2) _ _ _ _ _ _
14. Chic (2) _ _ _ _ _ _ _
15. Periodical (3) _ _ _ _ _ _ _ _
16. Excess (3) _ _ _ _ _ _ _ _
17. Western show (3) _ _ _ _ _
18. Fruit juice (2) _ _ _ _ _ _
19. Against the law (3) _ _ _ _ _ _ _
20. Famous (2) _ _ _ _ _

RINGERS

Each of the five Ringers is composed of five rings. Use your imagination to rotate the rings so that you spell four 5-letter words reading from the outside to the inside when all five rings are aligned correctly.

Solutions on page 329

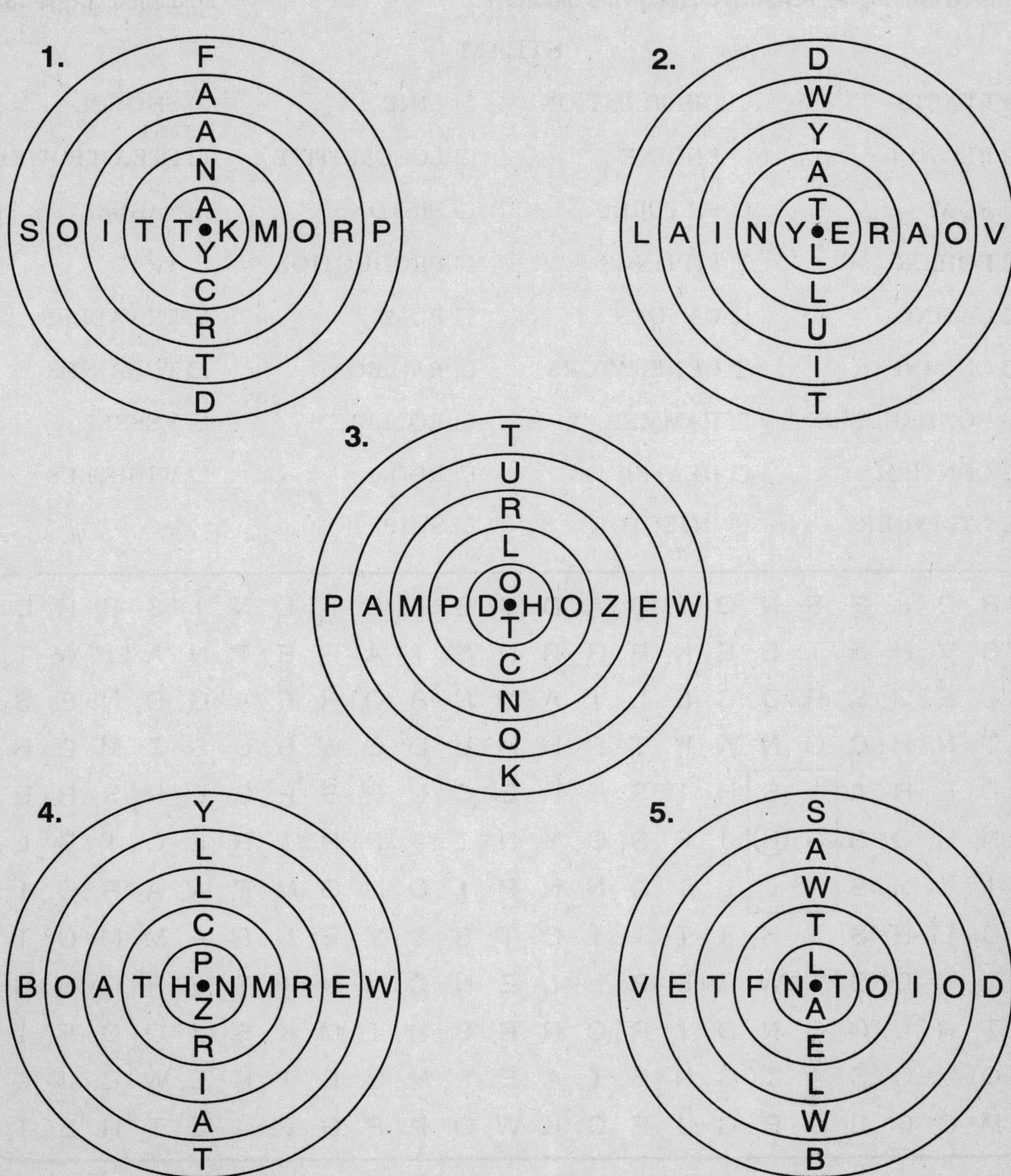

Boxes

All the entries in the list are words related to steam. An entry can begin at any point and will read either clockwise or counterclockwise around the edges of a box (sometimes a square and sometimes a rectangle). BLASTS is boxed in the diagram.

Solution on page 332

STEAM

- ☑ BLASTS
- ☐ BLOWER
- ☐ BOAT
- ☐ BOILER
- ☐ CASING
- ☐ CHIMNEYS
- ☐ CONDENSERS
- ☐ CONTROLS
- ☐ CYLINDER
- ☐ DISTILLATION
- ☐ ENGINE
- ☐ FILTERED
- ☐ FITTINGS
- ☐ GAUGES
- ☐ GENERATORS
- ☐ HAMMER
- ☐ HEATER
- ☐ INJECTOR
- ☐ LINE
- ☐ LOCOMOTIVE
- ☐ PISTON
- ☐ PRODUCTION
- ☐ PUMP
- ☐ RAILROAD
- ☐ ROLLER
- ☐ ROOM
- ☐ SHIP
- ☐ SHOVEL
- ☐ STEAM POWER
- ☐ TABLES
- ☐ TRAP
- ☐ TRAWLERS
- ☐ TURBINES
- ☐ VESSEL
- ☐ WHISTLES

```
H O J E S N G I O A D Y E L B F L N I S B R U
S V H R T E E N R G R N S T A R E T N A I W T
L E G S R D S E L I A M N B O H E A G C N E S
T N H C O N W P T R H M U D O W B U S T M C H
D E R A T S H I S P R E C N R S P G E R S R E
N H C G S B J F S G Y N T J P H I R L C T B L
I L Y B A L L I D N N P I O N G M P W A R O I
C L E S T H J T T I O T S S Y E L E A M M O T
I V E S I W R S B L L E N C M N I T V P G N H
T R L C O N D I R O R R B H I M K S J O D F I
O V O S A T C N B T A E L M U B T R E W E J L
M O C L O R G J E C K W O P P D P A L T R E T
```

Alphabetics

Each of the answer words starts with a different letter of the alphabet. The words are in the diagram reading forward, backward, up, down, diagonally, and always in a straight line. Words may overlap. Not all the letters in the diagram will be used. The number in parentheses is the number of letters in the word.

Word list on page 334

Solution on page 332

A _ _ _ _ _ _ _ _ _ _ (10)
B _ _ _ _ _ _ _ _ _ _ _ (11)
C _ _ _ _ _ _ _ _ _ _ _ (11)
D _ _ _ _ _ _ _ _ (8)
E _ _ _ _ _ (5)
F _ _ _ _ _ _ _ _ (8)
G _ _ _ _ _ _ _ (7)
H _ _ _ _ _ _ (6)
I _ _ _ _ _ _ _ _ _ (9)
J _ _ _ _ _ _ _ (7)
K _ _ _ _ _ _ _ _ _ (9)
L _ _ _ _ _ _ _ (7)
M _ _ _ _ _ _ _ _ (8)

N _ _ _ _ _ _ (6)
O _ _ _ _ _ _ (6)
P _ _ _ _ _ _ _ (7)
Q _ _ _ _ _ _ _ _ (8)
R _ _ _ _ _ _ _ _ (8)
S _ _ _ _ _ (5)
T _ _ _ _ _ (5)
U _ _ _ _ _ (5)
V _ _ _ _ _ (5)
W _ _ _ _ _ _ (6)
X _ _ _ _ _ _ _ _ _ (9)
Y _ _ _ _ _ _ (6)
Z _ _ _ _ _ (5)

```
W Z S E L B A P A C N I S H R O L B Q U Y B D
N O I T A L E R Z V N W T C O M E R E T N I W
X S Q L O N Y Z T A I X A I T K N O M X C Y Z
N E Y N T R W Q M I W X Y G A P J T E S R E V
W L T E I O E Y N L F E R L R R R H W S A N A
O R R R L A R G A X L I T O O G R E A T E R N
D U S L A I T N E D E R C Q O P V R T F Q U E
K O E N A I T N N Z E R O I U D H H M N E O N
C Y O D E E N A U D E R U T A N B O U T I J T
O O E C R I H H N O G B E O D L C O N N A E
N M I N U S E U Q J F F R I D E L D G E G A P
K N I A T N U O M S K P T A N N O I T S E U Q
```

WORD SEEK 3

Secret Message

After you have located and looped all the words in the diagram, read the leftover letters to find a Secret Message. Words in the diagram read forward, backward, up, down, and diagonally, and always in a straight line.

Secret Message on page 334

Solution on page 332

- ☐ ALERT
- ☐ AREA
- ☐ AUTHORITY
- ☐ AWARE
- ☐ CAREFUL
- ☐ CATCH
- ☐ CHECK
- ☐ CITY
- ☐ COMPLY
- ☐ DIRECTIONS
- ☐ DISTRICT
- ☐ DUTY
- ☐ ENFORCE
- ☐ FINE
- ☐ HEEDFUL
- ☐ HELPFUL
- ☐ INFORM
- ☐ KEEN
- ☐ LANE
- ☐ LAWS
- ☐ LEGAL
- ☐ LOCAL
- ☐ MONITOR
- ☐ NOTICE
- ☐ OBEY
- ☐ OBSERVANT
- ☐ OFFICIAL
- ☐ ORDERS
- ☐ PARKING
- ☐ PATROL
- ☐ PUBLIC
- ☐ RANKS
- ☐ REGARD
- ☐ REGULATE
- ☐ RESPECT
- ☐ ROAD
- ☐ RULES
- ☐ SAFETY
- ☐ SECTOR
- ☐ SERVE
- ☐ SIDEWALKS
- ☐ SIGNS
- ☐ STOP
- ☐ STREETS
- ☐ TIME
- ☐ TOWN
- ☐ UNIFORM
- ☐ URBAN
- ☐ WARN
- ☐ WATCHFUL
- ☐ ZONES

```
R T O L U F H C T A W I N F O R M R O F I N U
R O A B S R O A M W Y T E F A S R E T L E E A
E W T E S M B R C A R E F U L M U A A E Y S U
S N R C P E I A D R F I P E M E L G K T T T T
P V A L E L R H N E C U T Z O N E S I I U E H
E S Y L H S R V E I B E R C N L S C M J D E O
C O B S I D E W A L K S N O I T C E R I D R R
T H C T A C G L I N P O P A T R O L S O D T I
S A E I S D A C J U T F B S O E T K T E F S T
T E T C A N R A W I H E U E R L N S R T I N Y
O R I O K C D K C L O C A L Y A E S I G N S E
P A R K I N G E T A L U G E R T L U F D E E H
```

Patchwords

It's a crazy quilt and a Word Seek combined! Each of the words in the list can be found in an irregular-shaped patch in the puzzle diagram. Each letter in the diagram will be used once; the patches do not overlap. We have located one word to start you off.

Solution on page 332

AMERICAN REVOLUTION

- ☐ ARMY
- ☐ ATTACK
- ☐ BATTLES
- ☐ BOLD
- ☐ BOSTON
- ☐ BRAVE
- ☐ BRITISH
- ☐ CANNONS
- ☑ CAPTURE
- ☐ COLONIES
- ☐ CONCORD
- ☐ COURAGE
- ☐ DEFEND
- ☐ FLAG
- ☐ FORCES
- ☐ FORTS
- ☐ FREEDOM
- ☐ HARBOR
- ☐ HEROES
- ☐ HISTORY
- ☐ INDEPENDENCE
- ☐ KING
- ☐ LEXINGTON
- ☐ MARCH
- ☐ NATIONHOOD
- ☐ NAVY
- ☐ PATRIOTS
- ☐ PROUD
- ☐ REDCOATS
- ☐ SHIPS
- ☐ SPIES
- ☐ START
- ☐ STRIVE
- ☐ UNIFORMS
- ☐ VICTORIES

S	T	R	O	L	D	B	R	O	T	S	S	E	O	R
D	F	O	B	H	T	A	Y	S	N	I	H	N	O	E
O	N	O	I	A	T	L	C	A	O	S	O	S	T	H
O	H	K	T	R	B	E	S	N	N	E	B	T	C	I
N	E	I	A	N	O	R	N	C	E	I	R	O	S	V
D	F	N	G	S	E	S	E	D	A	P	T	I	H	G
S	E	D	C	O	I	P	E	N	C	N	U	P	S	A
T	R	O	M	N	R	D	P	A	T	O	R	E	F	L
V	I	D	S	C	O	D	E	R	S	T	F	O	R	S
E	E	E	T	O	I	N	M	T	N	G	I	T	C	E
F	R	S	R	I	C	O	A	H	I	B	R	I	S	H
C	K	T	T	A	P	L	R	C	X	E	L	D	U	O
A	T	A	O	C	N	O	E	S	I	N	U	A	R	R
N	T	A	E	D	I	B	V	M	F	A	E	G	U	P
A	V	Y	R	S	E	R	A	R	O	R	M	Y	O	C

Crossed Names

Fill in the squares of each diagram to form the name of a famous person. The first name may appear in either the across or down boxes. Use only the letters given above the diagram. The letter shown in each diagram is shared by both the first and last names.

Solutions on page 329

1. IJLRRSWY

2. AEIRRTTU

3. EEGHIKPST

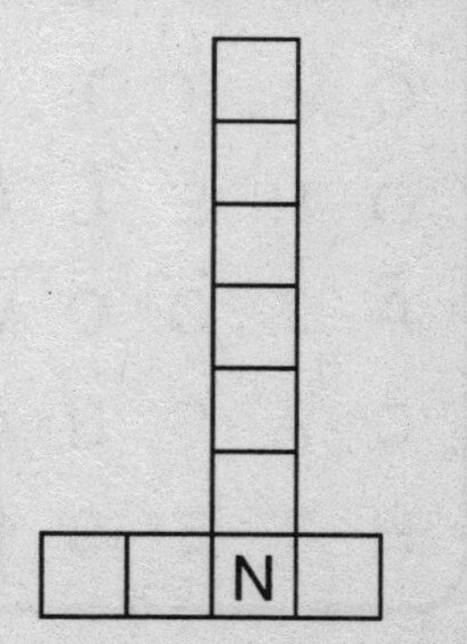

Wizard Words

The Wizard is wise and humorous. To complete his words first loop all the words in the word list, then read the leftover letters to reveal the missing words that will complete the Wizard's Words. Words in the diagram read forward, backward, up, down, and diagonally, and always in a straight line. Words often overlap, and some letters may be used more than once.

Wizard's Words on page 334

Solution on page 332

COWBOY POETS ______ _____ __ ______ ______ ___ _____ ________!

- ☐ BRANDING
- ☐ BRONCO
- ☐ CAMP
- ☐ CANYONS
- ☐ CATTLE DRIVES
- ☐ CATTLEMEN
- ☐ CHAPS
- ☐ COMPOSITION
- ☐ COOK
- ☐ CORRAL
- ☐ COWBOY HAT
- ☐ COWHAND
- ☐ COWPOKE
- ☐ COYOTES
- ☐ CREATIVE
- ☐ DUSTY
- ☐ EXPRESS
- ☐ GEAR
- ☐ HERD
- ☐ HORSE
- ☐ IMAGINATIVE
- ☐ LINES
- ☐ LITERARY
- ☐ MULE
- ☐ NATURE
- ☐ POETIC
- ☐ PONY
- ☐ RANCHER
- ☐ REINS
- ☐ RHYMES
- ☐ RIDERS
- ☐ RODEO
- ☐ ROPES
- ☐ SADDLE
- ☐ SPURS
- ☐ STABLE
- ☐ STAGECOACH
- ☐ SUBJECTS
- ☐ SUNSET
- ☐ TOPICS
- ☐ TOUGH
- ☐ TRACKS
- ☐ TRAILS
- ☐ VERSE
- ☐ WAGON
- ☐ WESTERN
- ☐ WORDS
- ☐ WORK
- ☐ WRANGLER

```
E V I T A N I G A M I S R A N C H E R U T A N
S L L O O S R E D I R E S S U B J E C T S E R
S N U H C P N O G A W V E E N G P O N Y K F E
T O I M O U I R D R A I M P R S M K O O C E T
A S N E R R I C A E S R Y O C P E B P D V P S
G L T O R S S E S E O D H R O A X W R I M H E
E I P M A C G E L O V E R S E H O E T O G S W
C A T T L E M E N B L L I O N C H A T U N K H
O R E L G N A R W D A T E K W S E T O Y O C R
A T C O W H A N D L I T E R A R Y T S U D A O
C A S N O Y N A C O N A S O C G N I D N A R B
H T E S N U S E N I L C O W B O Y H A T G T E
```

Missing Vowels

Before you can loop these names of young animals, you must first fill in the circles in the diagram with the missing vowels A, E, I, O, and U. Words in the diagram read forward, backward, up, down, and diagonally, and always in a straight line. Circle each word when you find it and cross it off the list. Words will often overlap, and some letters may be used more than once. Not all of the letters in the diagram will be used. We have filled in and circled BUNNY as an example.

Solution on page 332

ANIMAL YOUNGSTERS

BUNNY	FAWN	KITTEN	PUPPY
CALF	FILLY	LAMB	SHOAT
CHICK	FINGERLING	LEVERET	SMOLT
COCKEREL	FLAPPER	NESTLING	SPRAG
CODLING	FLEDGLING	OWLET	SQUAB
COLT	FOAL	PARR	SQUEAKER
CYGNET	GOSLING	PIGLET	TADPOLE
DUCKLING	GRILSE	POLLIWOG	TINKER
EAGLET	HEIFER	POULT	WHELP
ELVER	JOEY	PULLET	YEARLING

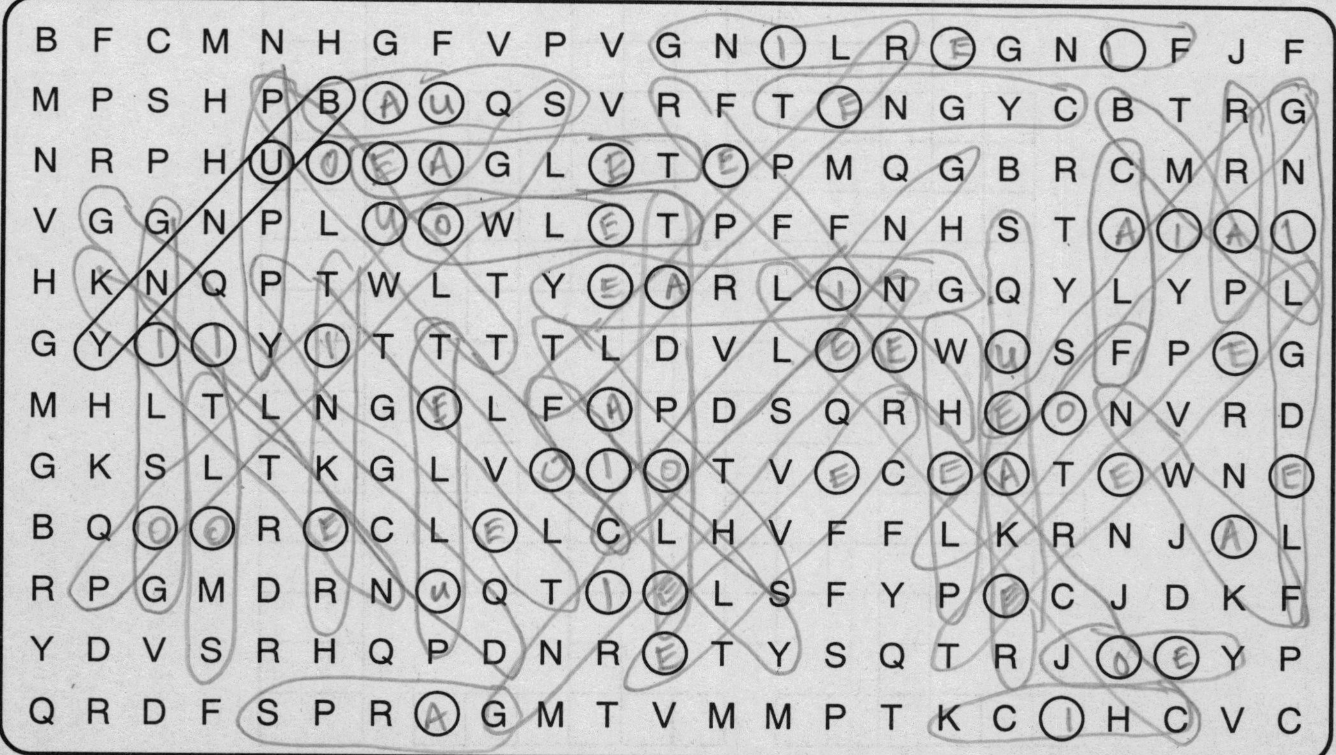

MASTERWORDS

Using only the ten letters shown, fill in the diagram by forming words across and down to achieve the highest possible score. Each letter has a given value, so try to use the high-value letters as much as possible. You may repeat letters as often as you wish, even within words. Do not repeat words in the diagram. Foreign words, abbreviations, and words starting with a capital letter are not allowed.

When the diagram is completely filled, add up your score. Count each letter, line by line, going across only. Put the total for each line in the boxes at the right.

Our solution with a score of 340 on page 330

A	B	E	F	I	L	R	T	U	Y
1	5	5	4	3	3	4	1	2	2

SCORE

TOTAL

CRYPTO-FAMILIES

Each Crypto-Family is a list of related words in code. Each Family has its own code. When you have identified a word, use the known letters to help decode the other words in the Family.

Solutions on page 329

1. ON YOUR FEET
Example: Loafers

PFISFT SFFJD
NFPYDUNWBD
XFPPLDUQD
IUQKJUVD
KLEFDGWD
GUKG GWWED
DQWLYWBD
DEUVVWBD
DLQNLED
VRXVD

2. WEATHER FORECAST
Example: Dew point

SETLYR
OLGGR
OGTD
FLNWY
DWGYSFWEE
HCTGP
AEWXXVCY
HELCCWZO
OPTCN
ACZZXR

3. "CROSS" WORDS
Example: Fire

CQDEJVA
DVHAEXN
TYX
DHXXQAE
CEJEDP
DHE
MJAU
XVYU
TVM
TVAQC

4. BRITISH POETS
Example: Browning

APTID
BYVZL
LSYJJYP
ZYDDPLID
UIUY
LUYDLYT
JYVT
AQTDL
GIDDY
VQGYD

5. GRAMMAR LESSON
Example: Interjection

SBKS
YTSXTSFT
BNUTFX
VHBSBKS
MEQTHN
FBSUKSFXPBS
VMYYPQT
FWMKYT
VHTVBYPXPBS
VWKHMW

6. WALK ON
Example: Hike

WCYMUU
SOYHF
OSRUK
WOBGCKY
WCYBC
TYMSKGOQK
TUMQ
CYKOQ
CYBQXK
WCYDQK

HOW TO SOLVE: Fill in as many boxes as you can to form eleven words starting with the given letters. No letter may be repeated in the word itself, in the word above, or in the word below. For each word the number of letters needed to earn the maximum score is indicated by the number of boxes.

HOW TO SCORE: Each letter used is worth one point. If you use all 26 letters of the alphabet, give yourself a bonus of ten points. Include the given letters in all scoring.

Our solutions on page 329

Sample:

Word	Score
SAMPLE	6
RING	4
CLOUDY	6

In this sample the word RING cannot be RINGER because the letter R would be repeated in that word and because the letter E appears above in SAMPLE. It cannot be RUNG because U is below in CLOUDY.

1.

WORDS	SCORE
H A _ _ _	
M I _ _ _	
J A _ _ _ _	
P _ _ _ _	
M A _ _ _ _	
C R _ _ _ _ _	
S P _ _ _	
M _ _ _ _	
S _ _ _	
P R _ _ _ _	
B _ _ _	
TOTAL	

2.

WORDS	SCORE
S Q _ _ _ _ _	
T _ _ _ _	
G L _ _ _	
S _ _ _ _	
O _ _ _	
R _ _ _ _	
M _ _ _ _	
P R _ _ _ _ _	
S _ _ _	
N I _ _ _ _ _	
B O _ _ _ _	
TOTAL	

LETTER POWER

P	L	A	Y					
1	1	1	1					4

L	E	T	T	E	R			
2	1	1	2	2	1			9

P	O	W	E	R				
2	1	1	3	2				9

22

Use your Letter Power to earn the highest score by repeating letters in each answer and from one answer to another as often as you can. There are many possible choices, so we suggest you pencil in your words lightly. Use a maximum of eight letters for each answer.

SCORING: Do not add your score until you have all your answers, since you may want to make changes. A letter is worth 1 point the first time it is used in your answers, 2 the second, 3 the third, etc. Add the points earned in each answer and put the total in the box at the right. Then compare your total score with ours.

1. Salad-bar item
2. Biblical name
3. Pop song
4. Eating utensil
5. Indian tribe
6. Revolutionary War battle site
7. Explorer
8. High-school term
9. Coin
10. Academy-Award-winning film

TOTAL

Our solutions with a score of 467 points on page 329

ANAGRAM MAGIC SQUARE

Rearrange the 5-letter word in each box to form another word. The anagrammed word will answer one of the clues. Put the number of that clue into the small square and write the anagram on the dash. The numbers in each row and column will add up to 65. Write the first letter of each anagram on the correspondingly numbered dash at the bottom of the page; and, presto!, the saying will appear. We have put in one anagram and its clue number and set its first letter on the proper dash. **Solution on page 329**

SNORE ☐ ___	SHALE ☐ ___	LASER ☐ ___	STAIN ☐ ___	LEASE ☐ ___	= 65
TRACE *1* *CRATE*	NERVE ☐ ___	MANSE ☐ ___	OVERT ☐ ___	RASPY ☐ ___	= 65
SHOAT ☐ ___	RUNIC ☐ ___	SHIRE ☐ ___	RESTS ☐ ___	SANER ☐ ___	= 65
ELTON ☐ ___	NEATH ☐ ___	DETER ☐ ___	LOWED ☐ ___	ARTIE ☐ ___	= 65
LORRE ☐ ___	TORTE ☐ ___	STENO ☐ ___	CEDAR ☐ ___	MANET ☐ ___	= 65
= 65	= 65	= 65	= 65	= 65	

1. Box
2. Aquatic mammal
3. Comes close to
4. Wooden pin
5. British noblemen
6. Intended
7. Ancient Scandinavian
8. Treasure-____
9. Charters
10. Patriot Allen
11. Shiny fabric
12. Furious
13. Reminders
14. At no time
15. Solemn promises
16. Cornered
17. Curl of hair
18. Gets better
19. Actor Flynn
20. Jet of water
21. Bring upon oneself
22. Titles
23. Actor Nick ____
24. Artist's stand
25. Sped

C																								
1	2	3	4	5	6	7	8	9	10	11	12	13	14	15	16	17	18	19	20	21	22	23	24	25

SPLIT AND SPLICE

Place the 6-letter answer to clue 1 in the first row of the diagram. The answers to the next two clues are 3-letter words made up of the letters of the first answer. Thereafter each answer contains the letters of the word above it plus one letter. In the sixth row the 6-letter answers split to form 3-letter words. For the lower part of the diagram the pattern is reversed: each answer contains the letters of the word above it minus one letter, and pairs of 3-letter answers combine to form 6-letter words. We have set one answer to help you begin.

Solution on page 330

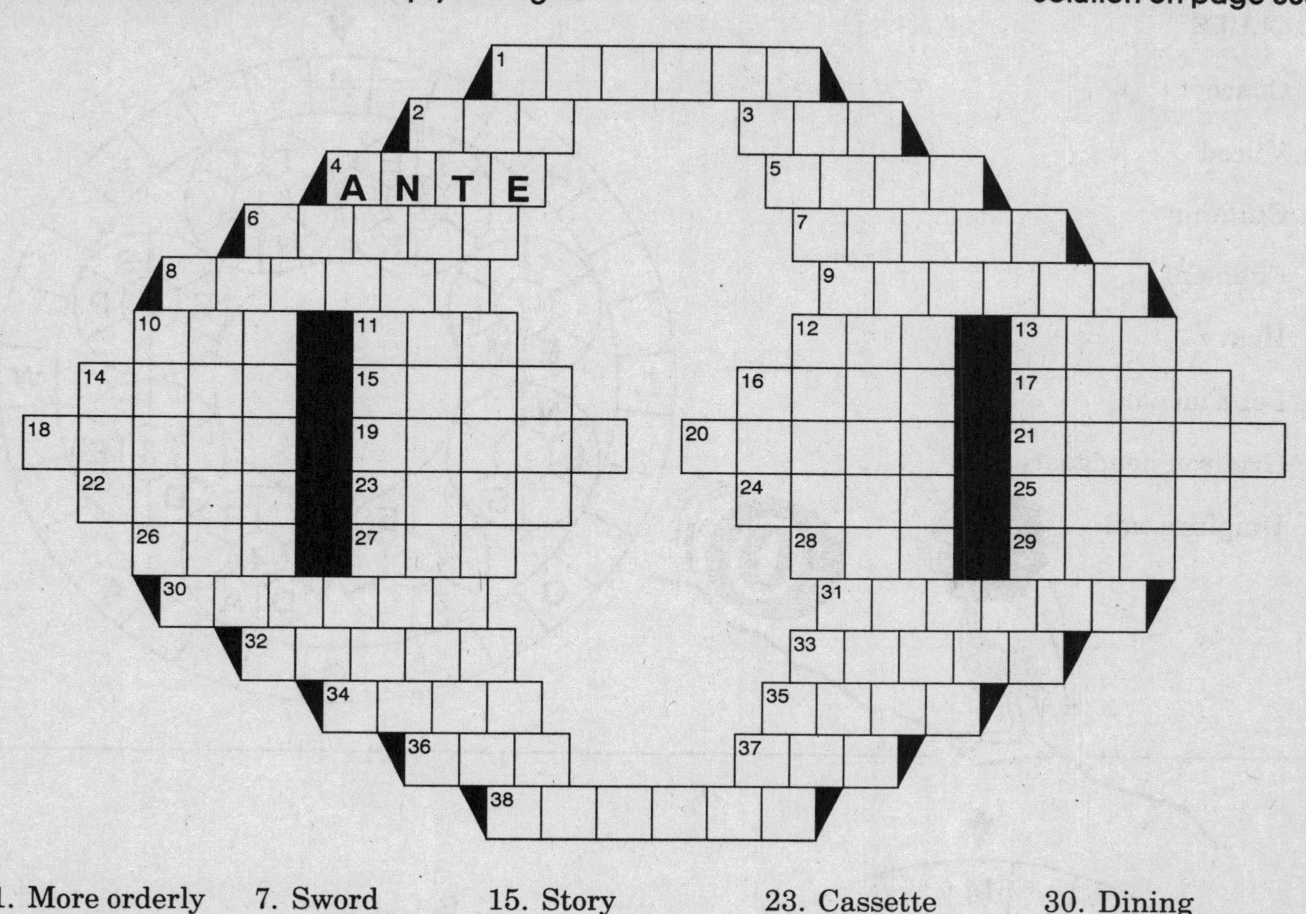

1. More orderly
2. Tennis-court divider
3. Period in history
4. Poker wager
5. Endure
6. Representative
7. Sword
8. Snarl
9. Cook slowly
10. Pester
11. Lease
12. Tease
13. "____ of Love"
14. Pealed
15. Story
16. French cheese
17. Flower holder
18. Rye or wheat
19. Skirt fold
20. Wedding star
21. Lotion
22. Broad smile
23. Cassette
24. Urgent
25. Emblem
26. ____ rummy
27. Oolong or pekoe
28. Primary color
29. Tavern beverage
30. Dining
31. Vendor
32. Titan
33. Birch's kin
34. Opposed: pref.
35. Valley
36. Writer Fleming
37. Conducted
38. Used a hammer

WHEELS

Answer the clues for the 6-letter words, which go clockwise around the inner Wheels starting at the heavy lines. Three letters of each are given. Then place the three letters you added in the adjoining spaces in the outer Wheel so that a message can be read starting at the arrow and proceeding clockwise.

Solution on page 329

A. CLUES

1. Concept
2. Voiced
3. Cunning
4. Filament
5. Heavy
6. Lend an ear
7. Gridiron headgear
8. Umpire's call

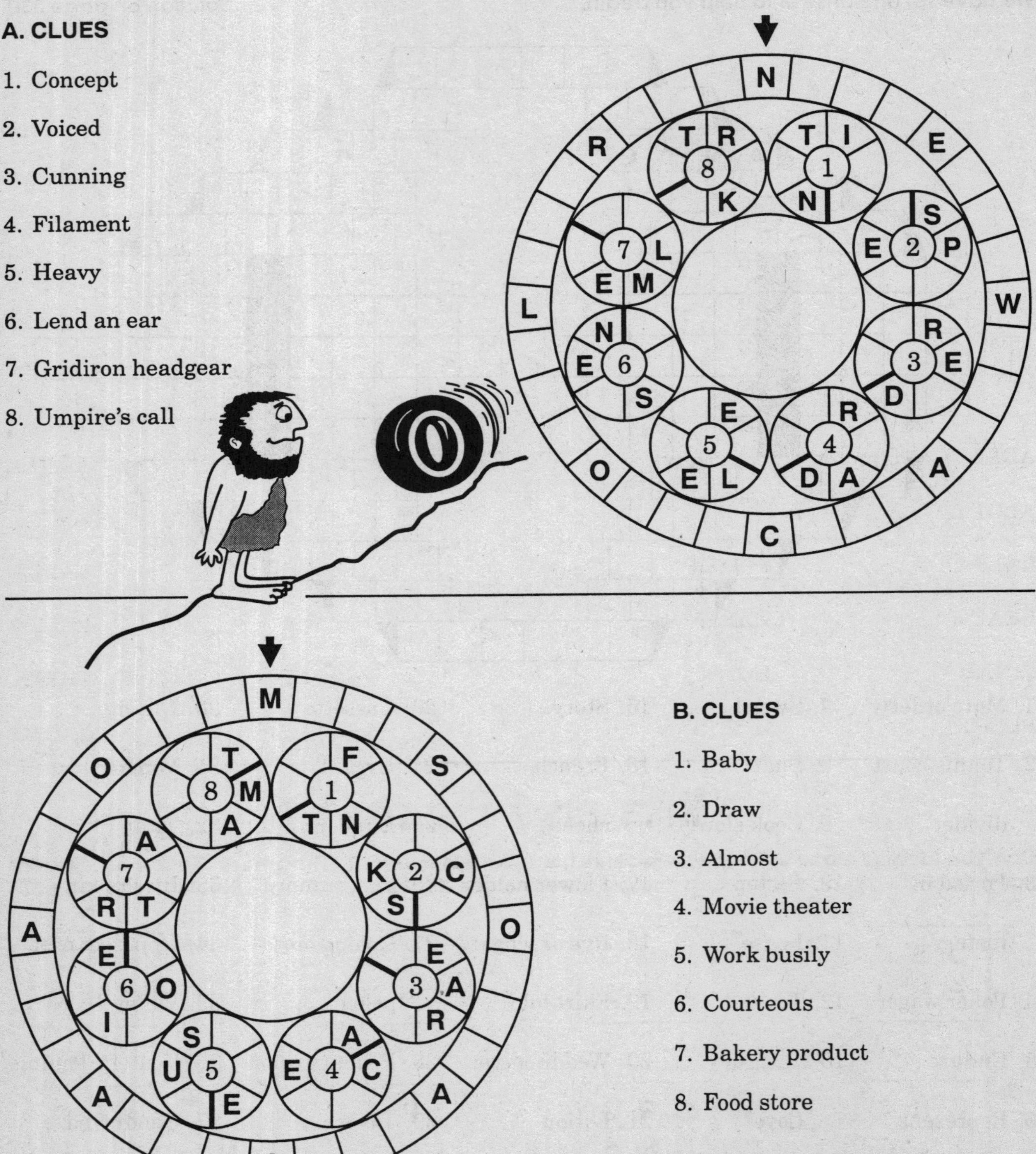

B. CLUES

1. Baby
2. Draw
3. Almost
4. Movie theater
5. Work busily
6. Courteous
7. Bakery product
8. Food store

CIRCLES IN THE SQUARE

The twenty 5-letter words all fit in the diagram. All words begin and end in a dark circle. Horizontal words read from left to right; all other words read from top to bottom. We have placed one letter in the diagram.

Solution on page 330

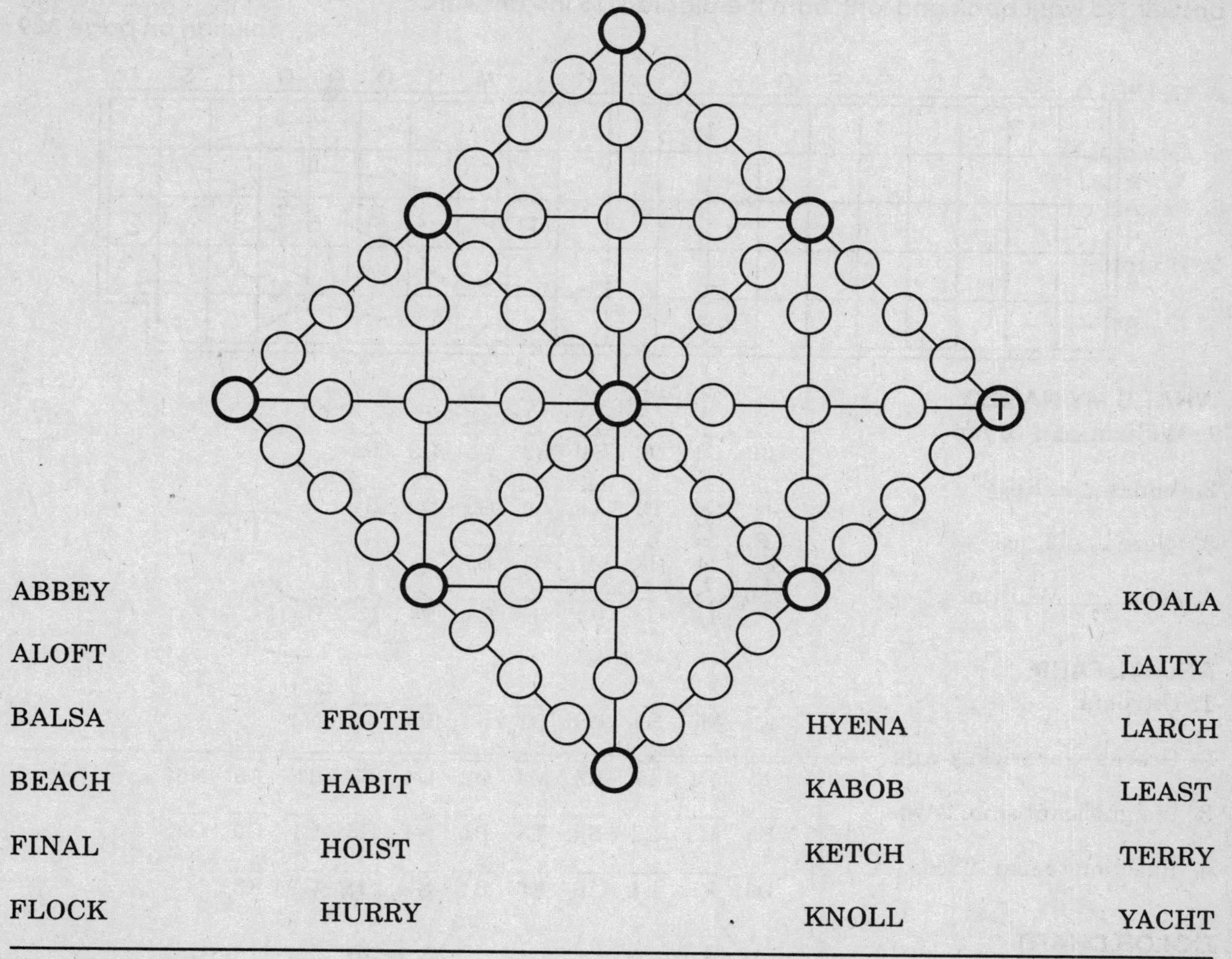

ABBEY
ALOFT
BALSA
BEACH
FINAL
FLOCK
FROTH
HABIT
HOIST
HURRY
HYENA
KABOB
KETCH
KNOLL
KOALA
LAITY
LARCH
LEAST
TERRY
YACHT

Bits and Pieces

Can you identify these U.S. vice presidents from the Bits and Pieces shown in the boxes? The first names are always on the top and the last names on the bottom.

Solutions on page 328

1. U B E / P H R
2. N D O / H N S
3. L T E / N D A
4. R A L / O R D
5. C H A / I X O
6. O R G / U S H
7. P I R / G N E
8. A R R / R U M

WORD GAMES

Place the answers to the Word Games onto the blanks at the right and then transfer the letters into the corresponding locations in the diagram. When the puzzle is completed, a rhyming verse will be revealed reading across the diagram. Some letters in the diagram are used in more than one answer, so work back and forth from the diagram to the answers.

Solution on page 329

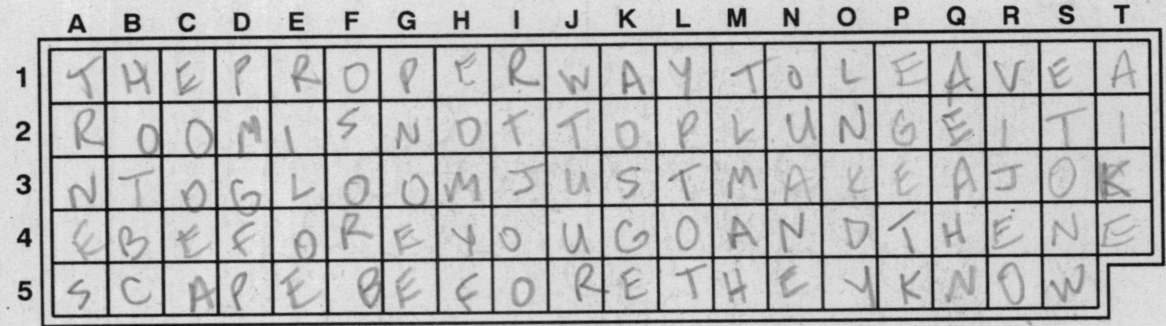

WHAT'S MY NAME?

1. William ____ Bryan — I3 C4 O2 S4 R2 Q5 D3 F2
2. James ____ Riley — J1 Q4 T2 A1 B5 G3 D2 B4
3. Clare ____ Luce — F5 I4 S3 M1 B1 E5
4. John ____ Whittier — P2 I1 G4 P3 G2 O1 T4 C5 D4

ANIMAL FARM

1. Diploma — K3 M5 H1 G5 D1 F2 P5 T2 N4
2. Greeks' war trick: 2 wds. — I2 F4 I5 R3 M4 O2 Q4 F3 I1 A5 N5
3. Insignificant sum: 2 wds. — B5 M5 E2 B5 T3 P1 N4 H5 C1 G5 O4
4. Reaction to fear: 2 wds. — D3 F1 L4 A5 K5 B4 N2 M3 G1 K3

COLOR CHART

1. Brains: 2 wds. — K4 J5 N3 H4 H3 M4 M1 J2 A4 J5
2. Cocktail: 2 wds. — L2 T2 Q5 O3 E3 K1 O4 O5
3. Academic's place: 2 wds. — E2 R1 C2 A2 L1 L5 E4 S5 Q2 E1
4. Cavern in Capri: 2 wds. — F5 M2 J4 R4 P2 F4 N1 B3 A1 B2

THREE + THREE = ONE

1. TAT + MOO = P4 K2 D2 Q1 L5 C3
2. GUY + ROT = L1 R5 K4 J3 A2 S2
3. INK + PAN = A3 T1 D5 P5 R2 S4
4. NOD + TEA = O4 H2 G2 Q3 L3 S1

PUZZLE DERBY

Ladies and gentlemen, the horses are at the starting gate. Select your favorite (A, E, I, O, or U), and the race is on. First fill in the blanks with the answers to the clues. Vowels always go above numbered dashes and consonants above the unnumbered ones. All answers have something in common. Then, to find out who wins the race, move the horses around the track according to the number values under the vowels.

Solution on page 330

Example: A L O U D (A = 2, O = 4, U = 1) **: move 2 spaces ahead in Lane A, 4 in Lane O, and 1 in Lane U.**

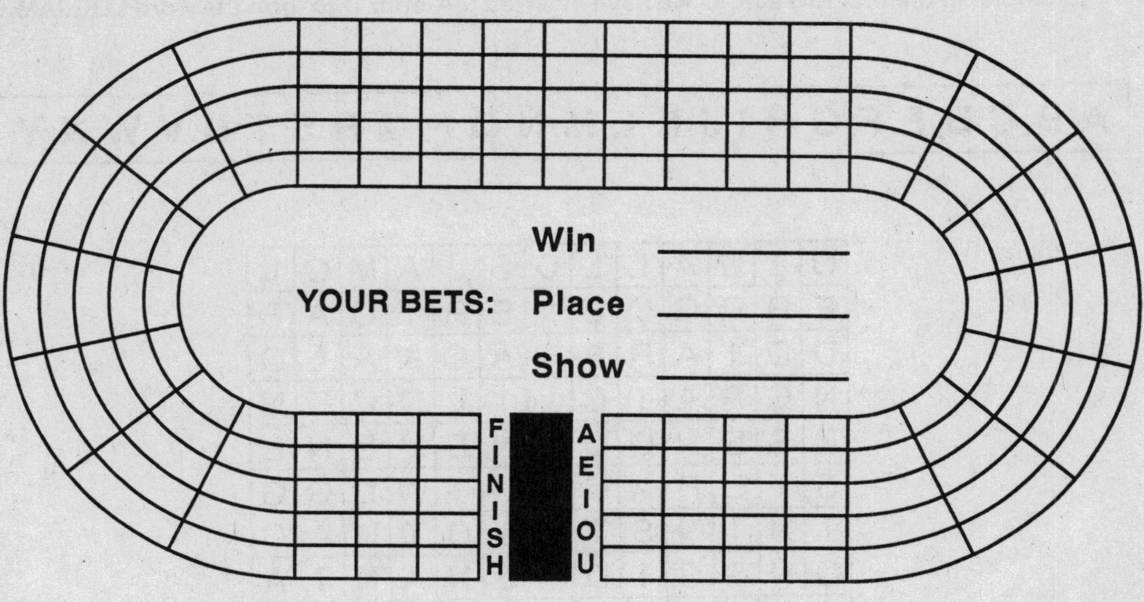

Clue	1	2	3	4	5	6	7	8	9
1. Exact copy		4	C	S	3		5	L	3
2. Eurasian bird	B	5		L	F	3			
3. Grape plantation		4	N	2		5			
4. Circle width		2	4	M	3		4		
5. Professional associate		6	L		2	3	G	6	4
6. Unshod		4	R	3	F	6	3		
7. Smart aleck	W	4	S	6	2	C		2	
8. Skilled hunter	N	3	M	R	2				
9. Stenography			5		T	H	6		
10. 15th Greek letter	2		6	C	R	3			

ALPHABET SOUP

Insert a different letter of the alphabet into each of the 26 empty boxes to form words of five or more letters reading across. The letter you insert may be at the beginning, the end, or in the middle of the word. Each letter of the alphabet will be used only once. Cross off each letter in the list as you use it. All the letters in each row are not necessarily used in forming the word.

Our solution on page 331

Example: In the first row across we have inserted the letter O to form the word LOGJAM.

A B C D E F G H I J K L M N Ø P Q R S T U V W X Y Z

O	L	U	A	L	L	**O**	G	J	A	M	C	L
E	P	R	G	O	E		E	R	T	C	A	B
U	D	I	A	R	F		A	C	K	A	L	O
N	G	R	A	I	C		I	L	D	R	E	N
E	S	E	N	O	U		N	E	V	E	N	E
S	T	O	R	A	G		O	T	W	U	G	G
T	N	I	N	S	T		N	C	T	U	A	G
O	N	S	S	I	D		E	N	A	N	T	A
J	O	J	E	C	F		A	M	E	V	O	C
A	N	D	G	H	T		R	I	E	N	D	R
O	C	R	Y	E	A		T	R	T	M	I	S
E	S	S	B	B	E		R	I	G	H	T	V
H	I	A	R	G	M		S	T	E	R	I	U
A	S	P	R	I	N		I	S	T	E	M	P
I	I	N	F	O	R		R	G	O	E	S	S
E	L	L	M	A	N		L	A	C	E	N	P
B	P	O	E	T	I		R	T	H	I	M	B
O	O	J	E	L	L		T	R	I	S	H	M
A	J	U	W	I	L		O	W	O	R	T	T
A	I	A	D	O	C		E	T	I	D	O	N
D	T	F	J	O	R		I	Z	I	R	I	U
X	A	B	R	O	N		E	A	G	E	A	T
L	D	I	S	T	A		C	E	P	I	N	N
N	W	I	N	D	O		W	E	L	I	C	T
R	E	O	S	P	E		A	D	E	L	U	B
U	R	A	F	R	E		U	E	N	T	B	H

BIG QUESTION

Start at the arrow and put the answers to the clues into the diagram in the order in which they are given. Every answer word overlaps the previous answer word by one letter or more. The first letters of all the answer words are shown in the diagram. When the Big Question is filled, place the eight numbered letters into their corresponding spaces in the square at the bottom to reveal the answer to the riddle.

Solution on page 330

Riddle: What kind of crowd rushes to the post office?

1. Royal abode
2. Middle
3. Wear away
4. Merry adventure
5. Skillful
6. Slide instrument
7. Burdensome
8. Theater attendant
9. Legacy
10. Representative
11. Doorway
12. Forefathers
13. Strew
14. Concise
15. Solon
16. Decoration
17. Confide
18. Play a guitar
19. Baseball official
20. Succeed in dieting
21. Large string instrument
22. Ore deposit

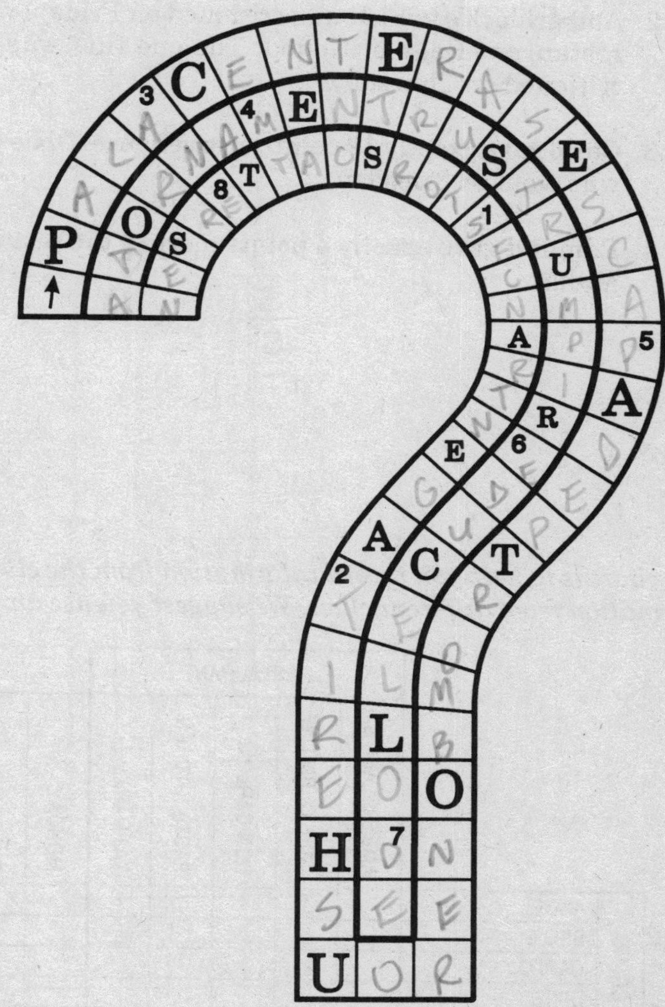

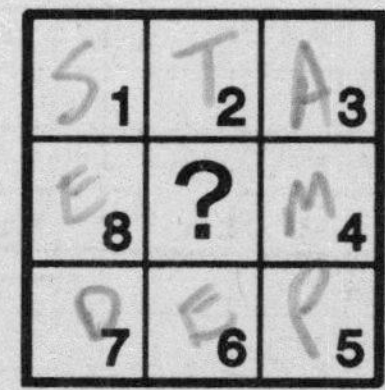

LOGIC PROBLEM

POINTS OF EXCELLENCE

To compile information for its regional restaurant guide, Orbis Publishing is rating area restaurants using a "points of excellence" system. Last week, Orbis sent each of five different restaurant critics to a different restaurant (one was Cafe Christine), each on a different weekday. Each restaurant was given a different number of points of excellence. From the information provided, determine the critic (one was Angel) who rated each restaurant, the day on which each critic conducted his or her critique, and the number of points of excellence (1, 4, 5, 8, or 12) received by each restaurant.

1. Belle (who was sent out on Monday) isn't the critic who went to Don Carlo's.

2. Amberblack's (which was critiqued on Friday) was given exactly 3 points fewer than the restaurant Belle critiqued. The one that was given exactly 1 point of excellence was critiqued on Thursday.

3. Carlo gave exactly 12 points of excellence. Dixie (who went to Pasta Kitchen) isn't the one who went on Tuesday.

4. Edmund gave exactly 4 points more to the restaurant he rated than were given to Taj Mahal.

This chart is to help you record information from the clues as well as the facts you deduce by combining information from different clues. We suggest you use an "X" for a "no" and a "•" for a "yes."

		RESTAURANT					DAY					POINTS				
		AMBERBLACK'S	CAFE CHRISTINE	DON CARLO'S	PASTA KITCHEN	TAJ MAHAL	MONDAY	TUESDAY	WEDNESDAY	THURSDAY	FRIDAY	1	4	5	8	12
CRITIC	ANGEL															
	BELLE															
	CARLO															
	DIXIE															
	EDMUND															
POINTS	1															
	4															
	5															
	8															
	12															
DAY	MONDAY															
	TUESDAY															
	WEDNESDAY															
	THURSDAY															
	FRIDAY															

Solution on page 330

JACKPOT

Solve all three parts of this puzzle and you will reveal the Jackpot quotation reading across!
Solution on page 331

M R E N N I D N I E
T W X V M E D O S Y
N O I T C A D A L E
E O T P E Q E I B L
R B V R Y R S A W L
U S I S L T I M I D
C T N E E T N A N M
O V E R J O Y E D I
R I Y V B N W L E R
D Z L E L S I A R E

CROSSWORD

This is a standard crossword except there is no clue for 23 Across. It is the start of the Jackpot quotation.

ACROSS

1. Monk's wear
5. Powder
9. Melville novel
10. Lollapalooza
11. One of the planets
12. Rooney of "60 Minutes"
13. Engenders
15. Record again
19. Health resort
22. Fragrant wood
23. See instructions
25. Struck attitudes
26. Distress call
27. Shoulder scarves
29. Grouchy ones
33. Unaccompanied
36. The ____ Ranger
37. One of the Cartwrights
38. Lotion ingredient
39. Grant
40. Specks

DOWN

1. Search thoroughly
2. Actor Sharif
3. Had on
4. Runner-up
5. Kitchen appliance
6. ____ Arbor
7. Directed
8. Weep
14. Cryptogram breaker
16. Appends
17. El ____, Texas
18. Historical periods
19. Undermines
20. Scheme
21. Likewise
24. Greet
28. Dinner course
30. ____ contendere
31. Cluster
32. Observes
33. Pouch
34. Lyric poem
35. Young boy

WORD SEEK

Solve as a regular Word Seek puzzle. The letters from the center row are missing. Fill them in as you solve to reveal the second part of the Jackpot quotation.

WORD LIST

Action
Admire
Aisle
Alley
Battery
Best
Cord
Current
Daisy
Destiny
Dinner
Doll
Exit
Grease
Hinder
News
Novelty
Oil
Overjoyed
Owl
Pine
Preserve
Spread
Timid
Widen

FRAMEWORK

Solve as a regular Framework. Then read across the center line to complete the Jackpot quotation.

WORD LIST

3 Letters
Bag
Buy
Cue
Nod
Rap
Say

4 Letters
Able
Gulp
Silo

5 Letters
Choir
House
Image
Lasso
Pasta
Roger

7 Letters
Algebra
Embrace
Nourish
Nursery
Proceed
Speaker

WHICH WAY WORDS

Starting with the correspondingly numbered circle, fit the answer to each clue into the connected circles, one letter in each. The five horizontal lines with the heavily outlined circles will contain related 9-letter entries.

Solution on page 330

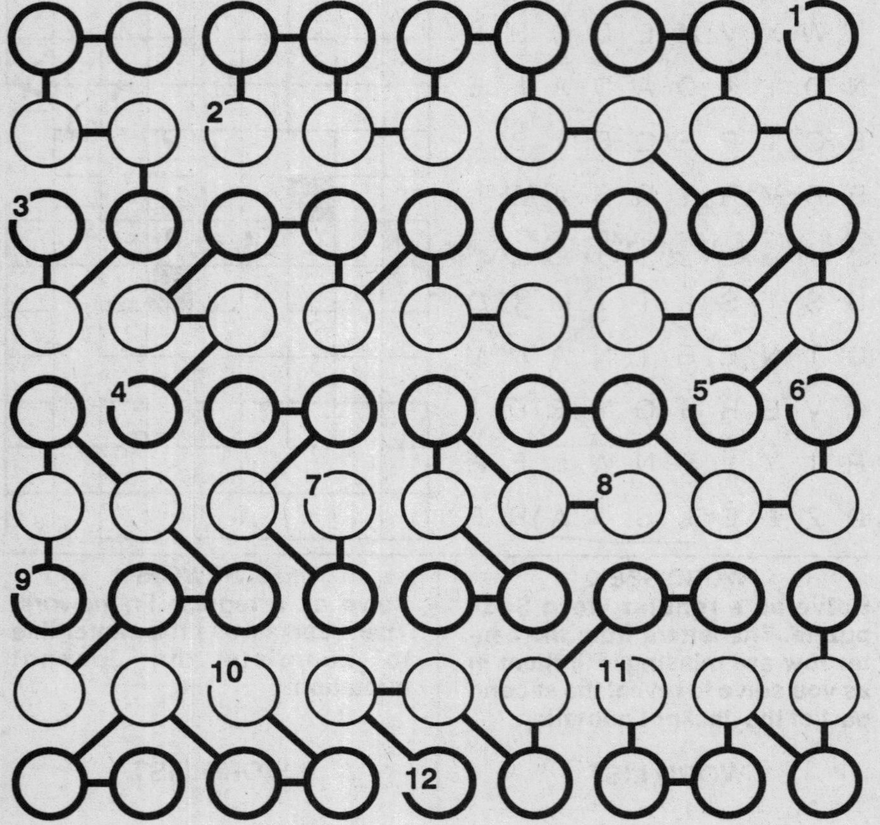

CLUES

1. Plumed bird
2. Bullets
3. Porch
4. Temporary
5. Angularly cut
6. Clan emblem
7. Trim
8. Fill in
9. Mediums' meetings
10. Titter
11. Flashlight need
12. Excellent

Place Your Number

The large square below is divided into four smaller squares—A, B, C, and D—and each smaller square is divided into four sections—North, East, South, and West. Use the clues to number the sections. Each section will contain a different number from 1 through 16.

Solution on page 331

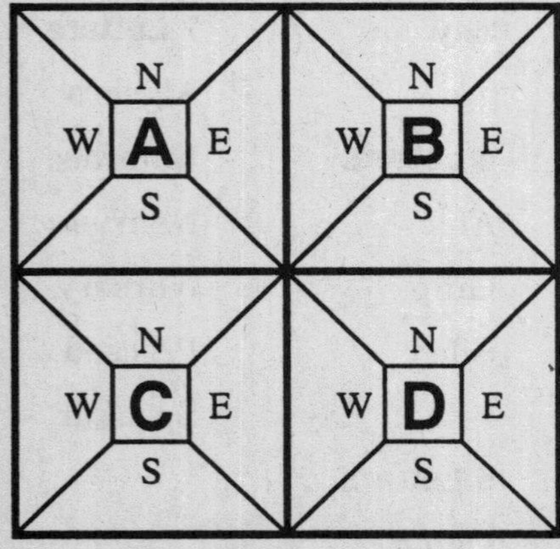

1. All of the South numbers contain the digit 1.
2. All of the East numbers are evenly divisible by 3.
3. Square A contains only double-digit numbers.
4. Square B contains four consecutive numbers.
5. Square C contains only single-digit numbers.
6. All of the numbers in square D are even.
7. A-South is two less than A-North.
8. C-East is half of D-West, which is half of D-East.
9. A-West is twice B-West, which is twice C-West.

STRETCH LETTERS

These words, listed alphabetically by length, are to be entered in the diagram across only. Words do not read down. When writing in a blank taller than a square, stretch the letter to the full height of the blank. The stretched letters are part of more than one entry.

Solution on page 330

• HIGH FINANCE •

4 Letters
Cash
Fine
Loan
Mint
Post

5 Letters
Asset
Audit
Debit
Money
Repay
Spend

6 Letters
Budget
Credit
Ledger
Refund

7 Letters
Account
Actuary
Capital
Expense
Payment
Premium
Receipt

8 Letters
Currency
Disburse
Interest
Monetary
Mortgage
Proceeds

9 Letters
Liability
Liquidate
Reimburse
Resources

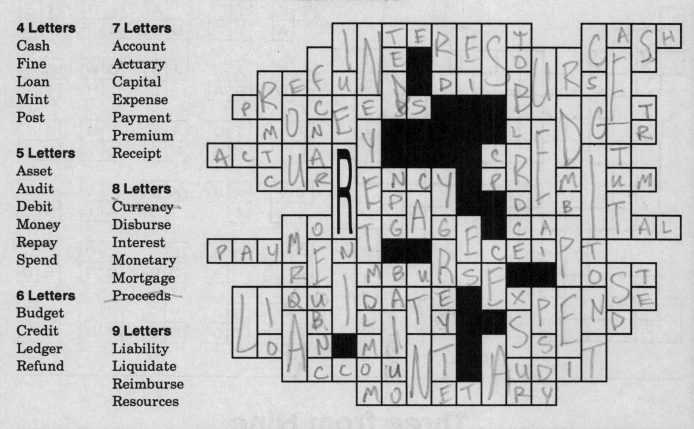

Blips

Place one of the given letters in each circle to form nine 3-letter words reading from top to bottom. Use each letter only as many times as it is listed.

Solution on page 330

A Z M Y N E D R O D E K T

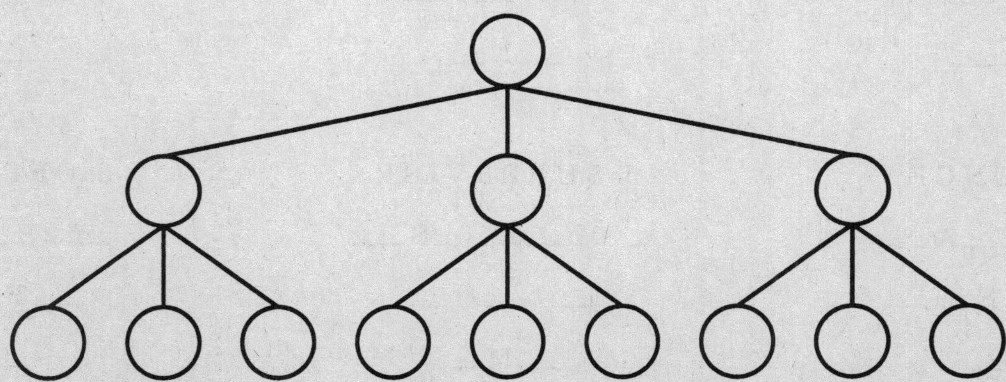

JIGSAW PUZZLE

When you have put the pieces of the Jigsaw Puzzle into their correct places in the diagram, they will form a crossword puzzle with words reading across and down. Do not turn the pieces. The heavy lines in the diagram will help you locate their proper places.

Solution on page 331

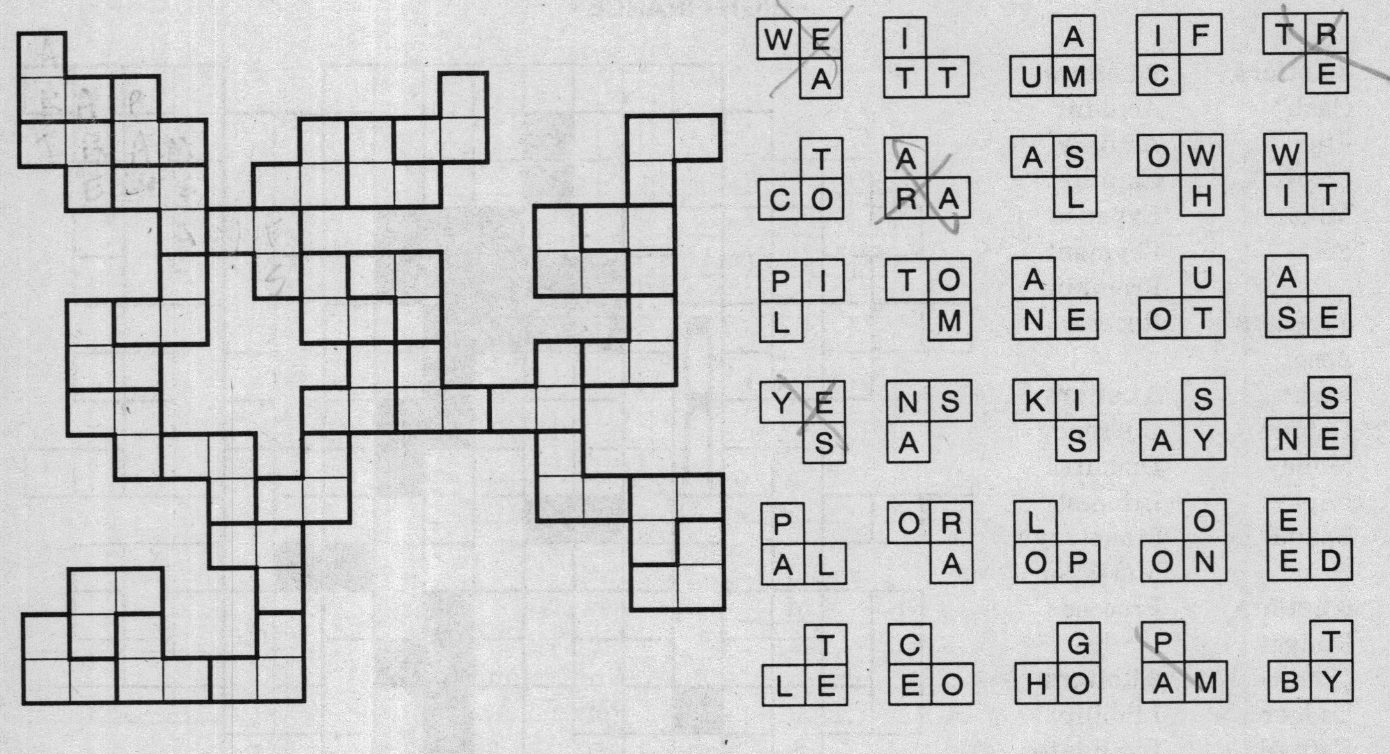

Three from Nine

Place the letters of the 9-letter words on the dashes, one letter per dash, to spell a 7-letter word, a 5-letter word, and a 3-letter word. Each letter of a 9-letter word will be used once.

Solutions on page 330

1. TRANSFORM

__A__H__M__

__A__O__

__I__

2. BLUEPRINT

__A__A__L__

__N__I__

__N__

3. INSULATED

__O__B__E__

__R__I__

__C__

4. DILIGENCE

__O__G__A__

__R__N__

__R__

5. SUPERVISE

__M__R__S__

__I__O__

__M__

6. ORCHESTRA

__P__I__O__

__P__C__

__I__

WORDFINDER

The answers to the clues are in the diagram in their corresponding rows across and down, but the letters are rearranged and mixed together. Each letter is used only once, so be sure to cross it out when you have used it. All the letters will be used. The first letter of each word is shown outside the diagram and next to each clue. We have filled in the first answer as an example.

Solutions on page 330

	G	U	K	H	Y	R	Q	A	T	C	M
L	S	Y	M	A	E	G	W	K	I	U	R
W	A	I	O	T	C	U	E	Y	R	P	H
F	U	A	E	M	N	I	T	R	O	Y	L
P	E	N	U	K	T	H	L	D	A	F	I
S	R	E	D	W	L	T	Y	O	K	I	A
J	I	T	W	S	K	E	N	M	U	A	O
N	D	S	A	C	I	L	R	H	P	E	Y
O	N	Z	R	L	G	A	U	I	E	T	D
B	F	R	N	I	O	M	D	U	H	L	E
D	M	G	I	O	S	V	A	E	L	R	U
V	T	D	L	E	A	F	I	S	M	O	C

ACROSS

Tepid L UKEWARM
Wave W ______
Seer's offering F ______
Acclamation P ______
To the heavens S ______
Fragrant flower J ______
Low point N ______
Arrange O ______
Nearly overflowing B ______
Disclose D ______
Singer V ______

DOWN

Jewels G ______
Shaky U ______
Understand K ______
Poisonous herb H ______
Egg centers Y ______
Legitimate R ______
Dorm courtyard Q ______
Nautical call A ______
Victory T ______
Confirm C ______
Tune M ______

BUILD-A-PYRAMID

Use all the jumbled letters to build a pyramid so that each word contains all the letters of the word above it plus one additional letter. A starting letter has been set in the top square of the diagram.

Solution on page 331

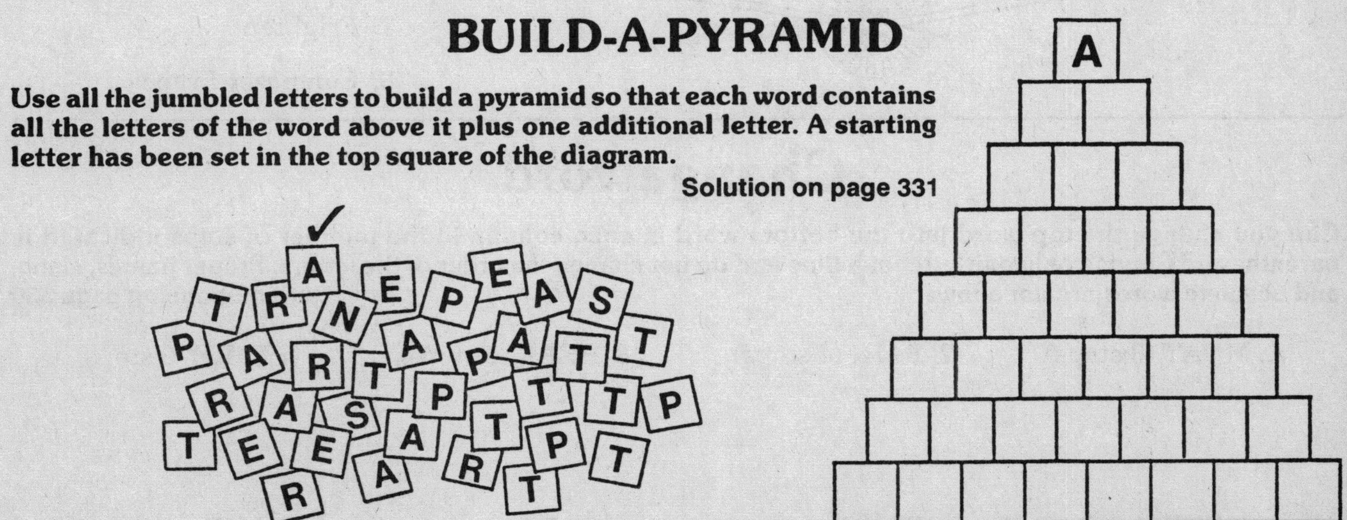

Headings

Use the letters in each Heading to fill in the blanks to complete words related to the Heading. Cross out each letter as you use it.

Solutions on page 330

1. DIFFERENT THINGS TO WRITE

___ A B L ___

___ ___ D D L ___

___ E ___ I ___ I ___ ___ O N

S O ___ ___

___ E P ___ R ___

M Y ___ ___

___ ___ O R Y

R ___ V ___ E ___

2. VARIOUS MUSICAL INSTRUMENTS

D ___ ___ ___

___ ___ O L ___ ___

___ R ___ ___ P ___ T

B A ___ ___ O O ___

___ E L ___ ___

G ___ ___ ___ A R

H ___ ___ P

___ ___ M I ___ E N

3. RACE CAR DRIVERS' VOCABULARY

___ E H ___ ___ L E

F ___ ___ G

___ ___ N K ___

___ ___ P I ___

___ I ___ T O ___ ___

S T ___ ___ ___

T ___ ___ ___ K

C ___ ___ ___ S E

Fan Words

Place the 5-letter answers to the clues into the fan to discover an 8-letter word reading across the outlined area. As an added help, pairs of answers are anagrams (1 is an anagram of 2, 3 is an anagram of 4, etc.).

Solution on page 330

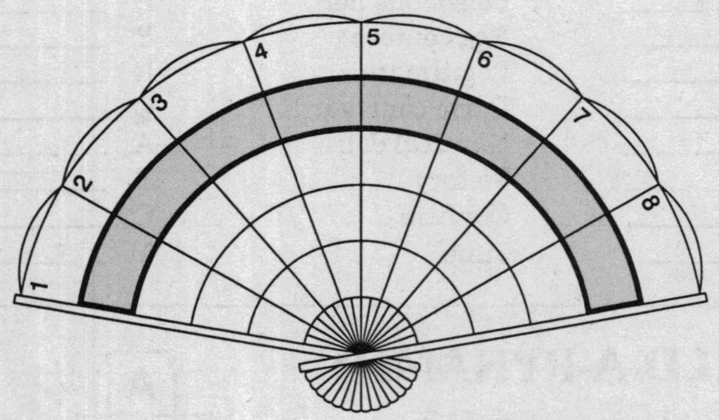

1. Fall flower
2. Signs of weeping
3. Beginning
4. Rock
5. Gulf of Aden land
6. Foe
7. Frighten
8. Composer Franck

Changaword

Can you change the top word into the bottom word in each column in the number of steps indicated in parentheses? Change only one letter at a time and do not change the order of the letters. Proper names, slang, and obsolete words are not allowed.

Our solutions on page 330

1. MOAT (3 steps)
2. PAIN (4 steps)
3. BEAR (5 steps)
4. FARE (6 steps)

MOTE

PANE

BARE

FAIR

ABACUS

Slide the abacus beads across the wires to form five related words reading down. All the beads will be used. Keep in mind that the beads are on wires and cannot jump over one another. An empty abacus is provided for you to work in.

Solution on page 331

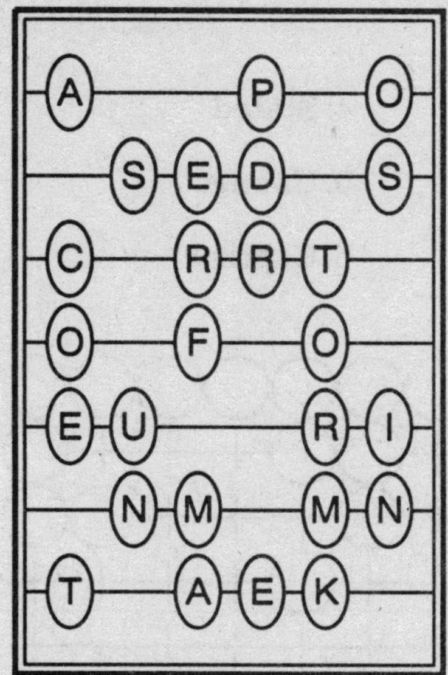

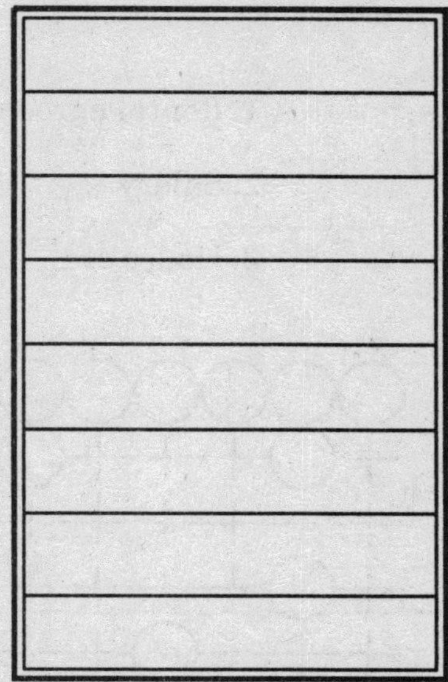

ACCORDION WORDS

Reduce each word one letter at a time until it is as short as possible. Each deletion must leave a new word. Do not change the order of the letters.

Our solutions on page 330

Example: OLIVE: Live, Lie.

1. FORGET: ____________________
2. HEAVIEST: ____________________
3. FLATTERY: ____________________
4. STOLID: ____________________
5. MANAGER: ____________________
6. CRUMBLE: ____________________
7. SCREAM: ____________________
8. COUPLET: ____________________
9. HOWLED: ____________________
10. MALIGNED: ____________________

CRISSCROSS

Beside each diagram are six groups of scrambled letters. Rearrange each group of letters to form a word, and then fit the words into the diagrams to read across or down in crossword fashion.

Our solutions on page 331

1.

VCSIEH
NEELEV
CRFNOE
IHCCEO
TEULOT
ITWINT

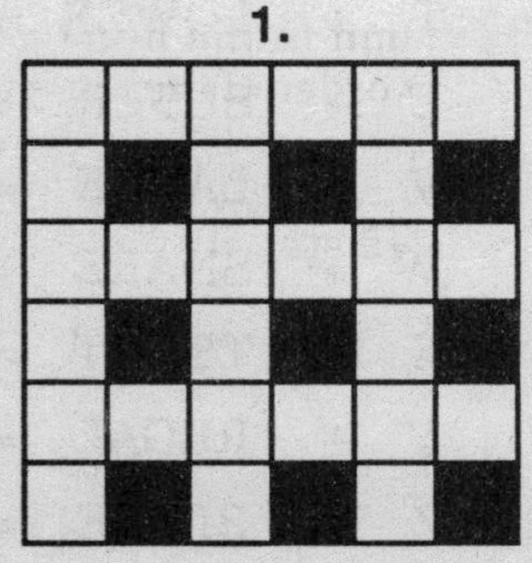

2.

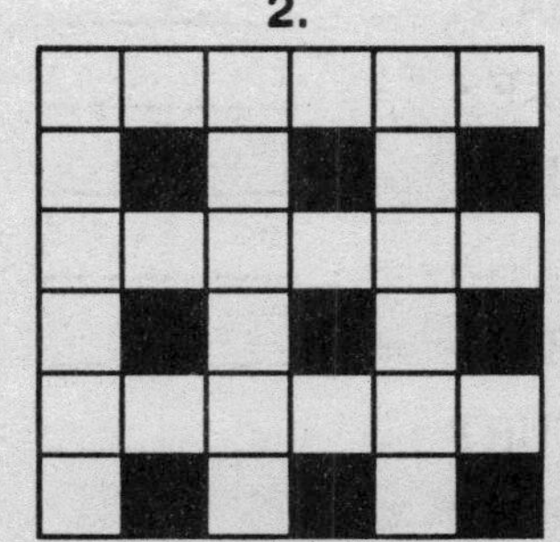

ONGTAU
MVELOU
GREEMA
OVRLUE
REWESK
HIVSAN

SPECULATION

Write the answer to each clue in the correspondingly numbered line across—one letter per circle. Next transfer the answer letters to the circles at the top to reveal a famous quotation. Note: Circles in the same vertical column contain the same letter.

Solution on page 330

1. Rental agreement
2. Salary
3. House of ____
4. Stated
5. Change
6. Captive

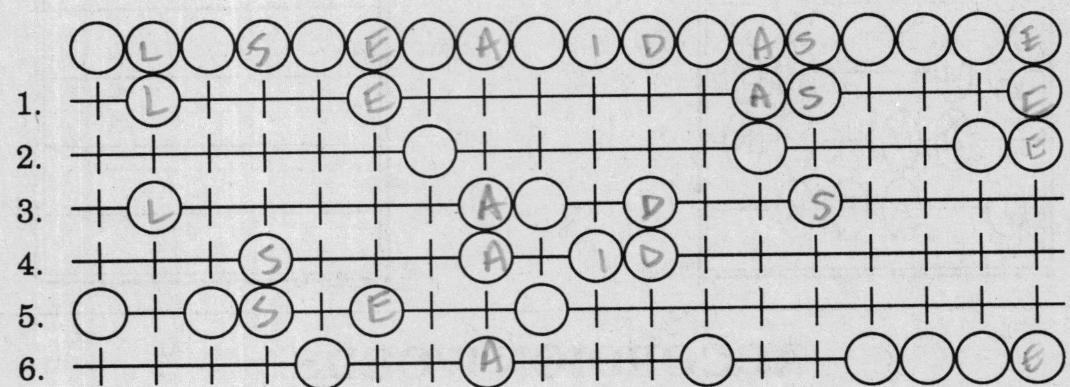

ALPHABET PLUS

Form common 6-letter words by rearranging each word and adding the letter of the alphabet shown with it. The word SENATE (the letters of TEENS plus the letter A) has been filled in for you.

Our solutions on page 330

A	+	TEENS	=	SENATE	N	+	FREED	=	______
B	+	LONGE	=	______	O	+	DRAWN	=	______
C	+	STORE	=	______	P	+	TRACE	=	______
D	+	HEART	=	______	Q	+	UNITS	=	______
E	+	THIGH	=	______	R	+	TINES	=	______
F	+	MINOR	=	______	S	+	ALONG	=	______
G	+	MEANT	=	______	T	+	LOWER	=	______
H	+	RAKES	=	______	U	+	SUPER	=	______
I	+	SALVE	=	______	V	+	LARGE	=	______
J	+	GLEAN	=	______	W	+	SNARE	=	______
K	+	TRIES	=	______	X	+	TENET	=	______
L	+	OVERT	=	______	Y	+	REGAL	=	______
M	+	SCOUT	=	______	Z	+	BLARE	=	______

INSERT-A-WORD

Insert a word from Group B into a word from Group A to form a longer word. Each word is used only once. For example, if the word FAR appeared in Group A and THE appeared in Group B, the answer would be FATHER (FA-THE-R).

Solution on page 330

GROUP A	GROUP B	
1. PIE	LEAS	1. ______
2. PARABLE	SENT	2. ______
3. PER	RAT	3. ______
4. REND	PARK	4. ______
5. PREDICT	ITCH	5. ______
6. KING	CREATION	6. ______
7. PRICE	DON	7. ______
8. REAL	EVER	8. ______
9. PURE	RIGHT	9. ______
10. SLED	NOW	10. ______
11. FEN	AMEN	11. ______
12. ABLY	ACT	12. ______

PICTURE PAIRS

Some of these designs match up as pairs, and some designs have no mates. Can you discover the designs that do not match in three minutes or less?

Solution on page 331

JIGSAW SQUARES

Your goal is to fit the PUZZLE PIECES into their proper places in the diagram to reveal a quotation. Fill the diagram by placing the PUZZLE PIECES horizontally into their corresponding sections of the diagram. There are 16 sections, identified by letter-number combinations (A-1, A-2, A-3, etc.). The quotation reads left to right, line by line. A black square indicates the end of a word. One PUZZLE PIECE has been entered for you.

Solution on page 331

PUZZLE PIECES

A-1	A-2	A-3	A-4	B-1	B-2	B-3	B-4
O	AND	E	A	A	A	D	E
R	HIS	UP	H	H	FE	I	N
AN	CKED	WO	ED	S	OME	ND	W
ON	FFIC	DIAL	PH	AS	PHO	NE	HI
PI		NOON	HOU	IS	WERE	THE	RE
ONE ✓			RKER	WI		WHER	TH
				TER			AUGH

C-1	C-2	C-3	C-4	D-1	D-2	D-3	D-4
E	S	N	D	B	T	CLI	Y
KI	AN	U	S	D	IT	FOL	IV
EXT	TWO	AN	V	E	OTH	HUNG	UP
IRS	ENSI	ON	AN	AS	TWO	OUSL	CKS
OICE	TCHE	FEMA	ED	BY	TANE		LOWE
		SWER	LE	GO			
			PSTA	IMUL			

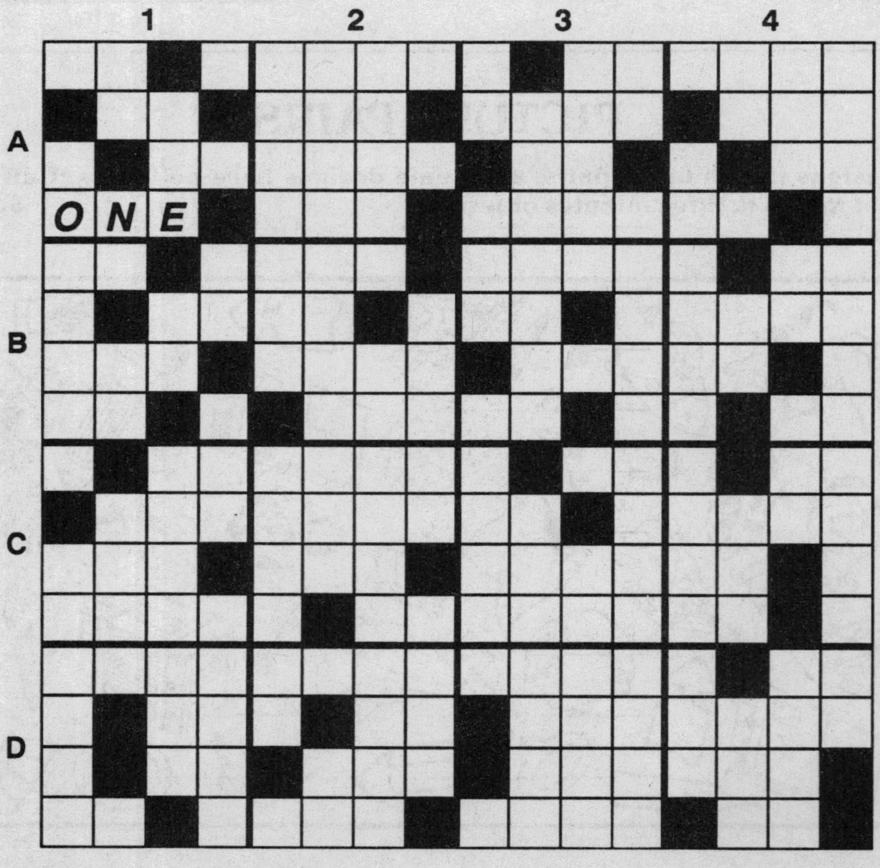

1 2 3 4

A

ONE

B

C

D

THREE'S COMPANY

This alphabetical list of seemingly unrelated words actually contains fifteen groups of three related items. Your job is to sort them out into those fifteen groups using each item only once. The trick is that some of the items could be used in more than one list, but only one arrangement of all the items will work. Remember, use each item only once and have exactly three items in each group. **Solution on page 331**

Akita	Chicory	Emperor	Kyoto	Queen
Atlanta	Cinnamon	Ersatz	Lincoln	Serve
Basket	Cool	Foot	Lob	Sleet
Beagle	Cotton	Frost	Mustard	Snow
Bogus	Court	Ginger	Niven	Swell
Brinkley	Cusack	Great	Nutmeg	Taffeta
Candy	Dalmatian	Hail	O'Hara	Tennyson
Carradine	Denim	Imitation	Osaka	Tokyo
Cashmere	Denver	Keats	Pharaoh	Volley

---

1. Poets ________ ________ ________
2. Tennis terms ________ ________ ________
3. Plants ________ ________ ________
4. State capitals ________ ________ ________
5. Rulers ________ ________ ________
6. Japanese cities ________ ________ ________
7. Spices ________ ________ ________
8. Weather words ________ ________ ________
9. Famous Johns ________ ________ ________
10. Fake ________ ________ ________
11. Groovy ________ ________ ________
12. Dog breeds ________ ________ ________
13. Fabrics ________ ________ ________
14. Famous Davids ________ ________ ________
15. Before ball ________ ________ ________

CODEWORD

Codeword is a special crossword puzzle in which conventional clues are omitted. Instead, answer words in the diagram are represented by numbers. Each number represents a different letter of the alphabet, and all of the letters of the alphabet are used. When you are sure of a letter, put it in the code key chart and cross it off in the alphabet box. A group of letters has been inserted to start you off.

Solution on page 331

1 N	14	
2	15	
3	16	
4	17	
5	18	
6	19	
7 I	20	
8	21	
9	22	
10	23	
11	24	
12	25	
13 K	26	

8	12	6	4	■	■	6	11	12	3	■	3	15	26	9
12	20	7	12	■	15	14	12	1	10	■	15	20	12	10
13 K	7 I	1 N	18	■	25	26	7	10	2	■	6	20	15	14
10	21	10	■	18	12	15	20	■	■	14	4	23	9	10
2	10	3	2	26	12	19	■	24	20	5	10	■	■	■
■	■	■	12	15	14	■	16	5	15	1	2	15	26	23
11	26	15	17	23	■	6	5	7	14	10	■	20	7	10
4	15	21	10	■	6	14	10	20	10	■	19	15	19	15
10	13	10	■	15	3	15	26	2	■	16	5	10	10	26
25	10	26	12	11	7	14	23	■	11	5	26	■	■	■
■	■	■	26	7	9	10	■	17	10	15	20	12	5	6
6	14	15	7	2	■	■	24	12	1	23	■	15	19	10
4	15	20	10	■	8	15	5	1	14	■	15	26	10	15
12	22	10	1	■	15	22	20	10	6	■	18	10	1	14
2	7	10	14	■	3	10	20	2	■	■	12	2	2	6

A	~~N~~
B	O
C	P
D	Q
E	R
F	S
G	T
H	U
~~I~~	V
J	W
~~K~~	X
L	Y
M	Z

Quotagram

Fill in the answers to the clues. Then transfer the letters to the correspondingly numbered squares in the diagram. The completed diagram will contain a quotation.

1. "The ___-Nine Steps" ___ ___ ___ ___ ___ ___ 5 21 46 24 36 17
2. Highest mountain ___ ___ ___ ___ ___ ___ ___ 34 11 22 47 3 30 43
3. Animated ___ ___ ___ ___ ___ 10 51 18 33 45
4. Pillow covers ___ ___ ___ ___ ___ 4 13 32 25 40
5. British prime minister ___ ___ ___ ___ ___ 6 16 49 20 29
6. Nevertheless ___ ___ ___ ___ ___ ___ 8 31 14 27 39 44
7. Prevent ___ ___ ___ ___ ___ ___ ___ 50 19 9 41 1 37 28
8. Liqueur flavoring ___ ___ ___ ___ ___ 7 15 23 52 12
9. Fourteen-line poem ___ ___ ___ ___ ___ ___ 35 26 42 38 2 48

Solution on page 331

1	2	3	4	■	5	6	7	8	■	9	10	11	12	■	13	14	15	16	17	■
18	19	■	20	21	22	23	24	■	25	26	27	28	29	30	■	31	32	33	34	■
35	36	37	38	39	40	■	41	42	■	43	44	45	46	47	■	48	49	50	51	52

CRYPTO-FAMILIES

The directions for solving are given on page 15.
Solutions on page 331

1. POWER FOLLOWERS
Example: Mower

QTVY
NZVFY
IYDDHSFX
ZSFD
IYVYSTF
IPTMDZ
PTJID
YHVSF
NZVR
QVID

2. SECRET IDENTITIES
Example: Zorro

WBARGNCZ
NG. SRGGFEFM
YKZR GCZDRG
DGRRZ JKGZRS
LKZQRG LKNCZ
MCASCFZ NCGORY
WAFQRG-NCZ
SJR JBYU
GKVFZ
VCSNCZ

3. BEWARE!
Example: Jeopardy

GWEPJ
EPLZ
NVRBWE
SVKVEN
OWRVQW
WOWEBWRQU
GPHAVJJ
WIGTLMEW
HSEWVH
MRQWEHVPRHU

4. PRESIDENTIAL MIDDLES
Example: Fitzgerald

NHTXVF
DXYVHZ
RYTUFEZ
NXSYN
UFIXGN
IYTZFV
XDGXR
UHVGB
XTXV
AXRXTYHT

5. CARIBBEAN ISLANDS
Example: Martinique

WBXWBTQR
BFLZNCCB
LZBTICQZJI
RE. CZGNB
FIPNR
SBYBNGB
BFENLZB
WBXWZTB
EXNFNTBT
YQFERIXXBE

6. IN THE FUTURE
Example: Eventually

AO HQY AO
PHWMV
HQJQ
MVMPJQZ
EMVMHLWMV
FSUJXCQZ
CQ YFM WCXM
EMQUMLJVWE
FPWCXHWMPO
NJXMYHO

BOWL GAME

To bowl a strike (20 points) you must create a 10-letter word using all the letters in each pin. The letter on top in the pin is the first letter of the strike word. To bowl a spare (10 points) use the same 10 letters to form two words. Splits are not allowed: you may not divide the strike to form a spare. For example, SWEETHEART may not become SWEET and HEART. Our solutions with a perfect score of 300 points on page 331

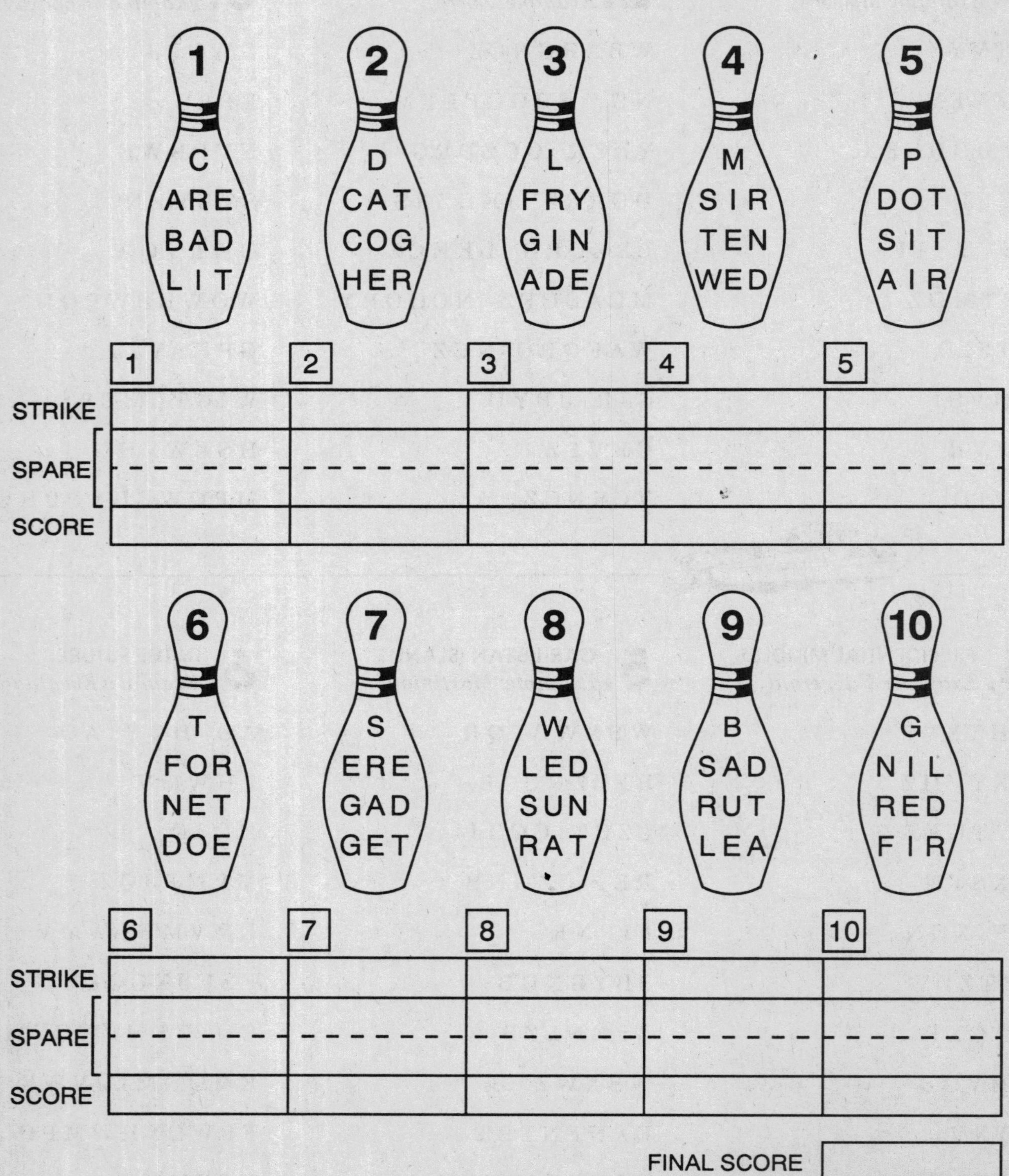

SUM TOTALS

Place one digit (1 to 9, no zeros) in each square so that the sum of the numbers in each group of squares across or down is the number given. The number below a diagonal is the sum of the numbers below it. The number to the right of a diagonal is the sum of the numbers to the right of it. IMPORTANT: No digit is used more than once in any group of squares leading to a sum. One group of digits has been given for you.

Solutions on page 331

■	■	24\	11\	6\	15\	■	■	■	10\	9\	■	41\	11\
■	\13					■	19\	6\16			\3		
■	17\29					13\17					\8		
\16			■	21\11					16\	17\	16\15		
\12			4\22					\21					■
■	7\	44\10			■	13\	22\	6\26					13\
\10					13\15	1				23\	\14		
\10			\29			8					13\15		
\9			12\	11\16		4			\12				
■	\28					■	19\	13\	28\16			19\	8\
■	22\10					4\29					\5		
\17			■	4\	16\21					17\	9\16		
\16			\20					\21					■
\10			\8			■	■	\26					■

IN AND AROUND

Place the 4-letter answers to the clues into the diagram, from the outside to the inside. When you have finished, two 12-letter words will be revealed, reading from 1 to 12 on both the outermost ring and the third ring from the outside.

Solution on page 331

1. Do the Australian crawl
2. Sharpen a razor
3. Single time
4. Chamber
5. Heavy book
6. Drinks slowly
7. Terrible tsar
8. Clothing
9. Cure
10. Laundry vats
11. Songstress Fitzgerald
12. Profound

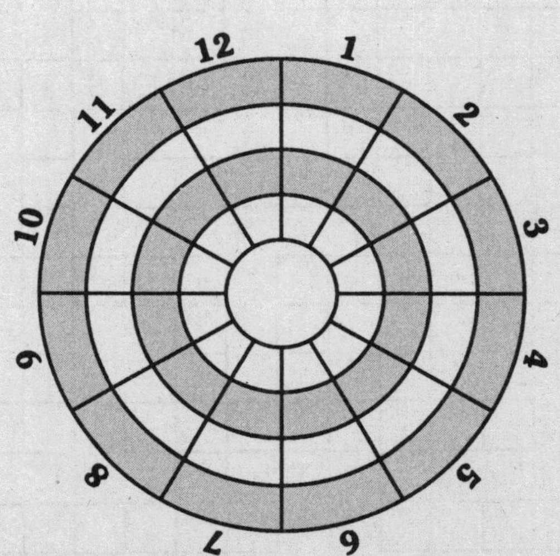

Framework 1

Finches

These words are listed in alphabetical order according to length. Fit them into their proper places in the Framework. This puzzle has been started for you with the entry NESTLING. Now look for an 8-letter entry starting with T. Continue working this way until the puzzle is completed.

4 Letters
Acts
Bath
Bill
Cute
Down
Eggs
Gold
Head
Itch
Mate
Pins
Plan
Seed
Tail
Tree
Type
Upon

5 Letters
Alike
Breed
Cages
Calls
Emits
Green
Habit
Hatch
Haven
Molts
Nests
Pecks
Perch
Preen
Roost
Small
Songs
Spice
Stand
Twins
Wings

6 Letters
Aurora
Aviary
Breast
Bronze
Cherry
Clutch
Common
Exotic
Flight
Grooms
Orange
Senses
Sleeps
Treats
Yellow

7 Letters
Hungers
Painted
Plumage
Redhead
Scratch
Species
Waxbill

8 Letters
Behavior
Brooding
Colorful
Crimsons
Feathers
Lavender
Nestling ✓
Postures
Toenails

Solution on page 337

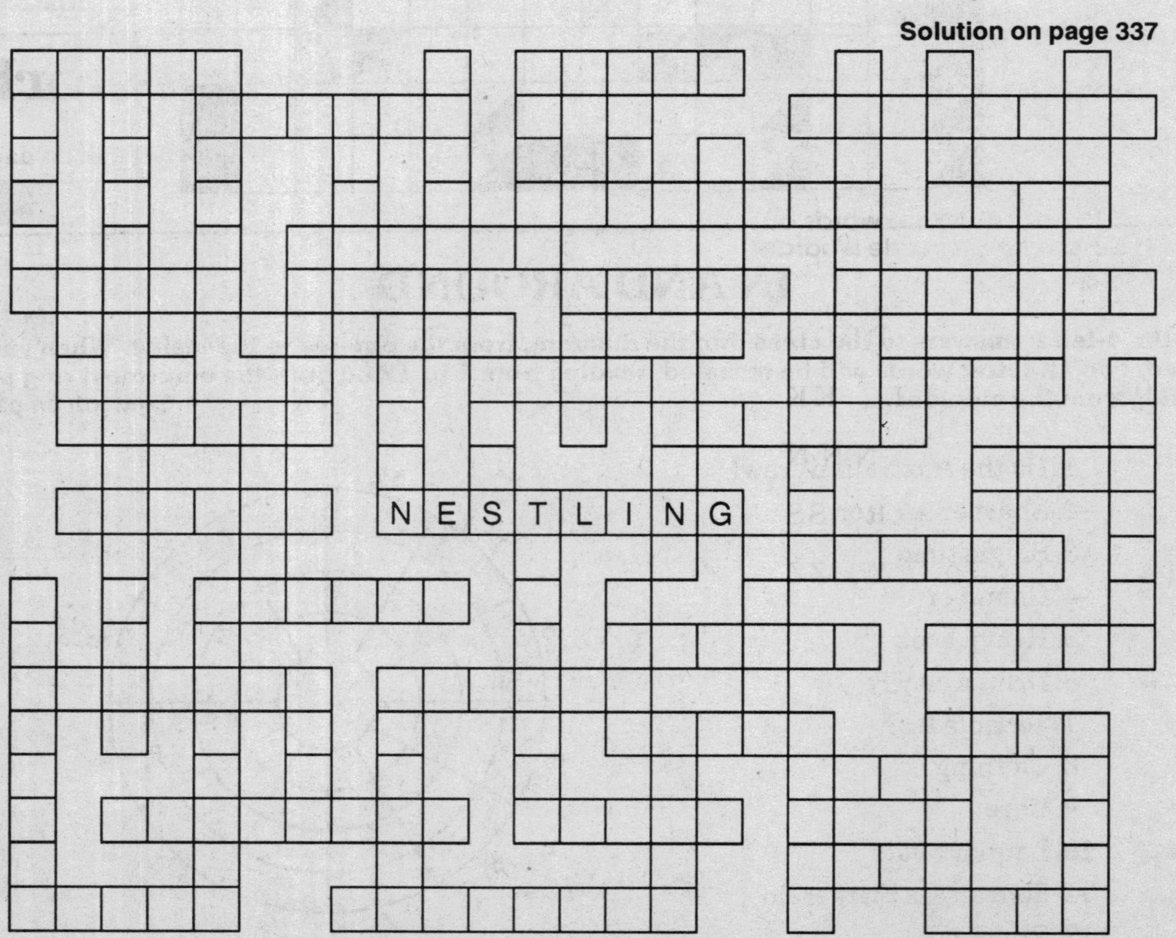

Framework 2

Revelation

When this Framework has been completed, read the circled letters in order from left to right, and they will reveal a message, which can be found on page 334.

First word on page 351

Solution on page 336

3 Letters
Asp
Elk
Err
Fir
Hot
Law
Men
Tie

4 Letters
Abut
Dawn
Deem
Frog
Idea
Like
Male
Name
News
Nuts
Romp
Site
Stem
Swan

5 Letters
Hunts
Inset
Kilts
Magic
Robot
Sheer

6 Letters
Affirm
Agreed
Eaglet
Flinch
Length
Master
Owners
Writer

7 Letters
Enchant
Isthmus

8 Letters
Distance
Relation
Wrestler

Framework 3

Framelinks

First word on page 351

Solution on page 336

Fill in the empty squares in the diagram with the given letters. All the words are common words, but the puzzle is harder than it looks.

AAA BB CCC DDDD

EEEE F HHH KK

LLLL MM NNNN

OOO PPPPP RRR SS

TTTT UU W YY ZZ

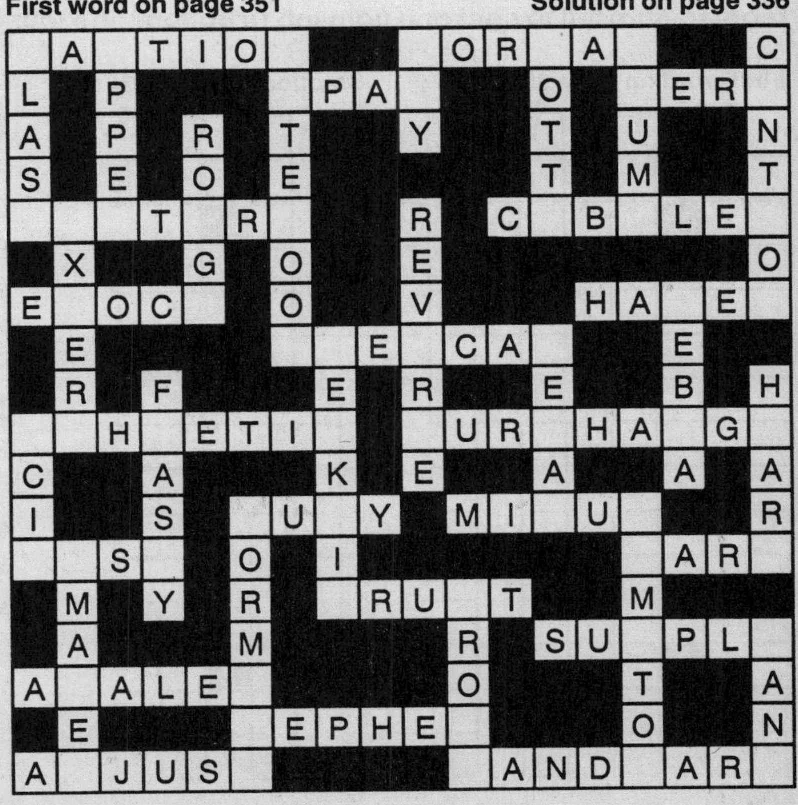

Framework 4

Number Frame

First number on page 351 Solution on page 336

3 Digits	5 Digits	6 Digits
433	16130	417349
461	17394	449577
845	21256	501584
988	24153	532675
	32745	564893
4 Digits	50109	612184
1023	54737	681209
1982	55843	701271
2655	59074	728303
3207	72655	729198
3529	73863	735986
3674	79324	824674
4863	81928	948875
7051	91276	

Framework 5

Shadowbox

When this Framework has been completed, the shadowed boxes will contain four related words reading from left to right and from top to bottom. The four related words are given on page 334.

First word on page 351 Solution on page 336

3 Letters		
Arc	Igor	Lashed
Con	Nose	Remove
Era	Owes	Sahara
Fee	Pole	Sunday
Few	Rita	Umpire
Nee	Semi	Urgent
Toe	Silo	
War	Soar	**7 Letters**
		Cinders
4 Letters	**5 Letters**	Gas tank
Aces	Plato	Magical
Atom	Since	Secrets
Boar	Title	
Epic	Toast	**8 Letters**
Ergo		Holsters
Ices	**6 Letters**	Reindeer
	Eerier	

Spring Cleaning

Framework 6

3 Letters
Age
Buy
Eat
Ego
Era
Kit
Lot
Low
Own
Run
Sag
Say
Sun
Try
Use

4 Letters
Anti
Asks
Ease
Even
Ever
Help
Inch
Lead
Near
Onto
Rags
Sand
Sink
Skin
Snap
Soap
Them
Toil
Type

5 Letters
Ashen
Brush
Elbow
Empty
Grass
Green
Grime
Haven
Heavy
Nasty
Pinch
Pride
Range
Smart
Speed
Thing
Trips
White

6 Letters
Attics
Energy
Garage
Garden
Noises
Places
Propel
Scours
Strong
Switch
System
Tested
Trunks

7 Letters
Closets
Element
General
Glasses
Hurried
Inspire
Invites
Kitchen
Laundry
Options
Several
Washing
Windows

8 Letters
Articles
Basement
Clothing
Estimate
Examples
Remember
Spilling

9 Letters
Fireplace
Neighbors
Observing
Scrubbing
Sensitive
Versatile

10 Letters
Dining room
Family room
Impossible

First word across on page 351

Solution on page 337

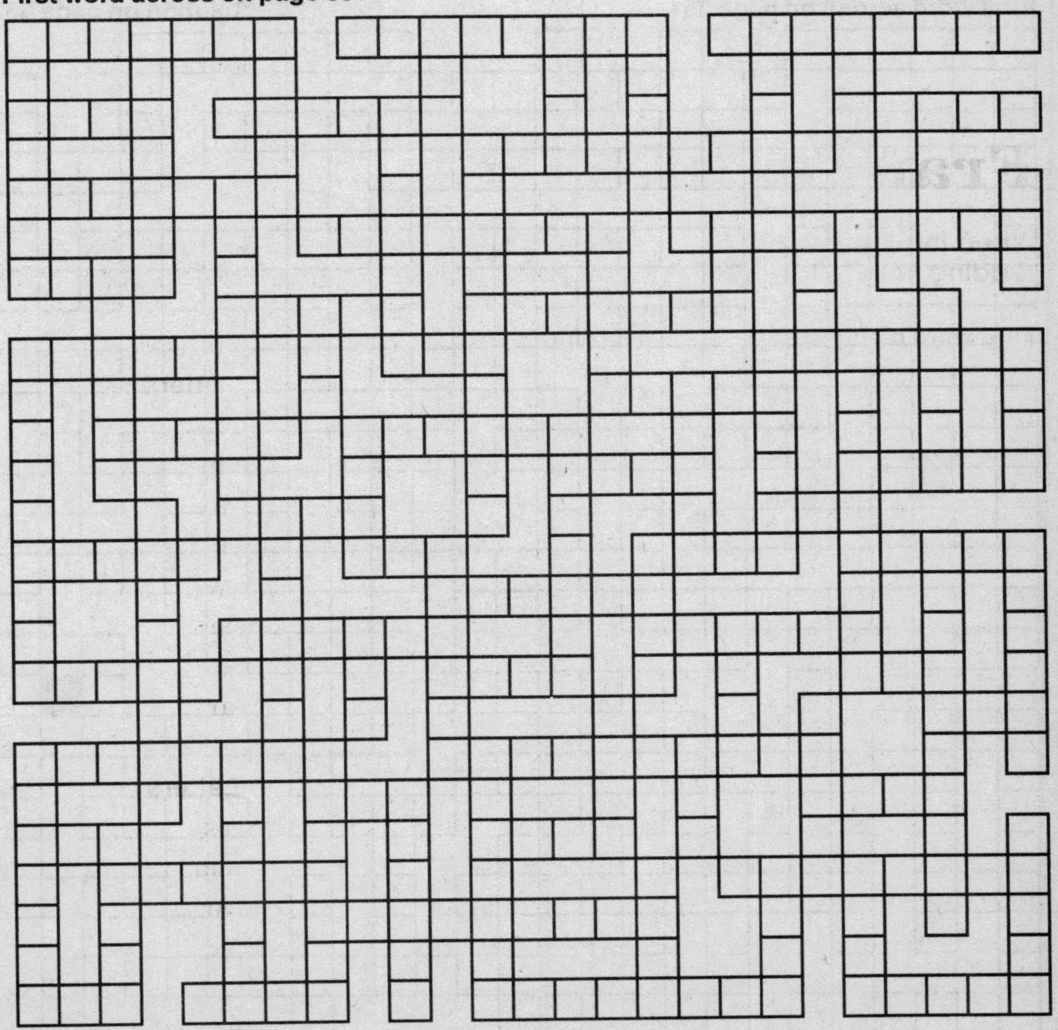

Framework 7

Carnival Glass Patterns

Our Framework expert needed 19 minutes to complete this puzzle. Your solving time: ______.

3 Letters
Arc
Bee
Fan
Hen
Owl
Sea
Web

4 Letters
Bell
Cane
Coal
Coin
Crab
Duck
Elks
Emus
Fern
Iris
Kiwi
Lacy
Leaf
Lion
Neva
Pony
Rays
Rose
Stag
Star
Swan

5 Letters
Acorn
Aztec
Bugle
Chain
Daisy
Flute
Forks
Fruit
Grape
Lilac
Peach
Plaid
Prism
Robin
Tracy
Triad
Tulip
Wheat

6 Letters
Colony
Double
Oxford
Parade
Puzzle
Ripple
Sunray
Sydney

7 Letters
Concave
Concord
Crackle
Hobnail
Lattice
Ostrich
Round-up
Ski Star
Tornado

8 Letters
Brocaded
Farmyard
Graceful
Imperial
Kangaroo
Nautilus
Rosalind
Soutache
Treebark
Venetian
Vineyard

9 Letters
Blueberry
Butterfly
Pineapple
Snow Fancy

10 Letters
Australian
Chatelaine
Kookaburra
Springtime
Sweetheart

First word across on page 351

Solution on page 337

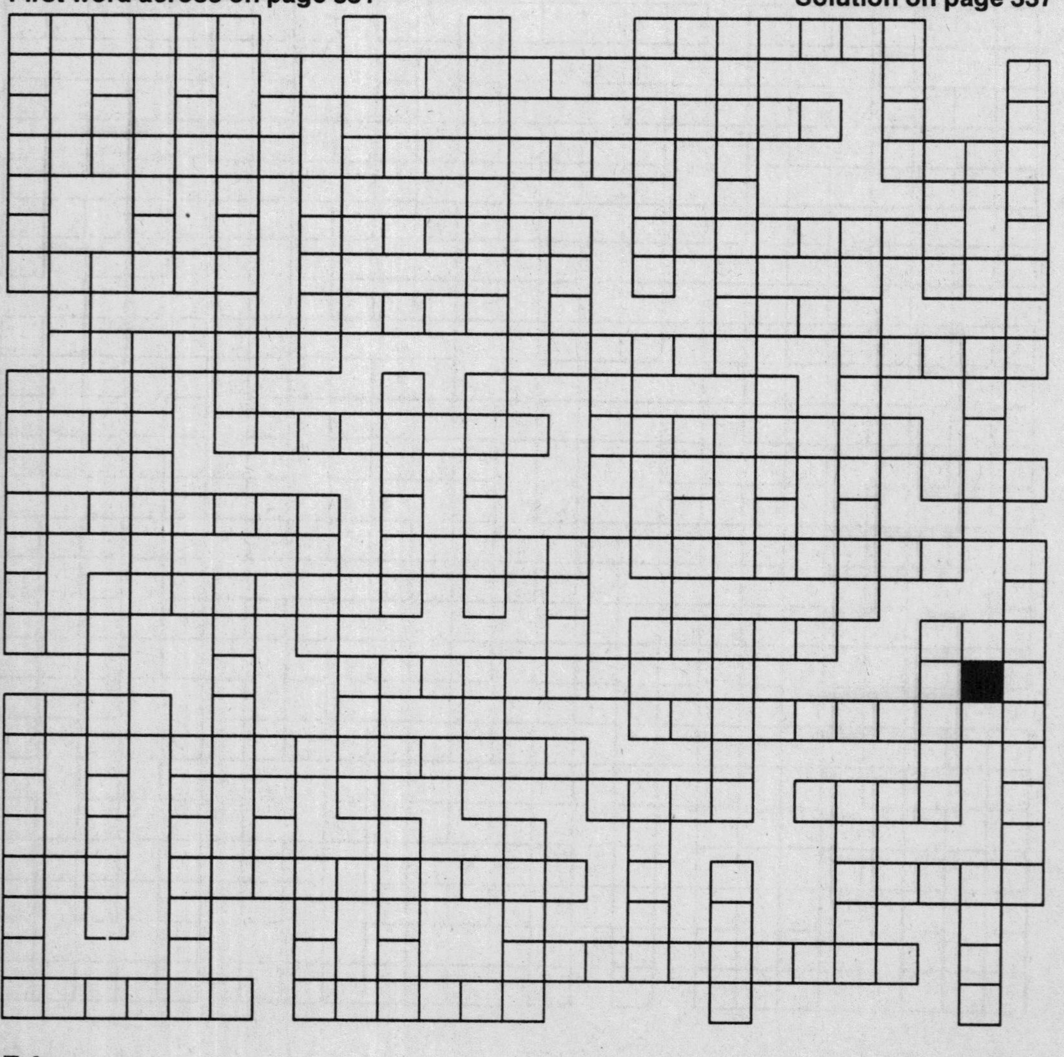

Fuchsia Fantasy

Framework 8

Our Framework expert needed 14 minutes to complete this puzzle. Your solving time: ______.

3 Letters
Age
Art
Enl.
Eye
Gay
Imp
Pry
Red
Set
Tag
Tie
Top
Web

4 Letters
Aton
Care
Disk
Earl
Ends
Ewer
Hues
Inga
Load
Mass
Neat
Plan
Puff
Size
Stem
Stub
Trim
Type
Warm
Yard

5 Letters
Aglow
Amber
Beads
Earth
Elfin
Erect
Errol
Great
Habit
Istar
Light
Norma
Perky
Plant
Roots
Rufus
Young

6 Letters
Ablaze
Detail
Emilie
Notice

7 Letters
Aviator
Ecstasy
Elegant
Hispano
Impress
Inspect
In white
Miramar
New data
Olympia
Papilio
Rosanna
Spilled
Wet peat
You tend

8 Letters
Cardinal
Even drop
In leaves
Old shrub

9 Letters
Claret Cup
Ina Claire
Kitty O'Day
One flower
Swingtime

10 Letters
Apply water
Black Pearl
Direct spot
Inca Maiden
Pee Wee Rose
Periwinkle
Red Firefly
Silverbell
Torpilleur

12 Letters
Bubble hanger
Normal growth

First word across on page 351

Solution on page 337

Framework 9

Poolside Living

3 Letters
Act
Air
Eel
Ham
Ivy
Law
Out
Sun
Tie
Wet

4 Letters
Acer
Arch
Deck
Eden
Lean
Mill
Neat
Play
Pump
Rail
Rest
Rock
Romp
Sail
Snug
Tend
Twig
Worn

5 Letters
Acids
Bathe
Extra
Habit
Ledge
Meter
Novel
Patio
Rinse
Space
Spill
Strip
Tests

6 Letters
Cabana
Dreamy
Filter
Garden
Gauges
Indoor
Insure
Ladder
Repair
Splash
Styles

7 Letters
Ammonia
Deflate
New pair
Setting

8 Letters
Aqua ball
Oval pool
Speakers
Swimming

9 Letters
Aqua slide
Cute girls
Fiberglas
Roomy area
Wall slope

10 Letters
Face piping
Icy ripples
Night light
Slat fences

11 Letters
Overcrowded
Rectangular
Skimmer weir

12 Letters
Paddle tennis
The first jump

14 Letters
Do not run or push
Small fountains
Tropical plants

First word across on page 351

Solution on page 337

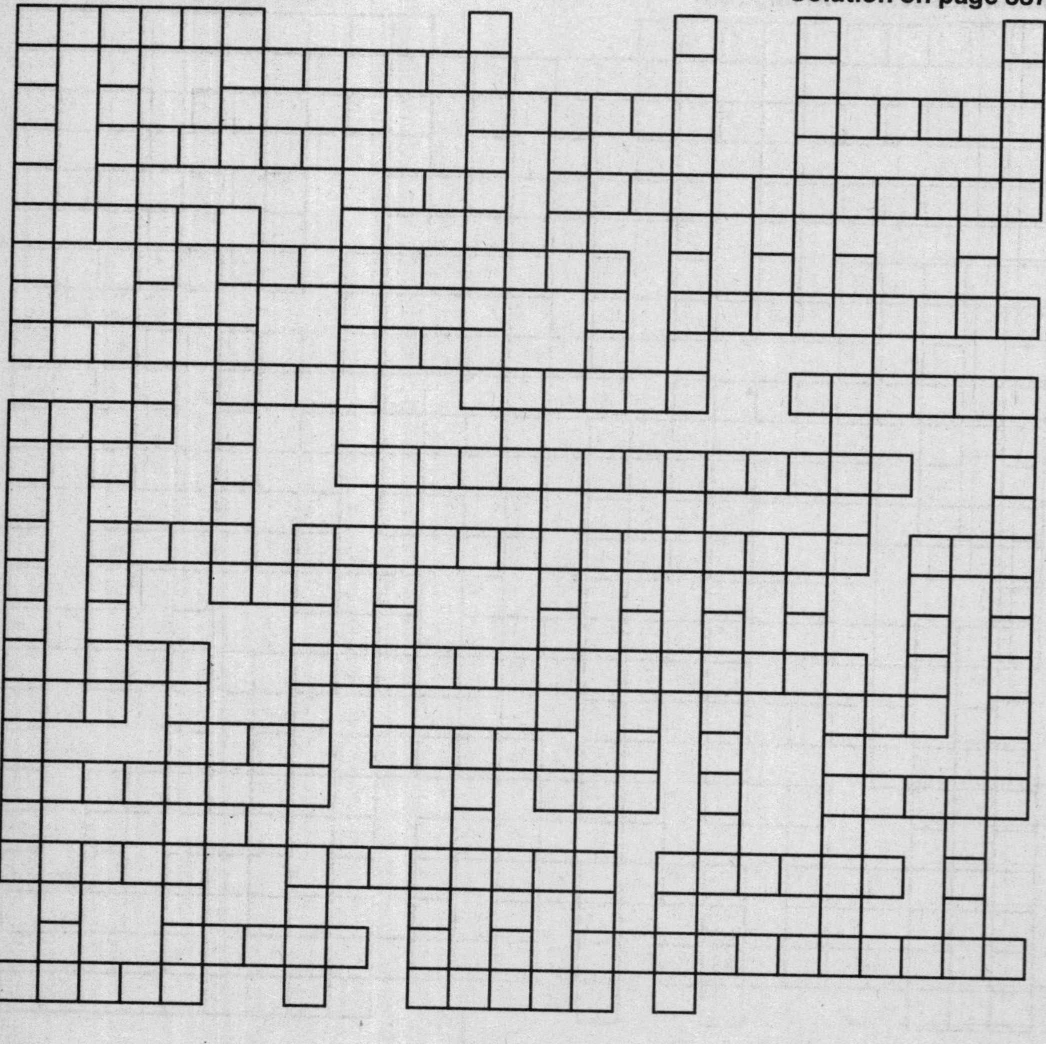

Starts With A Vowel

Framework 10

Our Framework expert needed 19 minutes to complete this puzzle. Your solving time: ______.

4 Letters
Acid
Atop
Easy
Epic
Into
Iris
Onto
Oust

5 Letters
Aaron
Annul
Aroma
Egret
Eland
Essay
Oasis
Onion
Oriel
Uncle

6 Letters
Accrue
Apiece
Ascend
Atomic
Eerily
Enigma
Exotic
Impala
Instep
Octave
Oracle
Unseat

7 Letters
Alluded
Amplify
Antacid
Arduous
Armhole
Average
Echidna
Elastic
Endless
Expense
Improve
Utility

8 Letters
Ambition
Anywhere
Eighteen
Election
Electric
Encumber
Enormous
Ignition
Implicit
Indolent
Official
Optimism
Organize
Oriented
Original
Ultimate
Usurious

9 Letters
Aerospace
Antitoxin
Archducal
Editorial
Energetic
Epicurean
Expatiate
Indelible
Overissue
Upholster

First word across on page 351

Solution on page 337

SPLIT AND SPLICE

Place the 6-letter answer to clue 1 in the first row of the diagram. The answers to the next two clues are 3-letter words made up of the letters of the first answer. Thereafter each answer contains the letters of the word above it plus one letter. In the sixth row the 6-letter answers split to form 3-letter words. For the lower part of the diagram the pattern is reversed: each answer contains the letters of the word above it minus one letter, and pairs of 3-letter answers combine to form 6-letter words.

Solution on page 333

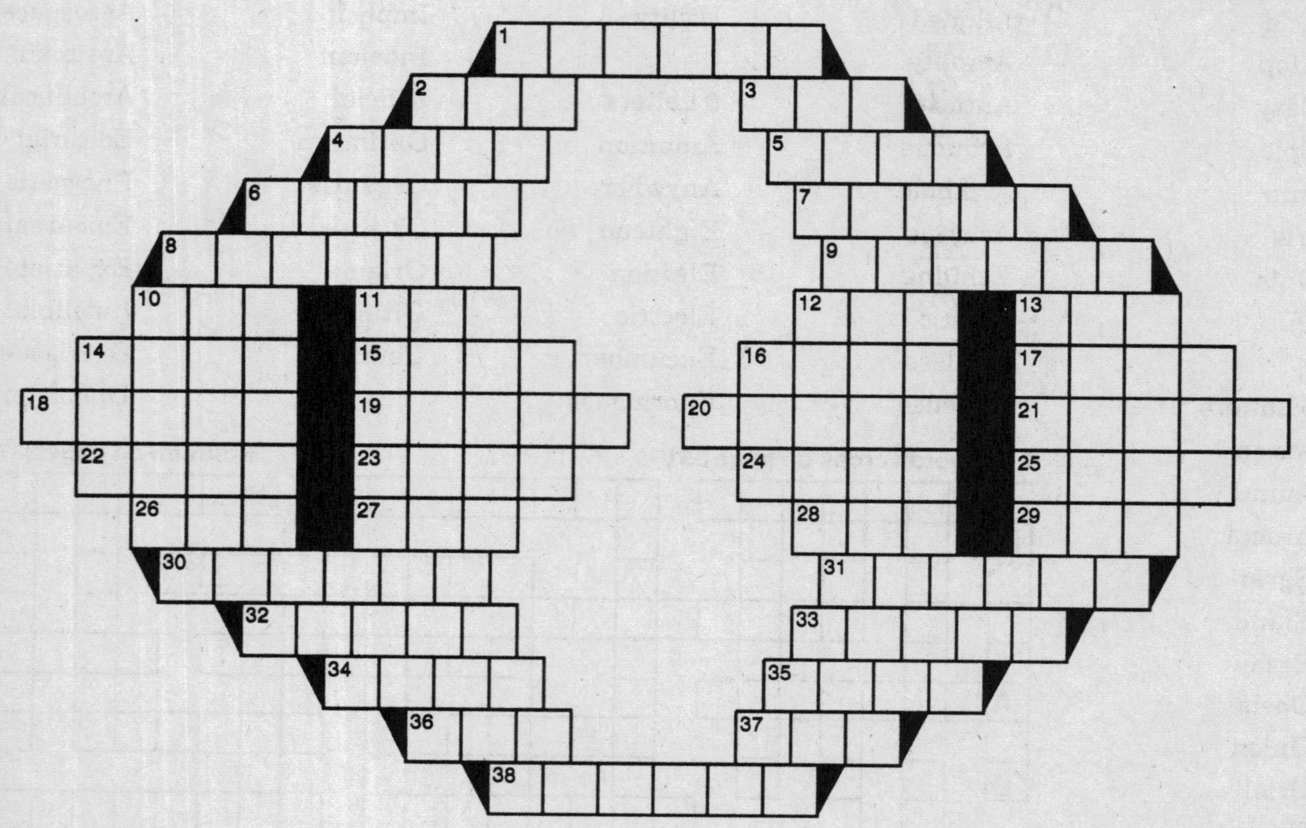

1. Temporary bypass
2. Decay
3. Payable
4. Three musicians
5. Family quarrel
6. Planet's path
7. Hungry
8. Small nightclub
9. Money back
10. Steal from
11. Take a chair
12. Lair
13. Animal pelt
14. 1980 Wimbledon winner
15. Elevator man
16. Ms. Ferber
17. Sod
18. Swedish actress
19. Labors
20. Mr. Previn
21. Orchard yield
22. Boast
23. Ms. Lane
24. Peruse
25. Fissure
26. Dust cloth
27. Petroleum
28. Historical period
29. Evergreen
30. Bunker daughter
31. More just
32. Slow, in music
33. Blazing
34. Target
35. Passenger charge
36. Flight record
37. Cup handle
38. In abundance

PICTURE THIS

You do not need any special art training to produce a picture in the empty grid. Use the letter-number guide above each square and carefully draw what is shown into the corresponding square in the grid.

Solution on page 336

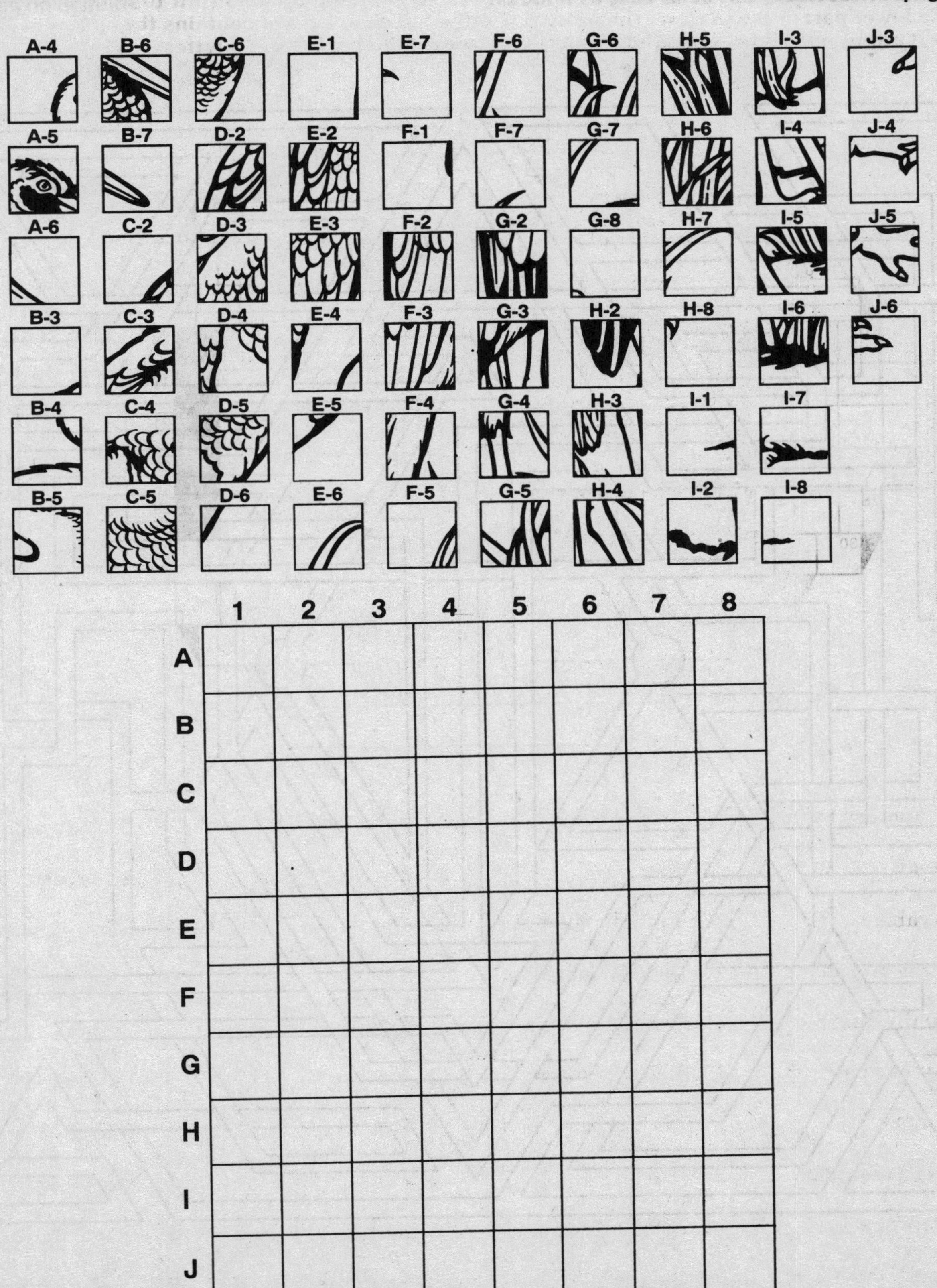

MAZE

The paths in this 3-dimensional maze cross over and under one another. There are no dead ends. The trick is to find the one path that goes from one circle to the other and back again. Do not use any path more than once. It may not be as easy as it looks!

Solution on page 335

Window Boxes

There is a common 4-letter word hidden in each strip of letters in Column I. Think of the strips in Column II as open and closed windows. Then match each letter strip with its correct Window Box so that the 4-letter word will show. There are different possibilities, but there is only one way in which each letter strip and each window strip are used once.

Solution on page 335

Example: P L O D E N T — P O E T

COLUMN I	COLUMN II
1. C H A M C A K	a.
2. Y O R E L K T	b.
3. B L A B S M Y	c.
4. E M O U R S T	d.
5. S K O A R L E	e.
6. S L A I P A M	f.
7. W H A R G E F	g.
8. G U R T O V E	h.
9. V E N C A E L	i.
10. A S N I E O W	j.

PUZZLER

       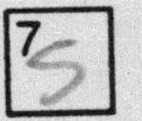 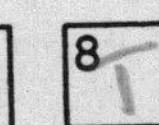

I am a word of eight letters.

My 7, 1, 6, 3, 3 is a booth.

My 5, 6, 1, 8, 3, 2 is a herd of cows.

My 7, 3, 4, 2, 8 is frozen rain.

My 7, 6, 3, 1 is a food seasoning.

My 3, 6, 5, 2 is a dainty fabric.

My 7, 4, 6, 8, 1, 3, 2 is a northwestern city.

My 5, 6, 3, 3 is a short visit.

Solution on page 335

TRIANGLE SUMS

The two diagonals divide the diagram on the right into four large triangles. Place the nine squares on the left into the diagram so that the sums of the four numbers in those triangles are equal. If a square is divided, place it in the diagram in a square that is divided the same way.

Solution on page 336

9 8 3/2

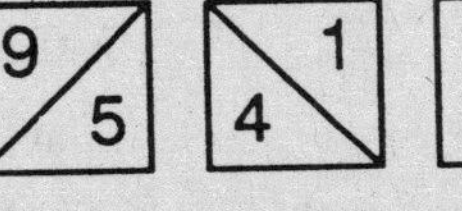

4

2

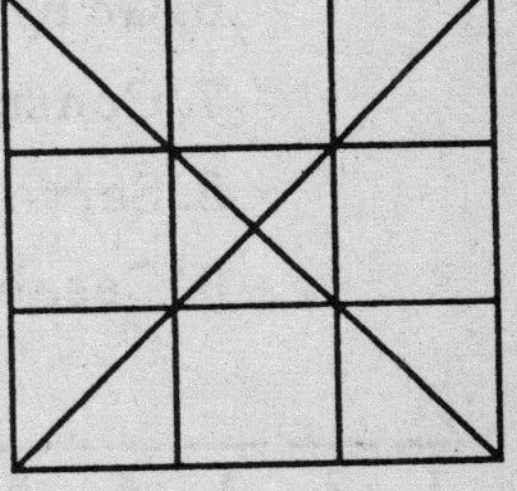

ANAGRAM MAGIC SQUARE

Attention Anagram Magic Square Fans! Solve this puzzle just as you would any other Anagram Magic Square (see page 14 for directions), but the added challenge is that this puzzle uses 6-letter words instead of 5-letter words. It shouldn't be too much of a stretch for you, but we've filled in the first answer to help you get moving along. Good luck!

Solution on page 335

SPINET ☐ ___	ASHORE ☐ ___	RENTAL 1 *ANTLER*	FINEST ☐ ___	AGREES ☐ ___	= 65
LAGERS ☐ ___	SLIEST ☐ ___	TINGES ☐ ___	PLANES ☐ ___	STREAM ☐ ___	= 65
LISTEN ☐ ___	CLEANS ☐ ___	CRATER ☐ ___	PARSON ☐ ___	LEMONS ☐ ___	= 65
BEATER ☐ ___	ASLEEP ☐ ___	RANTED ☐ ___	CHASER ☐ ___	PARENT ☐ ___	= 65
CAINES ☐ ___	WASHER ☐ ___	DRAINS ☐ ___	RAVELS ☐ ___	DEARER ☐ ___	= 65
= 65	= 65	= 65	= 65	= 65	

1. Branched horn
2. Exploration
3. Maven
4. Cover completely
5. Javelins
6. Go by, as time
7. Consume
8. Server
9. Casabas, e.g.
10. Foot part
11. Piercing looks
12. Ship's rope
13. Missing-person finder
14. Swarm about
15. Beguile
16. Bookworm
17. Gaudy trimming
18. Raspy
19. Passionate
20. Neighbor of Mount Vesuvius
21. Driveway parts
22. Lubricate
23. Kickback
24. Cays
25. Lowest points

A																								
1	2	3	4	5	6	7	8	9	10	11	12	13	14	15	16	17	18	19	20	21	22	23	24	25

SYL´´LA-CROS´TIC

Fill in the answers to the clues by using all the syllables in the Syllabox. The number of syllables to be used in each answer is shown in parentheses. The number of letters in each answer is indicated by the dashes. Each syllable will be used once. When the words are correctly filled in, their first and last letters, reading down, will reveal an epigram preceded by its author's name.

Solution on page 335

✻ SYLLABOX ✻

A A AL AL AP BE CA CLU DI DIS DOW E EL EX FIN FORE GA GER I IN ISH KAR LIM LOW MA ~~MEN~~ NAV NORM NOUR O O OT PANE PET PI POW ~~RA~~ RIN ~~SAC~~ SIVE THI TI TINCT ~~TO~~ TOR TUDE VAN WIN WOW ZEAL

1. California capital (4) S A C R A M E N T O
2. Conference (2) _ _ _ _ _ _
3. Blurred (3) _ _ _ _ _ _ _ _ _ _
4. Feed (2) _ _ _ _ _ _ _
5. Harmonica's kin (4) _ _ _ _ _ _ _
6. Fanatic (2) _ _ _ _ _ _
7. Permit (2) _ _ _ _ _
8. Plate of glass (3) _ _ _ _ _ _ _ _ _ _
9. Abyssinia, now (5) _ _ _ _ _ _ _ _
10. Thumb's neighbor (3) _ _ _ _ _ _ _ _ _ _
11. River to the North Sea (2) _ _ _ _
12. Scoop (3) _ _ _ _ _ _ _ _ _
13. Marine gastropod (2) _ _ _ _ _ _
14. Talent (3) _ _ _ _ _ _ _ _
15. Henry the ____ (4) _ _ _ _ _ _ _ _ _
16. Couch (2) _ _ _ _ _
17. Fate (2) _ _ _ _ _
18. Regular (2) _ _ _ _ _ _

FLOWER POWER

The answers to this petaled puzzle will go in a curve from the number on the outside to the center of the flower. Each number has two 5-letter words. One goes in a clockwise direction and the second in a counterclockwise direction. Try working from both sets of clues to fill the flower.

Solution on page 335

CLOCKWISE

1. Prepares the way
2. Twelve
3. Hue
4. Behaved foolishly
5. Passover meal
6. Flavor
7. Snooped
8. Flax fabric
9. Swore
10. Right now
11. Raft wood
12. Scottish landowner
13. Not drunk
14. Work of fiction
15. Book jacket
16. Dwelled
17. Sublease
18. Graded

COUNTERCLOCKWISE

1. Fainter
2. Passe
3. Desire wrongfully
4. Napped
5. Shoe bottoms
6. "Dragonwyck" author
7. Consumer advocate
8. Ran easily
9. Sunshade
10. Copier powder
11. Curtsied
12. Burdened
13. Mixed greens
14. Clamorous
15. Hooded snake
16. Adored
17. Stream
18. Make merry

ESCALATORS

Write the answer to clue 1 in the first space. Drop one letter and rearrange the remaining letters to answer clue 2. Put the dropped letter into Column A. Drop another letter and rearrange the remaining letters to answer clue 3. Put the dropped letter into Column B. Follow this pattern for each row in the diagram. When completed, the letters in Column A and Column B, reading down, will spell related words or a phrase.

Solutions on page 334

1

1. Clean carrots
2. Frighten
3. Organs of hearing
4. Husky sounding
5. Beach
6. National flower
7. Meal
8. Fixed gaze
9. Take a break
10. Transfer designs
11. Heat milk
12. Clothed
13. Take into custody
14. Fall flower
15. Leading actor

	A		B	
1		2		3
4		5		6
7		8		9
10		11		12
13		14		15

2

1. Paper fastener
2. Dish
3. Story
4. Eastern world
5. Male singer
6. Lease payment
7. Classical dance
8. Dining board
9. Flog
10. Buy stocks
11. Beer mug
12. Transmitted
13. Look for
14. Collision
15. Curved monument
16. Slice of bacon
17. Portion
18. Singe

	A		B	
1		2		3
4		5		6
7		8		9
10		11		12
13		14		15
16		17		18

3

1. Western homesteader
2. Go in
3. Adolescent
4. Ocean mammals
5. Wetland
6. Killed
7. Step taken
8. Caper
9. Jargon
10. Miracle
11. Male bee
12. Went on horseback
13. Purify
14. Deduce
15. Lacy plant
16. Individual
17. Unlocks
18. Sit for a portrait
19. Maddens
20. Cookstove
21. Close by

	A		B	
1		2		3
4		5		6
7		8		9
10		11		12
13		14		15
16		17		18
19		20		21

FILL-IN

The entries for this puzzle are given to you, listed alphabetically according to length. Across and Down words are all mixed together, and you are to find their proper places in the diagram. **Solution on page 335**

3 Letters
Act
Ail
And
Ass
Aye
Bit
Cam
Can
Cap
Car
E'en
Ell
Elm
Ems
Ens
Gee
Ice
Ins
Map
Mil
Ned
Oar
Par
Pas
Ree
Tie
Ton

4 Letters
Acid
Acme
Aden
Aloe
Also
Alto
Aria
Arid
Asea
Asps ✓
Atar
Cite
Date
Dead
Earl
Ears
Erne
Este
Ever
Evil
Fare
Inee
Into
Lade
Lana
Lane
Late
Lava
Lena
Line
Loan
Lorn
Made
Mere
Mesa
Mine
Mink
Moat
Mole
Nest
Open
Palm
Path
Peel
Peso
Pine
Pisa
Poll
Pone
Rate
Reel
Rent
Rile
Sang
Sell
Send
Shay
Shoe
Shot
Site
Soil
Sole
Soot
Sore
Star
Stem
Tans
Tart
Teen
Tool
Tore
Trim
Trot
True
Vent
Vino

5 Letters
Arena
Atone
Crate
Evade
Lease
Liner
Panel
Short
Slant
Spite

6 Letters
Assent
Attire
Eleven
Harden
Harken
Mantle
Pastel
Patent
Pistol
Praise
Relate
Retell

7 Letters
Antlers
Tremble

8 Letters
Colorado
Foothold
Gasoline
Handrail
Steelers
Virginia

13 Letters
South Carolina

A
S
P
S

DIAL-A-GRAMS

These messages are in a number code based on the familiar telephone dial. Each number represents one of the letters shown with it on the dial. You must decide which one. A number is not necessarily the same letter each time.

Solutions on page 335

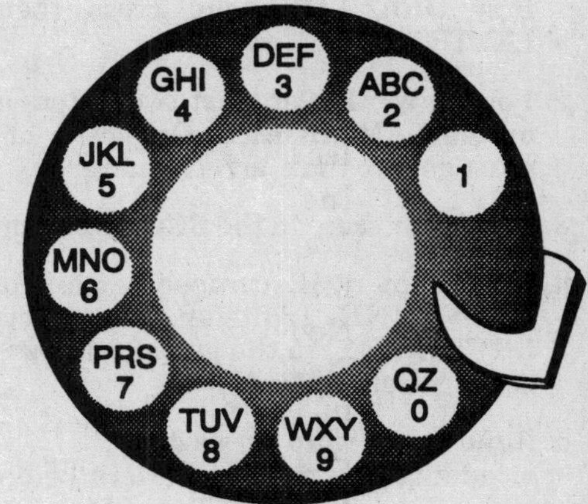

A. 2 2855364'7 628464
2255 226 23 43273 367
22688 4253 2 6453.

B. 64554667 63 93277 246
467737 9373 66 244437
8426 2287.

C. 2 232837'7 3528 8245 47 8733
46 79466464 263 86 9276 684377
63 326437.

D. 843 6673 2 336253 3825 082257, 843
6673 437 382554647 428437 276863 437.

E. 2 6653 226 344 86337476863 27 3278
27 48 226 9255 22683 476863.

F. 7663 66847 226 4327 2 228'7 76627.

G. 2 548836 2887 487 2229 83384 28
84733 86 749 93357 63 243.

H. 843 732 2722 47 22688 843 7403 63
843 6245 66 2 24453'7 548853 346437.

I. 2684 70843 263 6286787 273 56696 27
4653474.

TO PLAY:

1. Enter the first seven LETTERBOX letters onto the first DRAWLINE and cross them off in the LETTERBOX.
2. Form a word of at least two letters across or down on the GAMEBOARD. One letter of the first word must go into the starred square.
3. Tally your score in the SCORE column.
4. Carry down all unused letters onto the next DRAWLINE. Transfer enough letters from the LETTERBOX, in the given order, so that you have seven letters to work with.
5. Build a new word or words by:
   a. adding one or more letters before and/or after words on the GAMEBOARD.
   b. adding one or more letters at right angles to words on the GAMEBOARD.
   c. adding a word parallel to one on the GAMEBOARD.

IMPORTANT: All adjoining letters must spell out complete words.

6. Continue working this way until all the letters from the LETTERBOX have been used.
7. Asterisks (*) are "wild" letters and may represent any letter you choose, but once used they cannot be changed.

NOTE: Proper names, foreign words, and abbreviations are not allowed. No word may appear twice on the GAMEBOARD.

TO SCORE:

Score every letter in each new word as follows:

1. Letters in unnumbered squares count 1 point.
2. Letters in numbered squares count the given value of the square.
3. Double the score of a word containing a circle.
4. Triple the score of a word containing two circles.
5. Add 20 points if all seven letters from a DRAWLINE are used in one play.

Can you beat our game of 295 points given on page 335?

LETTERBOX

O	Q	P	D	E	I	C	R	D	*	L	A	B	U	S	Y	F	E	T	O	N	E	S	M	O	R	X	O	I	L
A	K	E	N	A	W	A	T	J	H	I	E	N	V	R	O	A	Z	S	I	N	R	E	U	T	U	T	*	G	O

DRAWLINES **SCORE**

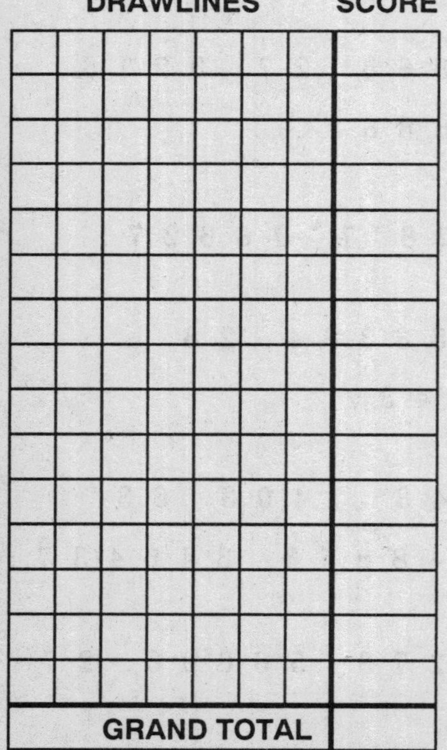

GAMEBOARD

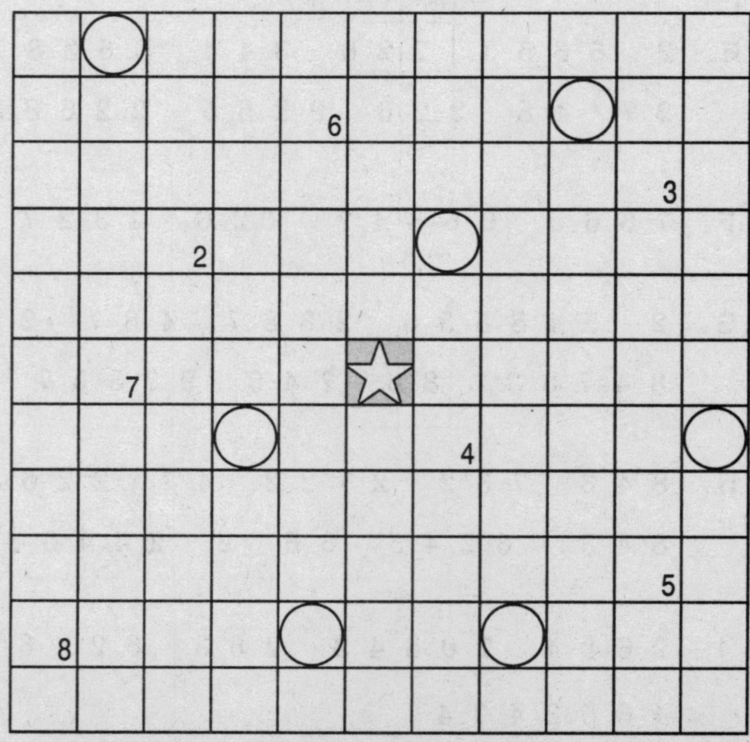

MASTERWORDS

Using only the ten letters shown, fill in the diagram by forming words across and down to achieve the highest possible score. Each letter has a given value, so try to use the high-value letters as much as possible. You may repeat letters as often as you wish, even within words. Do not repeat words in the diagram. Foreign words, abbreviations, and words starting with a capital letter are not allowed.

When the diagram is completely filled, add up your score. Count across only, each letter, line by line. Put the total for each line in the boxes at the right.

Our solution with a score of 360 on page 335

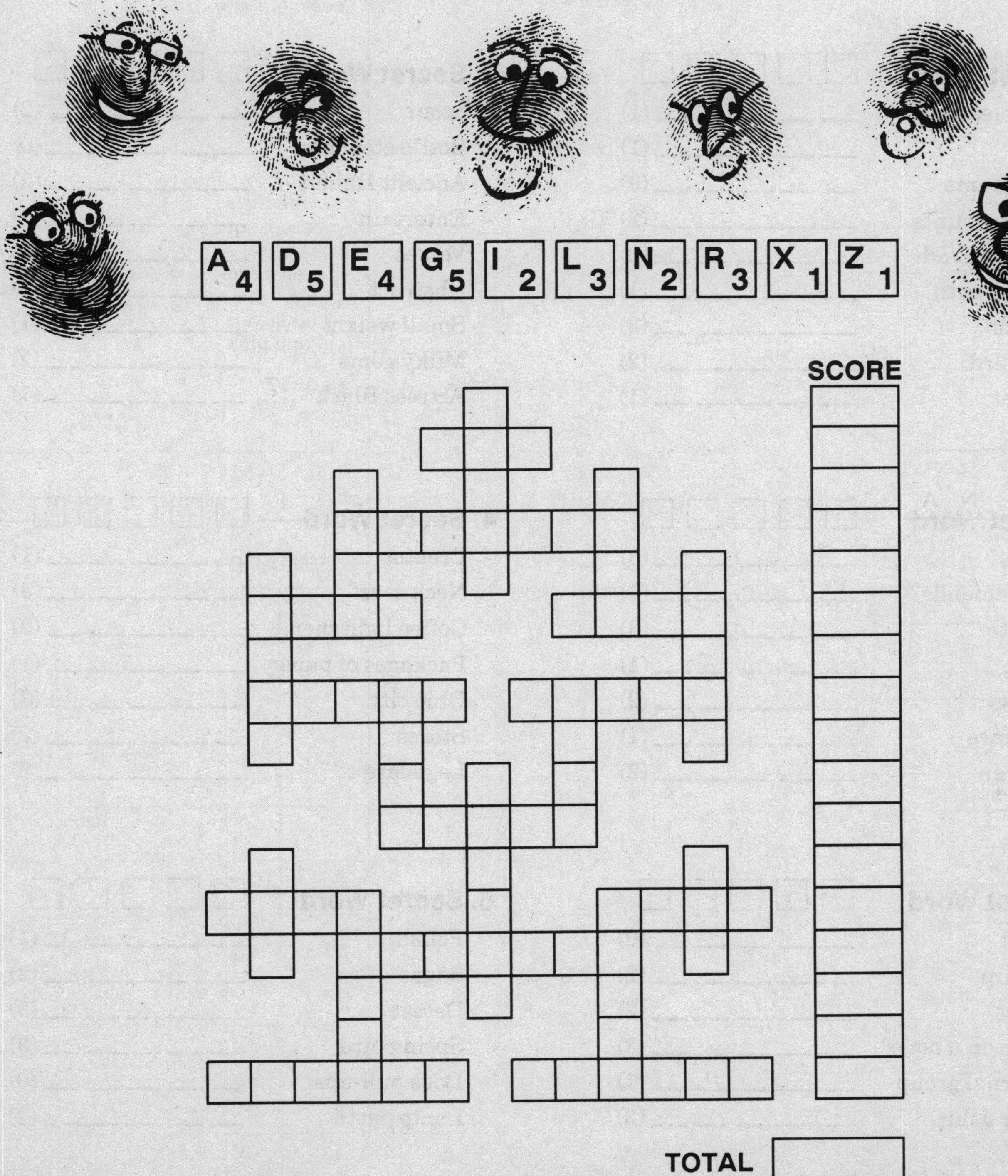

Secret Word

Discover the 5-letter Secret Words by the process of elimination and deduction. Fill in the blanks with the 5-letter answers to the clues. The number in parentheses next to each answer tells you how many of the letters in that word are also in the Secret Word. A zero next to an answer indicates that none of the letters in that word is in the Secret Word. After you have determined the correct five letters, rearrange them to form the Secret Word. No letter is repeated in any Secret Word or within any answer word. The first letters of the answers, reading down, spell out a hint to the Secret Word.

Solutions on page 335

1. Secret Word ☐☐☐☐☐

More pleasant _ _ _ _ _ (1)
Foyer _ _ _ _ _ (1)
Work teams _ _ _ _ _ (0)
English counts _ _ _ _ _ (2)
Piece of bread _ _ _ _ _ (2)
Take an oath _ _ _ _ _ (1)
Ward off _ _ _ _ _ (3)
Poe's bird _ _ _ _ _ (2)
Hanker _ _ _ _ _ (1)

2. Secret Word ☐☐☐☐☐

Scour _ _ _ _ _ (2)
Bottle stoppers _ _ _ _ _ (0)
Ancient Italian _ _ _ _ _ (2)
Entertain _ _ _ _ _ (3)
Verses _ _ _ _ _ (1)
Obstruct _ _ _ _ _ (2)
Small weight _ _ _ _ _ (1)
Milky gems _ _ _ _ _ (2)
Actress Black _ _ _ _ _ (1)

3. Secret Word ☐☐☐☐☐

Craves _ _ _ _ _ (3)
Make amends _ _ _ _ _ (0)
Bee bite _ _ _ _ _ (3)
Odor _ _ _ _ _ (1)
Lifeless _ _ _ _ _ (2)
Brilliance _ _ _ _ _ (1)
Frighten _ _ _ _ _ (2)

4. Secret Word ☐☐☐☐☐

Creator _ _ _ _ _ (1)
Neck scarf _ _ _ _ _ (3)
Coffee lightener _ _ _ _ _ (0)
Packages of paper _ _ _ _ _ (1)
Ohio city _ _ _ _ _ (3)
Stores _ _ _ _ _ (2)
Legislate _ _ _ _ _ (2)

5. Secret Word ☐☐☐☐☐

Pulled _ _ _ _ _ (0)
Worship _ _ _ _ _ (2)
Memos _ _ _ _ _ (2)
Chews on a bone _ _ _ _ _ (3)
Fraternal group _ _ _ _ _ (1)
Singer John _ _ _ _ _ (2)

6. Secret Word ☐☐☐☐☐

Polish _ _ _ _ _ (1)
Sagas _ _ _ _ _ (2)
Detest _ _ _ _ _ (3)
Spring bird _ _ _ _ _ (3)
Does pull-ups _ _ _ _ _ (0)
Lamp parts _ _ _ _ _ (2)

BULL'S-EYE SPIRAL

This is a new target for those who can think in circles. The game works two ways, outward and inward. If you're outward bound, guess the word that fits clue 1-3. Then go on to clue 4-7 and so on. If you're stuck with an outward-bound word, try the inward clues. Work both ways to hit the Bull's-Eye.

Solution on page 335

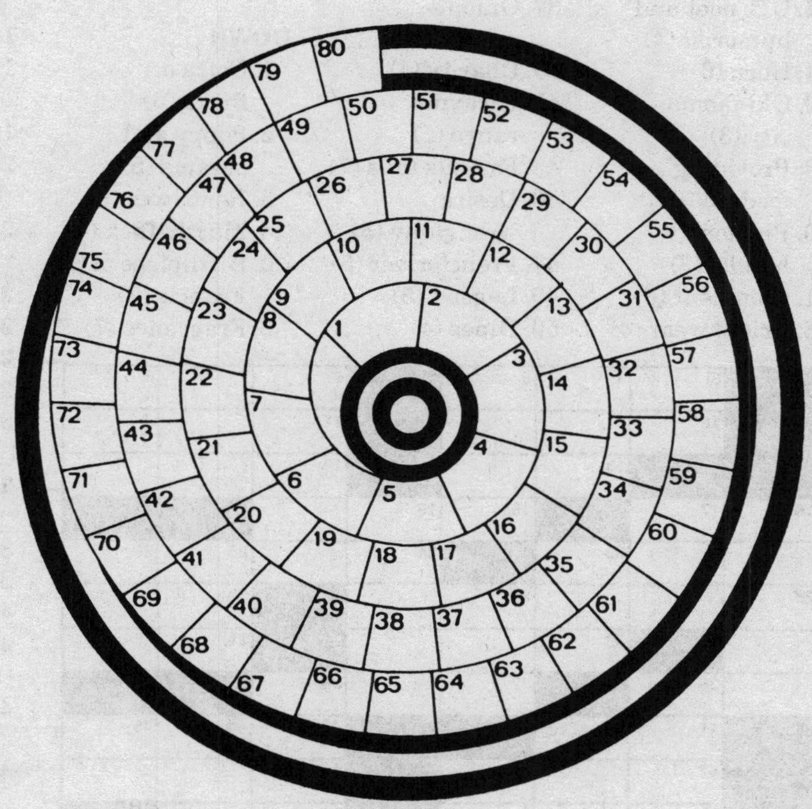

OUTWARD

1-3. Do ____ disturb!
4-7. Onionlike vegetable
8-12. Cognizant
13-18. Salad ingredient
19-23. Officer trainee
24-28. Autumn beverage
29-35. Laundry worker
36-41. Reduce in rank
42-46. Small drum
47-50. TV's Gomer ____
51-55. Elegant house
56-63. Turkish prayer towers
64-68. World carrier
69-75. Holds in high esteem
76-80. More wan

INWARD

80-74. Fall back into a bad habit
73-66. Complete turn-around
65-60. Food sampler
59-54. Zoo resident
53-48. Full of high spirits
47-41. Court dealing with wills
40-37. Heavy book
36-30. Mirrored chest-of-drawers
29-21. Acted the fortuneteller
20-16. Stage performer
15-11. Mario Andretti, for one
10-6. Not asleep anymore
5-1. Singer ____ John

DOUBLE TROUBLE

Not really double trouble, but double fun! Solve this puzzle as you would a regular crossword, EXCEPT place one, two, or three letters in each box. The number of letters in each answer is shown in parentheses after its clue.

ACROSS

1. Concise (5)
3. Greek letter (4)
6. Stoles (4)
9. Land measure (4)
10. Hardy heroine (4)
11. Eurasia's ____ Mountains (4)
12. Smidgen (3)
13. Noted boxer (3)
14. Bed cover (5)
15. Squabble (4)
18. Location (4)
20. Crazy (3)
22. U.S. poet and humorist (4)
24. Horn (6)
27. Oklahoma city (3)
28. Providing food (8)
30. Pitcher handle (3)
31. Comment (6)
33. Bridal wear (4)
34. Neither's partner (3)
35. Marsh stalk (4)
37. Onion's relative (4)
39. Charity (4)
41. Peruvian range (5)
43. Famous falls (7)
46. Desire wrongfully (5)
47. French river (5)
49. Legend (5)
50. Dines (4)
51. Singer John (5)
52. Strasbourg season (3)

DOWN

1. Cotta or firma (5)
2. Poppy and sesame (5)
3. Reno item (3)
4. Marsh duck (4)
5. Birthplace of St. Francis (6)
6. Fragrance (7)
7. Nutmeg covering (4)
8. Sailor (4)
9. Play part (3)
16. Flapjack (7)
17. Vintner's employee (6)
19. Snarl (6)
20. Juanita's mom (5)
21. Eden resident (4)
23. Apian home (4)
25. Thin (4)
26. Gaffe (5)
29. Cairo's river (4)
32. Takes into custody (7)
36. Actor Day-Lewis (6)
38. Chef's tool (5)
39. Nook (6)
40. Veal, e.g. (4)
42. Pastry chef's forte (7)
44. Marble (5)
45. Tillable (6)
48. Eternity (3)

■	1	2	■	3	4	5	■	6	7	8
9			■	10			■	11		
12			■	■	13		■	14		
■	■	15	16	17	■	18	19		■	■
20	21	■	22		23	■	24		25	26
27		■	28			29		■	30	
31		32		■	33			■	34	
■	■	35		36	■	37		38	■	■
39	40		■	41	42	■	■	43	44	45
46			■	47		48	■	49		
50			■	51			■	52		■

Solution on page 335

Crypto-Riddle

To read this riddle, you must first solve this simple substitution code. **Solution on page 338**

QUESTION:

C U J X ' G X U S K F L L S V S T B S E S X C S S T J P S C S Y S V J T K J P J F Y S V ?

ANSWER:

N T S N L X U S W F G G S Y Y F T O C J X B U S G , C U F Y S X U S N X U S V N T S F G C J X B U F T O B S Y Y G .

PATHFINDER

Follow one continuous winding path from Start (W) to Finish (S) to discover the hidden quotation. Each word starts with one of the circled letters. The last letter of one word is next to the circled first letter of the next. The number of letters in each word in the quotation is given below the answer blanks. The path does not cross itself, and no letter is used more than once. Not all the letters in the diagram will be used.

Solution on page 335

START (column 7) — FINISH (column 17)

(F)	O	H	E	N	P	(W)	H	U	A	I	G	I	N	H	O	S	E	I	U	U	O	B
I	E	P	(T)	R	O	P	E	Q	P	L	B	E	S	N	N	I	R	O	A	(A)	T	(A)
L	R	W	O	A	T	Y	H	N	L	H	E	U	(B)	O	I	D	F	(F)	S	N	W	G
E	B	S	(F)	R	C	G	M	H	(T)	I	M	(F)	W	E	N	G	(O)	P	(T)	D	Y	N
R	V	T	D	T	H	L	U	A	R	U	W	I	(T)	H	A	Z	A	H	N	S	P	I
M	I	(T)	H	E	C	A	E	(B)	T	S	R	Y	S	L	(W)	T	R	P	A	P	T	S
O	E	R	Y	N	I	H	(L)	H	A	E	O	(A)	N	A	E	P	T	(S)	K	I	U	L
U	(T)	I	T	I	L	J	U	Y	B	N	T	(T)	G	S	E	N	M	A	R	L	E	V
S	H	E	T	R	V	X	(B)	W	E	N	R	E	H	O	L	(W)	L	L	Y	B	N	Y
P	Y	(L)	A	P	R	H	R	T	(I)	D	U	O	S	E	A	U	T	(A)	N	E	H	(T)
O	R	K	N	U	G	I	B	O	E	R	C	E	U	S	P	N	I	E	O	S	F	D
M	P	A	I	L	A	E	U	A	K	I	X	T	V	H	Y	D	(P)	T	C	E	(A)	N

WHEN ___ ___ ___ ___ ___
4 3 5 4 7 3

___ ___ ___, ___ ___ ___
3 5 4 3 5 5

___ ___ ___ ___ ___ ___
4 1 8 6 3 4

___ ___ ___ ___ ___ ___
3 4 8 5 3 4

___ ___ ___ ___ ___.
3 3 9 2 7

FINISH THE FOURS

Place letters into the empty squares in the diagram to form a string of overlapping 4-letter words. A 4-letter word begins in each numbered square. If you choose the correct letters, they will reveal a fictional character, reading in order from left to right.

Solution on page 335

1 P	A	2	E	L	3 L		N	4 D	A	M	5	I	N	6	7	P	8 E	X		9 T
I		10 T	A	11 S		I	12 T	R		13 P	A	14	E	15 A	M	O	16	E	P	T

DOUBLE CROSSER

Fill in the missing letters in the crossword diagram, making sure that no word is repeated. Then transfer those letters to the correspondingly numbered dashes below the diagram to reveal a quotation. The author's name will appear in the shaded boxes. **Solution on page 335**

■	14	A	D	E	■	2	A	33	■	■	■	A	D	43
10	A	T	E	R	■	E	V	A	D	E	■	7	R	A
E	M	O	31	E	■	C	13	M	E	38	■	R	4	B
L	A	M	E	■	F	A	N	■	42	N	A	M	E	L
■	■	■	C	H	I	N	■	■	■	E	R	A	S	E
■	S	E	T	O	N	■	A	L	34	■	A	N	35	1
■	A	T	O	N	■	■	S	27	A	20	■	■	■	■
■	C	15	3	29	11	C	26	23	N	37	40	N	6	■
■	■	■	■	R	O	U	E	■	■	A	32	36	A	■
A	9	T	I	■	19	R	N	■	25	R	O	T	8	■
24	T	A	M	39	■	■	■	17	E	E	N	■	■	■
16	A	M	P	A	5	■	G	E	30	■	C	21	O	W
U	M	28	■	P	E	R	O	N	■	S	18	A	V	E
R	E	E	■	A	W	A	41	D	■	P	A	R	E	D
E	N	12	■	■	■	22	E	S	■	A	D	E	N	■

_ 1 _ 2 _ 3 _ 4 _ 5 _ 6   _ 7 _ 8   _ 9 _ 10 _ 11 _ 12 _ 13 _ 14

_ 15 _ 16   _ 17 _ 18 _ 19 _ 20 _ 21 _ 22   _ 23 _ 24   _ 25 _ 26 _ 27

_ 28 _ 29 _ 30 _ 31 _ 32 _ 33   _ 34 _ 35   _ 36 _ 37 _ 38 _ 39 _ 40 _ 41 _ 42 _ 43

Give and Take

Change the 4-letter words on the left to the 5-letter words on the right by giving and taking letters. Add one letter to the word on the left to form a 5-letter word. Then subtract one letter from that word to form a new 4-letter word. Next add a letter to form a new 5-letter word; subtract a letter to form a new 4-letter word. Finally, add a letter to form the word given on the right. The order of the letters may be rearranged in forming new words. **Our solutions on page 338**

Example: VEST, STOVE, TOES, THOSE, SHOT, SHORT

1. COWL ________ ______ ________ ______ SPOIL
2. GEAR ________ ______ ________ ______ LATHE
3. HAVE ________ ______ ________ ______ RANGE
4. MILE ________ ______ ________ ______ STALE
5. PINE ________ ______ ________ ______ SPANK
6. TEAK ________ ______ ________ ______ DECKS
7. WEAR ________ ______ ________ ______ TRAYS

PYRAMID POWER

Fill in the Pyramid with the 6-letter answers to the clues. Each answer fits into a triangle (which consists of six circles connected with lines) either clockwise or counterclockwise. The words in neighboring triangles will share letters. The answer to the first clue is ALLUDE; it has been placed into the diagram for you. You must determine where the other answers belong. As a solving aid, you will find that the answers to the clues are in alphabetical order.

Solution on page 339

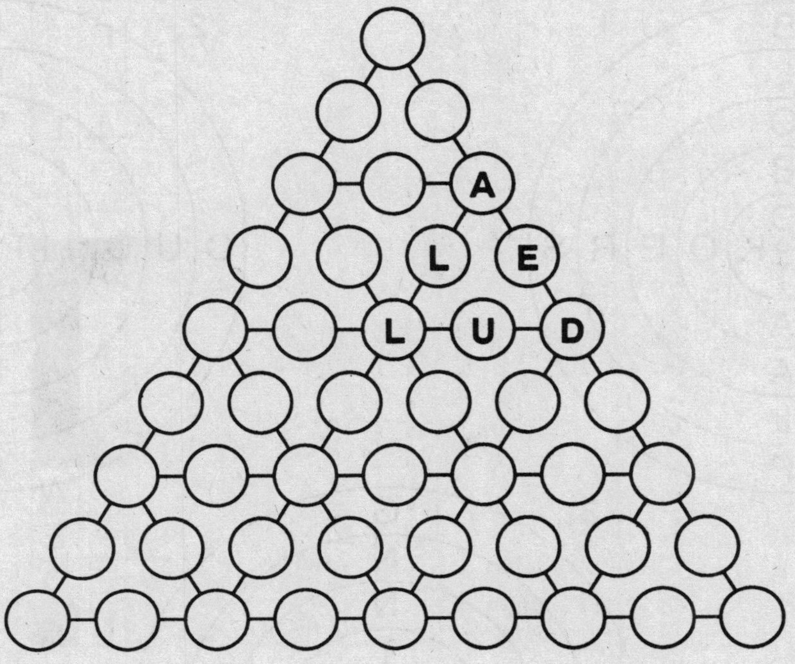

1. Refer indirectly A L L U D E
2. Visitor ______
3. Outdoorsman ______
4. Waltzed ______
5. Rely ______
6. Lawn tools ______
7. Gives the slip ______
8. Borrower's benefactor ______
9. Smaller ______
10. Prescribes ______
11. Chopped pickles ______
12. Drives off ______
13. Vacation hotel ______
14. Hurried ______
15. Sterling ______
16. Ocean craft ______

TWO AT A TIME

All 26 letters of the alphabet are to be pulled from the 13 words—Two at a Time! The remaining letters in each word will form a new word, sometimes by rearranging. For example, in the first word take out E and Z, rearrange the letters, and you have the word LEGAL.

Our solution on page 338

A B C D ~~E~~ F G H I J K L M N O P Q R S T U V W X Y ~~Z~~

1. ~~Gazelle~~ Legal
2. Awakens
3. Hijacks
4. Swerved
5. Exhorts
6. Hastily
7. Quakers
8. Ballads
9. Campers
10. Griddle
11. Infants
12. Rompers
13. Resolve

RINGERS

Each of the five Ringers is composed of five rings. Use your imagination to rotate the rings so that you spell four 5-letter words reading from the outside to the inside when all five rings are aligned correctly.

Solutions on page 339

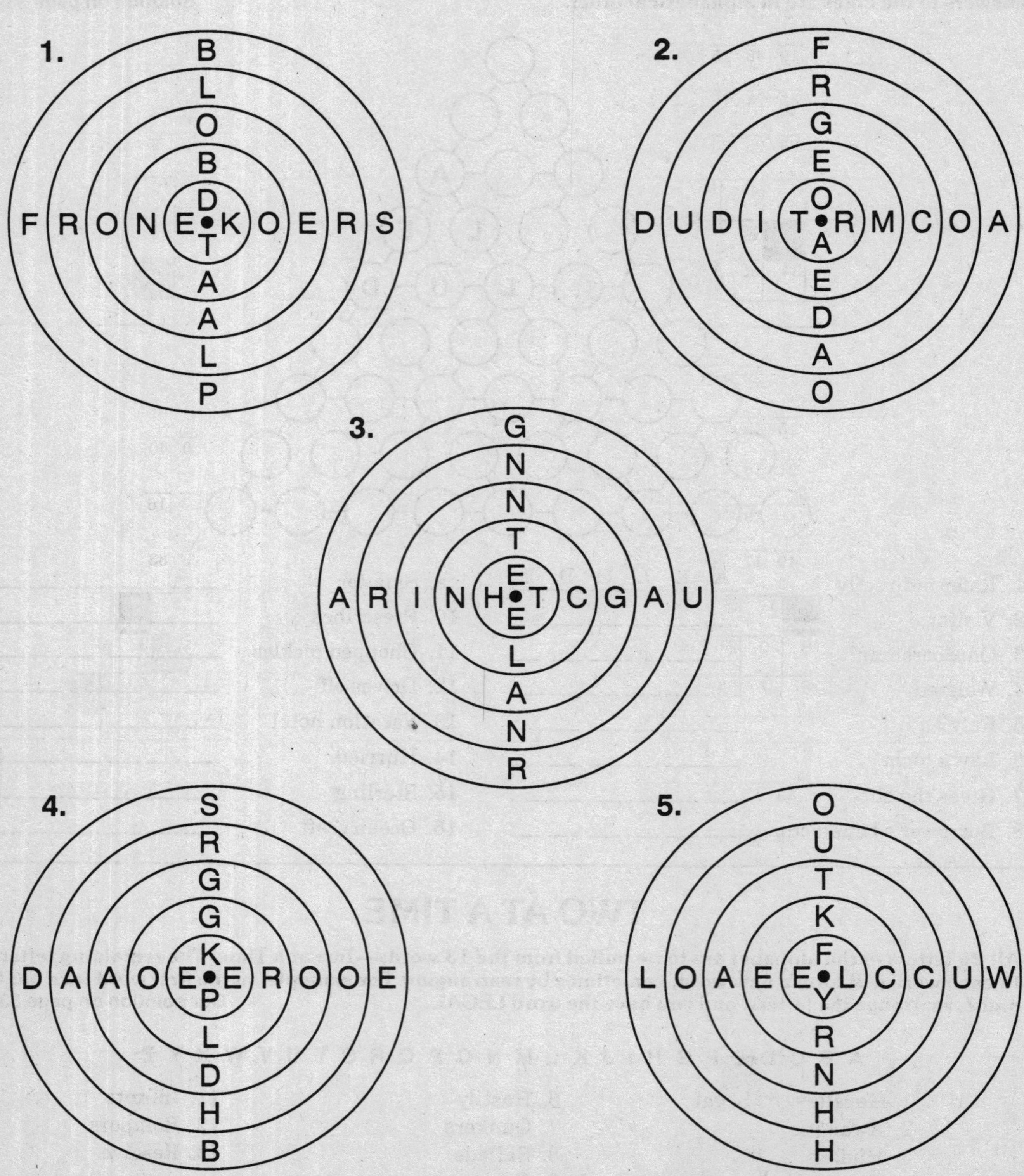

QUOTAGRAMS

Fill in the answers to the clues. Then transfer the letters to the correspondingly numbered squares in the diagram. The completed diagrams will contain quotations.

Solutions on page 338

A.

1. Evolve — 2 20 16 35 12 8 29
2. Signal warning — 19 46 25 4 22 9
3. Shade of red — 45 24 18 38 32 1
4. Maxims — 36 28 33 41 23 37
5. Triumphant — 10 7 31 44 11 14 39
6. Fold — 21 42 30 5 26 17
7. Ultimate — 27 34 15 40 6 3 43 13

1	2	3	4	5	6	7	8	9		10	11	12	13		14	15	16
17	18		19	20	21	22	23	24		25	26		27	28	29	30	31
32	33	34	35		36	37		38	39	40	41	42	43	44	45	46	

B.

1. Beneficial — 11 22 36 9 50 45 35
2. Decade unit — 15 48 37 5
3. Athletic team — 21 14 32 47 28 42 23
4. Dock — 7 19 34 46 27
5. Unrestrained — 49 17 6 30 12
6. South American country — 18 26 38 4 8 20 43
7. Adolescent — 1 44 25 10 40
8. Sycophant — 31 2 41 13 16
9. Villain — 29 24 39 3 33

1	2	3		4	5	6	7		8	9		10	11	12		13	14	15		16
17	18		19	20	21	22		23	24	25	26		27	28	29	30	31		32	33
34	35		36	37	38	39	40		41	42		43	44	45	46	47	48	49	50	

C.

1. Flirt — 43 37 73 74 66 3 17 30
2. Sail spar — 23 29 52 27 8
3. Very fast cats — 79 40 16 72 35 10 71 2
4. Contaminated — 70 75 36 46 54 5 22
5. Display counter — 67 25 18 68 15 1 42 80
6. "Mrs. ____" — 59 69 64 55 62 45 7
7. Rapidly spreading blaze — 19 53 76 61 32 57 21 48
8. Nice's locale — 50 28 78 14 56 33
9. Holiday — 12 63 51 6 24 44 49 38
10. Book division — 47 4 13 77 39 26 31
11. Waterfalls — 34 60 9 65 20 11 41 58

1	2		3	4	5		6	7	8	9		10	11	12	13	14	15	16		17	18	19	20
21	22	23		24	25	26	27	28		29	30	31	32	33	34	35	36	37	38		39	40	41
42	43	44	45	46	47	48		49	50		51	52	53	54	55	56	57	58	59		60	61	62
63	64	65	66	67		68	69	70	71		72	73	74	75	76		77	78	79	80			

CRYPTOGRAMS

Each of these Cryptograms is a message in substitution code. THE SMART CAT might become MRX DGYUM LYM if M is substituted for T, R for H, X for E, etc. One way to break the code is to look for repeated letters. E, T, A, O, N, R, and I are the most often used letters. A single letter is usually A or I; OF, IS, and IT are common 2-letter words; try THE or AND for a 3-letter group. The code is different for each Cryptogram.

Solutions on page 340

1. IY YKXDUYOX PDCIXD'Q NJYUW, ZXI QYOXIFCAZ — HAMIFCAZ — BYPA YA GHGXD. BYA'I PHCI SYD GXDSXUICYA IY CQQLX SYDIF. QCAUX IFX WXM IY ZYYB PDCICAZ CQ DX-PDCICAZ, ZCKX MYLDQXJS QYOXIFCAZ IY XBCI.

2. RMRKV XAJR XOR NTMRKWJRWX GXXRJDXH XT OGWZSR TBK GLLGAKH AX ITHXH JTKR, GWZ XOR KRHBSXH GKR UTKHR XOGW AL UR OGZ OGWZSRZ XORJ TBKHRSMRH.

3. AZ LRE CSAFG CSV TML RZ CSV CQMFHOQVHHRQ AH SMQI, LRE HSREPI CQL OVCCAFO HRWVTSVQV RF CSV HCQMAOSC MFI FMQQRT.

4. JX TSDO SDARS JG ROZUAZO AMUQ TSDO JQKSVZ, TSDO DBIZZB EJCC GSSQ HZ TSDO NSEQXUCC.

5. DSU LPS DEPS GDBEPFLUF FRLU FEEWM. GA NEH JEU'F YSWGSKS GF, BHF L CEEJ FEEW GU FRS RLUJM EA L BEEP ZEPXDLU.

6. WGRGDZ SK RYJ DQKR XJWGRSVGF RSDJ QV RYJ IJWM RQ RYJ TJMKQZ CYQ YWK ZQ FJWAJK RQ MWHJ.

7. FULH EIJL JLH OTEQUDARL DH INWTRDBTIH, MIS QDH ULDA BUL ALKIAB GIA JTWLE DAISHO.

8. I RTW TB NTRFQHRRJ GFDTNF NTXMWIHMJ AQFM JTNFTMF ISSJ I RHWWRF SHCW.

9. QLNP TPLTIP FJMZB FJKF FJP X.Q. RPKFJPG WXGPKX MQ K TPGOPUF PHKNTIP LO K ZLZ-TGLTJPF LGEKZMVKFMLZ.

10. K YWVF LKU WM DUH XFD WM UHTHY KRYKWO JD KMI JFH VQHYI JD MFDX FWL MDLHJFWUP VFHKZHY.

11. CYDIJGP DNTXYD LHS YGCD, EHI T SYCHMJGU CJYI TQDL NYQXD.

12. YPEWXVZTH XVSX VSY FWWT HIWSXCK JVWSQWTWA FK PRWIQIPABJXZPT ZY CWHZYCSXZPT.

13. WCFAAKXQ THCXR EHN XFQN XHEI OU NVK UFCXN TKAK HE HEK QORK HEXJ.

14. ECOO TJGB XKUMBIMV XCUZ IMMB KDV LMU K EJKP PKUUBMHH.

15. LXQJ EZJ MZW YQSE LGZIQDE HZEL — VYDQEE JUV NZFD FL.

16. RID QSLLDFR ZSFI EHD PEVLIR QB RID REOD.

DIAGRAMLESS FILL-IN

For this fill-in puzzle we have given you all of the E's that appear in the diagram, but none of the black squares. As you solve the puzzle remember to put a black square at the beginning and end of each answer and to balance each black square with its symmetrical counterpart on the opposite side of the diagram.

Solution on page 338

3 Letters
Add
Ade
Ail
Aim
Ala
Ale
And
Ape
Art
Ate
Axe
Aye
Did
Die
Eel
Egg
Ell
Els
Era
Ere
Err
Ewe
Hat
Ill
Inn
Ira
Jam
Jar
Lad
Lap
Les
Lid
Lot
Nap
Old
One
Ope
Owl
Pea
Per
Ran
Ray
Rig
Roe
See
Tar
Tee
Tie
Yap

4 Letters
Arms
Dams
Date
Ella
Else
Erie
Harm
Heat
Hope
Lair
Meet
Mold
Napa
Odds
Peel
Pope
Tara
Urge

5 Letters
Annex
Enter
Yodel

6 Letters
Aromas
Purple

							E							E		E
																E
								E				E	E			
			E			E										
			E									E				
				E									E	E		
									E							E
		E												E		
			E				E									
E																
										E						
	E	E														

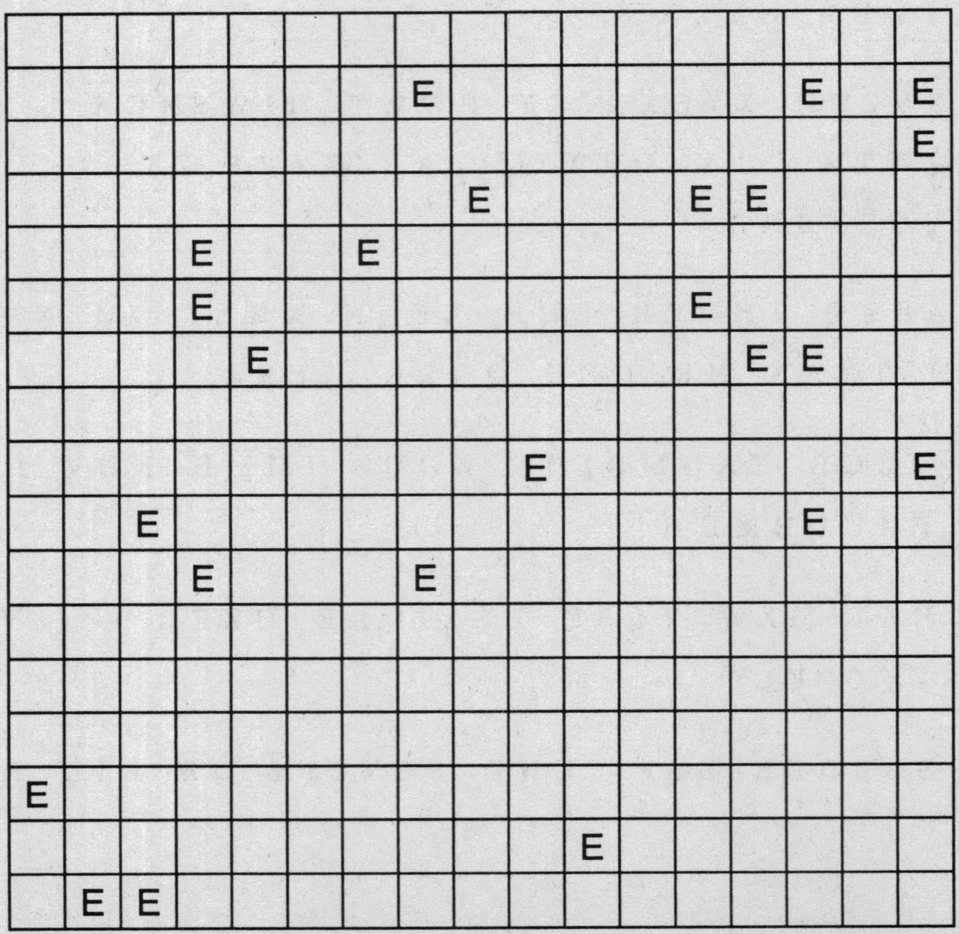

HOW TO SOLVE: Fill in as many boxes as you can to form eleven words starting with the given letters. No letter may be repeated in the word itself, in the word above, or in the word below. For each word the number of letters needed to earn the maximum score is indicated by the number of boxes.

HOW TO SCORE: Each letter used is worth one point. If you use all 26 letters of the alphabet, give yourself a bonus of ten points. Include the given letters in all scoring.

Our solutions on page 338

Sample:		
	S A M P L E _	6
	R I N G _ _ _	4
	C L O U D Y _	6

In this sample the word RING cannot be RINGER because the letter R would be repeated in that word and because the letter E appears above in SAMPLE. It cannot be RUNG because U is below in CLOUDY.

1.

WORDS	SCORE
L _ _ _	
I N _ _ _ _ _	
A _ _ _	
P E _ _ _ _ _	
M _ _ _ _	
H E _ _ _	
B R _ _ _	
O _ _ _ _	
M _ _ _	
W I _ _ _	
R U _ _ _ _	
TOTAL	

2.

WORDS	SCORE
T O _ _ _	
M _ _ _	
P L _ _ _ _	
C _ _ _ _	
W H _ _ _ _ _	
P L _ _ _	
W I _ _ _	
A D _ _ _ _	
W _ _ _	
A C _ _ _ _ _	
V _ _ _	
TOTAL	

MATCHMAKER

Fill in the missing first letter of each word in the column on the left. Next, look for a related word in the group at the right and put it in the blank in the second column. When the puzzle is completed, read the first letters of both columns in order, from top to bottom, to reveal a song title.

Solution on page 338

___ unday ________________

___ pset ________________

___ enny ________________

___ aster ________________

___ ice ________________

___ ute ________________

___ ctive ________________

___ os ________________

___ guana ________________

___ ree ________________

___ adio ________________

___ pparent ________________

___ rade ________________

___ llinois ________________

___ emon ________________

___ ota ________________

___ weet ________________

Angeles, Candy, Class, Dial, Eggs, Independent, Indiana, Inert, Irate, Lizard, Obvious, Orange, Pretty, Sour, Tuesday, Upsilon, Xavier.

HOW MANY SQUARES?

This diagram is filled with squares small, medium, and large. Try to count them all. There may be more than you think!

Solution on page 339

STRETCH LETTERS

These words, listed alphabetically by length, are to be entered in the diagram across only. Words do not read down. When writing in a blank taller than a square, stretch the letter to the full height of the blank. The stretched letters are part of more than one entry. **Solution on page 338**

UNITED STATES CITIES

4 Letters
Erie
Nome
Reno

5 Letters
Boise
Miami
Omaha
Tampa

6 Letters
Albany
Austin
Denver
Ithaca
Newark
Pierre
Racine
Toledo

7 Letters
Atlanta
Chicago
Detroit
Houston
Madison
Olympia
Orlando
Seattle
Trenton

8 Letters
Aberdeen
Billings
Columbia
Honolulu
Portland

9 Letters
Anchorage
Baltimore
Fairbanks
Milwaukee
Nashville

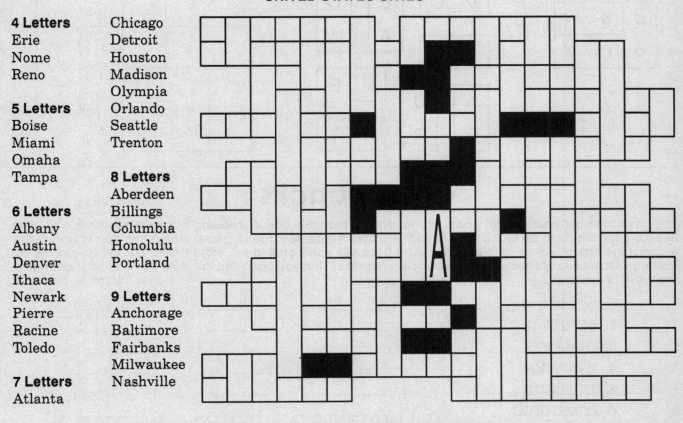

PLACE YOUR NUMBER

The large square below is divided into four smaller squares—A, B, C, and D—and each smaller square is divided into four sections—North, East, South, and West. Use the clues to number the sections. Each section will contain a different number from 1 through 16. **Solution on page 339**

1. All of the numbers in square A are even.
2. All of the numbers in square D are single digits.
3. The total of all the East numbers is 11.
4. Square C contains the square roots of two of the numbers in square B.
5. The total of all the West numbers is twice the total of all the numbers in square D.
6. The total of all the numbers in square A equals the total of all the North numbers.
7. The largest of the South numbers is the only even one.
8. The total of all the numbers in squares A and C minus the total of all the numbers in squares B and D equals the number in A-North.

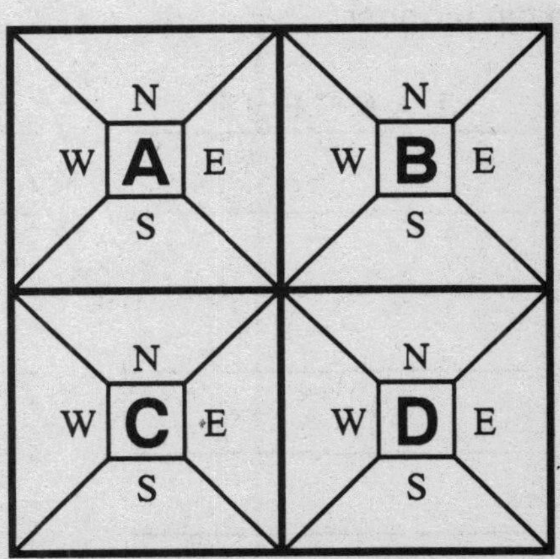

Letter Tiles

Form four words reading across and five words reading down by placing the eight Letter Tiles into the diagram. Horizontal tiles go into horizontal spaces, vertical tiles into vertical spaces. In the example, three tiles fit together to form the words SAW, ONE, SO, AN, and WE.

Solution on page 339

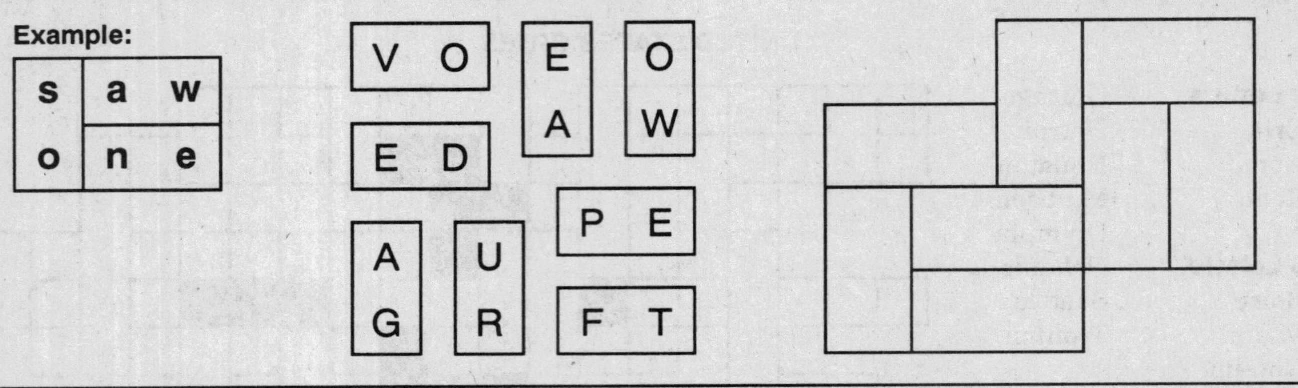

Throwbacks

You have to throw your mental gears into reverse to play this game. Reading backward there are at least three 4-letter words to be found in each of the longer words. You can skip over letters, but don't change the order of the letters. For example, in the word DECLARE you can find the word RACE reading backward by starting with the next-to-last letter and skipping over the L, but you can't find the word READ without changing the order of the letters.

Our solutions on page 338

1. DELTAS ________ ________ ________
2. RENEWAL ________ ________ ________
3. LAMENTS ________ ________ ________
4. TANAGER ________ ________ ________
5. TRIOXIDE ________ ________ ________
6. APERIODIC ________ ________ ________
7. YEARBOOKS ________ ________ ________
8. OLIGOPOLY ________ ________ ________

Hexagrams

One of the letters in the hexagons has been circled because it and the letters in the six surrounding hexagons can be unscrambled to form a seven-letter word (in this case LARGESS). We were able to form 10 other words in this manner.

Our solutions on page 338

LARGESS ________ ________ ________ ________ ________ ________ ________ ________ ________ ________

S L A B
E (G) S N T
Y R A A I E
O D A W P R F
W O R E T Y
F R T A H
L U E R

Crackerjacks

Find the answer to the riddle by filling in the center boxes with the letters needed to complete the words across and down. When you have filled in the Crackerjacks, the letters reading across the center boxes from left to right will spell out the riddle answer.

Solution on page 339

RIDDLE: What is the ideal occupation for someone always willing to write a wrong?

	EF	
KIN		LK
	RT	

	O	
TA		ET
	AN	

	EM	
AL		T
	ALD	

ANSWER: ____________________

Alpha Quotes

Reveal the quotes by eliminating the letters of the alphabet that are not part of the quotes. The unused letters go in alphabetical order from A to Z.

Solutions on page 338

1. E A T I B Q C U E D T E T F E I S G L E H A I J R
N I K N G L T M O Y N A W O N W I P T Q H R Y O
U S R T U M O V U T W H C X L Y O S E Z D .

2. A S H B O W C M E A D E P H A F R A O H G H W
I H O J A T E K C R A L C K M E R N S O I N B P
E D A N Q D I L L S R H O S W Y O U T A C U R
V U M W M Y X M U Y M M Z Y .

Build-A-Pyramid

Use all the jumbled letters to build a pyramid so that each word contains all the letters of the word above it plus one additional letter. A starting letter has been set in the top square of the diagram.

Our solution on page 339

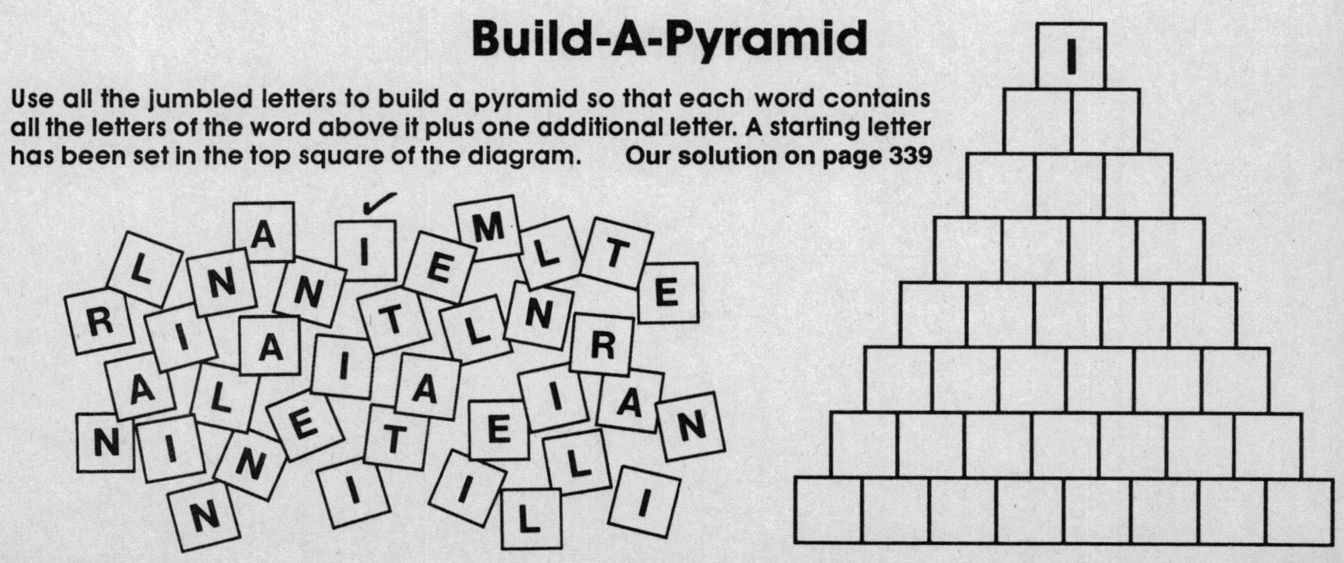

Word Seek 7

Match Words

Two-word terms related to the Tour de France are hidden in the diagrams below. The first word of each answer is in the left diagram; the second part is in the right diagram in the same location reading in the same direction. Words read forward, backward, up, down, and diagonally, and always in a straight line. For example, BUMPY ROUTE is formed by combining BUMPY from the left diagram and ROUTE from the right diagram.

Word list on page 334

Solution on page 332

```
P M U B Y S L K G Y L F A
S O G I P F I U C L H L T
O U W O L L E Y B I C A P
S N R A I Y A P M A U T E
T T E A M P C T O D B Q E
A A R L K M H Q E L R U T
R I E O P U A B U E S I S
C N K R N B S L G I P C O
R K R E G G E A P L E Y I
O B L A I C E P S N E M D
U Y T E F A S L I B C R Y
G U P H I L L C M F A S T
H G U O T F A S L H R Y E
```

```
J S B J O E I T J E R T Y
E T L M V W S O R G B I E
R R Y E S R E J L A C R B
A A N C M E U L I T T E M
R T I M E T G S G S W S I
C E T Y B U R T H N E T L
L G D A L O O L K S A H C
I Y L I C R U T A L L O F
R M O O R K P H D G U I H
O B E L C Y C I B R S G L
A T E M L E H C S F N L O
D S P R I N T E I P A C E
S E L I M P O C E F F L L
```

YOUR WORD LIST
(24 entries)

Missing Vowels

Before you can loop these words about HAWAII, you must first fill in the circles in the diagram with the missing vowels A, E, I, O, and U. Words in the diagram read forward, backward, up, down, and diagonally, and always in a straight line. Circle each word when you find it and cross it off the list. Words will often overlap, and some letters may be used more than once. Not all of the letters in the diagram will be used. We have filled in and circled AIEA as an example.

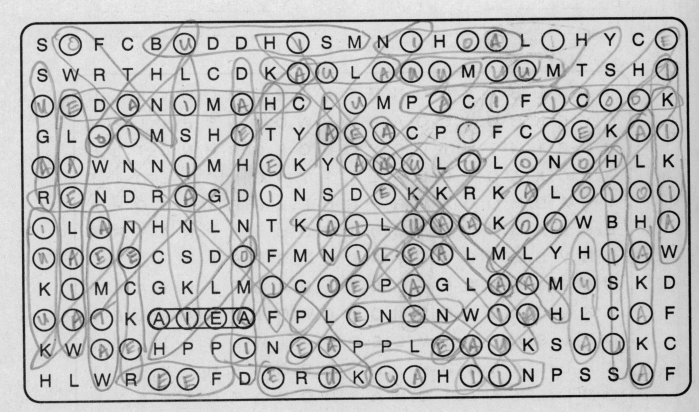

Solution on page 332

HAWAII

AIEA ✓
AKAKA
ALOHA
BUDDHISM
CHAMINADE
COOK
DIAMOND
  HEAD
FIFTIETH
GARDNER
HALEAKALA
HAMAKUA
HIBISCUS
HILO
HONOLULU
HULA
KAHOOLAWE
KAILUA
KAMEHAMEHA
KANEOHE
KAPIOLANI
KAUAI
KAULA
KILAUEA
KUKUI
KURE
LANAI
LAYSAN
LISIANSKI
LUAU
MACADAMIA
MARO
MAUI
MOLOKAI
MUUMUU
NECKER
NENE
NIHOA
NIIHAU
OAHU
PACIFIC
PEARL CITY
PINEAPPLE
POI
REEF
SUGAR
UKULELE
WAIALEALE
WAIKIKI
WAIMEA
WHALES

S	○	F	C	B	○	D	D	H	○	S	M	N	○	H	○	○	L	○	H	Y	C	○
S	W	R	T	H	L	C	D	K	○	○	L	○	○	○	M	○	○	M	T	S	H	○
○	○	D	○	N	○	M	○	H	C	L	○	M	P	○	C	○	F	○	C	○	○	K
G	L	○	○	M	S	H	○	T	Y	○	○	○	C	P	○	F	C	○	○	K	○	○
○	○	W	N	N	○	M	H	○	K	Y	○	○	○	L	○	L	○	N	○	H	L	K
R	○	N	D	R	○	G	D	○	N	S	D	○	K	K	R	K	○	L	○	○	○	○
○	L	○	N	H	N	L	N	T	K	○	○	L	○	○	○	K	○	○	W	B	H	○
○	○	○	○	C	S	D	○	F	M	N	○	L	○	○	L	M	L	Y	H	○	○	W
K	○	M	C	G	K	L	M	○	C	○	○	P	○	G	L	○	○	M	○	S	K	D
○	○	○	K	A	I	E	A	F	P	L	○	N	○	N	W	○	○	H	L	C	○	F
K	W	○	○	H	P	P	○	N	○	○	P	P	L	○	○	○	K	S	○	○	K	C
H	L	W	R	○	○	F	D	○	R	○	K	○	○	H	○	○	N	P	S	S	○	F

Word Seek 9

Alphabetics

Each of the answers starts with a different letter of the alphabet. The answers are in the diagram reading forward, backward, up, down, and diagonally, and always in a straight line. Not all the letters in the diagram will be used. The dashes indicate the length of each answer. We have looped the first word, ATTIC, for you.

Word list on page 334

Solution on page 332

A T T I C

B _ _ _ _ _ _ _ _

C _ _ _ _ _

D _ _ _ _ _ _ _

E _ _ _ _ _ _

F _ _ _ _

G _ _ _ _ _ _

H _ _ _ _ _

I _ _ _ _ _

J _ _ _ _ _

K _ _ _ _ _ _ _ _ _

L _ _ _ _ _

M _ _ _ _ _ _ _

N _ _ _ _ _

O _ _ _ _ _ _ _ _

P _ _ _ _ _ _

Q _ _ _ _ _ _

R _ _ _ _ _ _

S _ _ _ _ _ _

T _ _ _ _ _

U _ _ _ _ _ _ _

V _ _ _ _ _

W _ _ _ _ _ _

X _ _ _ _ _

Y _ _ _ _ _ _ _

Z _ _ _ _ _ _ _

J A S L B I Y H O N M T L O E Z M O C V K L D
O Y E K C O J C O A R T H W O C W T P I L E H
V D Z I H T U I U O Y O B O E G R H N O T L E
A F C X A O T Q U A L I T Y N G N G I E D T T
I L A O M O D A E R P S D E B P F I L S O H A
E E L A M M N L R G U I U D U I X P N A T R T
A R V E E T B U E I A D Y I S Q E L Y R A L C
W E E J R A W N T E B R E H S D R F E Y A A E
S K L D A B E O F M O F E W O I X A A W L E I
O C L S A R M G M E E R F A I W E Y P I L M Y
S A U C A E B U H I D G S R G T S H C A R R T
O M M L T A L T O N A T U G N A R O E L A Y H

Zigzag

The entries in this Zigzag puzzle will be found in the diagram in an unusual way. They do not read in straight lines; rather, each entry has one bend in it. Circle each word when you find it in the diagram, as we did with ZIGZAG, and cross it off the list. Words often overlap, and some letters may be used more than once. Not all the letters in the diagram will be used.

Solution on page 332

Agents	Dominate	Imperfect	Orthopedic	Stunts
Agriculture	Essence	Kingdom	Paintings	Sword
Antic	Establish	Lessons	Preview	Terrible
Bombast	Finish	Levees	Promises	Unsettle
Breaks	Fired	Meter	Quotient	Vestment
Cavort	Fortunate	Miracle	Reclaims	Willow
Convert	Genesis	Noisier	Reservoir	Wrestle
Debt	Girls	Omnipotent	Rubber	Yearn
Divided	Heavenly	Order	Shanty	Zigzag ✓

```
R O E T A N D O R T H O P E D R E I O N S N E
E M T N U T S I E L T W F I N I S S N S R P L
B S N T R G G R V N S R C I E H K I N A S E T
B D R I N E R H E I D E D G R N M O E G T E T
U O E I P I S I S R E S S E N O E N Y C D E L
F R T B B O T E C I Q T D C D E P S E S S O T
Z N P L Q E T O R O L L E B S R L F I N K R M
M I S E S R N E U V S B O T E M R C U S O A Q
O A G E N U V S N Q A M N V E E H E A V E R W
R P T Z T T E E H T B E I L V T P R A R N O D
P N A I S L R T S A M E W A E E I M B C L W E
A G R I C U T E Y T N R E C L M R W I L Y S R
```

Poet's Corner

To solve this puzzle, locate and loop in the diagram all those words which are underlined in the poem. Words in the diagram read forward, backward, up, down, and diagonally, and always in a straight line.

Solution on page 332

Answer to a Child's Question

Do you ask what the birds say? The sparrow, the dove,
The linnet, and thrush say "I love, and I love!"
In the winter they're silent, the wind is so strong;
What it says I don't know, but it sings a loud song.
But green leaves, and blossoms, and sunny warm weather,
And singing and loving—all come back together.
But the lark is so brimful of gladness and love,
The green fields below him, the blue sky above,
That he sings, and he sings, and forever sings he,
"I love my Love, and my Love loves me."

—Samuel Taylor Coleridge

```
S M O S S O L B U T T H E H T A H T H R U S H
F V S I K R A L S L R E E H B S R E H T A E W
T O E R P M O U U K E V O L D N A C K Y T D G
I H R Q B U N E N F O O J L G N E C D N N N K
T T S E D S W S N D M L E H L L A V F X O A S
A C L S V S R K Y Y S I D N A B O W O R D W A
H O O M B E T Y H G F X R L Q T O S T L H R U
W N R M T N R N N N E J O B I R D S S A Y S O
G A E N E D B I E L O V E K R N P N T I N M Y
W C I E Z A S E F L I G O A L I N T H E V I O
H W D D R L R T D N I W P B M T H E Y R E H D
S E V O L G N I G N I S E V A E L W T I T U B
```

Boxes

All the entries in the list below are one-word movie titles. An entry can begin at any point and will read either clockwise or counterclockwise around the edges of a box (sometimes a square and sometimes a rectangle). BETRAYAL is boxed in the diagram. Solution on page 332

~~Betrayal~~	Fantasia	Juggernaut	Ransom
Betrayed	Frankenstein	Kismet	Safari
Carousel	Gandhi	Lassiter	Sahara
Casablanca	Gaslight	Mirage	Sayonara
Cimarron	Gigi	Nighthawks	Stagecoach
Comanche	Hawaii	Oklahoma	Stowaway
Crisis	Hercules	Oliver	Svengali
Cynara	Indiscreet	Psycho	
Destry	Jaws	Ramona	

S N O W S H A M O C S I R A S A R O M F N I E
A F R A J T U A X R E D A H A W A R A R E N T
R A Y O U N G N I E X N O C Y O N O M A R Y S
I S T A G G E R L E T I M A N Y I C O N K E N
O H V I E W T H A C A C H R A W R E H C H A M
P C A O C R I S S P O N O R C S C W S U O B Y
S Y U M F A K O A B L A R I S I U L E X R T E
P R I G A I L A M O R G I R E K E S L C A S B
H I G I N S A H O E M E M O V I N S K A Y E D
D N A R T A I N G T S V E L I G P O W A Y S Y
B U Y C E N N A R K I C N S F H T H A W G T R
D H A L B R S O M F L A G A G T J I I A W O J

Word Seek 13

Wizard Words

The Wizard is wise and humorous. To complete his words first loop all the words in the word list, then read the leftover letters to reveal the missing words which will complete the Wizard's Words. Words in the diagram read forward, backward, up, down, and diagonally, and always in a straight line. Loop each word when you find it and cross it off the list. Words often overlap, and some letters may be used more than once.

Wizard's Words on page 334

Solution on page 332

THE SECURITY GUARD'S ____ ____ __ ______ ____ ____ ____ ______!

ACTIVE	CHECK	HALT	PRECAUTIONARY	SAFEGUARD
ALERT	CLOSE	HIRED	PRESENCE	SAFETY
ARMED	CONTROL	HOURS	PROPERTY	SECURE
AVERT	DEFENDER	KEEN	PROTECTOR	SIGN
AWAKE	DEPOT	KEEP	PRUDENT	STOP
AWARE	DOORS	MUSEUM	PURPOSE	TASK
BUILDINGS	DUTY	NIGHT	READY	TIME
CAREFUL	EMPLOYED	OFFICES	ROAM	UNIFORMS
CAUTIOUS	FENCE	PATROL	ROOMS	VIGILANT
CENTER	GATES	PLACE	ROUNDS	WATCHMAN

```
S A F E T Y C T S D N U O R O T C E T O R P K
D O O R S D A R M E D N S E C N E S E R P O E
D T E O P S U N W T A I T N A L I G I V E E E
R L I O K R T T S O F F I C E S O M A O R V N
A E T M A E I C Y P R O P E R T Y R D E D I A
U S C S E A O A C E L R T H E I E E T E E T M
G K T N E D U R P D O M L K P S F N R N Y C H
E O C S E Y S E E S R S A F O E E I F T O A C
F H E E E F O F E R T W H L N C H C L D L C T
A N I G H T L U K U A O C D M U E S U M P C A
S I G N E C A L P O P W E S O P R U P R M K W
B U I L D I N G S H Y R A N O I T U A C E R P
```

Heads & Tails

In this special Word Seek, you will form a continuous chain of looped words. The last letter of each word will be the first letter of the next. The number of letters in each word is given in parentheses. We have started you off with the first three words.

Word list on page 334

Solution on page 332

MERRY (5)	______ (6)	______ (4)
YELL (4)	______ (4)	______ (6)
LODE (4)	______ (4)	______ (6)
______ (6)	______ (5)	______ (7)
______ (7)	______ (6)	______ (4)
______ (6)	______ (4)	______ (6)
______ (6)	______ (5)	______ (4)
______ (5)	______ (7)	______ (6)
______ (4)	______ (5)	______ (5)
______ (5)	______ (5)	______ (5)

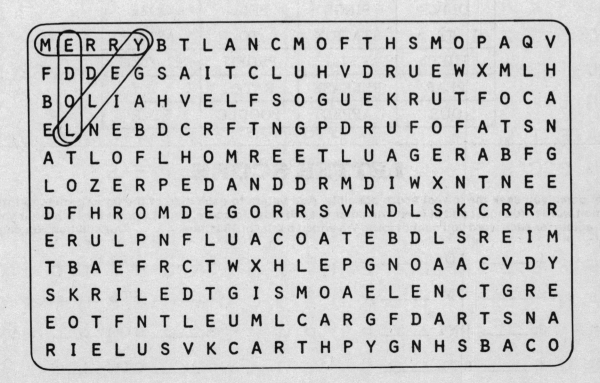

```
M E R R Y B T L A N C M O F T H S M O P A Q V
F D D E G S A I T C L U H V D R U E W X M L H
B O L I A H V E L F S O G U E K R U T F O C A
E L N E B D C R F T N G P D R U F O F A T S N
A T L O F L H O M R E E T L U A G E R A B F G
L O Z E R P E D A N D D R M D I W X N T N E E
D F H R O M D E G O R R S V N D L S K C R R R
E R U L P N F L U A C O A T E B D L S R E I M
T B A E F R C T W X H L E P G N O A A C V D Y
S K R I L E D T G I S M O A E L E N C T G R E
E O T F N T L E U M L C A R G F D A R T S N A
R I E L U S V K C A R T H P Y G N H S B A C O
```

WHAT'S LEFT?

Following the instructions, cross off words in the diagram. When you are finished, the remaining words will form a quotation reading left to right, line by line. **Solution on page 338**

1. Cross off all words that contain exactly two E's.
2. Cross off all two-letter words in columns A and D.
3. Cross off all words that are names of fruit.
4. Cross off all words above, below, or beside a word starting with C.
5. Cross off all words that are anagrams of STARE.
6. Cross off all words in column C that begin with and end in a vowel.
7. Cross off all words that sound the same as another word in the diagram but are spelled differently.
8. Cross off all words that contain two consecutive O's.

A	B	C	D
WHEN	HITCH	ARENA	PLEASE
CHERRY	IN	FORE	BE
MONEY	HOUR	YOUR	RECEIPT
TEARS	IGLOO	INDIGO	FOR
SO	FOUR	WAGON	PEACH
OLIVE	SIEGE	SELL	OOZE
IT	STATION	TO	ASTER
THEIR	CELL	PROFIT	ELATED
PEAR	RELEASE	RATES	A
OUR	APPLE	POODLE	STAR

LETTER SCORE

In this game you seek the lowest score possible. Add letters to each side of the letter groups to form ten common words. You must add at least one letter to each side. To score, count 1 point for each letter you add and 7 points for each word you cannot form. We added a total of 25 letters. **Our solutions on page 338**

1. ______ IO ______
2. ______ UM ______
3. ______ RYI ______
4. ______ RTL ______
5. ______ RTU ______
6. ______ USI ______
7. ______ STL ______
8. ______ UGA ______
9. ______ CTA ______
10. ______ TLA ______

CROSS NUMBERS

Place the number answer to each clue into its proper square in the diagram. If you are stuck on an answer, use the equations across and down to fill in the missing numbers. **Solution on page 339**

A. The Prime Minister of England lives at ____ Downing Street.
B. Number of face cards in a standard deck of playing cards
C. Woodrow Wilson served as U.S. president for ____ terms.
D. Number of hours in a week
E. D-Day was June ____, 1944.
F. Number of centavos in a peso
G. In 1990, the cost of a first-class postage stamp was ____¢.
H. Number of dots on the highest numbered domino
I. A trapezoid has ____ sides.
J. Donald Duck has ____ nephews.
K. Number of boroughs in New York City
L. The atomic number of hydrogen is ____.
M. Number of runs in a grand slam
N. A ringer in horseshoes is worth ____ points.
O. There are ____ cardinal virtues.
P. Number of fluid ounces in a pint
Q. ____ people appear in the painting "American Gothic."
R. Number of oceans on Earth
S. 1400 hours is equivalent to ____:00 p.m.
T. Number of fangs in a rattlesnake's mouth
U. "Stalag ____"
V. Bolivia is bordered by ____ countries.
W. A touchdown is worth ____ points in football.
X. Number of letters in the name of the capital of New Zealand
Y. Number of reeds on a clarinet

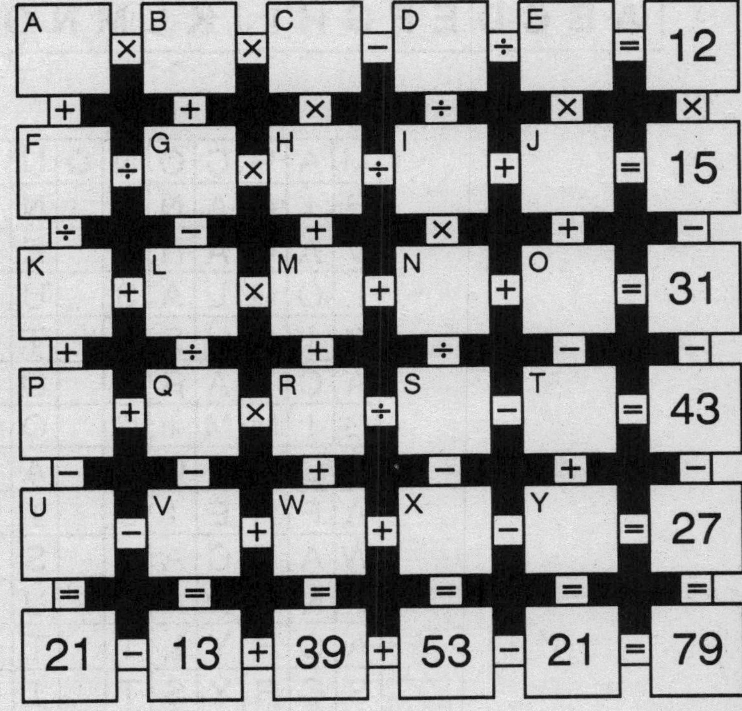

LINE 'EM UP

Line up the inner and outer rings to discover a 12-letter word. Use your imagination to rotate the rings so that the first letter of the word is opposite the number 1, the second letter opposite the number 2, and so forth. When you have lined up the first letter with number 1 correctly, the rest of the numbers will indicate the order of the letters in the word.

Solution on page 339

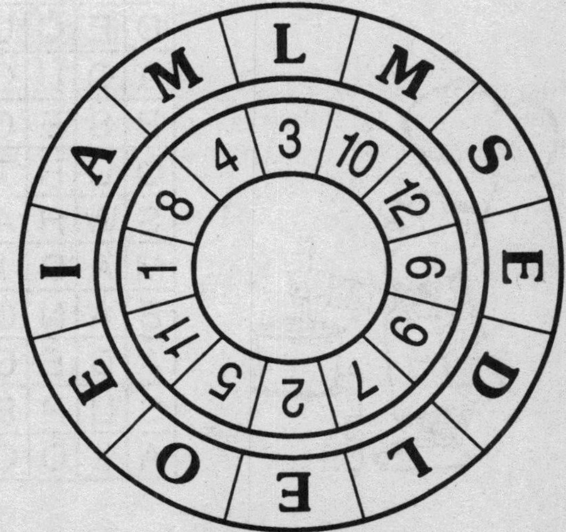

ALPHABET SOUP

Insert a different letter of the alphabet into each of the 26 empty boxes to form words of five or more letters reading across. The letter you insert may be at the beginning, the end, or in the middle of the word. Each letter of the alphabet will be used only once. Cross off each letter in the list as you use it. All the letters in each row are not necessarily used in forming the word.

Our solution on page 339

Example: In the first row across we have inserted the letter Q to form the word CONQUEST.

A B C D E F G H I J K L M N O P ~~Q~~ R S T U V W X Y Z

M	A	R	C	O	N	**Q**	U	E	S	T	I	C
B	I	G	A	N	D		N	I	M	A	L	E
V	A	C	A	R	A		E	L	I	D	O	R
L	O	G	L	A	S		U	R	P	L	E	X
C	I	S	H	E	L		T	E	D	O	N	G
A	C	T	A	R	I		O	U	Q	U	E	T
G	I	M	M	I	C		O	B	I	C	A	S
R	O	U	P	O	L		A	L	A	X	Y	E
A	F	R	E	I	G		T	E	E	P	E	L
W	A	N	C	A	I		S	I	G	H	T	Y
K	N	O	W	A	D		U	S	T	I	C	K
A	C	R	Y	L	I		T	E	R	R	O	W
S	C	R	Y	S	T		I	R	L	I	A	N
D	O	O	P	O	S		I	B	L	E	N	T
S	C	A	R	T	O		N	E	D	L	A	Y
P	E	C	A	B	I		A	R	R	E	L	A
D	E	Q	U	A	L		Y	L	E	N	G	S
A	Q	U	O	A	S		L	U	M	I	N	E
P	S	E	C	O	N		E	M	A	T	E	D
O	U	R	T	A	J		W	E	L	T	R	E
S	W	H	A	R	M		S	T	A	R	D	O
M	A	D	I	V	I		E	N	T	U	R	Y
B	A	N	Q	U	E		P	O	R	N	I	C
A	B	E	G	O	R		A	C	C	I	N	E
S	U	R	E	A	L		Z	E	A	V	E	N
A	L	D	O	M	A		H	Y	T	H	M	Y

BRICK BY BRICK

Rearrange this stack of bricks to form a crossword puzzle. The clues will help you fit the bricks into their correct places. Row 1 has been filled in for you. Use the bricks to fill in the remaining spaces.

Solution on page 339

ACROSS

1. Certain base
   Biscuit
   Serene
2. Hymn closure
   Evolve
   Century plant
3. Drizzle
   Stanza
   Store
4. Deprive
   Passes
5. Soil
   Fr. canonized woman
6. Crouch
   Legal thing
   Preach
7. Kick
   Container
   Type of liquor
8. Free (of)
   Aries
   Byron's before
   Gershwin brother
9. Anger
   Materialize
   Scheme
10. "____ of Endearment"
    "Cheers" owner
    Pee Wee of baseball
11. Appropriate
    10th president
12. Forced
    Outrage
13. Suffers
    General's helpers
    Toast spread
14. Orbit point
    Wheel part
    Actual
15. Bamboo
    Organic compound
    Only

DOWN

1. Some actors
   Small pole
   TV host Jack ____
2. Leave out
   Set of pages
   Primed
3. Tableland
   Beneath
   If not
4. Beg
   Gathered
5. Tank
   Files
6. Totter
   Beret, e.g.
   Vex
7. "You ____ My Sunshine"
   Hobos
   Short swims
8. Pine
   Part of HMS
   Munch
   Smidgen
9. Being, to Caesar
   Hot
   Make do
10. Irish dances
    Hockey great
    Runner-up
11. Make amends
    Ump's kin
12. Recreation vehicle
    Act
13. Sad word
    Nimble
    Robt. ____
14. Legends
    Beginners
    Singer Holly ____
15. New York team
    Growing out
    Robert or Elizabeth

BRICKS

LAP STE	TER ■■■	IRA LOT	PRE AIL	LOE ART
M■E PEA	POK STE	END LEO	E■A E■M	E■S D■E
■RE LER	D■■ IDE	RE■ R■P	RIS ERS	AT■ T■C
■RA ■AP	STA ■■■	RES ART	SES ■■■	ESE ■■■
N■A T■V	OFF S■O	SSE S■A	E■R R■M	RID IRE
MS■ APT	RVE EAR	EAL ERE	SQU PUN	■OR ON■
ATE GIN	■■E TH■	AME MIS	SAM ■TY	APS REE

DIAGRAM

	1	2	3	4	5	6	7	8	9	10	11	12	13	14	15
1	H	O	M	E	■	W	A	F	E	R	■	C	A	L	M
2															
3															
4															
5															
6															
7															
8															
9															
10															
11															
12															
13															
14															
15															

DIAMOND RINGS

To solve this jewel of a puzzle write in the 5-letter answer to each clue by putting one letter into the correspondingly numbered ring and the other four letters into the surrounding diamonds. The letters entered in the rings in each horizontal row will have the same position in each answer word for that row. For example, in one of the horizontal rows the letter in each ring will be the second letter of each answer word, and in another row the letter in each ring will be the third letter of each word. No two rows have the same position letter in the rings. When the diagram is completed, the letters in the rings will form a quotation, and the letters in the peripheral diamonds, reading all the way around in a counterclockwise direction from the arrow, will contain the name of the author and the source of the quote. To start you off we have entered SMITE, the answer to clue 1.

Solution on page 339

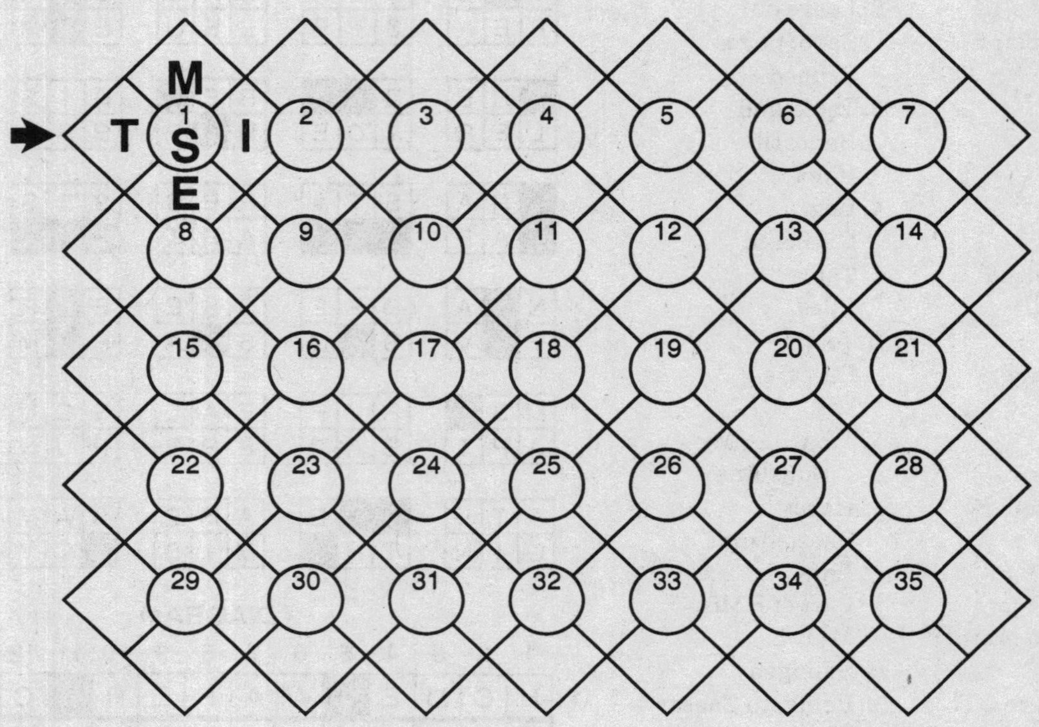

1. Strike
2. Pungent bulb
3. Dug up
4. Fairylike
5. Counterfeit
6. Some tests
7. Needs
8. Small lizard
9. Scandinavian
10. Team race
11. Hairy
12. Fisherman's basket
13. Circus performer
14. Short skirts
15. Crucifix
16. ____ de menthe
17. Nutcracker recipient
18. Municipal
19. Scottish landowner
20. Medicinal plants
21. Juliet's love
22. Notes
23. Aroma
24. Follow behind
25. Flat cap
26. Brother's daughter
27. Stingy
28. Prevent
29. Oarlock pin
30. Divulges
31. Zodiacal ram
32. Perspire
33. Prongs
34. Fragrant compound
35. Station

CRYPTO-FAMILIES

Each Crypto-Family is a list of related words in code. Each Family has its own code. When you have identified a word, use the known letters to help decode the other words in the Family.

Solutions on page 339

1. OFF TO SEE THE WIZARD
Example: Poppy Field

KGZU IMOFFYKI
QOJTYX QONJD
BGAJDTOAI
YBYKCMX JONU
JPQCKXMU MOPA
CGANOY YB
IJCKYJKPQ
XPKPNDU
NOA BCA
NPNP

2. CHINESE MENU
Example: Egg-drop soup

PHMZL HMBZ
KZQMTE LGBQ
DZDYOZ TFFLVZD
CFTSFT DFGK
VF OZMT
VZOFT BJMBQZT
JYKKX PYOMVX
ZEE HFVV
OFF DJG
DJHMOK SFYDS

3. TRADEMARKED
Example: Xerox

GOAYFOX
WLDQFEP
YADDXDZ
VOXH-ORH
CNQDZ
KDAJQE
PJEWJL WOCD
WNADXEA
CECPRJAD
QEAEHDZ

4. MILITARY LEADERS
Example: MacArthur

RNLLUV
WUVLJUWHFQ
WNFX NVLUVQ
ENQNV
VNRUZHUV
HBTHVCUKHF
ZHH
NZHMNVEHF
JHVJCBT XCNV
KNTCBVJLUV

5. CARTOONISTS
Example: Schulz

GILXHPL
AIHPGOHX
XETQHM
ZPITVQ
BLETHCEGH
AIVCQH
OPIG
CPGGHITVQ
PXXPUT
BIVHQEQB

6. ENDS IN "ION"
Example: Edit (Edition)

NMRBF
NEKDJKD
PJNJHH
WTAJPH
ECHJHH
TKDJKD
BRKH
FEPD
RNNEPW
DPRND

LOGIC PROBLEM

WILLOW WEDDINGS

The tiny town of Willow threw an engagement party when each of five of its young men, each newly graduated from a different university, announced his engagement to a woman he'd met while away at school. During the celebration, each couple announced their wedding date (each couple planned to marry on a different day). From the information provided, determine the woman (one is Ms. Jackson) and man (one is Mr. Kline) who make up each couple, the university each couple attended, and the wedding date (June 4, June 8, June 15, June 16, or June 20) set by each couple.

1. Mr. Black (who isn't the man who is engaged to Dr. Eloise Carroll) isn't the one who attended Kansas State University.

2. Mr. Lambert is engaged to neither Dr. Carroll nor the woman who graduated from the University of Michigan.

3. Dr. Richard Ambs's wedding date is exactly four days before Ms. Allen's, whose date is before that of the couple who met at Columbia University.

4. Of Dr. Carroll and Dr. Ambs (neither of whom attended Harvard University), one will get married June 4 and the other will get married June 20.

5. Ms. Harvey's wedding date is earlier than that of Mr. Lambert, but later than that of the couple who met at Ohio State University (whose wedding date isn't June 4).

6. The couple from Kansas State University set an earlier date than did Mr. Reed, who set an earlier date than did Miss Garrison.

7. The doctor who attended Columbia set a later date than the couple who met at the University of Michigan, whose date is immediately after that of Mr. Black.

This chart is to help you record information from the clues as well as the facts you deduce by combining information from different clues. We suggest you use an "X" for a "no" and a "•" for a "yes."

		MAN					UNIVERSITY					DATE				
		DR. AMBS	MR. BLACK	MR. KLINE	MR. LAMBERT	MR. REED	COLUMBIA	HARVARD	KANSAS	MICHIGAN	OHIO	JUNE 4	JUNE 8	JUNE 15	JUNE 16	JUNE 20
WOMAN	MS. ALLEN															
	DR. CARROLL															
	MS. GARRISON															
	MS. HARVEY															
	MS. JACKSON															
DATE	JUNE 4															
	JUNE 8															
	JUNE 15															
	JUNE 16															
	JUNE 20															
UNIVERSITY	COLUMBIA															
	HARVARD															
	KANSAS															
	MICHIGAN															
	OHIO															

Solution on page 340

PICTURE THIS

You do not need any special art training to produce a picture in the empty grid. Use the letter-number guide above each square and carefully draw what is shown into the corresponding square in the grid.

Solution on page 340

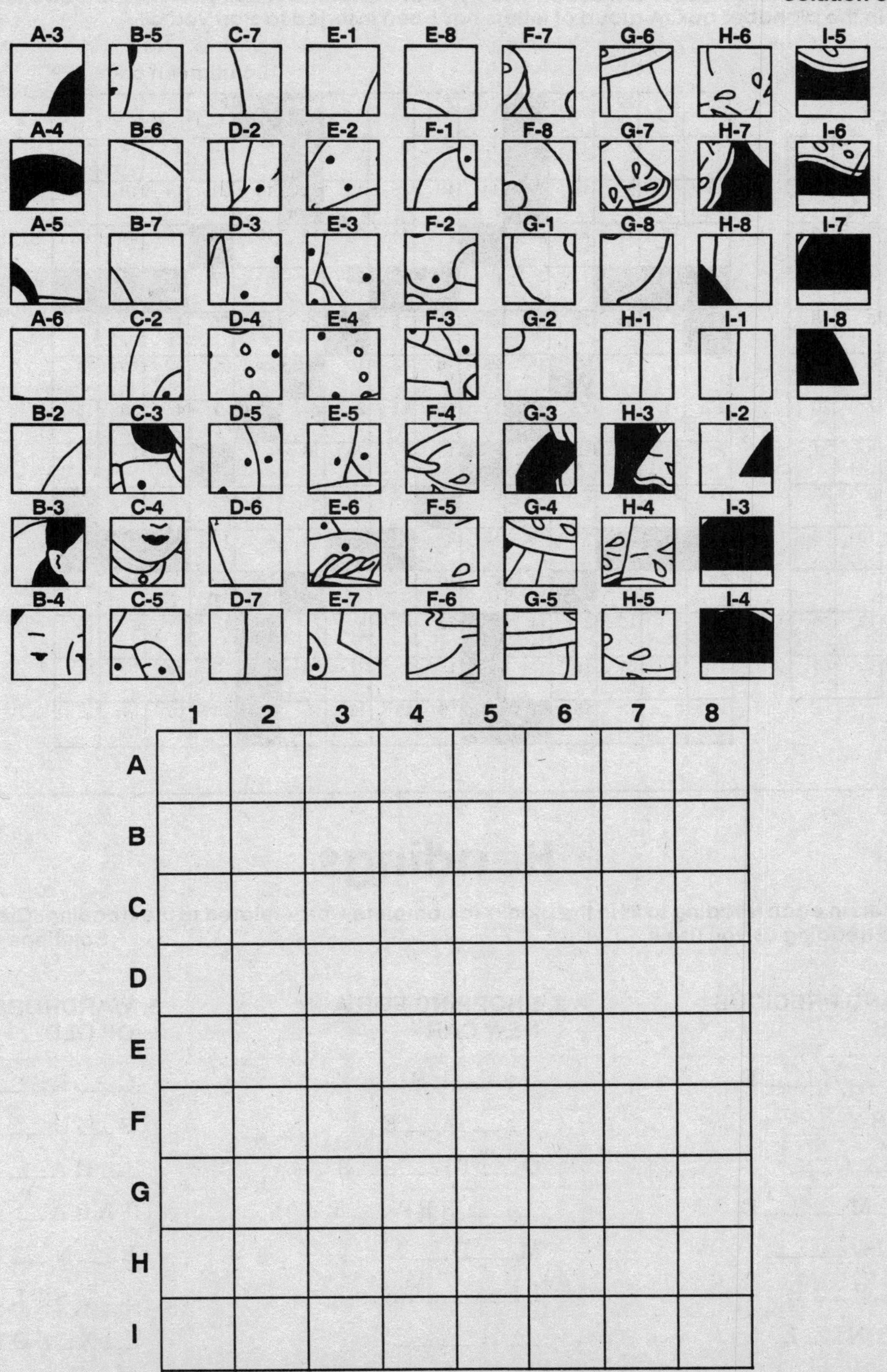

CODEWORD

Codeword is a special crossword puzzle in which conventional clues are omitted. Instead, answer words in the diagram are represented by numbers. Each number represents a different letter of the alphabet, and all of the letters of the alphabet are used. When you are sure of a letter, put it in the code key chart and cross it off in the alphabet box. A group of letters has been inserted to start you off.

Solution on page 339

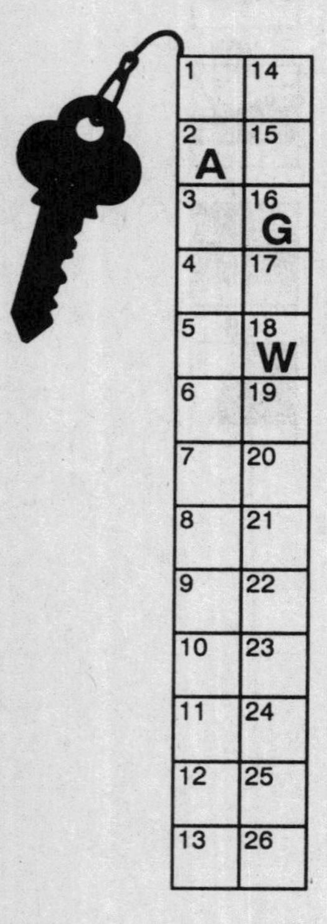

1	14
2 A	15
3	16 G
4	17
5	18 W
6	19
7	20
8	21
9	22
10	23
11	24
12	25
13	26

25	2	22	3	■	3	2	18	1	■	■	23	11	2	18
4	20	2	11	■	15	9	2	22	■	5	10	2	12	15
17	4	8	15	■	14	19	25	15	■	10	21	14	19	15
1	18	15	2	25	■	1	14	2	14	15	■	15	21	17
■	■	■	1	2	6	■	■	25	15	21	17	■	■	■
■	3	25	15	23	2	13	15	■	2	13	25	4	1	1
7	4	4	■	14	25	10	13	15	■	24	2	8	15	11
2	11	10	22	■	17	15	11	2	6	■	22	4	20	15
25	2	16	15	17	■	1	2	20	15	1	■	21	15	18
17	25	15	2	25	6	■	14	15	2	13	24	15	25	■
■	■	■	11	19	15	21	■	■	25	4	15	■	■	■
26	2	7	■	11	2	10	16	24	■	18 W	2 A	16 G	15	25
15	5	10	2	11	■	25	4	2	21	■	14	2	9	19
11	10	21	16	1	■	1	2	21	15	■	15	20	19	11
11	2	12	15	■	■	15	17	16	15	■	25	15	14	15

~~A~~	N
B	O
C	P
D	Q
E	R
F	S
~~G~~	T
H	U
I	V
J	~~W~~
K	X
L	Y
M	Z

Headings

Use the letters in each Heading to fill in the blanks to complete words related to the Heading. Cross out each letter in the Heading as you use it.

Solutions on page 338

1. RARE AND PRECIOUS STONES

__AP__HI__E

____BY

ZI____O__

__I__M____D

P__RID____

J____P__R

__P__N__L

2. SHOPPING FOR A NEW CAR

DE__LE__

____I__E

O__TI____S

____RRA__TY

M__D__L

LI____TS

__H____T

3. WARDROBE ITEMS OF OLD

C__RS____

P__U__E

__HA__L

TABA____

P__N__F____E

__USTL__

__X__OR__S

WORD MATH

In these long-division problems letters are substituted for numbers. Determine the value of each letter. Then arrange the letters in order from 0 to 9, and they will spell a word or phrase. **Solutions on page 339**

1.

```
             ROE
     ERE ) CIPHER
           CPSH
           ----
            OOHE
            PRTC
            ----
             TOCR
             IEIC
             ----
              CEY
```

0 _ 1 _ 2 _ 3 _ 4 _ 5 _ 6 _ 7 _ 8 _ 9 _

2.

```
              ALE
    ALEE ) ELATED
           HLTO
           ----
           ALHRE
           AOELA
           -----
            AOAOD
            ANLGD
            -----
             ANOG
```

0 _ 1 _ 2 _ 3 _ 4 _ 5 _ 6 _ 7 _ 8 _ 9 _

3.

```
             NIB
     NIB ) MUSLIN
           ULIT
           ----
            BULI
            BTHL
            ----
             UASN
             UUSA
             ----
              MSS
```

0 _ 1 _ 2 _ 3 _ 4 _ 5 _ 6 _ 7 _ 8 _ 9 _

4.

```
              RAG
    GOAL ) FRESCO
           EAAF
           ----
            LORC
            UCLE
            ----
             CRLO
             AGLU
             ----
             OSLR
```

0 _ 1 _ 2 _ 3 _ 4 _ 5 _ 6 _ 7 _ 8 _ 9 _

5.

```
             SEN
     ESS ) SHORES
           GOOS
           ----
            MEHE
            MSES
            ----
             NOGS
             IMHS
             ----
              MMB
```

0 _ 1 _ 2 _ 3 _ 4 _ 5 _ 6 _ 7 _ 8 _ 9 _

6.

```
               ETA
    TILE ) HEIGHTS
           HTWFL
           -----
            HIIFT
             SASI
             ----
             IELHS
             IIGEG
             -----
              HAAH
```

0 _ 1 _ 2 _ 3 _ 4 _ 5 _ 6 _ 7 _ 8 _ 9 _

FLOWER POWER

The answers to this petaled puzzle will go in a curve from the number on the outside to the center of the flower. Each number has two 5-letter words. One goes in a clockwise direction and the second in a counterclockwise direction. Try working from both sets of clues to fill the flower.

Solution on page 340

CLOCKWISE

1. Brimless hat
2. Gunpowder ingredient
3. Steer
4. Feeling
5. Jovial
6. Synagogue scroll
7. Certain golf club
8. Knack
9. The Statue of Liberty's light
10. Small fowl
11. Droll
12. French maid
13. North Dakota city
14. Monetary worth
15. Picked
16. Argument
17. "Don't ____ Me In"
18. Cessation

COUNTERCLOCKWISE

1. Uptight
2. Nick
3. Cotton fabric
4. Abdominal exercise
5. Scuffle
6. Luciano Pavarotti, e.g.
7. Most horrible
8. ____ Haute, Indiana
9. At the present time
10. Tree limb
11. Ridiculous sham
12. Cluster
13. April or June
14. "My Cousin ____"
15. Shrewd
16. Daphnis's love
17. Treat with disdain
18. Landlord's document

The entries for this puzzle are given to you, listed alphabetically according to length. Across and Down words are all mixed together, and you are to find their proper places in the diagram.

Solution on page 340

3 Letters
Ago
Ape
Ara
Dot
Ere
Hen
Ian
Ida
Inn
Men
Nee
Oat

4 Letters
Aver
Bees
Cabs
Chip
Clap
Cube
Dirt
Doer
Dose
Dove
Earn
Earp
Edit
Ends
Eras
Errs
Ever
Fred
Gape
Gels
Good
Home
Hove
Hump
Idea
Ides
Idol
Iron
Jams
July
Knew
Lets
Line
Lode
Lone
Lope
Lout
Love
Mere
Name
Odor
Ogee
Omar
Opal
Over
Past
Paul
Pelf
Pine
Poet
Port
Pout
Pump
Pups
Purr
Rate
Redo
Reel
Riot
Rode
Role
Seen
Sere
Sews
Slat
Slip
Slog
Sore
Spot
Stew
Tone
Toot
Tows
Twit
Upon
Worn

5 Letters
Begun
Genes
Grape
Heaps
Heart
Hides
Horns
Leads
Lease
Manse
Panes
Peace
Peels
Plane ✓
Riced
Share
Slash
Start
Teach
Treat
Treed
Weeds

6 Letters
Polite
Severs
Shovel
United

7 Letters
Camelot
Counter
Dangles
Kingdom
Pea soup
Persian
Snapper
Tedious

8 Letters
One-sided
Petulant
Shameful
Waddlers

9 Letters
Entertain
Eradicate
Fairyland
Great-aunt

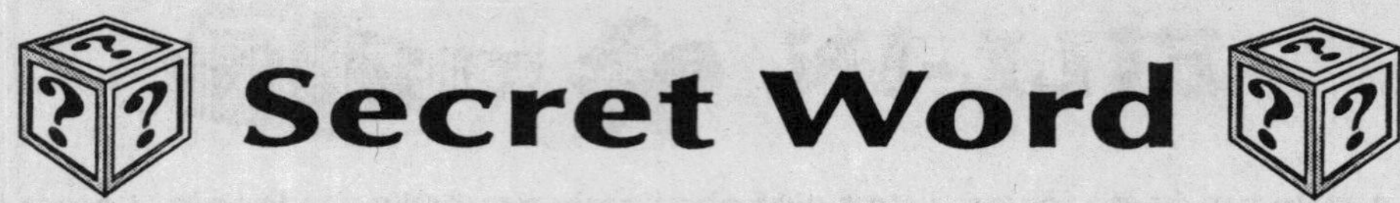

Secret Word

Discover the 5-letter Secret Words by the process of elimination and deduction. Fill in the blanks with the 5-letter answers to the clues. The number in parentheses next to each answer tells you how many of the letters in that word are also in the Secret Word. A zero next to an answer indicates that none of the letters in that word is in the Secret Word. After you have determined the correct five letters, rearrange them to form the Secret Word. No letter is repeated in any Secret Word or within any answer word. The first letters of the answers, reading down, spell out a hint to the Secret Word.

Solutions on page 340

1. Secret Word ☐☐☐☐☐

Enamel _____ (1)
Peruvian mountains _____ (1)
Layers _____ (2)
Aspirations _____ (2)
Coercion _____ (2)
Deduce _____ (0)
Elbow _____ (1)
Amsterdam residents _____ (3)
"____ Is Enough" _____ (1)
Face coloring _____ (2)

2. Secret Word ☐☐☐☐☐

Adhere _____ (0)
Laurel's partner _____ (3)
Cherub _____ (2)
Clasp _____ (1)
Actress Lavin _____ (2)
Cairo's country _____ (1)
Cozy corner _____ (1)
Pulverize _____ (2)
Sagas _____ (2)
Fashion _____ (2)

3. Secret Word ☐☐☐☐☐

Noel _____ (2)
Leaves out _____ (3)
Panorama _____ (1)
Oust _____ (1)
"Bolero" composer _____ (0)
Similar _____ (1)
Citrus fruits _____ (2)
Huron and Erie _____ (2)

4. Secret Word ☐☐☐☐☐

Chomp _____ (3)
Santiago's locale _____ (0)
Scottish skirts _____ (1)
Bay _____ (2)
Din _____ (2)
Fastens _____ (1)
Poet Dickinson _____ (1)
Child _____ (3)

5. Secret Word ☐☐☐☐☐

Performing _____ (2)
Eyed _____ (2)
New _____ (2)
Garnish _____ (0)
Courtroom event _____ (1)
Cowgirl Dale ____ _____ (3)
Strict _____ (2)

6. Secret Word ☐☐☐☐☐

Age _____ (2)
Radiates _____ (1)
Radio, TV, etc. _____ (1)
Neck backs _____ (3)
Sharp in taste _____ (3)
Kinder _____ (2)
Scheduled _____ (0)

SCOREMASTER

TO PLAY:

1. Write the first seven LETTERS across the first line of the PLAY CHART. Indicate the last letter used.
2. Form a word of at least two letters across or down in the DIAGRAM. One letter of the first word must go into the center square.
3. Tally your score, noting any bonuses (see key at bottom).
4. Carry down all unused LETTERS to the next line of the PLAY CHART. Transfer enough LETTERS, in the given order, so that you have seven LETTERS to work with.
5. Form a new word or words from each draw by:
   a. Adding one or more letters to an existing word.
   b. Building a new word at right angles to an existing word, by adding to it or incorporating one of its letters.
   c. Setting a new word parallel to an existing word, but remember all adjoining letters must form new words in crossword fashion.
6. Continue working in this way until all the LETTERS have been used or you can no longer form any words. If you need more lines for your PLAY CHART, use a separate piece of paper.

NOTE: Proper names, foreign words, and abbreviations are not allowed.

TO SCORE:

The value of each letter is given with it. The letter has the same value every time it is used. Be sure always to include all bonuses (see key at bottom). An additional 30 points is earned when you use all seven letters in the PLAY CHART in one turn. When two words are formed in the same play, the common letter (including any bonus) is scored with each word.

Our game with a score of 621 points on page 340

LETTERS

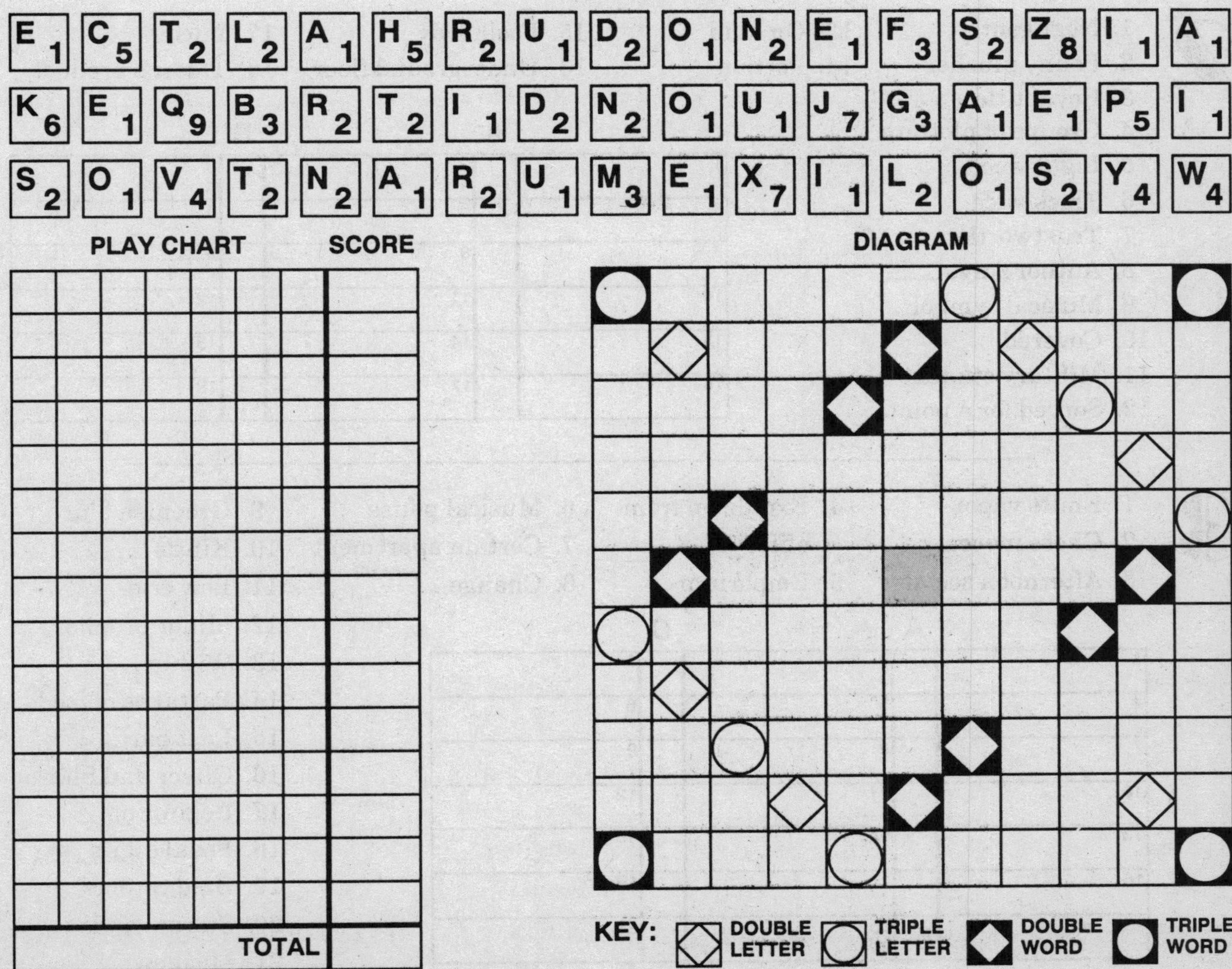

ESCALATORS

Write the 6-letter answer to clue 1 in the first space. Drop one letter and rearrange the remaining letters to answer clue 2. Put the dropped letter into Column A. Drop another letter and rearrange the remaining letters to answer clue 3. Put the dropped letter into Column B. Follow this pattern for each row in the diagram. When completed, the letters in Column A and Column B, reading down, will spell related words or a phrase.

Solutions on page 339

1

1. Take a chance
2. Accuse
3. Bundle cotton
4. Exclusively
5. Calls
6. Trade for money
7. For a short time
8. Sea mammal
9. Mend
10. Away
11. Sew loosely
12. Wagers
13. Kind of sock
14. Certain race
15. Nobleman

	A		B	
1		2		3
4		5		6
7		8		9
10		11		12
13		14		15

2

1. Negligent
2. Penny pincher
3. Royal title
4. Groups of plotters
5. Light wood
6. Thick slice
7. Trustworthy
8. Author Anya ____
9. Musical symbol
10. Covered
11. Military student
12. Served for a point
13. On land
14. Portion
15. Foolhardy
16. Underground floor
17. Lucid
18. Tatter's product

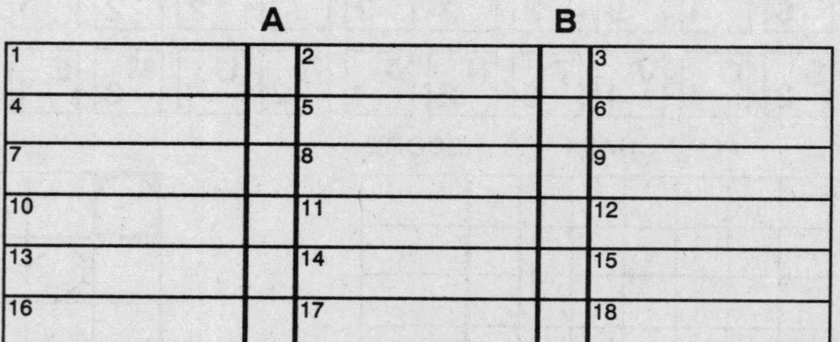

3

1. Emits vapor
2. Chess moves
3. Afternoon socials
4. Expulsion from office
5. Emporium
6. Musical pause
7. Certain apartment
8. Change
9. Greenish blue
10. King's ____
11. Low cries
12. Minor prophet
13. Within
14. Partakes of food
15. Last parts
16. Oliver and Sharon
17. Beginning
18. Pedal digits
19. Bald raptors
20. Storm winds
21. Meadows

	A		B	
1		2		3
4		5		6
7		8		9
10		11		12
13		14		15
16		17		18
19		20		21

WEAVER WORDS

The answers to the clues will form one continuous thread weaving across the top row, back on the second, etc. When the thread reaches the end of the bottom row, it will weave up the last column, down the next to last, and will finally end where it began in the upper left corner. The arrows will guide you. The last letter of each answer will be the first letter of the next answer. The numbers in parentheses tell you how many letters are in each answer. If you get stuck on a clue, mark it, count off the appropriate number of squares, and enter the answer to the next clue, remembering that it begins in the last square you counted off. You should be able to complete any missing answers when the thread weaves in the other direction.

Solution on page 341

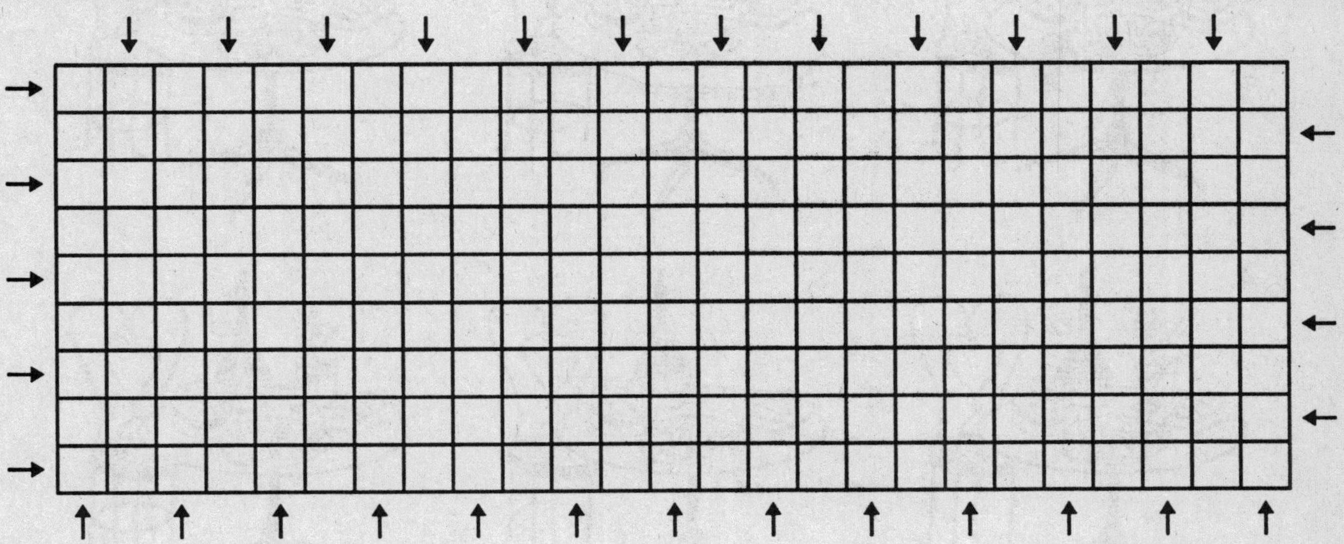

Memorable age (3)
Region (4)
Approving votes (4)
Steep slopes (6)
Ooze (4)
Egyptian king (7)
Hut (5)
Coat of paint (5)
Citrus juicer (6)
Narrow inlet (3)
Main artery (5)
Anteater (8)
Small barrels (4)
Mr. Snead (3)
Temperaments (5)
Belgrade native (4)
Gunny (6)
Column (6)
Relaxation (4)
Mountain path (5)
Reclined (4)
African river (4)
Devour (3)
Golf mounds (4)
Grin (5)
Disintegrate (5)
Mr. Hunter (4)
Mr. Bruce (5)
Tibetan monk (4)
Good-bye: Fr. (5)
Kitchen tool (7)
Voodoo cult (3)
Greek market (5)
Friends in need (6)
Tendon (5)
Hickory (6)
Prunes (5)
TV static (4)
Soggy (3)
Hartebeest (4)
Bedouin (4)
Malay island (6)
Nebraska city (5)
Forage plant (7)
Once more (4)
Network (3)
Road shoulder (4)
Florida city (5)
Angers (4)
Arrangement (5)
Harbor (4)
Slender (4)
Fruit juice (6)
"____ Daughter" (5)
Old knife (4)
Overhead trains (3)
Small drink (3)
Large violets (7)
Mixed greens (5)
Bo (5)
Young foxes (4)
Alike (7)
Uprising (6)
Roof worker (5)
Large rodent (3)
Clocks (5)
Chili sauce (5)
Sailor's cry (4)
Twelve months (4)
Tease (3)
Cyclist (5)
French artist (6)
Move around (9)
Jug (4)
Stitch again (5)
Moan (4)
Wife of Jacob (4)
Corridor (4)
Imparted (6)
Facts (4)
Totality (3)
Orchid garland (3)
Little devil (3)
Chirp (4)
Sore (7)
Circuit (3)
In addition (4)
Gapes (6)
Noiseless (6)
Art resort (4)
Feudal slave (4)
Less limited (5)
Smart knock (3)
French writer (6)
Lean (4)
". . . ____ of thee" (3)
Sea World whale (5)
Shadow (5)
Perform on stage (3)
Attempts (5)
Leg bone (4)
Zola heroine (4)
Indigo plant (4)
Rent contract (5)
Facilitated (5)
Cupola (4)
Heroic poem (4)
Chicken (6)
Wood nymph (5)
Fate (4)
Runs into (5)
Bias (5)
Child (3)
Delaware city (5)
Male sheep (3)
Mr. Brooks (3)
"Casablanca" actor (5)
"Pooh" donkey (6)
Ms. Gabor (3)
Sky altar (3)
Clumsy boats (4)
Droop (3)
Chat (3)
Prohibits (4)
Netting (7)
Golly! (3)

MATCH-UP

Can you find the two pictures that are identical?
Solution on page 339

LETTER POWER

P	L	A	Y					
1	1	1	1					4

L	E	T	T	E	R			
2	1	1	2	2	1			9

P	O	W	E	R				
2	1	1	3	2				9

22

Use your Letter Power to earn the highest score by repeating letters in each answer and from one answer to another as often as you can. There are many possible choices, so we suggest you pencil in your words lightly. Use a maximum of eight letters for each answer.

SCORING: Do not add your score until you have all your answers, since you may want to make changes. A letter is worth 1 point the first time it is used in your answers, 2 the second, 3 the third, etc. Add the points earned in each answer and put the total in the box at the right. Then compare your total score with ours.

Our solutions with a score of 353 points on page 340

1. U.S. state
2. Cocktail
3. Car part
4. Metal
5. Vegetable
6. Flower
7. Pasta
8. Opera composer
9. Fast-food outlet
10. Confection

TOTAL

DIAGRAMLESS FILL-IN

For this fill-in puzzle we have given you all of the E's that appear in the diagram, but none of the black squares. As you solve the puzzle remember to put a black square at the beginning and end of each answer and to balance each black square with its symmetrical counterpart on the opposite side of the diagram.

Solution on page 340

3 Letters
Ade
Alt
Ana
Any
Ara
Art
Ave
Ban
Chi
Cry
Ede
Eye
Fad
Hal
Hen
Ill
Leo
Mal
Mar
Mer
Pan
Phi
Rid
Sap
Sod
Sty
Tea
Ube
Use
Web
Yet

4 Letters
Alas
Alum
Apes
Aver
Baer
Cent
Cram
Ecru
Ella
Eras
Etna
Glad
Hurt
Ides
Late
Lido
Logs
Loll
Nero
Okay
Ones
Opal
Over
Pore
Prey
Rate
Reds
Rope
Ruse
Sate
Sere
Tret
Tune
Utah
Wash
Yips

5 Letters
Allay
Cadet
Caper
Dakar
Depot
Erode
Erred
Gravy
Grope
Grove
Hires
Homer
Image
Preen
Pride
Prong
Reeve
Romeo
Sleep
Snags
Trout
Under

6 Letters
Coasts
Deport
Harris
Poodle

7 Letters
Aerials
Customs
Embassy
Pitfall
Rhatany
Smeared

9 Letters
Churchill
Contracts
Orchestra
Plenitude
Submarine

														E						
					E				E		E									
				E						E					E	E				
											E									
																E				
									E											
		E						E											E	
					E								E							
							E													
										E										
											E									
		E																		
			E	E																
		E											E							
			E									E							E	
											E					E				
							E			E						E				
						E											E			
																E				

BOWL GAME

To bowl a strike (20 points) you must create a 10-letter word using all the letters in each pin. The letter on top in the pin is the first letter of the strike word. To bowl a spare (10 points) use the same 10 letters to form two words. Splits are not allowed: you may not divide the strike to form a spare. For example, SWEETHEART may not become SWEET and HEART.

Our solutions with a perfect score of 300 points on page 340

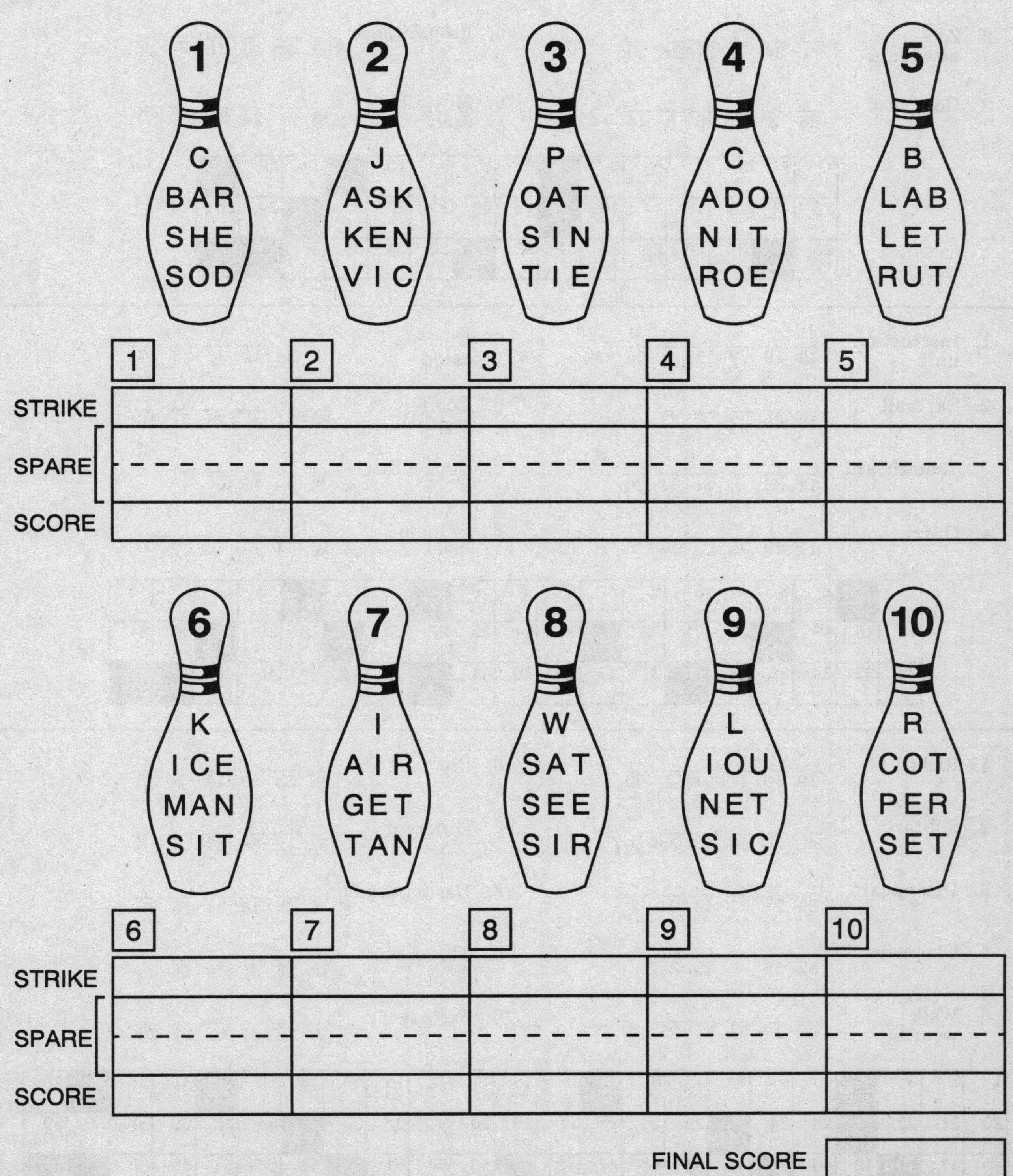

QUOTAGRAMS

Fill in the answers to the clues. Then transfer the letters to the correspondingly numbered squares in the diagrams. The completed diagrams will contain quotations.

Solutions on page 341

A.

1. Actress Loren — 22 12 4 34 30 15
2. Zoo attendant — 9 23 2 27 18 28
3. Goat wool — 36 3 20 29 8 14
4. Walk quietly — 19 16 1 11 26 35
5. Propositions — 33 25 10 31 6 17
6. Movie Thin Man — 13 21 24 32 5 7

1	2	3	4	5	6	■	7	8	9	10	■	11	12	■
13	14	15	16	17	18	■	19	20	21	22	23	■	24	25
26	■	27	28	29	30	31	32	■	33	34	35	36	■	■

B.

1. Instruction unit — 43 19 27 12 4 35
2. Ski trail — 13 38 22 2 33
3. Teeterboard — 42 36 6 41 24 20
4. Crazy — 11 29 39 1 18 45
5. Uncomplicated — 7 28 15 46 25 37
6. Comfort gently — 30 34 9 23 21 16
7. Sign of fire — 8 32 14 26 44
8. Shingle layer — 10 31 17 5 40 3

C.

1. Riches — 19 40 14 31 8 50
2. Solitary — 6 36 10 48 28
3. Disappear — 39 21 11 42 24 2
4. Choppers — 52 35 4 46 20
5. Walk wearily — 49 13 54 41 25 38
6. Sly — 9 53 30 45 1 33
7. Different — 17 12 56 47 29
8. Earlier than — 34 3 18 44 15 26
9. Threescore — 43 23 5 55 16
10. Fee payer — 7 32 37 51 27 22

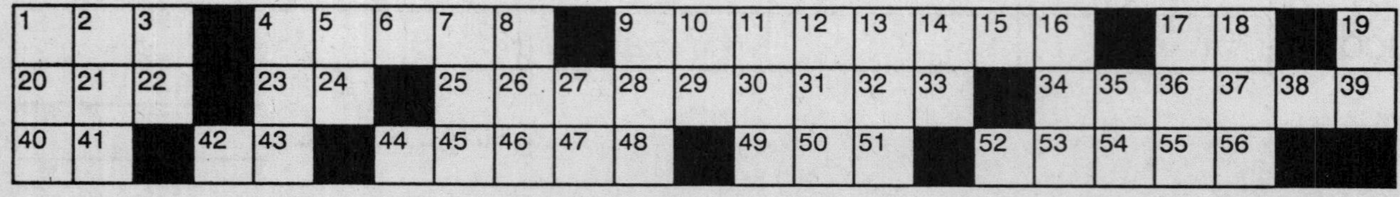

SYL´´LA-CROS´TIC

The directions for solving are given on page 34. Solution on page 341

✻ SYLLABOX ✻

A AB AN ANT BAR BER BOU BREL BRET CA ~~CAL~~ CAR CEN CI ~~CIP~~ COU DATE DER DI DI DO E E E E E EM EX FE FIT GA GA GA GART GO GO I I IST JEC JU KA KIN KO LAS LI LI LIC LOR LU MAN MI MI NAI NAR NER NO NOFF O O O OB OT OUT PE QUES RA RAN ~~RE~~ RI RI ~~RO~~ ROW SHEN SMITH STRO TATE TAY TION TION TO TO TO TRI TRIC TU TY U UM VAN VER YEV

1. Complement (4) R E C I P R O C A L
2. Paper tiger, perhaps (4) ___ ___ ___ ___ ___ ___ ___
3. Hassock (3) ___ ___ ___ ___ ___ ___ ___
4. Cooked in a sour cream sauce (3) ___ ___ ___ ___ ___ ___ ___ ___ ___ ___
5. Explain (4) ___ ___ ___ ___ ___ ___ ___ ___ ___
6. Canadian island (3) ___ ___ ___ ___ ___ ___ ___ ___ ___
7. Mediterranean islands (3) ___ ___ ___ ___ ___
8. Musical text (3) ___ ___ ___ ___ ___ ___ ___ ___
9. Liz or Rod (2) ___ ___ ___ ___ ___ ___
10. Tight (2) ___ ___ ___ ___ ___ ___
11. Modus ____ (4) ___ ___ ___ ___ ___ ___ ___ ___
12. Ensemble (2) ___ ___ ___ ___ ___ ___
13. Creator of basketball (2) ___ ___ ___ ___ ___ ___ ___ ___
14. Commercial restraint (3) ___ ___ ___ ___ ___ ___ ___
15. Reindeer's kin (3) ___ ___ ___ ___ ___ ___ ___
16. Slavery opposer (5) ___ ___ ___ ___ ___ ___ ___ ___ ___ ___ ___ ___
17. Infamy (5) ___ ___ ___ ___ ___ ___ ___ ___ ___
18. Emperor's title (3) ___ ___ ___ ___ ___ ___
19. Brazilian seaport (4) ___ ___ ___ ___ ___ ___ ___
20. Five-year-old, usually (4) ___ ___ ___ ___ ___ ___ ___ ___ ___ ___ ___ ___ ___
21. Conceited (4) ___ ___ ___ ___ ___ ___ ___ ___ ___ ___
22. Russian poet (4) ___ ___ ___ ___ ___ ___ ___ ___ ___ ___ ___
23. Disapproval (3) ___ ___ ___ ___ ___ ___ ___ ___ ___
24. Parasols (3) ___ ___ ___ ___ ___ ___ ___ ___ ___
25. Send regards (4) ___ ___ ___ ___ ___ ___ ___ ___ ___ ___
26. Mounted (4) ___ ___ ___ ___ ___ ___ ___ ___ ___ ___
27. Overjoyed (4) ___ ___ ___ ___ ___ ___ ___ ___ ___

Crostic Puzzle 1

Use the CLUES on the left to fill in the WORDS column. Then transfer each letter to the correspondingly numbered square in the diagram. (We have inserted WORD A as an example.) It is not necessary to know all the words to start solving. Work back and forth from the diagram to the WORDS column until both are filled. A black square indicates the end of a word. The completed diagram will contain a quotation, and the first letter of each word in the WORDS column, reading down, will spell the author's name and the source of the quotation.

CLUES	WORDS
A. Bach keyboard piece	T O C C A T A 14 133 93 78 3 75 84
B. Henry ____ Longfellow	100 63 8 52 132 113 141 153 105
C. Wiley Post, e.g.	35 55 101 79 139 95 120
D. Not fully developed	81 124 118 145 66 128 11 32
E. Vexes	31 61 48 137 62 23 18
F. Straw covering	69 65 46 146 151 60
G. Israeli seaport	50 38 117 82 125
H. United Kingdom division	138 85 6 115 68 71 47
I. Crude person	127 144 114 19 17
J. Greatest	88 102 83 121 64 33
K. Beloved	25 112 140 123 109 34 98 54 16 131
L. Aim	73 126 59 56 27 111 24 143 39
M. Innately	40 108 80 134 22 13 53 4 29
N. Receded	150 91 43 72 116
O. Flock guardian	9 76 12 119 20 51 94 136
P. Soda's partner	97 107 30 49 86 67
Q. Roman poet	26 122 110 90
R. Ineffective	58 15 42 142 28 106
S. Repulsive	5 1 152 129 149 96 41 45 44
T. "The Seven Year ____"	130 148 37 103
U. Free to wander	2 87 57 36 135 7 70 74 147
V. Chosen	21 89 77 10 104 92 99

Solution on page 352

		1 S	2 U	■	3 A A	4 M	5 S	■	6 H	7 U	8 B	9 O	■	10 V	11 D	12 O	13 M	14 A T	15 R		
	16 K	17 I	18 E	■	19 I	20 O	21 V	22 M	23 E	■	24 L	25 K	■	26 Q	27 L	28 R	29 M	■	30 P	31 E	
32 D	■	33 J	34 K	35 C	36 U	■	37 T	38 G	39 L	40 M	41 S	42 R	■	43 N	44 S	■	45 S	46 F	47 H	48 E	■
49 P	50 G	51 O	■	52 B	53 M	54 K	55 C	56 L	■	57 U	58 R	■	59 L	60 F	61 E	■	62 E	63 B	64 J	65 F	■
66 D	67 P	68 H	69 F	■	70 U	71 H	72 N	■	73 L	74 U	■	75 A T	76 O	77 V	■	78 A C	79 C	80 M	■	81 D	82 G
■	83 J	84 A A	85 H	■	86 P	87 U	88 J	89 V	90 Q	■	91 N	92 V	■	93 A C	94 O	95 C	96 S	97 P	98 K	99 V	■
100 B	101 C	102 J	103 T	■	104 V	105 B	106 R	■	107 P	108 M	109 K	■	110 Q	111 L	■	112 K	113 B	114 I	115 H	116 N	■
117 G	118 D	119 O	120 C	121 J	122 Q	123 K	■	124 D	125 G	126 L	■	127 I	128 D	129 S	■	130 T	131 K	■	132 B	133 A O	134 M
135 U	136 O	■	137 E	138 H	139 C	140 K	141 B	142 R	143 L	144 I	145 D	146 F	147 U	■	148 T	149 S	150 N	■	151 F	152 S	153 B

Crostic Puzzle 2

A. Short-legged dog — 95 128 146 75 177 73 51 55 169

B. Beekeeper — 90 65 39 112 83 42 52 148

C. Boastful pride — 3 58 84 176 123 137 105 91 79

D. Like some designs — 138 103 8 160 2 158

E. Reliance — 104 150 46 140 94 117 26 161 108 155

F. Vision — 11 116 67 21 121 136 164 12

G. Recite — 110 102 168 100 85 142 61

H. Driveway stones — 86 59 76 131 19 38

I. Building — 165 56 130 89 4 34 170

J. Unattached — 115 152 36 159 64

K. Guitarist/folk singer: 2 wds. — 44 88 154 127 143 49 132 16 87

L. Moderately slow, in music — 15 157 162 81 171 120 74

M. Game bird — 78 151 114 167 68 93 96 22

N. Firewood support — 54 33 133 125 18 50 62

O. Uncharged atomic particle — 70 32 124 163 82 9 135

P. Insistent — 41 80 77 147 97 71 118 7

Q. Unbelted dress — 31 23 53 45 92 144

R. Gushing — 101 40 37 17 119 20 25 156

S. Look — 174 109 5 60 107 63

T. Sock pattern — 141 113 166 28 1 173

U. Controls — 27 29 175 48 10

V. Type of pastry — 129 47 122 145 30 149

W. International understanding — 24 43 98 35 139 72 69

X. Bean — 106 13 57 6 134 14

Y. Outlying district — 126 153 172 99 66 111

Solution on page 352

		1 T	2 D	3 C	4 I	5 S	6 X	■	7 P	8 D	9 O	10 U	11 F	■	12 F	13 X	■	14 X	15 L		
16 K	17 R	18 N	19 H	■	20 R	21 F	■	22 M	23 Q	24 W	■	25 R	26 E	27 U	28 T	■	29 U	30 V	31 Q	32 O	33 N
34 I	35 W	■	36 J	37 R	■	38 H	39 B	40 R	41 P	■	42 B	43 W	■	44 K	45 Q	46 E	47 V	48 U	■	49 K	50 N
51 A	52 B	53 Q	■	54 N	55 A	56 I	■	57 X	58 C	59 H	60 S	61 G	62 N	■	63 S	64 J	65 B	66 Y	67 F	68 M	69 W
70 O	71 P	■	72 W	73 A	74 L	■	75 A	76 H	77 P	78 M	79 C	■	80 P	81 L	82 O	83 B	84 C	85 G	86 H	87 K	■
88 K	89 I	■	90 B	91 C	92 Q	■	93 M	94 E	95 A	■	96 M	97 P	98 W	99 Y	100 G	101 R	■	102 G	103 D	104 E	■
105 C	106 X	107 S	■	108 E	109 S	110 G	■	111 Y	112 B	113 T	114 M	115 J	116 F	■	117 E	118 P	119 R	120 L	121 F	122 V	123 C
124 O	125 N	126 Y	127 K	■	128 A	■	129 V	130 I	131 H	132 K	133 N	134 X	135 O	136 F	■	137 C	138 D	139 W	140 E	■	141 T
142 G	■	143 K	144 Q	145 V	146 A	147 P	■	148 B	149 V	150 E	■	151 M	152 J	153 Y	154 K	155 E	■	156 R	157 L	158 D	159 J
■	160 D	161 E	162 L	■	163 O	164 F	165 I	■	166 T	167 M	168 G	169 A	170 I	171 L	■	172 Y	173 T	174 S	175 U	176 C	177 A

Crostic Puzzle 3

A. Airship — 98 9 16 118 68 189 87 61 138

B. Pertinacious — 146 11 32 156 180 80 48 23 50

C. Tip — 174 35 193 192 163 116 172 63

D. All over — 34 18 75 6 73 13 54 92 43 101

E. Excessively lively — 164 17 122 2 100 78 25 69

F. Fully armed: 3 wds. — 70 160 33 109 105 42 110 82 165 178

G. Shining — 134 161 89 155 169 64 46 95

H. Clumsy — 72 37 197 121 58 76 45

I. Bulky — 88 119 145 67 167 21 183 173

J. Exercise room — 120 159 56 158 38 93 19 126 162

K. Underworld — 124 84 49 170 71

L. Customs — 141 102 55 150 27 184 24 107 10 94

M. Upper canine — 188 8 142 123 44 175 147 128

N. Excuses — 196 186 96 28 51 144 83

O. Breakfast meat — 166 5 47 201 91

P. River mouth — 86 132 171 53 133 187 200

Q. Georgia city — 39 181 117 1 41 103 30 185

R. ___ and Tobago — 108 127 97 113 90 139 149 59

S. Pacific island group — 57 111 143 182 129 36 154 99

T. Nonsense — 12 14 136 74 3 190 81

U. English poet — 131 157 79 191 77

V. Major Prophet — 22 140 60 152 114 148

W. Social group — 31 198 66 194 65 130 135 7 137

X. Improvised — 62 151 168 112 176 52 4 26 202

Y. Water nymph — 199 195 40 29 177

Z. Space to move — 179 115 106 20 104 153 125 15 85

Solution on page 352

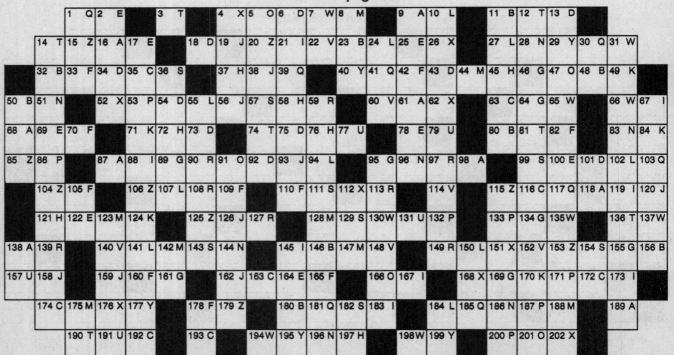

		1 Q	2 E	■	3 T	■	4 X	5 O	6 D	7 W	8 M	■	9 A	10 L	■	11 B	12 T	13 D	■		
	14 T	15 Z	16 A	17 E	■	18 D	19 J	20 Z	21 I	22 V	23 B	24 L	25 E	26 X	■	27 L	28 N	29 Y	30 Q	31 W	
■	32 B	33 F	34 D	35 C	36 S	■	37 H	38 J	39 Q	■	40 Y	41 Q	42 F	43 D	44 M	45 H	46 G	47 O	48 B	49 K	■
50 B	51 N	■	52 X	53 P	54 D	55 L	56 J	57 S	58 H	59 R	■	60 V	61 A	62 X	■	63 C	64 G	65 W	■	66 W	67 I
68 A	69 E	70 F	■	71 K	72 H	73 D	■	74 T	75 D	76 H	77 U	■	78 E	79 U	■	80 B	81 T	82 F	■	83 N	84 K
85 Z	86 P	■	87 A	88 I	89 G	90 R	91 O	92 D	93 J	94 L	■	95 G	96 N	97 R	98 A	■	99 S	100 E	101 D	102 L	103 Q
■	104 Z	105 F	■	106 Z	107 L	108 R	109 F	■	110 F	111 S	112 X	113 R	■	114 V	■	115 Z	116 C	117 Q	118 A	119 I	120 J
■	121 H	122 E	123 M	124 K	■	125 Z	126 J	127 R	■	128 M	129 S	130 W	131 U	132 P	■	133 P	134 G	135 W	■	136 T	137 W
138 A	139 R	■	140 V	141 L	142 M	143 S	144 N	■	145 I	146 B	147 M	148 V	■	149 R	150 L	151 X	152 V	153 Z	154 S	155 G	156 B
157 U	158 J	■	159 J	160 F	161 G	■	162 J	163 C	164 E	165 F	■	166 O	167 I	■	168 X	169 G	170 K	171 P	172 C	173 I	■
	174 C	175 M	176 X	177 Y	■	178 F	179 Z	■	180 B	181 Q	182 S	183 I	■	184 L	185 Q	186 N	187 P	188 M	■	189 A	
		190 T	191 U	192 C	■	193 C	■	194 W	195 Y	196 N	197 H	■	198 W	199 Y	■	200 P	201 O	202 X	■		

Crostic Puzzle 4

A. Vacation — 140 99 9 170 193 62 222

B. Sudden change: hyph. — 22 225 103 86 136 126 16 76 160

C. Fake diamond — 218 42 227 164 184 67 24 13 97 50

D. Large cetacean: 2 wds. — 41 75 154 111 104 29 59 203 209 143

E. California national park — 90 96 95 141 202 43 212 117

F. Restrains — 102 137 166 82 105 7 88 221 180

G. Shrewdness — 198 161 78 132 71 123

H. Independent — 181 70 36 130 18 87 58 195 144 175

I. Ordinary citizens: 2 wds. — 229 23 220 81 25 4 207 64 150 194

J. Spring bloom — 30 187 122 6 191 163 37 188

K. Court listing — 94 147 211 66 48 113

L. Extreme — 119 93 134 38 215 169 226

M. Thistlelike plant — 54 14 101 131 206 177 26 116 40

N. Runner-up's award: 2 wds. — 73 219 182 100 45 56 63 135 174

O. Large sandpiper — 5 57 217 8 214 34 89 28 108 171

P. Lots — 65 72 183 205 149 85

Q. Cheap car — 121 186 92 2 39 80 167

R. Rates — 115 17 109 3 146 145 10 120

S. Jobber — 68 118 165 156 133 44 173 204 196 32

T. Below zero: 3 wds. — 106 185 176 35 83 151 128 208 158

U. Nursemaid — 61 216 46 192 55

V. Represent — 139 224 112 124 114

W. Monroe film: 2 wds. — 110 159 178 148 60 20 190 69 52 157

X. Hard coal — 162 107 47 197 127 200 11 152 21 155

Y. Organization — 142 125 199 77 31 53

Z. Stretching muscle — 12 210 228 201 19 79

a. Newspeak — 168 84 74 15 98 27 223 51 138

b. Subtlety — 49 189 91 213 153 33 129 1 179 172

Solution on page 352

		1 b	2 Q	3 R	4 I	5 O		6 J	7 F	8 O	9 A	10 R	11 X	12 Z	13 C	14 M		15 a	16 B		
	17 R		18 H	19 Z		20 W	21 X	22 B	23 I	24 C		25 I	26 M	27 a	28 O	29 D	30 J	31 Y	32 S	33 b	
	34 O	35 T	36 H	37 J	38 L	39 Q	40 M	41 D		42 C	43 E	44 S		45 N	46 U	47 X	48 K	49 b	50 C	51 a	52 W
	53 Y	54 M	55 U		56 N	57 O		58 H	59 D	60 W	61 U	62 A		63 N	64 I	65 P	66 K	67 C		68 S	69 W
70 H	71 G		72 P	73 N		74 a	75 D	76 B	77 Y	78 G	79 Z	80 Q	81 I		82 F	83 T		84 a	85 P	86 B	87 H
88 F	89 O	90 E		91 b	92 Q	93 L	94 K	95 E		96 E	97 C	98 a		99 A	100 N		101 M	102 F	103 B		104 D
105 F	106 T	107 X	108 O	109 R		110 W	111 D	112 V	113 K		114 V	115 R	116 M	117 E		118 S	119 L	120 R		121 Q	122 J
123 G	124 V	125 Y		126 B	127 X	128 T	129 b		130 H	131 M	132 G	133 S		134 L	135 N		136 B	137 F	138 a	139 V	
140 A	141 E		142 Y	143 D	144 H	145 R		146 R	147 K	148 W	149 P	150 I	151 T	152 X	153 b	154 D		155 X	156 S	157 W	158 T
	159 W	160 B		161 G	162 X	163 J	164 C	165 S	166 F		167 Q	168 a	169 L	170 A	171 O	172 b		173 S	174 N	175 H	
176 T	177 M	178 W	179 b		180 F	181 H	182 N	183 P	184 C	185 T	186 Q	187 J		188 J	189 b		190 W	191 J	192 U	193 A	194 I
	195 H	196 S		197 X	198 G	199 Y		200 X		201 Z	202 E	203 D	204 S	205 P		206 M	207 I	208 T	209 D	210 Z	211 K
212 E	213 b	214 O	215 L		216 U	217 O	218 C	219 N	220 I	221 F	222 A		223 a	224 V		225 B	226 L	227 C	228 Z	229 I	

Crostic Puzzle 5

A. Free-for-all — 147 91 11 92 115 79 148 173 14 7

B. To the midpoint — 30 24 165 134 75 6 57

C. Croquet fields — 158 66 69 25 170

D. Became rotten, as eggs — 171 17 81 141 65 21

E. Almost: hyph. — 55 149 46 72 146 82 128 95

F. Greek letters — 86 62 157 150

G. Vespers — 135 168 85 127 58 34 20 98

H. Standards — 67 105 43 13 155

I. Kings' companions? — 22 120 59 102 76 162 47 144

J. Sidestep — 4 159 73 68 169

K. Pad — 61 56 45 74 37 89

L. Sounds of galloping — 40 44 93 83 35 103 53 29 104

M. Misfortunes — 112 142 117 152 18

N. Commonplace — 32 23 2 16 70 138 164 50 97 63

O. Animated — 123 137 153 27 172 77

P. Type of joint — 15 88 133 125 143 33 156 10 51

Q. Moves around confusedly — 5 96 54 116 28

R. Firefighting apparatus — 119 113 26 163 101 154

S. Maidens — 12 19 38 9 87 52 139

T. Bloodhound's action — 78 161 124 129 118

U. Omitted in pronunciation — 60 106 126 122 8 136

V. Come full circle — 131 175 107 151 132 111 31

W. Bedding item — 42 160 1 36 130 49

X. Debilitated — 166 3 84 80 39 110

Y. Itinerants — 121 140 48 100 109 90

Z. Salt Lake City auditorium — 94 145 114 41 64 174 167 99 71 108

Solution on page 352

		1 W	2 N	3 X	4 J	■	5 Q	6 B	7 A	8 U	9 S	■	10 P	11 A	12 S	■	13 H	14 A	15 P		
		16 N	17 D	18 M	■	19 S	20 G	21 D	■	22 I	23 N	24 B	25 C	26 R	27 O	28 Q	■	29 L	30 B		
31 V	■	32 N	33 P	34 G	35 L	36 W	37 K	38 S	■	39 X	40 L	41 Z	■	42 W	43 H	44 L	45 K	46 E	47 I	48 Y	■
49 W	50 N	51 P	52 S	■	53 L	54 Q	55 E	56 K	57 B	58 G	■	59 I	60 U	■	61 K	62 F	63 N	64 Z	65 D	■	66 C
67 H	68 J	■	69 C	70 N	71 Z	72 E	■	73 J	74 K	75 B	76 I	77 O	78 T	■	79 A	80 X	■	81 D	82 E	83 L	84 X
85 G	86 F	87 S	88 P	89 K	■	90 Y	91 A	■	92 A	93 L	94 Z	95 E	96 Q	97 N	98 G	■	99 Z	100 Y	101 R	■	102 I
103 L	■	104 L	105 H	106 U	107 V	108 Z	109 Y	■	110 X	111 V	112 M	113 R	■	114 Z	115 A	■	116 Q	117 M	118 T	119 R	■
120 I	121 Y	122 U	■	123 O	124 T	125 P	126 U	127 G	128 E	■	129 T	130 W	131 V	■	132 V	133 P	134 B	135 G	■	136 U	137 O
138 N	139 S	140 Y	141 D	142 M	143 P	144 I	■	145 Z	146 E	147 A	■	148 A	149 E	150 F	151 V	152 M	153 O	154 R	155 H	■	156 P
157 F	158 C	159 J	160 W	161 T	162 I	■	163 R	164 N	■	165 B	166 X	167 Z	168 G	169 J	170 C	■	171 D	172 O	173 A	174 Z	175 V

Crostic Puzzle 6

A. Histrionic — 54 47 3 193 12 79 97 176 15 164

B. Away from the coast — 186 64 82 148 160 140 115 94

C. Jumble — 9 5 96 125 135 114 130 55

D. Failure — 120 63 11 30 95

E. Support — 43 53 139 129 59 29 66 21 103 123

F. Reporter — 194 35 173 171 81 83 105

G. Whipped cream portion — 158 80 67 61 39 110

H. Vote in again — 57 37 108 145 17 127 106

I. Honshu port — 87 163 181 20 24 88 188 156

J. Sworn statement — 178 14 78 187 34 27 7 100 92

K. Obscurity — 75 10 131 180 165 151 146

L. Condones — 133 4 111 175 124 184

M. Secret — 141 153 183 6 143 28 190 65 41 74

N. Couch potato's entertainment — 154 161 86 58 36 1 19 182 91 119

O. Timely — 109 189 40 166 162 52 68 99 152

P. Beach structure — 2 104 159 132 174 144 60 44 138

Q. Of a European country — 118 168 150 71 121 46

R. Constables — 13 167 122 48 179 72 191 70

S. Peek — 98 38 126 84 107 185 172

T. Discharged — 26 56 49 112 73 22 8 42

U. Goddess of beauty — 136 149 93 18 177 90 32 62 69

V. Trail maker — 16 45 134 169 101 51 157 50 113 31

W. Ice pellet — 128 25 102 116 33 195 170 89 76

X. Measuring aid — 117 147 142 77 155 192 85 23 137

Solution on page 352

	1 N		2 P	3 A	4 L	5 C	6 M	7 J	8 T		9 C	10 K	11 D	12 A		13 R	14 J		15 A		
16 V	17 H	18 U	19 N	20 I	21 E	22 T		23 X	24 I	25 W	26 T	27 J	28 M	29 E	30 D	31 V		32 U	33 W		34 J
35 F	36 N	37 H	38 S	39 G	40 O	41 M	42 T		43 E	44 P		45 V		46 Q	47 A	48 R	49 T	50 V		51 V	52 O
53 E		54 A	55 C	56 T		57 H	58 N	59 E	60 P	61 G	62 U		63 D	64 B		65 M	66 E	67 G	68 O	69 U	70 R
	71 Q	72 R	73 T	74 M	75 K	76 W	77 X		78 J	79 A	80 G	81 F		82 B	83 F	84 S	85 X	86 N	87 I		88 I
89 W	90 U		91 N	92 J	93 U	94 B	95 D		96 C	97 A	98 S	99 O	100 J	101 V	102 W	103 E	104 P	105 F	106 H		107 S
108 H	109 O	110 G	111 L	112 T		113 V	114 C	115 B	116 W	117 X		118 Q	119 N		120 D	121 Q	122 R	123 E		124 L	125 C
126 S	127 H	128 W		129 E	130 C		131 K	132 P	133 L	134 V		135 C	136 U	137 X	138 P	139 E		140 B	141 M	142 X	
143 M	144 P	145 H	146 K		147 X	148 B		149 U	150 Q	151 K	152 O	153 M	154 N	155 X		156 I	157 V	158 G		159 P	160 B
161 N		162 O	163 I	164 A	165 K		166 O	167 R		168 Q	169 V	170 W	171 F	172 S		173 F	174 P	175 L		176 A	177 U
178 J	179 R	180 K		181 I	182 N	183 M	184 L		185 S	186 B		187 J	188 I	189 O	190 M	191 R	192 X	193 A	194 F	195 W	

TAKE A LETTER

The names of fifteen jobs are hidden in the 4-letter words. In the first row across take a letter from each word from left to right to spell one job; choose a different letter from each word to spell another; and choose one more to spell a third. One letter of each 4-letter word will be left unused. Do the same for the other rows, spelling the names of three jobs in each one.

Solutions on page 341

1.	FAIR	RANI	TART	EMIT	SIRE	RENT
2.	PEND	DADO	TRIO	SALT	ODOR	NARY
3.	MEWL	DATA	RICE	THIS	NEED	REAR
4.	CEDE	ROAN	SICK	TINT	IGOR	CORN
5.	WILT	AWAY	WARP	IDLY	SEED	TURN

1. __________ __________ __________

2. __________ __________ __________

3. __________ __________ __________

4. __________ __________ __________

5. __________ __________ __________

Mathboxes

Fill in the missing numbers across and down using only the digits given above the diagrams. Always perform the mathematical operations in order from left to right and from top to bottom.

Solutions on page 341

1 2 2 3 4 6 7 8

A.

1 2 3 3 4 4 4 4

B.

DOUBLE OCCUPANCY

Place the letter pairs on the left into the blank squares in the diagram to form 6-letter words reading across and down. Each pair will be used only once.

Solution on page 341

AC	DE	LE	NT
AN	DE	LI	NU
AS	DE	LO	ON
AS	ED	LU	PI
AS	EF	MA	RA
BA	EL	ME	RS
BE	EM	MI	RS
BU	ER	MI	ST
CA	ES	NE	ST
CA	ET	NE	TE
CE	FI	NG	TO
CO	GY	NI	UT
CU	KE	NS	VA
CU	LE	NS	VE

	LI		AL				DG	
HE	■	FI		■		TO	■	DE
	IN				UR		TE	
RE				TE				CE
	■		RS	■	AI		■	
		RE		GE		ER		
	CE				FE		ND	
TI	■	MO		■		NG	■	AR
	IO		ER				MO	

BORROW AND SCORE

Form words of four letters or more by combining the two given letters with as many letters from the word on the preceding line as you can. Letters may be used in any order. Place the letters you do not use in the UNUSED LETTERS column. To start add the letters DO to as many of the letters in the word PACT as you can and place the unused ones in the UNUSED LETTERS column. If you cannot form a word on a line, place all the letters from the preceding word in the UNUSED LETTERS column and start again as on line 1 with PACT. To score subtract the total of unused letters from 100. A score of 85 is very good.

Our solution with a score of 89 on page 342

PACT

	GIVEN LETTERS	WORDS	UNUSED LETTERS
1.	DO	______	____
2.	RY	______	____
3.	IN	______	____
4.	OR	______	____
5.	EP	______	____
6.	CH	______	____
7.	IL	______	____
8.	EO	______	____
		TOTAL	____

FOUR-FIT

Without changing the order of the letters, place the 4-letter words on the dashes to form 8-letter words. Each 4-letter word will be used once.

Solution on page 341

CAPE	GOAT	LINT	OMEN	PRAY
CLAY	INTO	MULE	ORAL	STAY
EPEE	LEAN	OGRE	PLOY	WIRE

1. ___GUIS_
2. _X__DIT_
3. _U_IN_R_
4. UN__E_D_
5. PR____SS
6. AD___B_E
7. ___ERI_R
8. P___SA_T
9. SI___AT_
10. _HA_M_C_
11. EM____EE
12. _A_T__SS
13. C__M__CE
14. ES___AD_
15. I_N_R_N_

How Many Triangles?

This diagram is filled with triangles small, medium, and large. Try to count them all. There may be more than you Think!

Solution on page 341

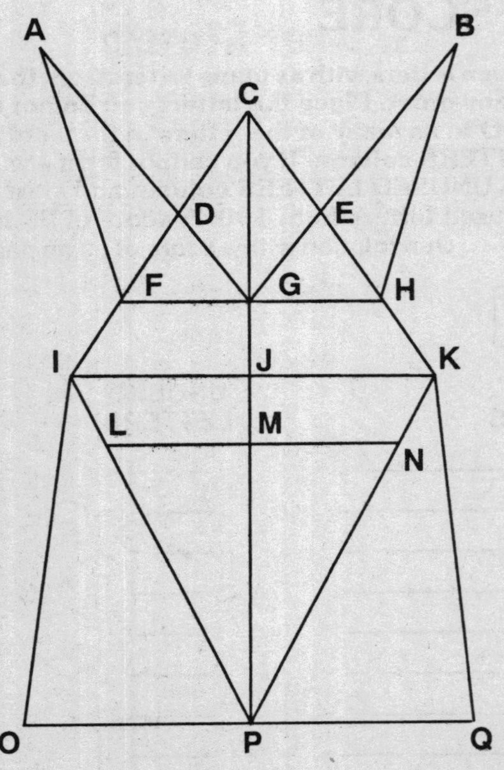

Hocus-Pocus

Fill in the diagram with words formed by unscrambling the letters so that an 8-letter word will be revealed reading down the outlined column. This is a bit tricky since the scrambled letters may form more than one word.

Solution on page 342

1. GILOC
2. NPORA
3. HARWT
4. ODYLE
5. UREPN
6. LFHAS
7. TLOEH
8. EAKND

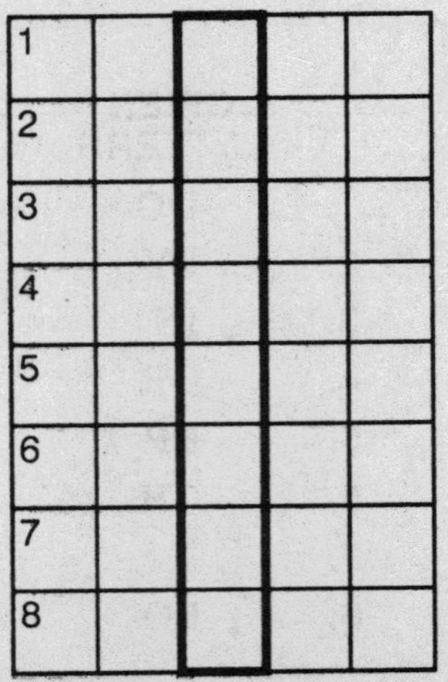

Classified Adds

Fill in the spaces with answers which begin and end with the given letters and fit the categories shown. Answers may be any length. For example, in number 1 below, you must think of a beverage beginning with the letter T and ending with the letter A, a musical group beginning with the letter A and ending with the letter A, and so on. There are many possible solutions.

Our solution on page 341

	BEVERAGES	MUSICAL GROUPS	OLD TESTAMENT MEN	INSECTS	TREES AND SHRUBS	
1.	T	A	A	L	G	M
2.	B	Y	S	M	O	K
3.	W	R	H	M	Y	W
4.	C	A	H	A	D	D
5.	M	K	S	L	E	M
6.	S	T	C	B	E	S
7.	R	M	A	M	H	K
8.	R	R	M	S	B	Y

Keyword

To find the Keyword fill in the blanks in words 1 through 10 with the correct missing letters. Transfer those letters to the correspondingly numbered squares in the diagram. Approach with care—this puzzle is not as simple as it first appears.

Solution on page 342

1	2	3	4	5	6	7	8	9	10

1. P___ACH
2. SPO___T
3. ___ASTE
4. STIL___
5. FL___SH
6. THI___K
7. CROW___
8. G___ANT
9. LEA___E
10. ___URRY

Number Sleuth

One of the numbers in the hexagons has been circled because it and the numbers in the six surrounding hexagons are all different. There are 12 others like this. Are you a sharp-eyed sleuth who can find them all?

Solution on page 342

LOGIC PROBLEM

SUMMER IN THE CITY

In the summertime, Ernest and four other inhabitants of the Regency Apartments enjoy adding color to their building by planting window boxes. Last summer, each person planted a different flower (begonias, marigolds, pansies, petunias, or zinnias) and a different foliage plant (caladium, coleus, English ivy, fern, or wandering Jew) in his or her window box. Each green-thumbed tenant lives on a different floor. From the information provided, determine the tenant who lives on each floor (1st, 3rd, 4th, 7th, or 10th), the flower each planted, and the foliage plant each planted.

1. Three of the tenants are the one who planted begonias, the one who planted English ivy, and Sarah.

2. Grace (who planted zinnias) didn't plant wandering Jew.

3. The one who planted wandering Jew lives on the tenth floor.

4. Maria (who didn't plant begonias) planted caladium. She doesn't live on the first floor.

5. The one who lives on the third floor planted petunias and English ivy.

6. Robert (who lives on the fourth floor) didn't plant ferns.

7. Marigolds were not planted by the tenant who lives on the seventh floor.

This chart is to help you record information from the clues as well as the facts you deduce by combining information from different clues. We suggest you use an "X" for a "no" and a "•" for a "yes."

		FLOOR					FLOWER					FOLIAGE PLANT				
		FIRST	THIRD	FOURTH	SEVENTH	TENTH	BEGONIA	MARIGOLD	PANSY	PETUNIA	ZINNIA	CALADIUM	COLEUS	ENGLISH IVY	FERN	WANDERING JEW
TENANT	ERNEST															
	GRACE															
	MARIA															
	ROBERT															
	SARAH															
FOLIAGE	CALADIUM															
	COLEUS															
	ENGLISH IVY															
	FERN															
	WANDERING JEW															
FLOWER	BEGONIA															
	MARIGOLD															
	PANSY															
	PETUNIA															
	ZINNIA															

Solution on page 341

WORD MERGERS

Rearrange the letters in each Word Merger to form two words using all the given letters only once. Then rearrange these same letters and merge them into one long word. You might want to form the long word first and then the pair of words. Score 5 points for each pair of words you form and 10 points for each long word. A score of 85 is good, 95 is very good, and 105 is excellent.

Our solutions with a perfect score of 120 points on page 341

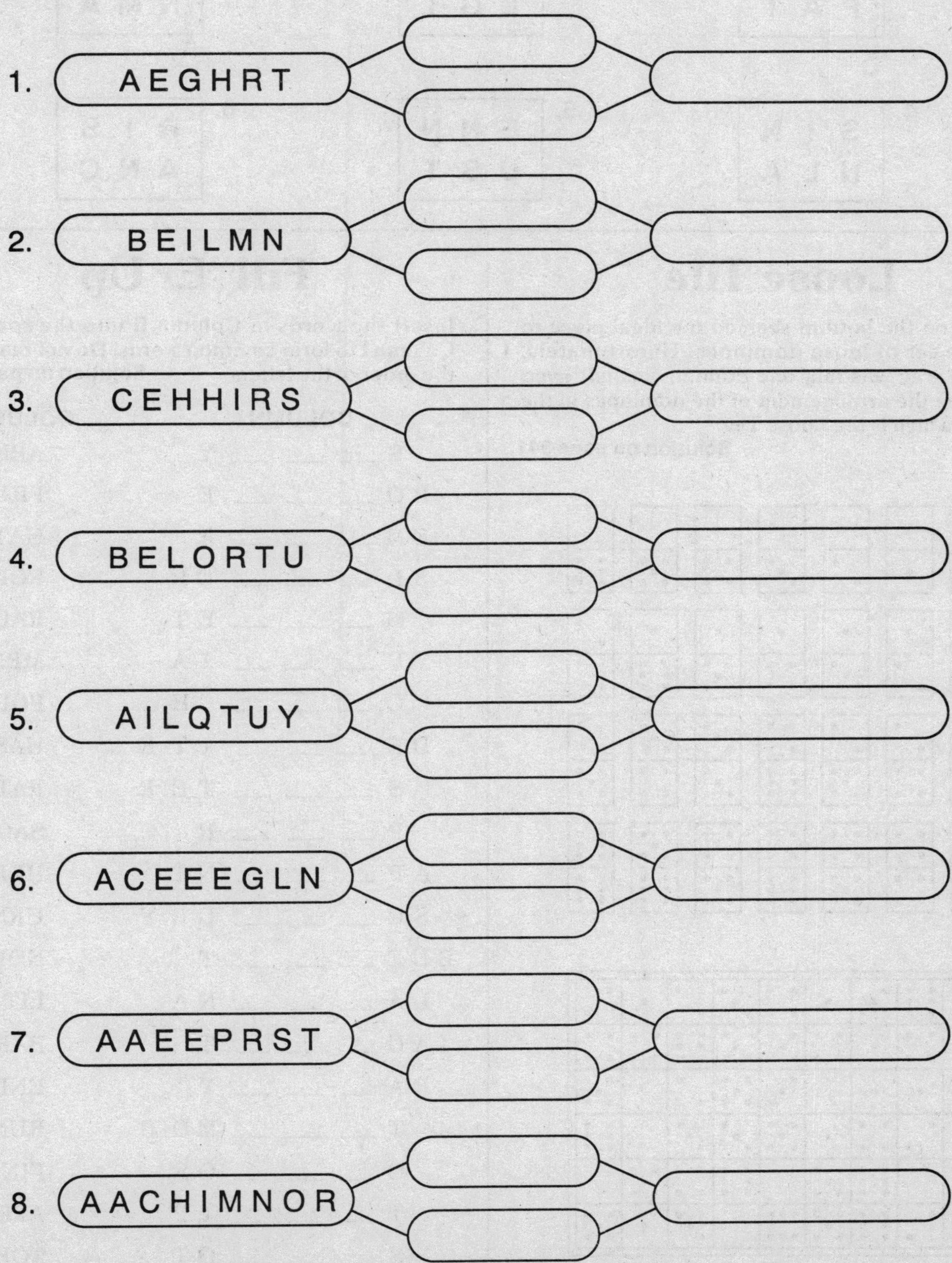

Bits and Pieces

Can you identify these European capitals from the Bits and Pieces shown in the boxes? The cities are always on the top and the countries on the bottom.
Solutions on page 341

1. A D R / P A I

2. U S S / L G I

3. E N H / N M A

4. S I N / N L A

5. E N N / U S T

6. R I S / A N C

Loose Tile

The tray on the bottom seemed the ideal place to store the set of loose dominoes. Unfortunately, when the tray was full, one domino was left over. Determine the arrangement of the dominoes in the tray and which is the Loose Tile.
Solution on page 341

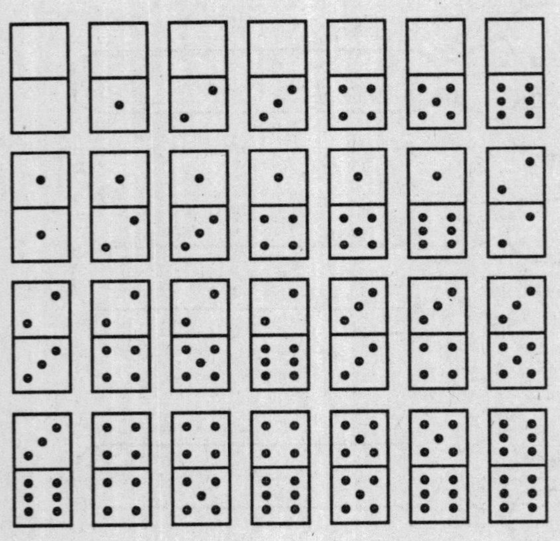

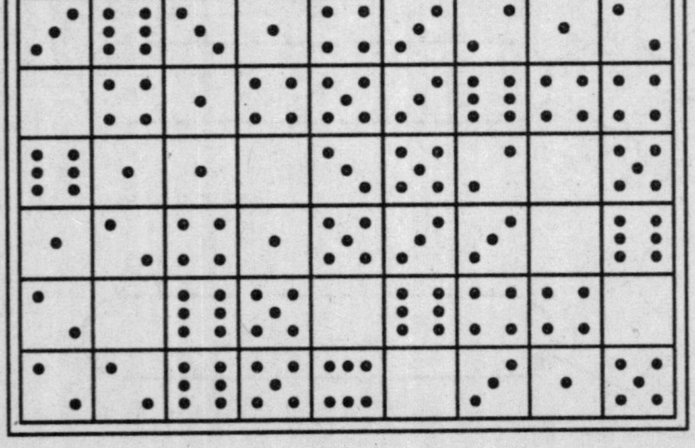

Fill 'Er Up

Insert the words in Column II into the spaces in Column I to form common words. Do not rearrange the order of the letters.
Solution on page 341

COLUMN I	COLUMN II
S __ __ __ Y	ARK
PO __ __ __ E	PIG
EM __ __ __ K	HAT
SL __ __ __ ER	ROD
M __ __ __ ET	RAG
U __ __ __ IA	MEN
C __ __ __ CH	POI
DE __ __ __ ITE	HAS
S __ __ __ TER	RAT
P __ __ __ R	SAG
AP __ __ __ NT	HER
SC __ __ __ GLY	URN
ELE __ __ __ T	NOW
LA __ __ __ NA	LIT
AG __ __ __ T	BAR
PA __ __ __ Y	END
T __ __ __ MOS	RUN
O __ __ __ OR	FIN
T __ __ __ IP	APE
S __ __ __ OT	TOP

Word Math

In these long-division problems letters are substituted for numbers. Determine the value of each letter. Then arrange the letters in order from 0 to 9, and they will spell a word or phrase.

Solutions on page 341

1.

```
           S A C
HIT | S L A C K S
      K T H B
        A C C K
        L H S M
          C I T S
          A H C K
            T S L
```

0 _ 1 _ 2 _ 3 _ 4 _ 5 _ 6 _ 7 _ 8 _ 9 _

2.

```
              H O P
EATS | P O T A T O
       O H A A
       E E A B T
         P P S O
         E A U S O
         E E A E T
           E E Y T
```

0 _ 1 _ 2 _ 3 _ 4 _ 5 _ 6 _ 7 _ 8 _ 9 _

3.

```
                G E E
TIME | I G N I T E S
       E H I A
       H A S E E
       H H G A T
         H R G T S
         H H G A T
             H S E M
```

0 _ 1 _ 2 _ 3 _ 4 _ 5 _ 6 _ 7 _ 8 _ 9 _

Middle of the Road

Place the correct missing letters into the diagram to form words reading across. Then read the filled-in letters down from top to bottom to reveal a message. Be careful—some of the words are tricky!

Solution on page 341

NORM _ LIZES
CLIM _
STR _ PPED
_ HIEF
LEA _ Y
_ OUND
LEAS _
ST _ FF
_ RACER
_ INER
RIVE _
SP _ RES
REVI _ ED
_ ASED
DE _ IDED
GREE _ HOUSE
H _ ARD
_ ERVE
STOR _
_ EADY
TUBE _
H _ RRIED
RAVE _
PAIN _
P _ SSE
P _ NCHED
STAR _
GR _ PE
_ OGGY
DIN _ Y
C _ RRY
DAI _ Y

BOWL GAME

To bowl a strike (20 points) you must create a 10-letter word using all the letters in each pin. The letter on top in the pin is the first letter of the strike word. To bowl a spare (10 points) use the same 10 letters to form two words. Splits are not allowed: you may not divide the strike to form a spare. For example, SWEETHEART may not become SWEET and HEART.

Our solutions with a perfect score of 300 points on page 341

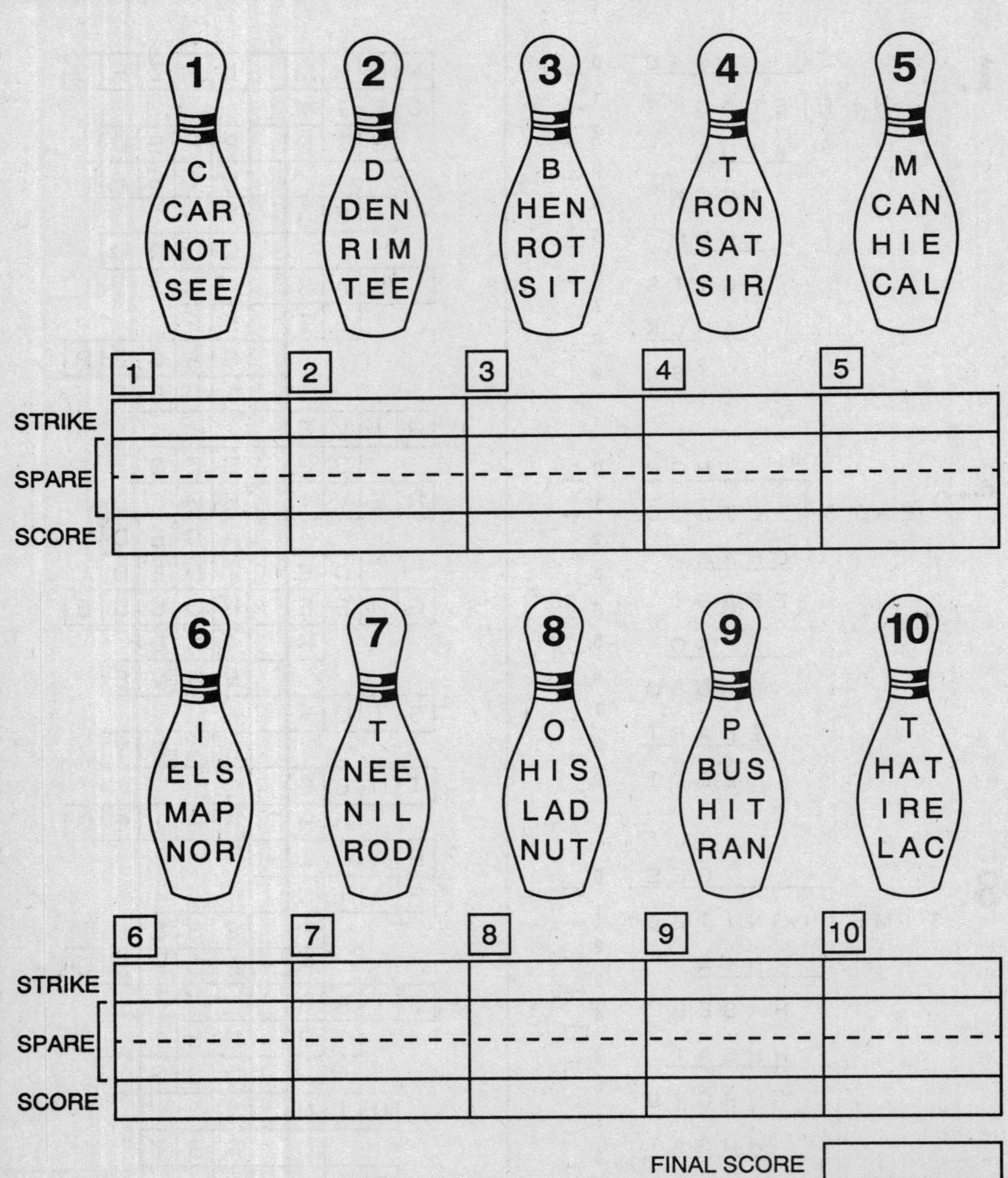

CODEWORD

The directions for solving are given on page 27.

Solution on page 342

1	14
2	15
3 M	16
4	17
5	18
6	19
7	20
8	21
9	22
10 A	23
11	24
12	25
13	26

4	23	26	8	22	9	19	2	■	24	20	3	5	12	13
11	■	1	■	17	■	1	■	6	■	17	■	13	■	12
20	4	20	10	8	■	16	13	12	4	2	8	22	17	9
22	■	17	■	12	■	■	■	10	■	1	■	6	■	10
13	22	9	19	2	7	20	8	8	26	■	25	12	8	8
13	■	4	■	■	■	17	■	■	■	4	■	■	■	12
12	17	2	13	10	17	25	12	15	■	23	12	5	2	■
8	■	12	■	18	■	8	■	12	■	22	■	13	■	5
■	7	13	12	12	■	12	18	2	12	17	4	22	14	12
21	■	■	■	4	■	■	■	12	■	■	■	14	■	13
20	5	1	17	■	24	1	20	13	17	10	8	22	4	3
21	■	25	■	4	■	20	■	■	■	8	■	8	■	12
21	10	25	23	16	10	13	15	4	■	10	13	12	17	10
8	■	20	■	10	■	4	■	22	■	13	■	9	■	2
12	17	13	10	9	12	■	4	2	10 A	3 M	5	12	15	12

PLACE YOUR NUMBER

The large square below is divided into four smaller squares—A, B, C, and D—and each smaller square is divided into four sections—North, East, South, and West. Use the clues to number the sections. Each section will contain a different number from 1 through 16. **Solution on page 342**

1. Each section contains exactly two even-numbered subsections.
2. D-West and D-South are both single-digit odd numbers.
3. Each North number is an even number.
4. A-South is one more than A-North, which is one more than A-East, which is one more than A-West.
5. D-East + D-West = A-East.
6. A-West, C-North, and D-North are all divisible by the number 4.
7. C-West is three times greater than B-East.
8. A-West is seven more than B-South.
9. B-North is three times greater than C-North, which is two times greater than C-South.

DOUBLE OCCUPANCY

Place the letter pairs on the right into the blank squares in the diagram to form 6-letter words reading across and down. Each pair will be used only once.

Solution on page 342

	ST		AL				UT	
LA	■	NE		■		ER	■	AS
	LE				AL		RA	
		IN		IT		DI		
	■		OT	■	AR		■	
LE				AT				PE
	IL				CH		AL	
TI	■	AN		■		NT	■	PI
	NE		ID				MO	

AL	GE	OI	SH
AN	GE	OR	ST
AP	GE	OR	ST
BL	GG	OR	TA
CA	GY	PA	TE
CE	HE	PE	TE
CH	IN	RB	TH
CH	IO	RE	TU
CH	KI	RE	TW
CL	LE	RE	TY
CY	LU	RI	TY
ED	ND	RI	VE
ES	NG	RY	WI
FL	NI	SA	WT

Give and Take

Change the 4-letter words on the left to the 5-letter words on the right by giving and taking letters. Add one letter to the word on the left to form a 5-letter word. Then subtract one letter from that word to form a new 4-letter word. Next add a letter to form a new 5-letter word; subtract a letter to form a new 4-letter word. Finally, add a letter to form the word given on the right. The order of the letters may be rearranged in forming new words.

Our solutions on page 341

Example: VEST, STOVE, TOES, THOSE, SHOT, SHORT

1. OPEN ______ ______ ______ ______ HOUSE
2. HEAD ______ ______ ______ ______ STAND
3. LINE ______ ______ ______ ______ DANCE
4. CARD ______ ______ ______ ______ SHARP
5. NAME ______ ______ ______ ______ PLATE
6. RACE ______ ______ ______ ______ HORSE
7. LAND ______ ______ ______ ______ SLIDE
8. FAST ______ ______ ______ ______ TRACK
9. HARD ______ ______ ______ ______ WIRED
10. TIME ______ ______ ______ ______ FRAME

SUM TOTALS

Place one digit (1 to 9, no zeros) in each square so that the sum of the numbers in each group of squares across or down is the number given. The number below a diagonal is the sum of the numbers below it. The number to the right of a diagonal is the sum of the numbers to the right of it. IMPORTANT: No digit is used more than once in any group of squares leading to a sum. One group of digits has been given for you.

Solution on page 342

■	22\	39\	17\	■	9\	4\	■	■	3\	20\	■	■	■
\8			5	4\6			8\	\11			7\	■	■
\34			8					42\10				11\	12\
\18			4		9\	44\14			3\10				
\12			28\	12\17			\7				27\17		
■	11\17						22\10			28\10			■
\27					\21				\17			39\	16\
\12					\15				\16				
■	■	24\15			13\10				9\25				
■	17\13			23\14			\28						15\
\15			10\18				14\14			14\	16\17		
\29					6\17			15\	7\12				
■	■	\17				\37							
■	■	■	\4			■	\8			\18			

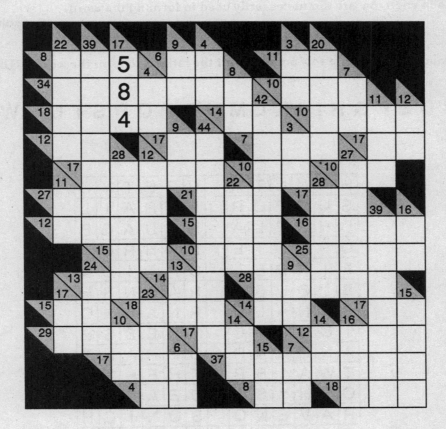

Crossout Quote

Cross out one letter in each box so that the remaining letters spell out a humorous quotation across from left to right.

Solution on page 342

T N	O H	E T	■	T R	A H	C A	T E	■	M W	H A	O Y	■	N C
A O	T N	■	B I	F E	■	T A	N O	■	A T	H R	T E	■	S G
W R	A I	F D	E T	■	N F	I O	R T	■	T G	E H	E T	■	V A
I N	S C	W T	O E	R L	L Y	■	T B	E O	■	W T	I H	E N	■
S B	T E	L R	O L	O N	W G	■	B C	A U	N T	■	T W	H R	E A
R T	S E	■	H T	E O	W N	■	M Y	O E	N U	■	B S	P E	T Y

ALPHABET SOUP

Insert a different letter of the alphabet into each of the 26 empty boxes to form words of five or more letters reading across. The letter you insert may be at the beginning, the end, or in the middle of the word. Each letter of the alphabet will be used only once. Cross off each letter in the list as you use it. All the letters in each row are not necessarily used in forming the word.

Our solution on page 342

Example: In the first row across insert the letter Z to form the word AZURE.

A B C D E F G H I J K L M N O P Q R S T U V W X Y Z

H	A	N	O	T	A		U	R	E	T	Y	S
S	U	M	P	O	R		E	R	R	A	I	L
C	H	A	P	L	A		N	G	U	A	G	E
U	P	R	O	T	E		E	N	H	R	O	Y
F	I	N	D	E	L		G	A	T	I	O	N
B	L	O	U	S	H		R	A	W	N	S	H
S	C	H	A	L	E		R	N	A	L	L	O
T	O	O	P	I	C		Y	N	E	S	S	E
A	N	C	H	A	R		O	P	H	A	N	T
T	W	A	I	B	R		T	H	E	R	L	Y
O	P	H	Y	S	I		U	E	A	T	E	D
R	A	V	E	N	O		S	O	N	I	C	H
P	O	S	I	R	E		A	R	D	Y	A	P
E	N	N	C	R	A		O	N	O	R	I	M
S	L	A	O	B	E		E	N	T	U	A	L
I	N	S	D	H	E		E	D	I	T	Y	E
C	O	G	L	I	M		S	E	Y	A	M	P
U	N	T	O	R	D		I	F	T	Y	E	N
E	S	Q	U	I	P		U	S	H	I	S	T
O	L	L	A	D	E		O	Y	F	A	N	D
T	A	R	O	U	N		G	B	A	R	T	N
B	E	A	U	T	I		U	L	N	P	A	M
A	C	E	R	E	C		A	G	R	I	N	D
F	A	N	W	H	E		E	C	T	I	O	N
E	N	L	I	V	I		U	A	L	A	M	C
E	X	A	P	R	O		Y	L	U	N	N	G

TO PLAY:

1. Enter the first seven LETTERBOX letters onto the first DRAWLINE and cross them off in the LETTERBOX.
2. Form a word of at least two letters across or down on the GAMEBOARD. One letter of the first word must go into the starred square.
3. Tally your score in the SCORE column.
4. Carry down all unused letters onto the next DRAWLINE. Transfer enough letters from the LETTERBOX, in the given order, so that you have seven letters to work with.
5. Build a new word or words by:
   a. adding one or more letters before and/or after words on the GAMEBOARD.
   b. adding one or more letters at right angles to words on the GAMEBOARD.
   c. adding a word parallel to one on the GAMEBOARD.

IMPORTANT: All adjoining letters must spell out complete words.

6. Continue working this way until all the letters from the LETTERBOX have been used.
7. Asterisks (*) are "wild" letters and may represent any letter you choose, but once used they cannot be changed.

NOTE: Proper names, foreign words, and abbreviations are not allowed. No word may appear twice on the GAMEBOARD.

TO SCORE:

Score every letter in each new word as follows:

1. Letters in unnumbered squares count 1 point.
2. Letters in numbered squares count the given value of the square.
3. Double the score of a word containing a circle.
4. Triple the score of a word containing two circles.
5. Add 20 points if all seven letters from a DRAWLINE are used in one play.

Can you beat our game of 367 points given on page 341?

LETTERBOX

E O R A V F D N I X Z E S B T N A O W E U L J R * E I T S Q
U A P T G R A N I O Y A H K O C S D L E M U * E T S R I N O

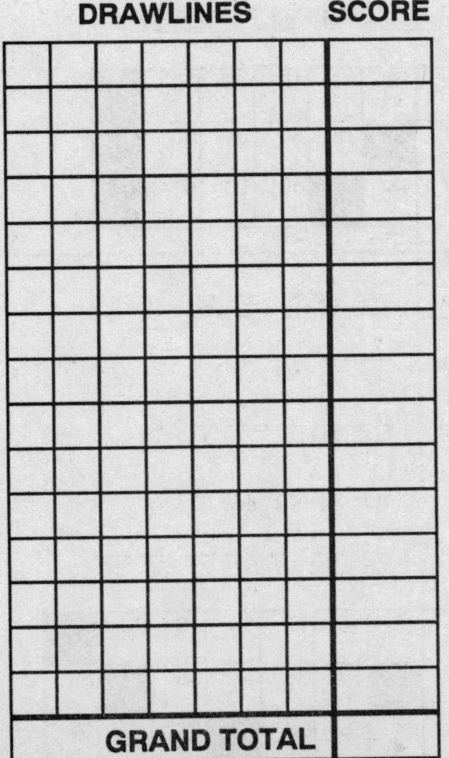

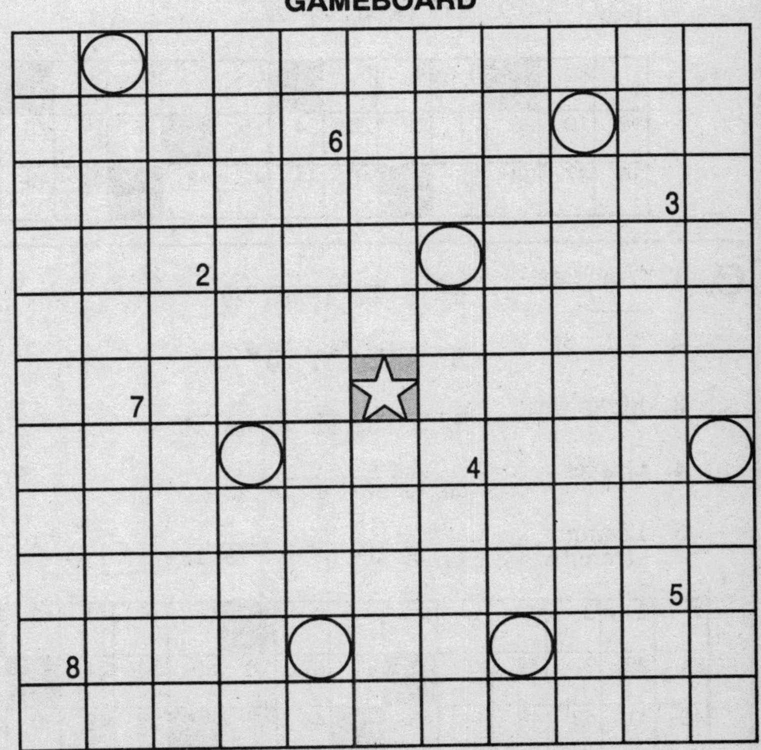

QUOTAGRAMS

Fill in the answers to the clues. Then transfer the letters to the correspondingly numbered squares in the diagram. The completed diagram will contain a quotation.

Solutions on page 342

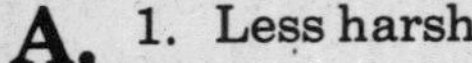

A.

1. Less harsh — 28 48 6 50 15 34 58
2. Indoor plant nursery — 19 22 52 36 46 60 11 3
3. Advantage — 56 8 27 12 53 5 24 62
4. Yearning — 7 20 38 29 44 13 42
5. Yale University's site — 61 43 23 2 37 47 32 17
6. During an annual span — 41 26 39 54 14 9 31 18
7. Song from "Annie" — 45 51 4 55 35 49 59 25
8. Guest — 33 10 21 16 1 57 40 30

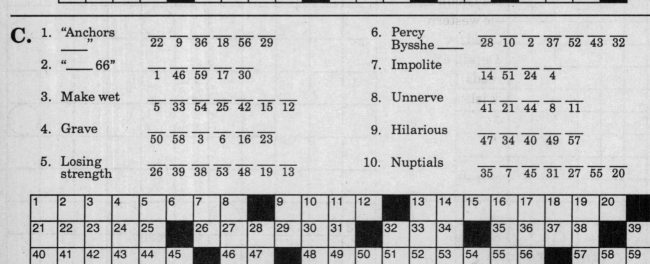

1	2	3		4	5	6		7	8	9		10	11		12	13	14	15	16
17	18		19	20	21		22	23	24		25	26	27	28	29	30		31	32
33	34	35		36	37	38		39	40	41		42	43	44	45		46	47	48
49		50	51		52	53	54	55	56		57	58	59	60	61	62			

B.

1. Come after — 17 41 6 33 45 36
2. Each one — 9 19 35 13 31
3. Save — 38 47 10 28 3
4. Irked — 21 1 50 15 30
5. Manuscript leaf — 2 18 40 37 27
6. Uses a strop — 25 11 26 43 14
7. Artist ____-Lautrec — 48 7 46 51 4 23 34 20
8. Beautiful — 39 29 42 32 16 44
9. Cleaning machine — 8 49 24 5 12 22

1	2		3	4	5		6	7	8	9		10	11	12	13	14	15	16	17	
18	19	20	21	22	23	24	25		26	27	28	29	30	31		32	33	34	35	
36	37	38	39		40	41	42	43		44	45	46		47	48		49	50	51	

C.

1. "Anchors ____" — 22 9 36 18 56 29
2. "____ 66" — 1 46 59 17 30
3. Make wet — 5 33 54 25 42 15 12
4. Grave — 50 58 3 6 16 23
5. Losing strength — 26 39 38 53 48 19 13
6. Percy Bysshe ____ — 28 10 2 37 52 43 32
7. Impolite — 14 51 24 4
8. Unnerve — 41 21 44 8 11
9. Hilarious — 47 34 40 49 57
10. Nuptials — 35 7 45 31 27 55 20

1	2	3	4	5	6	7	8		9	10	11	12		13	14	15	16	17	18	19	20	
21	22	23	24	25		26	27	28	29	30	31		32	33	34		35	36	37	38		39
40	41	42	43	44	45		46	47		48	49	50	51	52	53	54	55	56		57	58	59

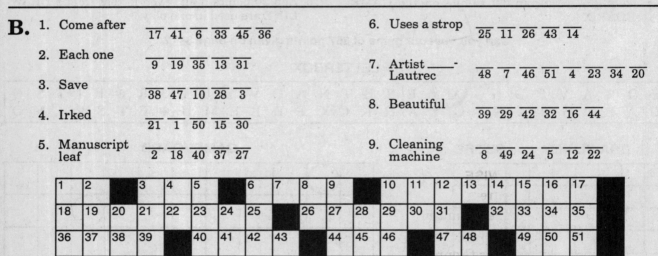

FLOWER POWER

The answers to this petaled puzzle will go in a curve from the number on the outside to the center of the flower. Each number has two 5-letter words. One goes in a clockwise direction and the second in a counterclockwise direction. Try working from both sets of clues to fill the flower. **Solution on page 342**

CLOCKWISE

1. Picture
2. Pepper or nutmeg
3. Kind of oil
4. Actress Glenn ____
5. Classic western
6. Glistened
7. Mare's-tail, e.g.
8. Seaweeds
9. Greek isle
10. Scent
11. Verge
12. Ruin
13. Fuzzy fruit
14. Window material
15. Tangle
16. Diminutive
17. Stains
18. Turn aside

COUNTERCLOCKWISE

1. Casino decoy
2. Oar
3. Unlocks
4. Country singer Black
5. Pizza portion
6. Push
7. Pursue
8. Unaccompanied
9. Duplicate
10. Quarrel
11. Sandwich need
12. Used a pen
13. First-rate
14. Davis of "Tootsie"
15. Limp
16. Eat between meals
17. Destroy
18. Flies high

ESCALATORS

Write the answer to clue 1 in the first space. Drop one letter and rearrange the remaining letters to answer clue 2. Put the dropped letter into Column A. Drop another letter and rearrange the remaining letters to answer clue 3. Put the dropped letter into Column B. Follow this pattern for each row in the diagram. When completed, the letters in Column A and Column B, reading down, will spell related words or a phrase.

Solutions on page 342

1

1. Cringes
2. Game tally
3. National flower
4. Stew slowly
5. Cavalry sword
6. Foundation
7. Enumerates
8. Talent seeker
9. Folding beds
10. Vehement speech
11. Made public
12. Peruse
13. Go by
14. Rings
15. Jump
16. Marvel
17. Provide a fund
18. Eider feathers

	A		B	
1		2		3
4		5		6
7		8		9
10		11		12
13		14		15
16		17		18

2

1. Rug
2. Crawled
3. Saucy
4. Youth lodging
5. The ones there
6. Foot digits
7. Gratify
8. Artist's stand
9. Otherwise
10. Sell to consumers
11. Change to fit
12. Rip
13. Kindling material
14. Attempted
15. Soil
16. Turning machines
17. Stops
18. Bind with rope

	A		B	
1		2		3
4		5		6
7		8		9
10		11		12
13		14		15
16		17		18

3

1. Buy on credit
2. Meal prayer
3. Be concerned
4. Baltimore bird
5. Tank ship
6. Vex
7. Feudal lord's home
8. Not fresh
9. Allows
10. Leg joints
11. Bowling alleys
12. Rational
13. Besmirch
14. Pasture
15. Ran away
16. With confidence
17. Entices
18. Aspersion

	A		B	
1		2		3
4		5		6
7		8		9
10		11		12
13		14		15
16		17		18

SYL''LA-CROS'TIC

The directions for solving are given on page 34. Solution on page 343

✱ SYLLABOX ✱

A A ~~A~~ AS CAR COL ~~DA~~ DI DIC ED EN ER ER FUL ~~GAN~~ GO GRA
HAI HI I IM IN KU LAT LET MA MAN NEF NO NON NOR NOV NUI
O O O OR OUT PAR PET PROP ~~PROP~~ REG REP RI RO SAN SHA
SIM TA TE TI TI TI TION U VY WIS

1. Publicity, of a sort (4) P R O P A G A N D A
2. Russian czar (3) _ _ _ _ _ _ _
3. Spaghetti-sauce seasoning (4) _ _ _ _ _ _ _
4. Picturesque (3) _ _ _ _ _ _ _ _
5. Japanese verse (2) _ _ _ _ _
6. Objective (4) _ _ _ _ _ _ _ _ _ _ _
7. Socket (2) _ _ _ _ _ _
8. Flowering shrub (4) _ _ _ _ _ _ _ _
9. Unsuitable (3) _ _ _ _ _ _ _ _
10. Turkey topper (2) _ _ _ _ _
11. Not alpine (2) _ _ _ _ _ _
12. Midwest state (3) _ _ _ _
13. Good name (4) _ _ _ _ _ _ _ _ _ _
14. Conformed (5) _ _ _ _ _ _ _ _ _ _ _
15. Egyptian queen (4) _ _ _ _ _ _ _ _ _
16. Rug (2) _ _ _ _ _ _
17. Boredom (2) _ _ _ _ _
18. Blue dye (3) _ _ _ _ _ _
19. Medicine man (2) _ _ _ _ _ _

CRYPTO-FAMILIES

Each Crypto-Family is a list of related words in code. Each Family has its own code. When you have identified a word, use the known letters to help decode the other words in the Family.

Solutions on page 342

1. SEWING NOTIONS
Example: Binding

MALLQVI
JQQSCQI
PBFFNJI
FUVQKS
IZAIINVI
PBZECQI
QCKIFAZ
LKFFQVJI
IJKLI
LAJI

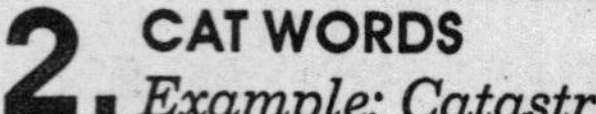

2. CAT WORDS
Example: Catastrophe

ALVCNRU
ALVLAXEPR
ALVOYMNIILY
ALVWLM
ALVOBXYS
ALVLAISRE
ALVAULII
ALVZLIF
ALVLPXINRE
ALVOYZLJI

3. BLUE CHASERS
Example: Jay

QKRY
JGC
SBRZV
QBVVAV
EGGAV
MWFV
JZRE
MGWTD
YVKKP
AMKXQV

4. PASS THE WORD
Example: Note

XGBGFYVU
UGUIYVHEWU
EQTLVXPD
ZWBBGXQH
PIUUWHQSWG
UQTTQJG
TLGGPD
PIUUGHXVYA
GEQXIYQVB
UGTTVFG

5. TURN ON THE HEAT
Example: Stove

ODITLBFY
QFGBMYF
XFBMM
FDSXY
JBQDOJB
XDU QPFSYF
AGDUAYF
GWYS
IBOFGHDWY
LGSCPY TGA

6. WHIPPERSNAPPER
Example: Tot

YRJVA
UQHVV ZGT
MXAAVPG
QXBBPM
JSZHSM
DICPSJVP
MTWP
OHOT
SPFOXGS
TXISEUMPG

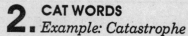

DOUBLE TROUBLE

Not really double trouble, but double fun! Solve this puzzle as you would a regular crossword, except place one, two, or three letters in each box. The number of letters in each answer is shown in parentheses after its clue.

ACROSS

1. In what place (5)
4. Pelt gatherer (7)
8. Laundry ramp (5)
10. Baking chamber (4)
11. Sleuth Queen (6)
12. Male sheep (3)
13. Transmitted (4)
14. Fall flower (5)
15. Was sore (5)
16. Closed (4)
18. Heater (5)
20. Capital of France (5)
22. Bemoan (6)
24. Kind-hearted (6)
27. Refined iron (5)
29. The ones here (5)
31. Teuton (6)
32. Ford failure (5)
34. Italian poet (5)
36. Prod (4)
37. Secret languages (5)
39. Coronet (5)
41. Said (6)
43. Lightweight velvet (5)
45. Steps over a fence (5)
48. French cleric (4)
49. Of thinking (6)
50. Theater paths (6)
51. Allows (4)
52. Leading lady (7)
53. Remainder (4)

DOWN

1. Which person's (5)
2. All tied up (4)
3. Leases (5)
4. Application (9)
5. "____ Well That Ends Well" (4)
6. Diva Roberta ____ (6)
7. Attorney Mason (5)
8. Place of worship (6)
9. Yoked (6)
15. Nemesis (7)
17. Hawaiian dance (4)
19. Carry on the back (4)
20. Glued (6)
21. Soars (5)
23. Actress Bara (5)
25. Take exception (5)
26. Scope (5)
28. Chose by vote (7)
30. Guards (9)
33. Ore deposit (4)
35. Salty drop (4)
38. Disbursed (5)
40. Dancer Fred ____ (7)
41. Horse barn (6)
42. Aids in wrong (5)
44. Star in Scorpio (7)
46. Small land masses (5)
47. For fear that (4)
49. Singer Davis (3)

Solution on page 342

1	2	3	■	4	5	6	7	■	8	9
10			■	11				■	12	
13			■	14			■	15		
■	■	16	17		■	18	19		■	■
20	21	■	22		23	■	24		25	26
27		28	■	29		30	■	31		
32			33	■	34		35	■	36	
■	■	37		38	■	39		40	■	■
41	42		■	43	44		■	45	46	47
48		■	49				■	50		
51		■	52				■	53		

Categories

For each of the categories listed can you think of a word or phrase beginning with each letter on the left? Count one point for each correct answer. A score of 15 is good, and 21 is excellent. **Our solutions on page 342**

	TOOLS	HORSES	GEORGIA CITIES	TREES	CAREERS
C					
L					
A					
M					
P					

Secret Word

Discover the 5-letter Secret Words by the process of elimination and deduction. Fill in the blanks with the 5-letter answers to the clues. The number in parentheses next to each answer tells you how many of the letters in that word are also in the Secret Word. A zero next to an answer indicates that none of the letters in that word is in the Secret Word. After you have determined the correct five letters, rearrange them to form the Secret Word. No letter is repeated in any Secret Word or within any answer word. The first letters of the answers, reading down, spell out a hint to the Secret Word.

Solutions on page 343

1. Secret Word ☐☐☐☐☐

Small rodent _____ (1)
Worrier's ailment _____ (2)
Blaze _____ (2)
Redden _____ (2)
Citrus fruit _____ (0)
Deserves _____ (3)
Western farm _____ (3)

2. Secret Word ☐☐☐☐☐

Shoulder gesture _____ (3)
Prowls _____ (3)
Ahead of time _____ (1)
Male duck _____ (1)
Affairs of honor _____ (2)
More mature _____ (0)
Magnificence _____ (1)

3. Secret Word ☐☐☐☐☐

Farm workers _____ (1)
Metropolitan _____ (0)
Soda sipper _____ (2)
Makes beer _____ (3)
Turn aside _____ (2)
Artless _____ (3)
Sink outlet _____ (1)
Bush _____ (1)

4. Secret Word ☐☐☐☐☐

Dried plum _____ (2)
Wrangle _____ (3)
Drive forward _____ (2)
Asian kingdom _____ (2)
Fork prongs _____ (0)
Likeness _____ (2)
Hospital worker _____ (2)
Visitor _____ (1)

5. Secret Word ☐☐☐☐☐

Sugar tree _____ (2)
Unskillful _____ (3)
Cacophonous _____ (2)
Grin _____ (2)
Ordeal _____ (1)
Drizzly _____ (0)
Vacant _____ (3)
Memorize _____ (1)
Tyrant Legree _____ (2)

6. Secret Word ☐☐☐☐☐

Sleep sound _____ (3)
Looking at _____ (2)
Zoo enclosures _____ (0)
Sea _____ (2)
Desert wanderer _____ (3)
Sediment _____ (1)
Modify _____ (2)
Goes by car _____ (2)
Long for _____ (2)

PICTURE THIS

You do not need any special art training to produce a picture in the empty grid. Use the letter-number guide above each square and carefully draw what is shown into the corresponding square in the grid.

Solution on page 343

A-8	B-9	C-8	D-6	E-4	F-3	G-2	G-10
A-9	B-10	C-9	D-7	E-5	F-4	G-3	H-1
A-10	C-2	C-10	D-8	E-6	F-5	G-4	H-2
B-4	C-3	D-1	D-9	E-7	F-6	G-5	H-3
B-5	C-4	D-2	D-10	E-8	F-7	G-6	H-7
B-6	C-5	D-3	E-1	E-9	F-8	G-7	H-8
B-7	C-6	D-4	E-2	F-1	F-9	G-8	H-9
B-8	C-7	D-5	E-3	F-2	G-1	G-9	H-10

	1	2	3	4	5	6	7	8	9	10
A										
B										
C										
D										
E										
F										
G										
H										

CHAIN REACTION

The answer to each clue is a word or phrase formed from two shorter words or syllables. Place the first part of the answer in the link with the corresponding number and the second part in the next link moving clockwise. Links with two numbers use the same word or syllable. The number of letters in each answer is shown in parentheses.

Solution on page 343

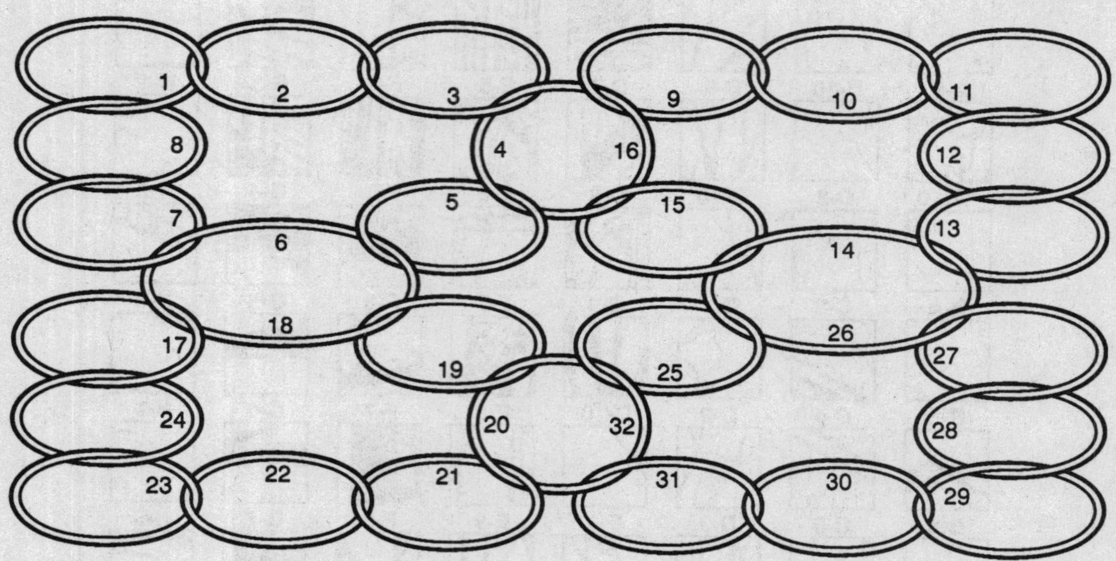

1. Bank customer's register (9)
2. Small paperback (7)
3. Release explosively (6)
4. Extempore (7)
5. Indoor court sport (8)
6. Ink writer (9)
7. Blunt (10)
8. Carte blanche (10)
9. Mr. Namath (11)
10. Snoopy's alter ego (7)
11. Last exercise segment (8)
12. Economic decline (8)
13. Baked pastry (8)
14. Cloudy (8)
15. Discarded item (7)
16. Peripherally of the established theater (11)
17. Umpire's opening shout (8)
18. Stadium (8)
19. Scenic road (7)
20. Shipping document (7)
21. Wallet (8)
22. Magazine insert (7)
23. Exceed socially (8)
24. Student stage production (9)
25. Temporary stop (7)
26. Exceed a bank balance (8)
27. Disadvantage (8)
28. Spine (8)
29. Parched (7)
30. Rehearsal (6)
31. Landing strip (6)
32. Ambush (6)

The entries for this puzzle are given to you, listed alphabetically according to length. Across and Down words are all mixed together, and you are to find their proper places in the diagram.

Solution on page 343

3 Letters
Air
Ami
Ate
Ave
Boa
Cod
Doe
End
Era
Ide
Irk
Les
Mat
Mel
Ode
Ran
Rat
Tar
Tee
Win

4 Letters
Abet
Apes
Area
Aria
Asea
Bulb
Code
Coma
Date
Deep
Dent
Dial
Dote
Edie
Elms
Elsa
Else
Emit
Erie
Erin
Eton
Ever
Evil
Gila
Hail
Hand
Hard
Hate
Helm
Hole
Hope
Idle
Lark
Late
Lave
Loot
Lore
Love
Melt
Mere
Mire
Near
Over
Pain
Pear
Peen
Peer
Pest
Pill
Pine
Pomp
Rapt
Rent
Rest
Roll
Runt
Salt
Sent
Sere
Shop
Slam
Sley
Slip
Smog
Soap
Solo
Stab
Tame
Tamp
Teas
Tine
Tire
To-do
Tole
Tort
Tote
Trio
Trip
Used ✓
Wave

5 Letters
Bared
Elate
Elder
Hedge
Homer
Lames
Petty
Relet
Scent
Slave
Stale
Stare
Tarot
Title

6 Letters
Demote
Gloves
Ideals
Regent
Scheme
Shaped
Tapers
Teeter

7 Letters
Minutes
Perused
Pleaded
Treacle

8 Letters
Bantered
Battered
Glitters
Measures
Positive
Standard
Stranded
Torments

U
S
E
D

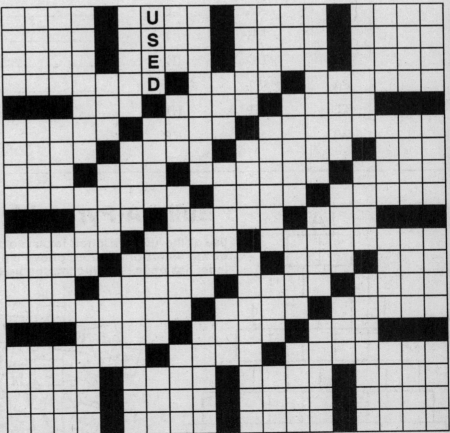

Crackerjacks

Find the answer to the riddle by filling in the center boxes with the letters needed to complete the words across and down. When you have filled in the Crackerjacks, the letters reading across the center boxes from left to right will spell out the riddle answer.

Solution on page 342

RIDDLE: What does a little crybaby eventually become?

	FR	
LE		UE
	ILE	

	ST	
APP		ACH
	NG	

	ALM	
CH		GE
	AC	

	HU	
RO		CE
	ITY	

ANSWER: ____________________

Scrambled Headwear

Match up each pair of letters in column A with pairs from columns B and C to form the names of eight items of headwear. Each letter pair will be used once. Do not switch the order of a pair of letters.

Solution on page 341

A	B	C	
BE	LM	MA	____________
BO	OC	RA	____________
CL	NA	LE	____________
FE	RB	ET	____________
HE	DO	IE	____________
PA	WL	AN	____________
TU	MP	HE	____________
WI	AN	ER	____________

Build-A-Pyramid

Use all the jumbled letters to build a pyramid so that each word contains all the letters of the word above it plus one additional letter. A starting letter has been set in the top square of the diagram.

Our solution on page 342

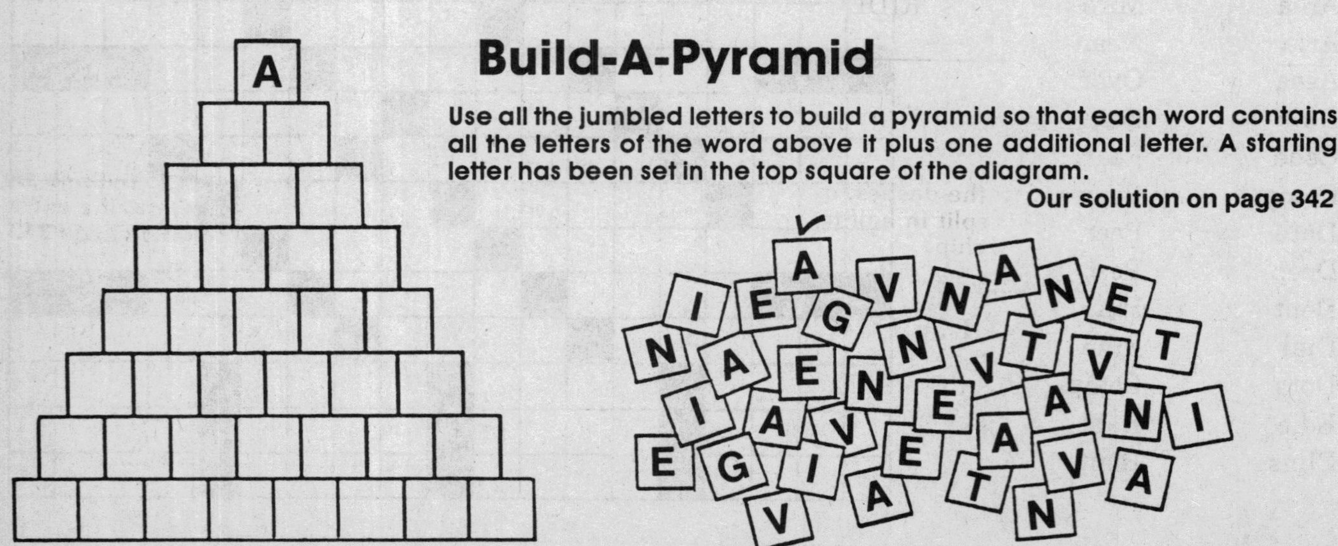

Abacus

Slide the abacus beads on the wires to form five related words reading down. All the beads will be used. Keep in mind that the beads are on wires and cannot jump over one another. An empty abacus is provided for you to work in.

Solution on page 344

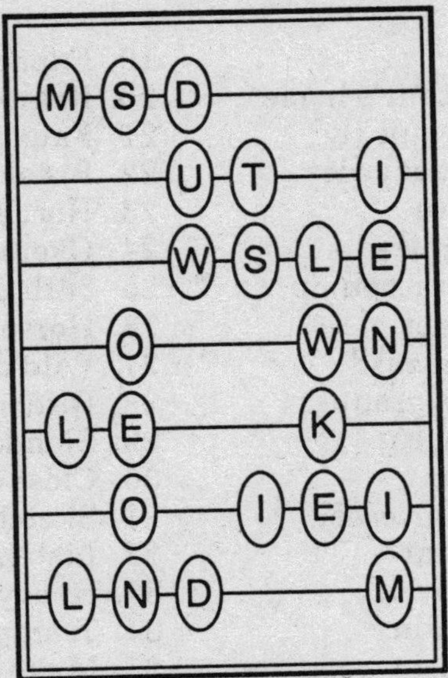

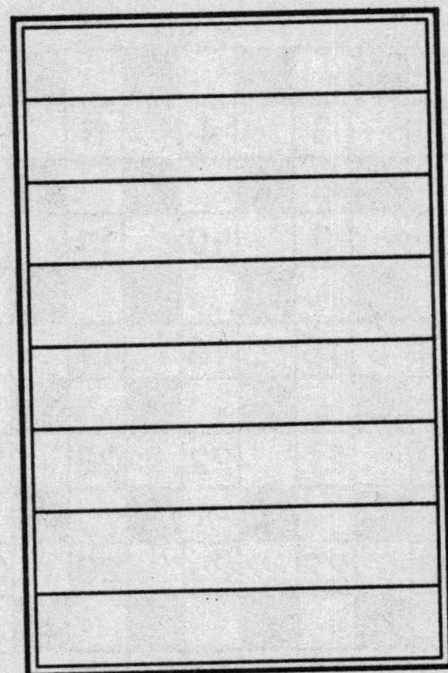

Changaword

Can you change the top word into the bottom word in each column in the number of steps indicated in parentheses? Change only one letter at a time and do not change the order of the letters. Proper names, slang, and obsolete words are not allowed.

Our solutions on page 342

1. MARS (3 steps)	2. BEST (5 steps)	3. PLUM (6 steps)	4. SPAR (7 steps)
HALL	RIDE	PEST	KING

Chips

Place the chips of words on the dashes, one letter per dash, to discover a saying. When a word contains an even number of letters, it is split in half to form two chips. If it contains an odd number of letters, the extra letter is added to the second chip.

Solution on page 343

NATI I HE CONC UR S CLOVER

LEAF WER ONAL T O FLO RETE

_ _ _   _ _ _ _ _ _ _ _ _ _   _ _ _ _ _ _ _ _   _ _ _   _ _ _ _

_ _ _ _ _ _ _ _ _ _   _ _ _ _ _ _ _ _ _ _ _ _

Square Deal

The answer to each definition is a 4-letter word which is to be entered into the four squares surrounding the corresponding number in the diagram. The word can start in any of the four squares and go in a clockwise or counterclockwise direction. The first word, MAZE, has been entered to start you off.

Solution on page 343

	M											
E	1	A	2		3		4		5		6	
	Z											
	7		8		9		10		11		12	
	13		14		15		16		17		18	
	19		20		21		22		23		24	
	25		26		27		28		29		30	
	31		32		33		34		35		36	

CLUES

1. Minotaur's home
2. Move quickly
3. Count calories
4. Chance
5. Recognized
6. Loafer or pump
7. Indolent
8. Golf hazard
9. Sports group
10. Anjou, e.g.
11. Distort
12. Sailing vessel
13. Pennant
14. Turn over
15. Fine rain
16. Ragout
17. Erode
18. Brass instrument
19. Expand
20. Rotate
21. Faux pas
22. Break suddenly
23. Hornet's home
24. Overseer
25. 38th president
26. Horse's foot
27. Wild disorder
28. Difficult
29. Slender
30. Close-fitting
31. Sketch
32. Listen to
33. Heavy book
34. Trampled
35. Make a scarf
36. Supply of money

Linkwords

Add a Linkword to the end of the word on the left and the beginning of the word on the right to form two compound words or phrases. The dashes indicate the number of letters in the Linkword. For example, if the words were PEANUT _ _ _ _ _ _ FLY, the Linkword would be BUTTER (Peanut butter, Butterfly).

Solutions on page 343

1. SWEET _ _ _ SOUP
2. TEXT _ _ _ _ REVIEW
3. CHAIN _ _ _ _ _ _ HEAD
4. SNOW _ _ _ _ SHARE
5. BLUE _ _ _ _ _ OUT
6. HORSE _ _ _ _ SPACE
7. HOUR _ _ _ _ _ CEILING
8. LIGHT _ _ _ _ _ _ BOARD
9. DEEP _ _ _ _ _ _ FRAME
10. WATER _ _ _ _ DOWN
11. STRAW _ _ _ _ _ _ CHILD
12. PARK _ _ _ SIDE

Dart Game

Complete 5-letter words reading outward from the center by placing the given letters correctly in the diagram blanks. Each letter will be used only once. All five words begin with the center letter.

Solution on page 342

B C D H L M N O T V Y

ROUNDABOUT

Go round and Roundabout in clockwise order using the clues to fill in the curving 6-letter words. When the diagram is complete, fill in the numbered boxes below the diagram with the correspondingly numbered letters to discover the answer to the riddle.

Solution on page 344

1-4. Butterfly, e.g.
3-6. Feeling sore
5-8. Strong, sudden flow
7-10. Flee
9-12. "Charlotte's Web" heroine
11-14. Cleared
13-16. Basement
15-18. Family room
17-20. Wasp
19-22. Bailey of the comics
21-24. Pilots
23-2. Scowls

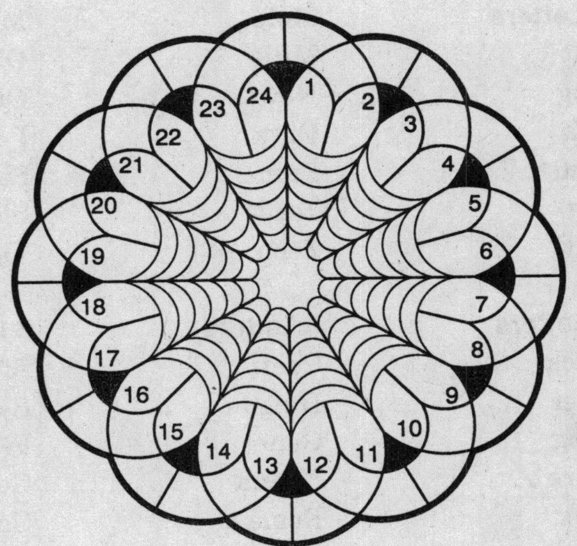

RIDDLE: What was the moth larva living on in the near-empty closet?

3

24	17	5	22	9	20	18	1	11	6

Circle Sums

Each circle, lettered A through I, has its own number value from 1 to 9. No two circles have the same value. The numbers shown in the diagram are the sums of the circles which overlap at those points. For example, 9 is the sum of circles D and E. Can you find the value of each circle?

Solution on page 343

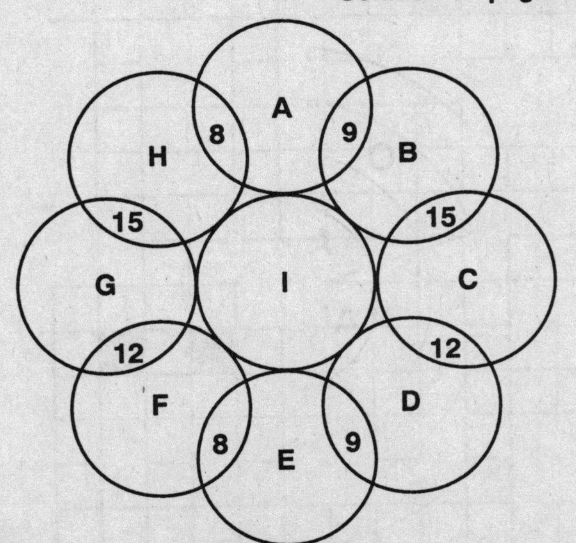

Associations

You can form a chain of associated words by filling in the blanks with the letters listed on the right. Each word you make will be associated in some way with the words above and below it. The initial letters of the words are already in place. Each letter on the right will be used only once.

Solution on page 343

FLOWER	A A A C D
T _ _ _ _ _	E E E E
H _ _ _ _ _ _ _ _	H I K
D _ _ _ _ _	L L L
T _ _ _ _ _	N O P
D _ _ _ _ _ _ _	R R S S
C _ _ _ _	T T T
WALK	U U

Framework 11

Animal Farm

These words are listed in alphabetical order according to length. Fit them into their proper places in the Framework. This puzzle has been started for you with the entry HARE. Now look for a 5-letter entry starting with H. Continue working this way until the puzzle is completed.

Solution on page 337

3 Letters
Cat
Dog
Elk
Gnu
Pig
Rat

4 Letters
Buck
Deer
Frog
Hare ✓
Ibex
Lion
Lynx
Mink
Mole
Mule
Newt
Oryx
Puma
Toad
Zebu

5 Letters
Coati
Dingo
Genet
Hyena
Koala
Lemur
Llama
Moose
Mouse
Okapi
Otter
Panda
Sheep
Sloth
Tiger

6 Letters
Alpaca
Badger
Fennec
Gerbil
Gopher
Iguana
Impala
Jackal
Lizard
Marten
Turtle
Wapiti

7 Letters
Chamois
Giraffe
Lemming
Leopard
Muskrat
Opossum

8 Letters
Antelope
Chipmunk
Elephant
Tortoise

9 Letters
Chameleon
Crocodile
Polar bear
Porcupine

10 Letters
Cacomistle
Jack rabbit
Prairie dog
Timber wolf

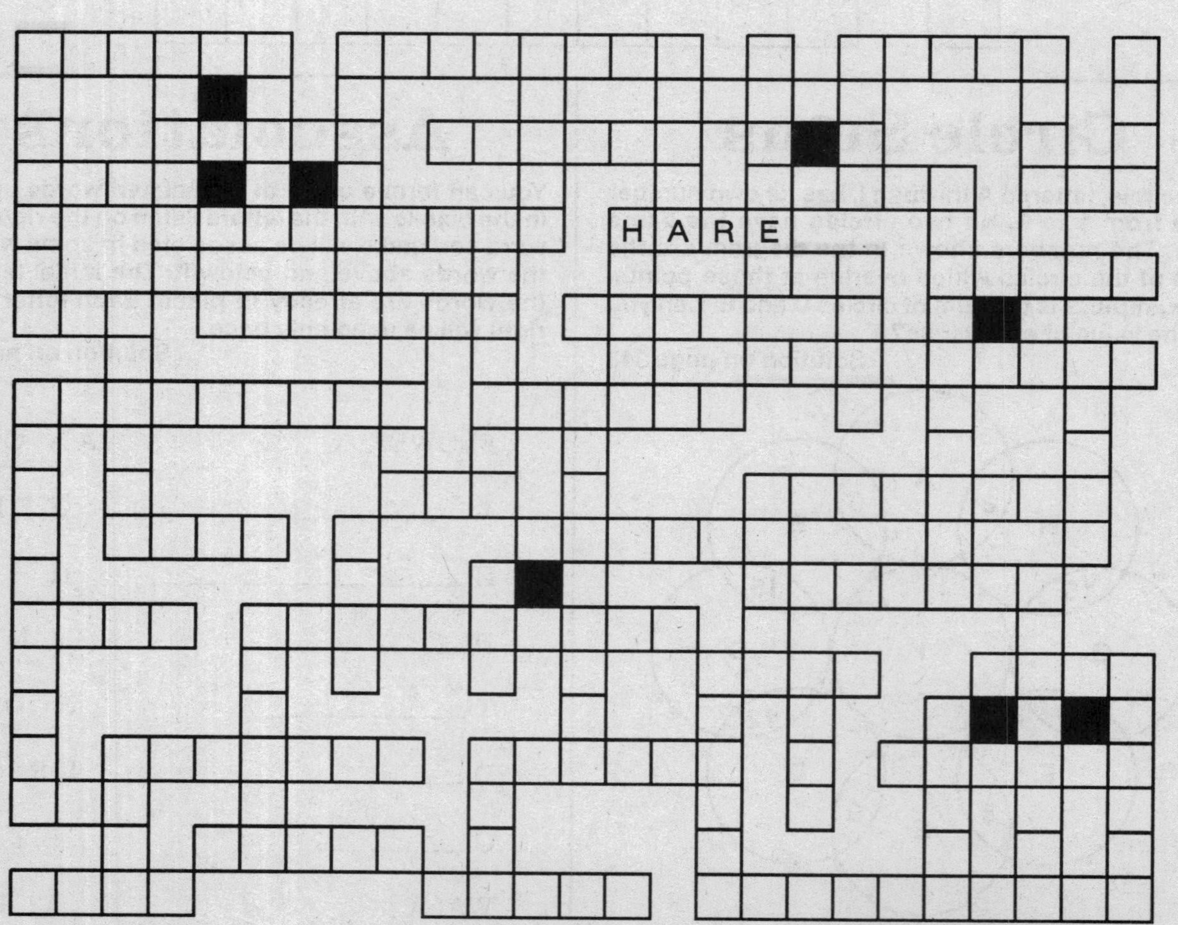

Framework 12

All Sevens

Solution on page 336

Abandon
Angular
Anodyne
Beehive
Bloomed
Destiny
Economy
Extract
Factory

Feather
Flotsam
Flyleaf ✓
Foghorn
Foolish
Hamster
Headset
Impeach
Insurer

Largess
Lottery
Maestro
Midyear
Neither
Pageant
Parasol
Snorkel
Tannery

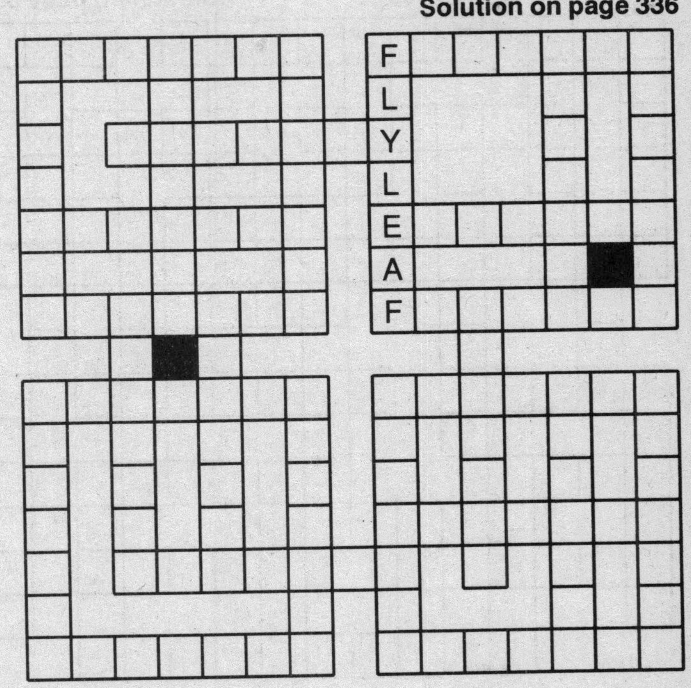

Framework 13

Revelation

When this Framework has been completed, read the circled letters in order from left to right, and they will reveal a bit of wisdom, which can be found on page 334.

First word on page 351

Solution on page 336

3 Letters
Elf
Gal
Nab
One
See

4 Letters
Corn
Kale
Open
Real
Sack

5 Letters
Glare
Kneel
Nerve
Occur
Panic
Rinse
Rouge
Swamp
Sweep
Yells

6 Letters
Canary
Verbal

7 Letters
Adamant
Advance
Cannery
Friends
Obverse
Theater

8 Letters
Fervency
Headrest
Viscount

9 Letters
Crossover
Perforate

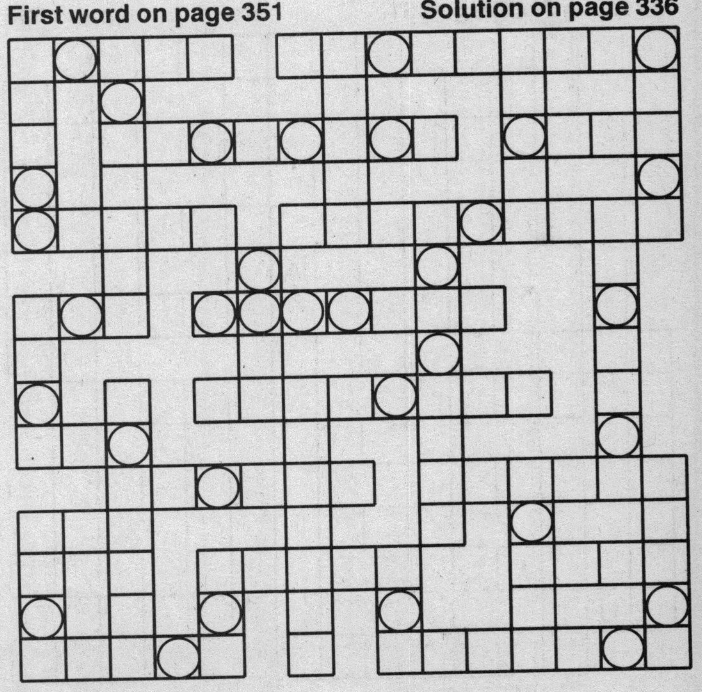

Framework 14

Hold Everything!

First word on page 351 Solution on page 336

3 Letters
Ark
Bag
Egg
Kit
Sac
Tin

4 Letters
Cans
Cart
Case
Cask
Desk
Ewer
Kegs
Oven
Shed
Sled
Till

5 Letters
Chest
Creel
Hooks
Igloo
Nests
Racks

6 Letters
Basket
Beaker
Bucket
Crocks
Dishes
Goblet
Sheath
Stalls

7 Letters
Cistern
Inkwell

8 Letters
Crucible
Decanter
Reticule
Skillets

Framework 15

Missing Vowels

All of the vowels (A, E, I, O, U) are missing from the words listed below. Work back and forth and complete the diagram. The words are in alphabetical order according to length. The word list is given on page 334.

First word on page 351 Solution on page 336

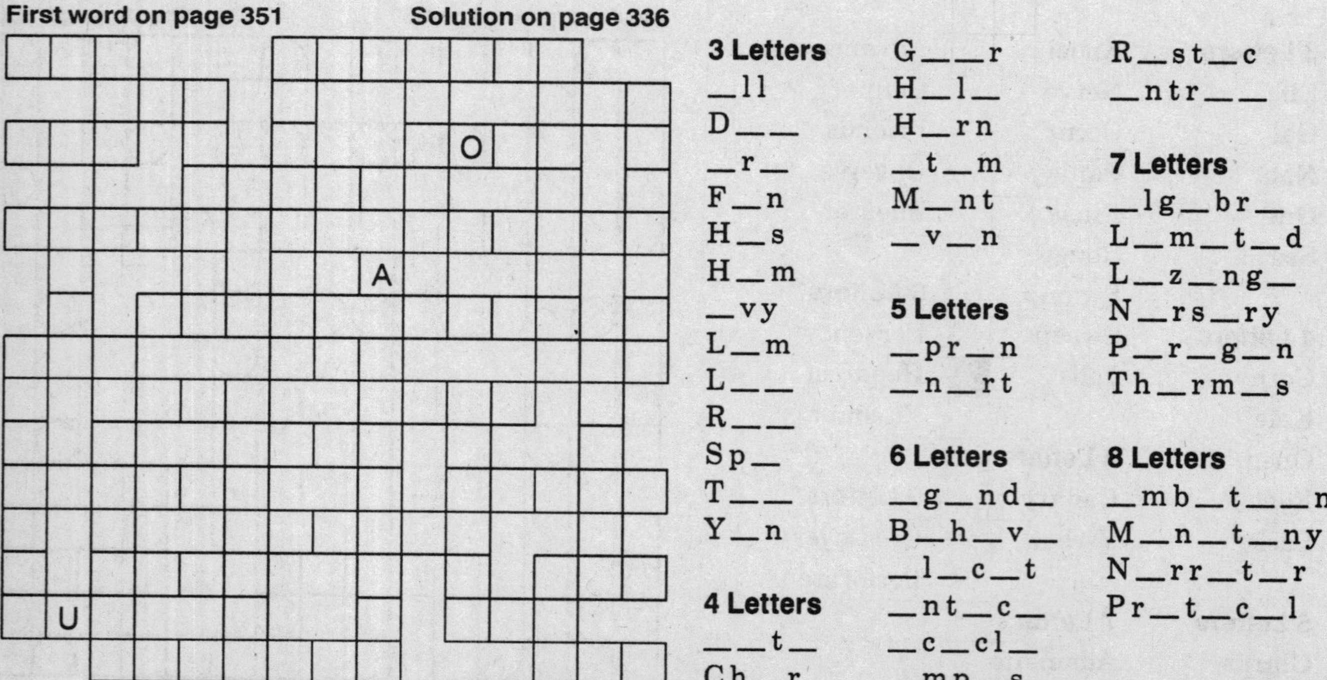

3 Letters
__ll
D__ __
__r__
F__n
H__s
H__m
__vy
L__m
L__ __
R__ __
Sp__
T__ __
Y__n

4 Letters
__ __t__
Ch__r
G__ __r
H__l__
H__rn
__t__m
M__nt
__v__n

5 Letters
__pr__n
__n__rt

6 Letters
__g__nd__
B__h__v__
__l__c__t
__nt__c__
__c__cl__
__mp__s__
R__st__c
__ntr__ __

7 Letters
__lg__br__
L__m__t__d
L__z__ng__
N__rs__ry
P__r__g__n
Th__rm__s

8 Letters
__mb__t__ __n
M__n__t__ny
N__rr__t__r
Pr__t__c__l

Going Up

Framework 16

Our Framework expert needed 19 minutes to complete this puzzle. Your solving time: ______.

3 Letters
Add
Eke
Get

4 Letters
Abet
Edge
Itch
Jump
Lift
Mend
More
Push
Rise

5 Letters
Build
Bulge
Crowd
Heave
Key up
Spree
Swell
Widen

6 Letters
Accrue
Better
Blow up
Crease
Deepen
Dilate
Extend
Gained
Gather
Jack up
Return
Spread
Upturn

7 Letters
Advance
Amplify
Auction
Augment
Auxesis
Balloon
Broaden
Develop
Distend
Enhance
Greaten
Improve
Magnify
Sharpen
Shoot up
Steepen
Thicken
Upsurge
Upswing
Uptrend

8 Letters
Compound
Lengthen
Maximize

9 Letters
Accession
Expansion
Extension
Increment
Intensify
Overladen
Propagate
Redoubles
Reinforce

First word across on page 351

Solution on page 337

Framework 17

Ah, Love!

3 Letters
Awe
End
Hug
Ilk
Low
One
Opt
Sit
Top
Use
Vow
Wed

4 Letters
Abet
Ache
Dare
Eden
Ever
Give
Glow
Hope
Imps
Item
Limp
Long
News
Plan
Play
Rapt
Rich
Rite
Smug
Spin
To-do
Upon
Urge
Wish
Wits
Zeal

5 Letters
Doubt
Elope
Faces
Grace
Groom
Heart
Image
Issue
Mirth
Sighs
Sweet
Tacit
Tower
Unity

6 Letters
Assent
Assure
Candid
Divine
Ideate
Kisses
Narrow
Reason
Simmer
Smiles
Swoons
Truest
Trysts
Vanity

7 Letters
Ballads
Elation
"Our song"
Perfume
Pretend
Romance
Secrets
Serious
Smitten
Snuggle
Sunsets
Undying

8 Letters
Insecure
Pleasure
Presents
Promises
Suspense
Undreamt

9 Letters
Entranced
Honeymoon
Warm words

10 Letters
Attraction
Engagement
Rendezvous

11 Letters
Anniversary
Enchantment
Endearments

First word across on page 351

Solution on page 337

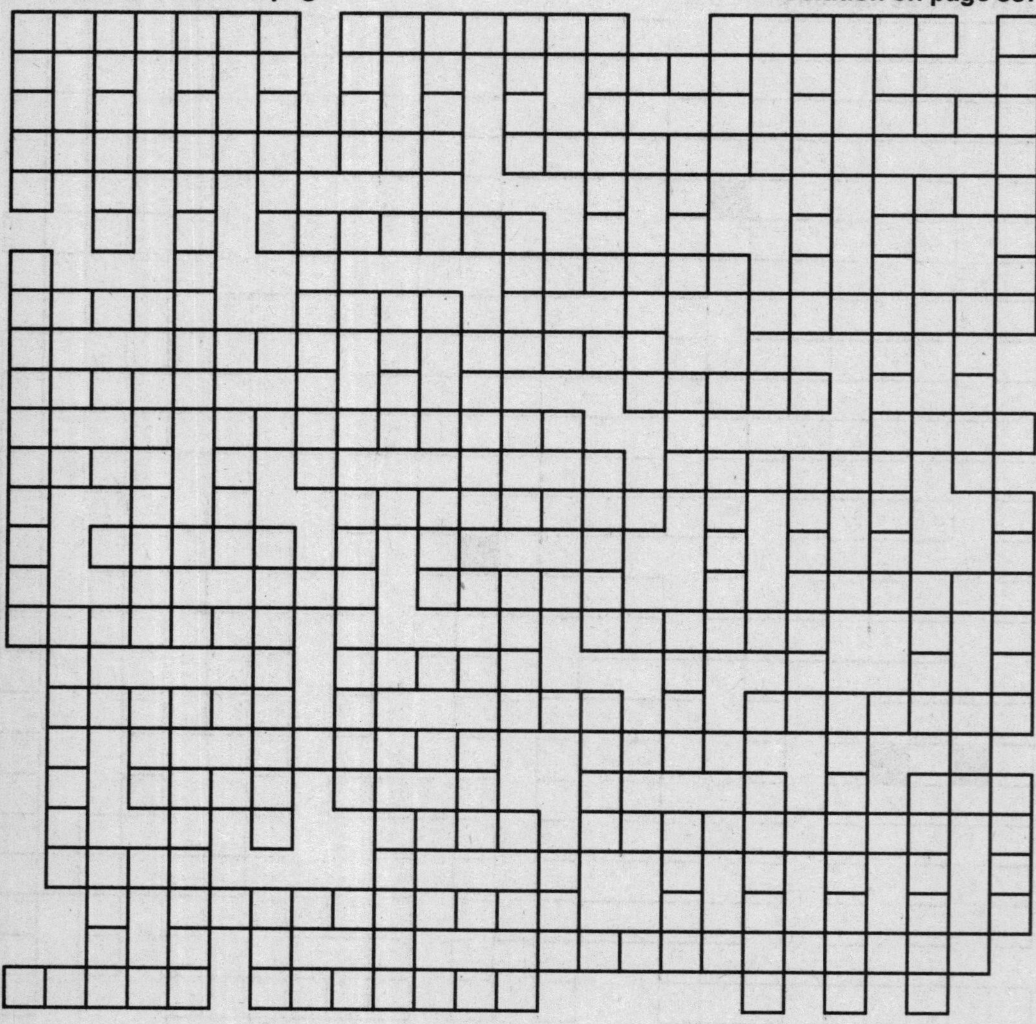

Framework 18

4 Letters
Arts
Exit
Hour
Lots
News
Note
Papa
Rate
Said
Soap
Time
Type
Urge
Vote
Ways

5 Letters
After
Delay
Drive
Early
Earns
Giant
Grade
Heeds
Ideas
Lease
Music
Parts
Pilot
Raise
Refer
Risks
Scene
Style
Terms
Treat
Views
Warms
Years

6 Letters
Action
Awards
Dangle
Option
Orders
Please
Reruns
Rovers
Series
Sports
Summer
System

7 Letters
Actress
Arrange
Classic
Express
Hostess
Insight
Popular
Preview
Reports
Seasons
Selects
Stories
Strange
Success
Traffic
Weather

8 Letters
Channels
Coverage
Identity
Programs
Reporter
Schedule
Sessions
Specials
Sponsors
Starring
Talk show

9 Letters
Absolutes
Adventure
Advertise
Announcer
Excellent
Game shows
Prime time
Represent

First word across on page 351

Solution on page 337

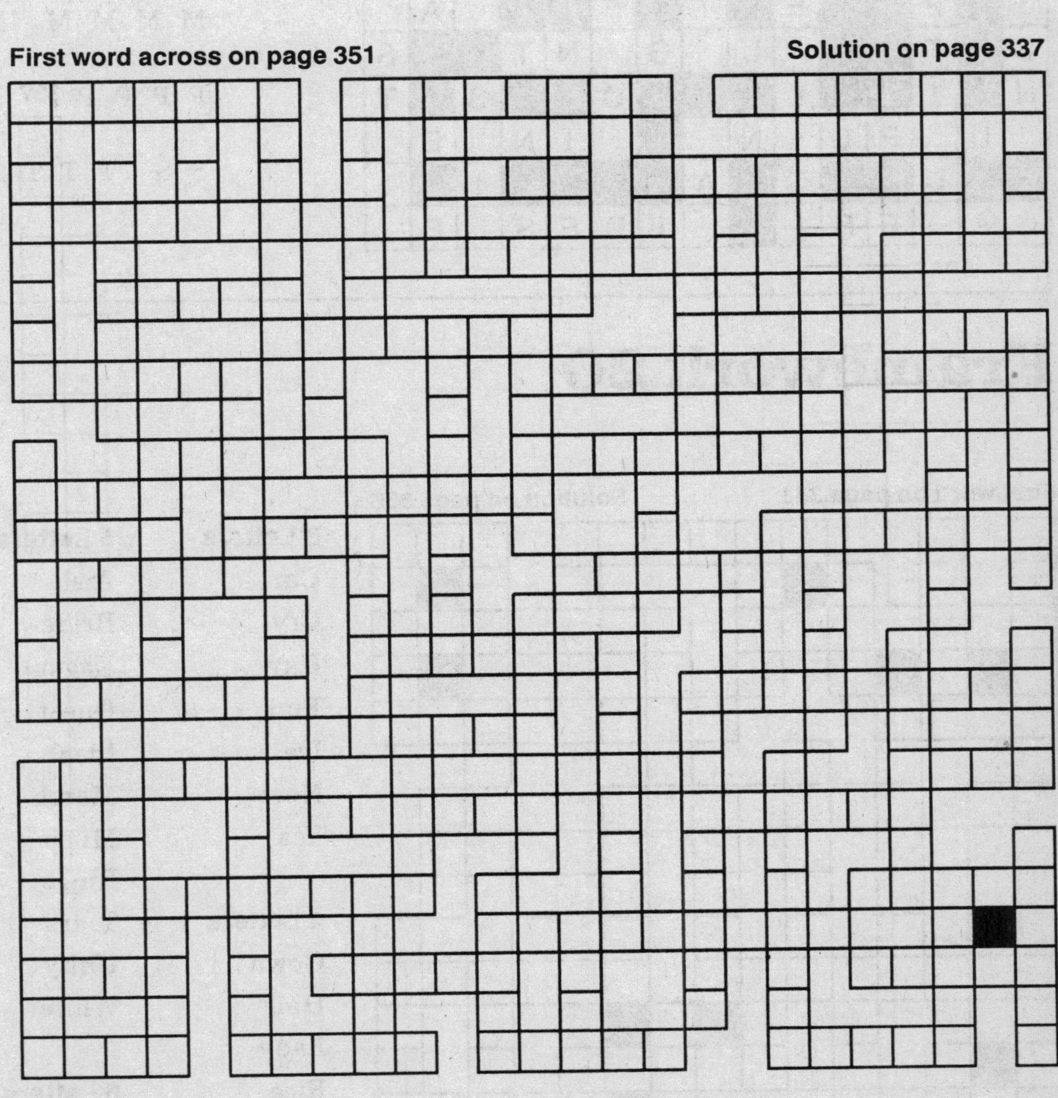

Framework 19

Framelinks

First word on page 351 Solution on page 336

	A	M	P	H		E	T	■		O		I	O	
O	■	■	■	■	E	■	■	■	A	■	R	■	■	E
P	■	■		E		T		N		■		S	E	
	H	I		■	T	■	O	■	■	■	M	■	■	V
O	■	■	A	■	U	■	T	■		M			S	
R	■	■		E		L		I		■	■	C	■	■
	E	A		■	E	■	■	■	P	■	■		L	
■	■	■	O	■	■	■		R		W	E		■	I
	L			E		■	O	■	R	■	■	O	■	L
I	■	P	■	■	E	■	I	■	F	■	■		A	
E	■	T	■	■		U		G		N	T	■	■	S
N	■	I	■	■	L	■	■	■	C	■	■	S	■	T
	U		P	L		N		■		I	N		E	
■	■	U	■	■	C	■	A	■	■	■	■	I	■	I
C	A		E	R		■		I	D	E	S		E	

Fill in the empty squares in the diagram with the given letters. All the words are common words, but the puzzle is harder than it looks.

A A C C C D E E E E

F F G G I I I K L L L

M M M M N N N O O

P P P P P R R R R R

S S T T T T T U W

Framework 20

Weddings Bells

First word on page 351 Solution on page 336

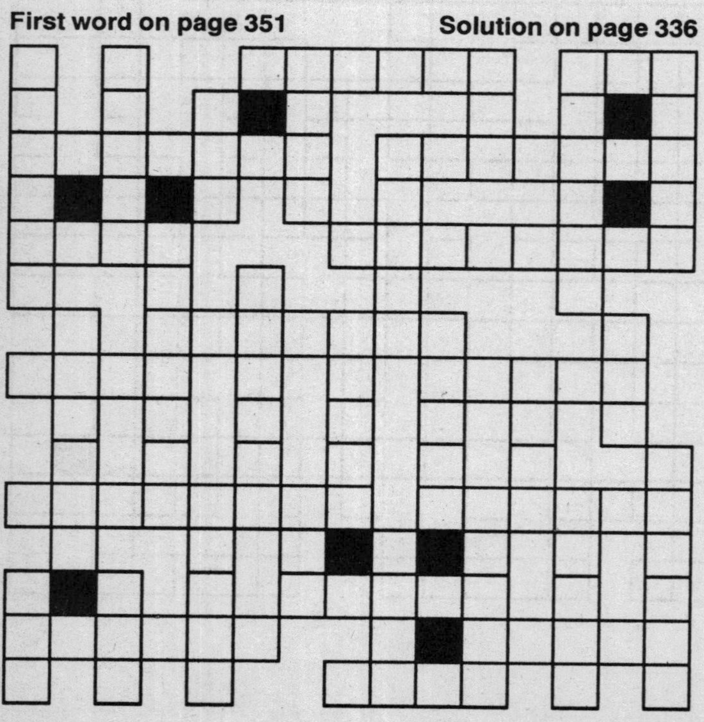

3 Letters
Car
Cry
Day
Fun
Ice
New
Yes

4 Letters
Gown
Hair
Lady
Rice
Veil
Wine

5 Letters
Aisle
Bride
Eager
Guest
Ideal
March
Music
Rings
Tears
Unity
White

6 Letters
Camera
Church
Clergy
Garter
Prayer
Singer
Tuxedo
Ushers

7 Letters
Best man
Bouquet
Embrace
Husband

8 Letters
Ceremony
Pictures

Framework 21

Seeing Red

First word on page 351

Solution on page 336

3 Letters
Ant
Bud
Hot
Ink
Out

4 Letters
Alga
Beet
Cent
Deer
Head
Mite
Snow
Soil
Star
Tape
Tide
Wood
Worm

5 Letters
Alert
Brick
Cedar
Coral
Cross
Osier
Roses
Shank

6 Letters
Clover
Fescue
Letter
Ribbon
Siskin

7 Letters
Blooded
Tanager

8 Letters
Lipstick

10 Letters
Poinsettia
Strawberry

Framework 22

Fiddler's Frame

It will take a little fiddling to solve this special Framework. Two or three letters will go in each box. The words are listed according to the number of boxes they will fill. We have filled in one example.

Solution on page 336

2 Boxes
Allow
Canal
Cared ✓
Class
Cones
Feed
Filly
Ingot
Lien
List
Mete
Moist
Oners
Peers
Pica
Pies
Rated
Tame
Used
Veers

3 Boxes
Angered
Congeal
Connote
Departs
Discus
Errands
Fiesta
Gophers
Greener
Husbands
National
Nuggets
Offered
Ongoing
Primal
Retreat
Scratch

4 Boxes
Animation
Bargained
Greatness
Lowercase
Negative

5 Boxes
Essentially
Incidental
Insinuation
Homestretch
Mennonites
Time-honored

6 Boxes
Consternation
Personalities
Photo finishes

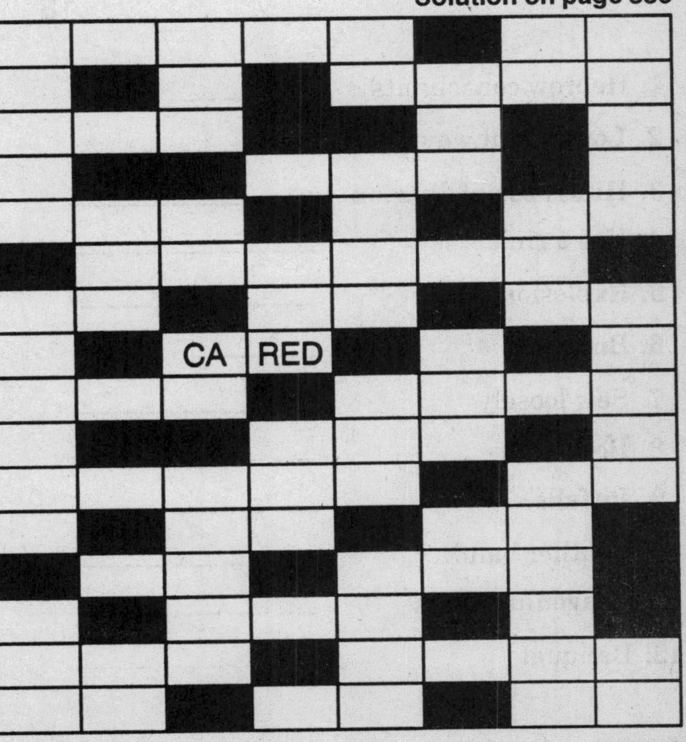

PUZZLE IN THE ROUND

To solve this challenging puzzle first fill in as many of the 5-letter answers next to their clues as you can. Next scramble the order of the letters, look for shared letters, and enter each letter into its correct place in the diagram. The letter in the center will be shared by all the answer words. The unshared letters will go in the outer ring and form the title of a book and its author's name, reading from 1 to 24. **Solution on page 344**

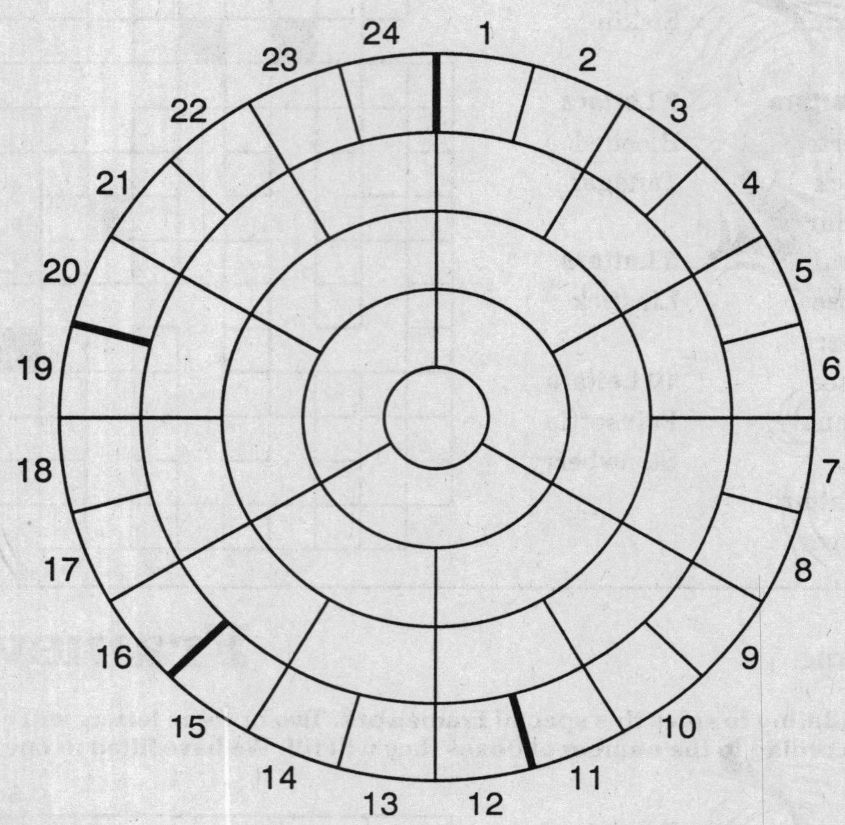

1. Hebrew consonants __ __ __ __ __
2. London subways __ __ __ __ __
3. Hindu social division __ __ __ __ __
4. Use a rink __ __ __ __ __
5. Explosion __ __ __ __ __
6. Brute __ __ __ __ __
7. Sew loosely __ __ __ __ __
8. Bother __ __ __ __ __
9. Pitfalls __ __ __ __ __
10. Leather band __ __ __ __ __
11. Leavening agent __ __ __ __ __
12. Banquet __ __ __ __ __
13. Raccoon's kin __ __ __ __ __
14. Poem division __ __ __ __ __
15. Intone __ __ __ __ __
16. One's equal __ __ __ __ __
17. Winged __ __ __ __ __
18. Procrastinator's motto __ __ __ __ __
19. Porterhouse __ __ __ __ __
20. Aesthetic sense __ __ __ __ __
21. Hurled __ __ __ __ __
22. Core __ __ __ __ __
23. Fatigued __ __ __ __ __
24. Prevailing tendency __ __ __ __ __

MATCH-UP

Can you find the two pictures that are identical?
Solution on page 343

SPIDER'S WEB

Rearrange the 4-letter answer to each clue on the left to form a 5-letter word ending with the center letter R. Place the 5-letter word in the Spider's Web at the corresponding number, reading inward. Each 5-letter word answers one of the clues on the right. For example, the answer to the first clue is NOSE. Rearrange these letters, add the given letter R, and form the 5-letter word SENOR, which is the answer to clue e. When completed, the outer ring of the web, reading from 1 to 18, will spell out the name of a major European port.

Solution on page 343

4-Letter Words

1. Snout
2. Apportion
3. Desert feature
4. Middle Eastern bread
5. Offspring
6. Layer
7. Whine
8. Milky gem
9. Vessel
10. Took the bus
11. Prong
12. Youth
13. Quality of sound
14. Ruminant
15. Pack animal
16. Swine
17. Average
18. Sphere

5-Letter Words

a. Drum
b. Down ____ (Australia)
c. Appointer
d. Come in
e. Spanish gentleman
f. Everglades denizen
g. Hoglike animal
h. Nocturnal mammal
i. More mature
j. Banish
k. Stately house
l. Employer
m. Command
n. Arctic bear
o. Transcriber
p. Celebrity
q. Ann ____, Michigan
r. Saltpeter

CRYPTIC GEOGRAPHY

A map of the United States is given below; the stars show the locations of two places. The names of the places and some interesting information about them are given in substitution codes (different letters are substituted for the correct ones). The code for each one is different. **Solutions on page 344**

1.

P B W V D W D

(place)

V L A   W D P A   " P B W V D W D "   N B P A X   Q S B P   D   X G D W T X L   R B S U   P A D W T W Z   " P B M W V D T W B M X . "   V L A   P B M W V D T W X   N B W V D T W A U   D   R A D H V L   B Q   Z B H U   D W U   X T H E A S ,   R L T N L   Z D E A   V L A   X V D V A   T V X   W T N C W D P A ,   " V L A   V S A D X M S A   X V D V A . "

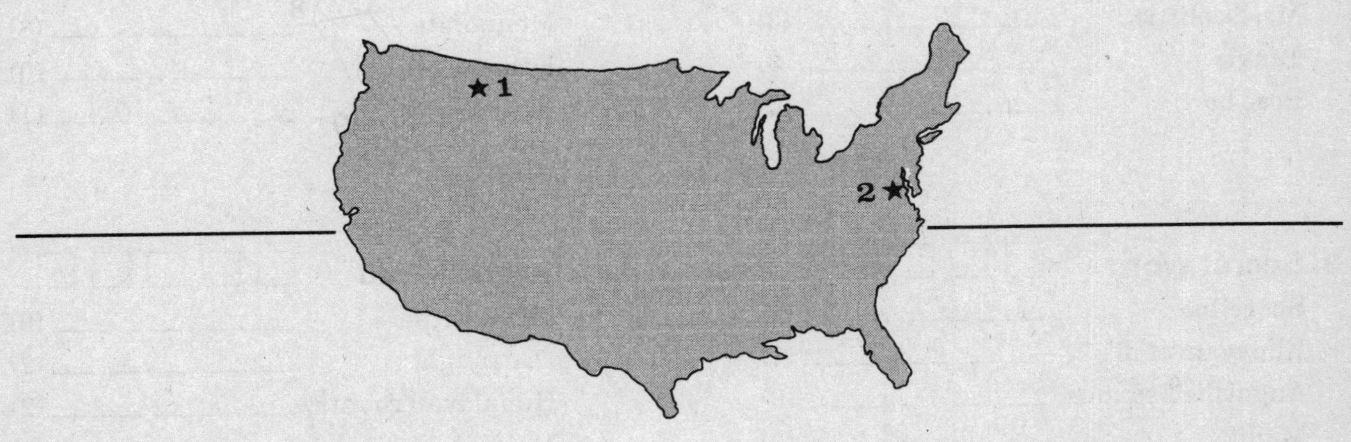

2.

T L C W D X M B G X ,   J . Y .

(place)

B W D C   Y D B R   T L C   J Z C D M X Z J   L X J   P L D J   G S B   N Z I G U Z   B W Z   I D U C B   N S D P J D X M C   T Z U Z   Z U Z Y B Z J .   M Z G U M Z   T L C W D X M B G X   Y W G C Z   B W Z   Z F L Y B   C V G B   L X J   W D U Z J   H L Q G U   V D Z U U Z   P ' Z X I L X B   B G   J U L T   V P L X C   I G U   B W Z   Y D B R .   B W Z   C B U Z Z B C   I G U H   C O S L U Z C   P D A Z   L   Y W Z Y A Z U N G L U J .   H L Q G U   L K Z X S Z C   J D L M G X L P P R   Y U D C C Y U G C C   B W D C   J Z C D M X ,   P Z L J D X M   B G   B W Z   Y Z X B Z U C   G I   M G K Z U X H Z X B   P D A Z   C V G A Z C   D X   L   T W Z Z P .

Discover the 5-letter Secret Words by the process of elimination and deduction. Fill in the blanks with the 5-letter answers to the clues. The number in parentheses next to each answer tells you how many of the letters in that word are also in the Secret Word. A zero next to an answer indicates that none of the letters in that word is in the Secret Word. After you have determined the correct five letters, rearrange them to form the Secret Word. No letter is repeated in any Secret Word or within any answer word. The first letters of the answers, reading down, spell out a hint to the Secret Word.

Solutions on page 344

1. Secret Word ☐☐☐☐☐

Group of twelve _ _ _ _ _ (1)
Thoughts _ _ _ _ _ (3)
Change gears _ _ _ _ _ (2)
Lift _ _ _ _ _ (1)
Many times _ _ _ _ _ (2)
Clamor _ _ _ _ _ (2)
Ms. Doolittle _ _ _ _ _ (3)
Tangle _ _ _ _ _ (3)
Rose barb _ _ _ _ _ (0)

2. Secret Word ☐☐☐☐☐

New _ _ _ _ _ (2)
Pains _ _ _ _ _ (3)
Hit _ _ _ _ _ (1)
Tribal leader _ _ _ _ _ (2)
Peruvian peoples _ _ _ _ _ (2)
Comes close to _ _ _ _ _ (2)
Mennonite _ _ _ _ _ (3)
Fork parts _ _ _ _ _ (0)
Radiates _ _ _ _ _ (1)

3. Secret Word ☐☐☐☐☐

Shoreline _ _ _ _ _ (1)
Khayyam et al. _ _ _ _ _ (1)
Anguished sounds _ _ _ _ _ (0)
Might _ _ _ _ _ (3)
Proprietor _ _ _ _ _ (3)
Canonized one _ _ _ _ _ (2)
Heroic poems _ _ _ _ _ (2)

4. Secret Word ☐☐☐☐☐

Mix together _ _ _ _ _ (0)
Distraught _ _ _ _ _ (2)
Himalayan country _ _ _ _ _ (2)
Mallards, e.g. _ _ _ _ _ (3)
Lies hidden _ _ _ _ _ (2)
Ferber et al. _ _ _ _ _ (2)
Scour _ _ _ _ _ (2)

5. Secret Word ☐☐☐☐☐

Unclear _ _ _ _ _ (1)
Ward off _ _ _ _ _ (2)
Poe's bird _ _ _ _ _ (2)
Compass direction _ _ _ _ _ (2)
Metal bar _ _ _ _ _ (3)
English county _ _ _ _ _ (2)
Hang in the air _ _ _ _ _ (0)

6. Secret Word ☐☐☐☐☐

Formally give _ _ _ _ _ (2)
African antelope _ _ _ _ _ (2)
Of high birth _ _ _ _ _ (2)
Rye fungus _ _ _ _ _ (2)
Governed _ _ _ _ _ (2)
More competent _ _ _ _ _ (3)
Spring forward _ _ _ _ _ (0)

BRICK BY BRICK

Rearrange this stack of bricks to form a crossword puzzle. The clues will help you fit the bricks into their correct places. Row 1 has been filled in for you. Use the bricks to fill in the remaining spaces.

Solution on page 344

ACROSS

1. Clerical garments
 Actor George ____
 Vex
2. Trim
 Dodge
 Actor Jannings
3. Vanishes
 Agile
4. Cognizant
 Catch
5. Pealed
 Nationality suffix
6. Hindu incarnation
 John ____ Passos
 Fast plane
7. Inscribed
 Toward the left
 Baden Baden, e.g.
8. Novelist Anne ____
 "A Bell for ____"
 Wharf
9. "Man ____ Fool"
 Fight site
 Facade
10. Vietnamese holiday
 Garden plot
 Ability
11. Debtor's letters
 Smack
12. Small beards
 Incensed
13. Fluff
 Burn completely
14. "Dies ____"
 TV's Arledge
 And others: abbr.
15. Building wings
 Colorado's ____ Park
 Information

DOWN

1. Orangutan, e.g.
 Court order
 Golf situation
2. Volcano's output
 Spring up
 Young woman
3. Excellent, in Dundee
 Of an occupation
4. Divide
 Joyce Carol ____
5. Speechify
 Border on
6. Evening love song
 "Butterflies ____ Free"
 Shamrock land
7. A Gabor
 Rated
 Son of Seth
8. Fence doorway
 Peter ____
 Aberdeen native
9. Arabian gulf
 "The 39 Steps" star and family
 Feminine name suffix
10. Minus
 Gold, to Juan
 Skirt styles
11. Cozy home
 Signal light
12. Buttes' kin
 Readied
13. Vague awareness
 So long, in London
14. Conflagration
 Exhausted
 Coup d'____
15. Insect pest
 Acidic-tasting
 Guido's high note

BRICKS

ALE / LAP	E■E / S■S	ES■ / NCI	RE■ / E■■	OS■ / RT■
IER / ONT	VAD / ATE	TAL / ATA	E■A / ■AR	ATE / T■I
■BE / OU■	■AW / ■■■	PAR / EVA	IRA / NER	ATA / TE■
ARE / RAN	R■D / APO	IRA / ELL	RIC / ISA	DAN / ENA
OON / STE	E■E / S■D	D■T / ■■S	■EN / G■■	NT■ / ■■■
E■R / S■E	SST / SPA	SNA / ■ES	TET / ■■I	■GO / LIN
■AV / WRO	E■E / POR	O■P / ■FR	TE■ / ATE	MIL / PRY

DIAGRAM

	1	2	3	4	5	6	7	8	9	10	11	12	13	14	15
1	A	L	B	S	■	S	E	G	A	L	■	M	I	F	F
2															
3															
4															
5															
6															
7															
8															
9															
10															
11															
12															
13															
14															
15															

LOGIC PROBLEM

HUDSON VALLEY CINEMA

The Hudson Valley Mall celebrated the opening of its five-theater cinema last night with a showing of five classics. A different movie was shown in each of the theaters, which are numbered 1 through 5. Among the many people who took advantage of the free showing were five married couples, each of whom watched a different movie. From the information provided, determine the woman and man who compose each couple, the movie each couple watched, and the theater in which each movie was shown.

1. The movie Thelma watched was shown in a higher-numbered theater than that showing the movie Trevor watched.
2. Sheena (whose husband isn't Neville) sat in a theater with a higher number than the one in which *Marian's Baby* was shown.
3. Liz watched *Psychic*, which wasn't shown in Theater 3.
4. Neither Sheena nor Valerie watched *The Roman* (which was shown in Theater 2).
5. Madge (who didn't watch *The Glob*) sat in a theater whose number was two higher than the one in which Albert sat but lower than the one in which *The Smiling* was shown.
6. Cyril sat in a theater numbered exactly one lower than the theater in which Fraser sat.

This chart is to help you record information from the clues as well as the facts you deduce by combining information from different clues. We suggest you use an "X" for a "no" and a "•" for a "yes."

		MAN					MOVIE					THEATER				
		ALBERT	CYRIL	FRASER	NEVILLE	TREVOR	MARIAN'S BABY	PSYCHIC	THE GLOB	THE ROMAN	THE SMILING	1	2	3	4	5
WOMAN	LIZ															
	MADGE															
	SHEENA															
	THELMA															
	VALERIE															
THEATER	1															
	2															
	3															
	4															
	5															
MOVIE	MARIAN'S BABY															
	PSYCHIC															
	THE GLOB															
	THE ROMAN															
	THE SMILING															

Solution on page 343

SYL´´LA-CROS´TIC

The directions for solving are given on page 34. Solution on page 344

✻ SYLLABOX ✻

A A ~~A~~ AN AS BAN BE CEL CEN CLE DI DINE DREW EC FA FAR FOOL GERED GI ~~HOL~~ I I ~~IC~~ IL IN ISH ISH IT LA LET LI LI LIST LON ME MIN NE NEP NI NO O O O OR OUS RAN REG RI RI RIGHT RO ROUS RUS SA SCAR SEAU SI SURE TA TAC TAU TER TES TU TUNE U UP VIEW WA ~~WORK~~

1. Jack, the dull boy (4) W O R K A H O L I C
2. Antiseptic (3) _ _ _ _ _ _
3. Extremely wicked (4) _ _ _ _ _ _ _ _ _
4. Zodiac bull (2) _ _ _ _ _ _
5. The Preacher in the Old Testament (5) _ _ _ _ _ _ _ _ _ _ _ _
6. Lover (3) _ _ _ _ _
7. African hunt (3) _ _ _ _ _ _
8. Meeting with a job seeker (3) _ _ _ _ _ _ _ _ _
9. Reproval (2) _ _ _ _ _ _ _
10. Synthetic fabric (2) _ _ _ _ _
11. Honorable (2) _ _ _ _ _ _ _
12. West African republic (4) _ _ _ _ _ _ _ _ _
13. Lessen (3) _ _ _ _ _ _ _ _
14. God of the sea (2) _ _ _ _ _ _ _
15. Large spider (4) _ _ _ _ _ _ _ _ _
16. Laid odds (2) _ _ _ _ _ _ _
17. President Jackson (2) _ _ _ _ _ _
18. Urbana students (3) _ _ _ _ _ _
19. Understood (2) _ _ _ _ _
20. Unwise (2) _ _ _ _ _ _ _
21. Pizza herb (4) _ _ _ _ _ _ _
22. French philosopher (2) _ _ _ _ _ _ _ _
23. Bright red (2) _ _ _ _ _ _ _
24. West African river (3) _ _ _ _ _ _
25. String player (2) _ _ _ _ _ _ _

DIAGRAMLESS FILL-IN

For this fill-in puzzle we have given you all of the E's that appear in the diagram, but none of the black squares. As you solve the puzzle remember to put a black square at the beginning and end of each answer and to balance each black square with its symmetrical counterpart on the opposite side of the diagram.

Solution on page 343

3 Letters
Ago
Air
Alt
Arc
Asp
Ass
Baa
Ban
Cot
Gin
Got
Hen
Hoe
Ill
Ney
Nit
Nob
Own
Sea
Toe
Try
Val

4 Letters
Abut
Agar
Ague
Alop
Anet
Area
Brag
Drew
Elba
Erle
Evil
Fred
Halo
Hear
Herd
Iago
Idle
Iles
Iris
Lama
Lamb
Lisa
Mash
Note
Ogre
Opah
Papa
Ream
Rely
Scow
Silt
Slap
Slat
Slur
Stoa
Stow
Tear
Till
Tsar
Tuba
Ugli
Vial
Weep
Yalu

5 Letters
Alibi
Boffo
Carat
Delta
Ebsen
Endue
Etape
Float
Isles
Lento
Maria
Muses
Ogive
Ovolo
Poilu
Prior
Sauna
Strap
Vales

6 Letters
Ardent
Behalf
Lapdog
Launch
Oporto
Parish
Terror
Wraith

9 Letters
Finlandia

10 Letters
Attraction
Distraught

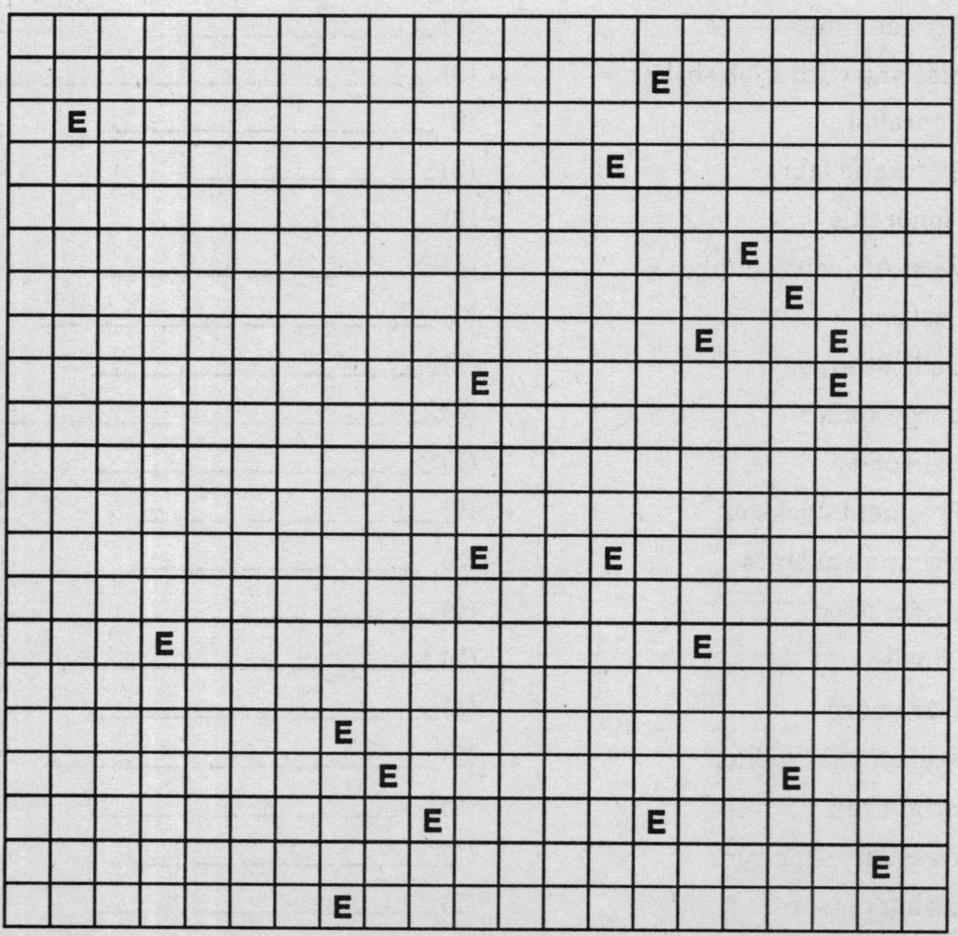

BOWL GAME

To bowl a strike (20 points) you must create a 10-letter word using all the letters in each pin. The letter on top in the pin is the first letter of the strike word. To bowl a spare (10 points) use the same 10 letters to form two words. Splits are not allowed: you may not divide the strike to form a spare. For example, SWEETHEART may not become SWEET and HEART.

Our solutions with a perfect score of 300 points on page 343

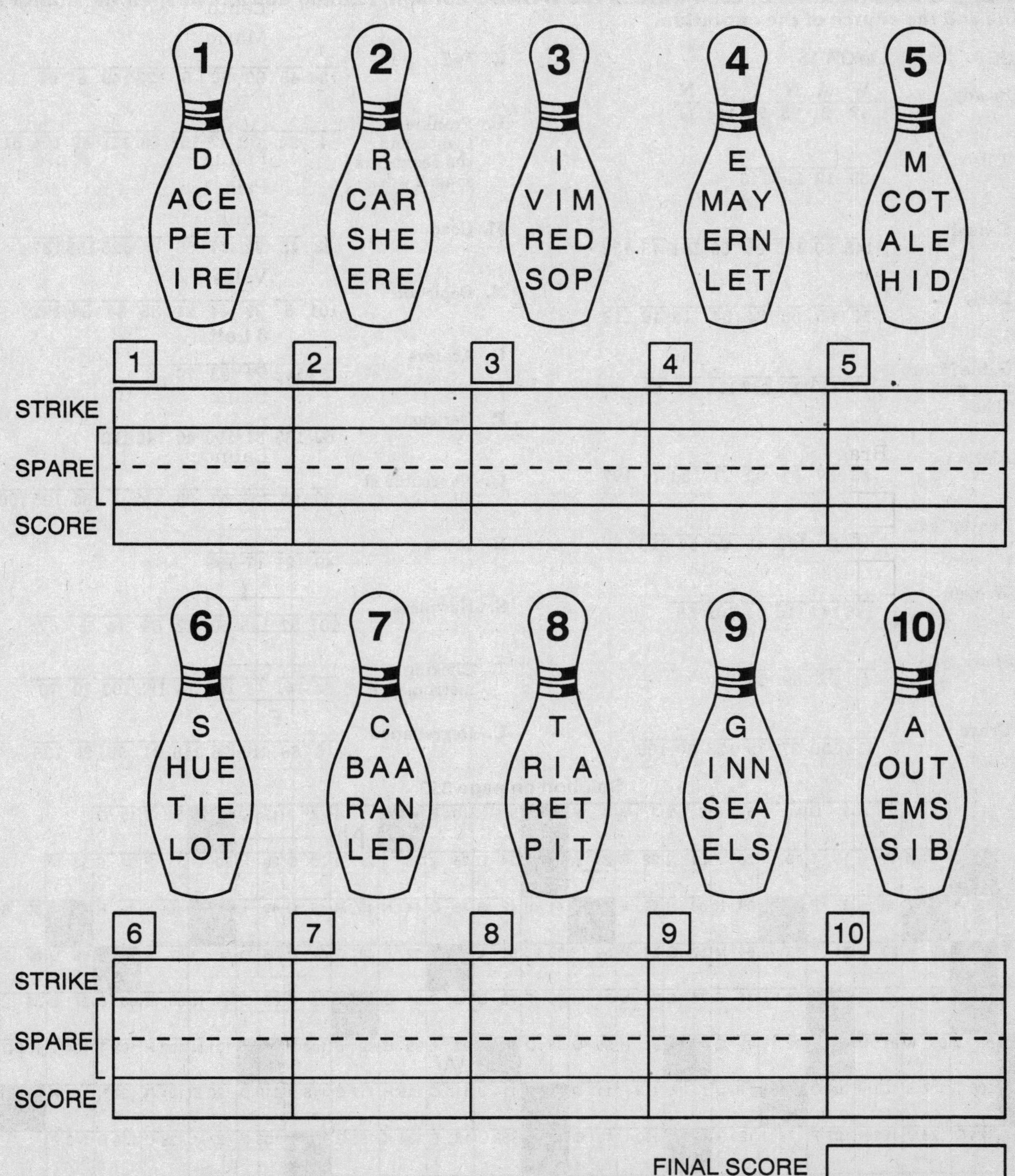

FINAL SCORE

Crostic Puzzle 7

Use the CLUES on the left to fill in the WORDS column. Then transfer each letter to the correspondingly numbered square in the diagram. (We have inserted WORD A as an example.) It is not necessary to know all the words to start solving. Work back and forth from the diagram to the WORDS column until both are filled. A black square indicates the end of a word. The completed diagram will contain a quotation, and the first letter of each word in the WORDS column, reading down, will spell the author's name and the source of the quotation.

CLUES	WORDS
A. Bawdy	W A N T O N 97 2 35 23 144 11
B. Tills	39 12 117 146
C. Casual	143 80 115 98 66 151 43 132
D. Burly	13 95 86 24 64 113 46 119
E. Gable/Monroe film, with "The"	75 120 10 148 154 32 85
F. Alarm	82 37 51 99 71 136 78 127
G. Denver team	15 30 135 81 42 55 129
H. Weaken	126 147 116 94 102 58
I. Shark type	41 92 59 26
J. Grave	114 150 27 19 128 60 108
K. Fed	134 48 90 20 9 123 149 8 52
L. Frankie Lymon and the Teenagers song: 2 wds.	4 34 130 47 156 88 111 89 104 61
M. Goad	33 45 72 77 56 7 125 155 137
N. Depiction	101 6 29 44 21 38 84 36 122
O. Achieve	152 142 28 63 79 3
P. Derision	62 133 31 100 40 140 112
Q. No trouble at all	96 93 131 57 83 124 1 65 105 109
R. Dress	49 121 17 139
S. Harmless	107 87 145 50 22 69 74 5 67
T. Clicking instruments	54 141 18 106 14 153 103 70 73
U. Degradation	16 68 110 76 118 91 53 25 138

Solution on page 353

		1 Q	2 A A	3 O	4 L	5 S	6 N	7 M	8 K	■	9 K	10 E	■	11 A N	12 B	13 D	■	14 T	15 G		
	■	16 U	17 R	18 T	19 J	20 K	21 N	22 S	23 A T	■	24 D	25 U	26 I	27 J	28 O	29 N	30 G	31 P	32 E	33 M	
34 L	35 A N	■	36 N	37 F	■	38 N	39 B	40 P	■	41 I	42 G	43 C	44 N	45 M	46 D	47 L	■	48 K	49 R	■	50 S
51 F	■	52 K	53 U	54 T	55 G	56 M	57 Q	58 H	59 I	60 J	61 L	■	62 P	63 O	64 D	65 Q	66 C	67 S	■	68 U	69 S
70 T	■	71 F	72 M	■	73 T	74 S	75 E	76 U	77 M	78 F	79 O	80 C	81 G	■	82 F	83 Q	84 N	85 E	86 D	87 S	88 L
■	89 L	90 K	91 U	■	92 I	93 Q	■	94 H	95 D	96 Q	■	97 A W	98 C	99 F	100 P	■	101 N	102 H	103 T	104 L	105 Q
■	106 T	107 S	108 J	109 Q	■	110 U	111 L	112 P	113 D	■	114 J	115 C	116 H	117 B	118 U	119 D	120 E	121 R	122 N	123 K	■
	124 Q	125 M	126 H	127 F	128 J	129 G	■	130 L	131 Q	■	132 C	133 P	134 K	135 G	■	136 F	137 M	138 U	139 R	140 P	
		141 T	142 O	143 C	144 A O	145 S	146 B	■	147 H	148 E	■	149 K	150 J	151 C	152 O	153 T	154 E	155 M	156 L		

Crostic Puzzle 8

A. Father of Pocahontas — 22 175 8 18 149 108 126 196

B. Fixed — 166 180 145 143 50 44 30 20 193 81

C. Captors — 69 150 113 43 4 146 16 52 67 107

D. Brightens up — 106 120 78 144 95 71 170 98 25

E. Magna Carta site — 84 122 118 21 7 186 183 101 168

F. Praising highly — 100 3 88 73 109 77 167 189 155 178

G. Dabbler — 131 179 91 154 42 72 28 177 57 114

H. Friendliness — 185 104 53 164 139 194 6 82 64 34

I. Love of self — 11 158 127 17 105 169 27 200 2 37

J. Rich: 3 wds. — 40 112 103 116 10 19 128 39 75 89

K. Security device: 2 wds. — 124 172 174 80 115 159 23 32 192 65

L. Bony — 36 197 201 26 133 1 62

M. Sigma Chi charmer — 74 148 171 163 33 51 117 12 190 141

N. Nevertheless: 3 wds. — 102 165 92 46 119 152 184 63 99 15

O. Makes coffee — 29 76 55 61 79

P. Practiced — 14 49 134 31 138 162 24 147 151

Q. Life of Riley: 2 wds. — 66 38 56 161 83 121 47 85 97 181

R. Ed Norton's milieu — 45 137 35 199 123 96

S. Italian part song — 136 176 5 58 90 130 191 160 68 86

T. Invisible: 3 wds. — 60 129 156 195 13 173 54 70 94 142

U. Liberated — 157 41 110 48 135 125 198 140 188

V. Clergyman's headgear: 2 wds. — 93 182 59 153 187 87 9 111 132

Solution on page 353

				1 L	2 I	3 F	4 C	5 S	6 H	7 E	■	8 A	9 V	10 J	11 I	■	12 M				
■	13 T	14 P	15 N	16 C	17 I	18 A	19 J	20 B	21 E	■	22 A	23 K	24 P	25 D	26 L	27 I	■	28 G	■	29 O	30 B
31 P	32 K	33 M	34 H	■	35 R	36 L	37 I	38 Q	39 J	■	40 J	41 U	■	42 G	43 C	44 B	■	45 R	46 N	47 Q	48 U
49 P	50 B	■	51 M	52 C	■	53 H	54 T	55 O	56 Q	57 G	■	58 S	59 V	60 T	61 O	62 L	■	63 N	64 H	■	65 K
66 Q	67 C	■	68 S	69 C	70 T	71 D	■	72 G	73 F	■	74 M	75 J	76 O	■	77 F	78 D	■	79 O	80 K	81 B	■
82 H	83 Q	■	84 E	85 Q	86 S	87 V	88 F	89 J	■	90 S	91 G	92 N	■	93 V	94 T	95 D	■	96 R	97 Q	98 D	99 N
100 F	101 E	■	102 N	103 J	■	104 H	105 I	106 D	107 C	108 A	■	109 F	110 U	111 V	112 J	113 C	114 G	■	115 K	116 J	117 M
118 E	■	119 N	120 D	■	121 Q	122 E	123 R	124 K	125 U	■	126 A	127 I	128 J	129 T	130 S	131 G	■	132 V	133 L	■	134 P
135 U	136 S	137 R	■	138 P	■	139 H	140 U	141 M	142 T	143 B	144 D	■	145 B	146 C	147 P	148 M	■	149 A	150 C	151 P	■
152 N	153 V	154 G	155 F	156 T	157 U	158 I	159 K	160 S	161 Q	■	162 P	163 M	164 H	165 N	166 B	167 F	168 E	169 I	■	170 D	171 M
■	172 K	173 T	■	174 K	175 A	176 S	177 G	178 F	■	179 G	180 B	■	181 Q	182 V	183 E	■	184 N	185 H	186 E	187 V	■
			188 U	189 F	190 M	191 S	192 K	193 B	194 H	195 T	196 A	■	197 L	198 U	199 R	■	200 I	201 L			

Crostic Puzzle 9

A. Balancing feat — 138 154 46 172 119 66 178 162 105

B. Handle with ____: 2 wds. — 155 51 186 149 196 159 114 73 103

C. Unerring — 34 98 129 151 194 179 82 41 111 167

D. Starch — 122 38 170 85 1 191 157

E. Ladle — 116 93 84 59 35

F. Lamb dish: 2 wds. — 69 94 37 18 44 7 108 144 133

G. Small cetacean — 56 13 118 120 150 71 182

H. Eva Gabor sitcom: 2 wds. — 163 132 171 188 148 87 81 190 117 96

I. March event — 95 198 79 104 26 161 58

J. Done in quick succession: hyph. — 135 192 70 74 23 17 109 176 53

K. Government report: 2 wds. — 173 141 57 21 165 47 134 86 39 65

L. Ron Howard sitcom: 2 wds. — 29 128 100 168 139 152 76 15 50

M. Frozen dessert: 2 wds. — 147 28 24 68 14 174 20 4

N. Browned — 12 78 25 124 72 102 40

O. Amuse — 106 54 61 5 10 19 123 115 201

P. William Randolph or Patricia — 164 145 64 166 31 55

Q. Daunted — 62 36 11 48 184 137 156 127

R. Current: hyph. — 199 63 140 2 136 121 153 49

S. Navigational route: 2 wds. — 88 97 110 169 90 33 45

T. Group of nine — 177 107 75 142 27 92

U. Soccer warning: 2 wds. — 42 131 160 180 197 187 77 175 101 52

V. Home of the Oilers — 126 113 143 16 91 99 181 80

W. Other — 189 193 202 30 3 60 112 130 22

X. Missile — 6 32 9 125 200 89

Y. Colonized: 2 wds. — 158 8 43 146 83 195 183 67 185

Solution on page 353

			1 D	2 R	3 W	4 M	5 O	6 X	■	7 F	8 Y	9 X	10 O	11 Q	12 N	13 G	14 M	15 L			
		■	16 V	17 J	■	18 F	19 O	20 M	21 K	22 W	■	23 J	24 M	25 N	26 I	■	27 T	28 M	29 L		
30 W	31 P	32 X	33 S	■	34 C	35 E	36 Q	37 F	38 D	39 K	40 N	■	41 C	42 U	■	43 Y	44 F	45 S	46 A	—	47 K
48 Q	49 R	50 L	51 B	52 U	53 J	54 O	55 P	■	56 G	57 K	58 I	59 E	60 W	■	61 O	62 Q	■	63 R	64 P	65 K	66 A
67 Y	68 M	69 F	70 J	71 G	72 N	73 B	■	74 J	75 T	■	76 L	■	77 U	78 N	79 I	80 V	81 H	82 C	83 Y	■	84 E
85 D	■	86 K	87 H	88 S	89 X	■	90 S	91 V	92 T	■	93 E	94 F	95 I	96 H	97 S	98 C	99 V	■	100 L	101 U	102 N
103 B	104 I	105 A	106 O	107 T	108 F	109 J	110 S	111 C	■	112 W	113 V	114 B	115 O	116 E	117 H	118 G	119 A	■	120 G	121 R	122 D
■	123 O	124 N	125 X	126 V	127 Q	■	128 L	129 C	130 W	131 U	132 H	133 F	134 K	135 J	136 R	■	137 Q	138 A	139 L	■	140 R
141 K	142 T	■	143 V	144 F	145 P	146 Y	147 M	148 H	149 B	■	150 G	151 C	152 L	■	153 R	154 A	155 B	156 Q	157 D	■	158 Y
159 B	■	160 U	161 I	162 A	163 H	■	164 P	165 K	■	166 P	167 C	168 L	169 S	170 D	171 H	172 A	■	173 K	174 M	■	175 U
		176 J	177 T	■	178 A	179 C	180 U	■	181 V	182 G	183 Y	■	184 Q	185 Y	186 B	■	187 U	188 H	■		
			189 W	190 H	191 D	■	192 J	193 W	194 C	■	195 Y	196 B	197 U	198 I	199 R	200 X	201 O	202 W			

Crostic Puzzle 10

A. Slight trace — 36 178 45 52 186 161 169 127 138 6

B. Oblivion — 187 27 55 103 173

C. Precise — 182 14 81 162 23

D. Green vegetation — 82 171 5 159 156 32 22

E. Addis Ababa's land — 33 41 170 78 153 15 176 141

F. Most destitute — 71 16 96 123 191 83 135 201

G. Employees — 195 152 47 9 98

H. Tricked — 154 104 75 34 43 54 205 197 168

I. Suit accessory — 106 31 48 150 180 158 3

J. Functioning — 76 130 28 136 149 72 113 108 167

K. West Indies religion — 164 125 129 84 11 93

L. Dominion — 122 198 65 66 89 146

M. Epsom oval — 10 4 131 40 184 193 25 21 49

N. Germanic language — 151 18 200 97 111 116 30

O. Honest — 105 94 139 121 24 124 64 46

P. Added moisture to — 185 188 39 194 183 68 67 53 199 8

Q. Harmful — 101 20 114 133 110 56 163 61 80

R. ___ Territories — 63 202 134 59 177 69 107 37 143

S. Long-tailed blackbird — 57 126 119 189 95 147 13

T. Purslane's kin — 145 50 60 117 70 174 17 132 144 128

U. Father of King Arthur — 115 26 42 19 166

V. Gunwale feature — 157 58 88 2 204 86 90 44

W. Secret organization — 172 35 112 160 73

X. Differently — 38 29 140 192 100 118 1 179 175

Y. ABC, e.g. — 51 165 91 92 99 77 190

Z. Shone forth — 7 74 87 85 181 203 109 142

a. Rare metallic element — 137 79 102 196 62 155 120 148 12

Solution on page 353

		1 X		2 V	3 I	4 M	5 D	6 A	7 Z	8 P		9 G	10 M	11 K	12 a		13 S	14 C	15 E		
16 F	17 T	18 N	19 U	20 Q	21 M	22 D		23 C	24 O	25 M	26 U		27 B	28 J		29 X	30 N	31 I	32 D	33 E	
34 H	35 W	36 A		37 R	38 X	39 P	40 M	41 E	42 U	43 H	44 V	45 A		46 O	47 G	48 I	49 M	50 T	51 Y	52 A	
53 P	54 H		55 B	56 Q	57 S	58 V	59 R		60 T	61 Q	62 a	63 R		64 O	65 L		66 L	67 P		68 P	
69 R	70 T	71 F	72 J		73 W	74 Z	75 H	76 J	77 Y		78 E	79 a		80 Q	81 C	82 D	83 F	84 K		85 Z	86 V
	87 Z	88 V	89 L		90 V	91 Y		92 Y	93 K	94 O	95 S	96 F	97 N		98 G	99 Y	100 X		101 Q	102 a	
103 B	104 H	105 O		106 I	107 R	108 J	109 Z	110 Q		111 N	112 W		113 J		114 Q	115 U	116 N	117 T		118 X	119 S
120 a	121 O	122 L	123 F		124 O	125 K	126 S		127 A	128 T		129 K	130 J		131 M	132 T	133 Q	134 R	135 F	136 J	
137 a	138 A	139 O		140 X	141 E	142 Z		143 R	144 T		145 T	146 L		147 S	148 a	149 J	150 I	151 N		152 G	153 E
154 H		155 a	156 D	157 V		158 I		159 D	160 W	161 A	162 C	163 Q	164 K	165 Y	166 U	167 J	168 H		169 A	170 E	171 D
	172 W	173 B	174 T	175 X		176 E		177 R	178 A	179 X	180 I	181 Z	182 C	183 P		184 M	185 P	186 A		187 B	188 P
189 S	190 Y	191 F	192 X	193 M		194 P		195 G	196 a	197 H	198 L	199 P	200 N		201 F	202 R		203 Z	204 V	205 H	

Crostic Puzzle 11

A. Little critter — 64 19 196 38

B. Bizarre — 165 89 200 26 65 162 49 85 133 37

C. Belladonna — 3 169 163 18 111 181 91 77 109 70

D. Shimmer and shine — 153 164 47 128 142 115 211

E. Role for Bea Arthur: 2 wds. — 137 151 207 12 213 203 104 193 188 76

F. Unmindful — 45 150 148 135 155 5 205 61 68

G. Pipe type — 69 132 72 98 2 90 160 53 152 190

H. Qualify — 185 136 63 32 59 84 156

I. Emu — 174 146 27 138 79 40

J. Abominable Snowman — 158 99 30 58

K. Sworn statement — 92 124 71 94 176 41 86 1 129

L. Perfect game for Clemens: hyph. — 117 106 201 102 6 17 87 131

M. River Phoenix's "Little ____" — 48 13 21 127 96 195

N. 1954 hit for The Penguins: 2 wds. — 43 122 107 171 210 191 143 34 97 9

O. Effluence — 16 206 44 46 167 22 105

P. Botched — 139 25 114 54 81 154 78

Q. ____ cypress — 75 198 112 141 95

R. Ceremonies — 39 189 159 175 7

S. "Crocodile Rock" singer: 2 wds. — 120 108 134 55 11 60 50 28 194

T. Devotee — 202 93 36 31 51 125 110 149 100 118

U. Massachusetts seaport: 2 wds. — 179 67 140 119 10 208 186 183 42 168

V. Fawcett-O'Neal sitcom: 2 wds. — 192 180 126 116 62 184 187 212 52 35

W. Valid — 24 166 4 121 178 33 170 161 182

X. Unimaginative: hyph. — 177 56 15 209 80 199 14 113 145 103

Y. Restored to vintage condition: 2 wds. — 123 197 66 82 20 173 204

Z. French female — 144 74 147 29

a. Mom's new hubby — 88 57 130 8 23 83 101 172 73 157

Solution on page 353

1 K	2 G	3 C	4 W		5 F	6 L		7 R	8 a	9 N	10 U	11 S	12 E	13 M	14 X		15 X	16 O		17 L	18 C
19 A	20 Y	21 M		22 O	23 a		24 W	25 P	26 B		27 I	28 S	29 Z		30 J	31 T	32 H	33 W	34 N	35 V	
36 T	37 B	38 A	39 R	40 I		41 K	42 U	43 N		44 O	45 F		46 O	47 D	48 M	49 B		50 S	51 T	52 V	
53 G	54 P	55 S	56 X	57 a		58 J	59 H		60 S	61 F	62 V	63 H		64 A	65 B	66 Y	67 U	68 F		69 G	70 C
	71 K	72 G	73 a	74 Z		75 Q	76 E	77 C	78 P		79 I	80 X		81 P	82 Y		83 a	84 H	85 B	86 K	87 L
	88 a	89 B	90 G	91 C		92 K	93 T		94 K	95 Q	96 M	97 N	98 G	99 J	100 T	101 a	102 L	103 X	104 E		105 O
106 L	107 N	108 S	109 C		110 T	111 C		112 Q	113 X	114 P	115 D	116 V	117 L	118 T		119 U	120 S		121 W	122 N	123 Y
124 K		125 T	126 V		127 M	128 D	129 K	130 a	131 L	132 G	133 B	134 S	135 F	136 H	137 E		138 I	139 P		140 U	141 Q
	142 D	143 N	144 Z	145 X		146 I	147 Z	148 F		149 T	150 F	151 E	152 G	153 D		154 P	155 F	156 H	157 a	158 J	159 R
160 G	161 W	162 B	163 C		164 D	165 B	166 W	167 O	168 U		169 C	170 W		171 N	172 a	173 Y	174 I	175 R	176 K		177 X
178 W		179 U	180 V		181 C	182 W	183 U	184 V	185 H		186 U	187 V	188 E		189 R	190 G	191 N	192 V	193 E	194 S	195 M
196 A	197 Y	198 Q	199 X		200 B	201 L	202 T	203 E		204 Y	205 F	206 O	207 E	208 U		209 X	210 N	211 D	212 V	213 E	

Crostic Puzzle 12

A. Subsequently — 32 109 74 169 27 62 145 86 131

B. Correspond — 63 93 37 16 157

C. Square dance routine: hyph. — 147 124 180 150 120 60

D. Put together — 65 64 161 153 44 20 132 119

E. Finishing coat — 84 172 136 57 178 13 156

F. Laughing hysterically: 2 wds. — 92 146 36 152 159 118 121 87 18 47

G. Gobi, e.g. — 78 143 103 85 15 166

H. Sure thing: hyph. — 179 75 122 52 167 80

I. Out of bounds: hyph. — 110 41 158 53 126 33 117 68 30

J. Count — 142 115 72 174 135 82

K. Finally: 3 wds. — 69 134 108 49 94 81 4 76 128 59

L. Instant — 19 46 66 54 77 104

M. Conifer, e.g. — 88 7 114 111 141 42 95 23 125

N. Blush — 160 138 89 24 8 168

O. Idle time — 29 165 48 12 22 123 3 177 6

P. Sheer fabric — 163 98 56 100 25 43 130

Q. System of letters — 129 70 148 28 83 45 127 97

R. Dozed — 50 175 154 96 10 137

S. Eggs on — 1 5 164 39 105

T. Wane — 107 11 133 162 90

U. Concern — 38 176 14 182 149 106 71 171

V. Country — 116 2 155 140 26 170

W. Cloth — 51 79 55 112 73 173 40

X. Surmise — 101 61 31 99 9

Y. Cared for — 151 35 102 91 21 144

Z. Shamus — 58 181 17 139 113 34 67

Solution on page 353

	1 S	2 V	3 O	4 K	■	5 S	6 O	7 M	8 N	9 X	10 R	■	11 T	12 O	13 E	14 U	■	15 G	16 B	17 Z	
18 F	19 L	20 D	21 Y	22 O	23 M	24 N	■	25 P	26 V	27 A	■	28 Q	29 O	30 I	■	31 X	32 A	33 I	34 Z	35 Y	36 F
■	37 B	38 U	39 S	40 W	■	41 I	42 M	43 P	44 D	■	45 Q	46 L	47 F	48 O	49 K	50 R	■	51 W	52 H	■	53 I
54 L	55 W	56 P	57 E	58 Z	59 K	60 C	61 X	■	62 A	63 B	64 D	■	65 D	■	66 L	67 Z	68 I	69 K	70 Q	71 U	72 J
73 W	74 A	75 H	■	76 K	77 L	78 G	■	79 W	80 H	81 K	82 J	83 Q	84 E	85 G	86 A	■	87 F	88 M	■	89 N	90 T
91 Y	92 F	93 B	94 K	95 M	96 R	■	97 Q	98 P	99 X	■	100 P	101 X	102 Y	103 G	104 L	■	105 S	106 U	107 T	108 K	■
109 A	110 I	111 M	■	112 W	113 Z	114 M	■	115 J	116 V	117 I	118 F	119 D	120 C	■	121 F	122 H	123 O	124 C	125 M	126 I	127 Q
128 K	■	129 Q	130 P	131 A	■	132 D	133 T	134 K	135 J	136 E	■	137 R	138 N	139 Z	140 V	141 M	142 J	143 G	144 Y	■	145 A
146 F	147 C	■	148 Q	149 U	150 C	151 Y	152 F	153 D	154 R	■	155 V	156 E	157 B	■	158 I	159 F	160 N	161 D	162 T	■	163 P
164 S	165 O	166 G	167 H	168 N	169 A	170 V	171 U	172 E	173 W	■	174 J	175 R	176 U	177 O	■	178 E	179 H	180 C	181 Z	182 U	■

FLOWER POWER

The answers to this petaled puzzle will go in a curve from the number on the outside to the center of the flower. Each number has two 5-letter words. One goes in a clockwise direction and the second in a counterclockwise direction. Try working from both sets of clues to fill the flower.

Solution on page 343

CLOCKWISE

1. Theater platform
2. Repulsive
3. Tranquility
4. Dirigible
5. Frolic
6. Singer John ____
7. Allow
8. Actor Eastwood
9. Salt water
10. Hoax
11. Site
12. Search blindly
13. Chart
14. Selected
15. Like a snake
16. Carve
17. Strike
18. Torrent

COUNTERCLOCKWISE

1. Peppery
2. Minnesota, e.g.
3. Book illustration
4. Neutral color
5. Fire
6. Expensive
7. Dirt
8. Brittle
9. Expressionless
10. Threefold
11. Publish
12. Flash
13. Elegance
14. Earthenware pot
15. Form
16. Extent
17. Cut sharply
18. Grin

ANAGRAM MAGIC SQUARE

Find an anagram for the 5-letter word in each box. The anagram will answer one of the clues. Put the number of that clue into the small square and write the anagram on the dash. The numbers in each row and column will add up to 65. Write the first letter of each anagram on the correspondingly numbered dash at the bottom of the page; and, presto!, the Anagram Magic saying will appear. To start you off, we have put in one anagram and its clue number and set its first letter on the proper dash at the bottom of the page.

Solution on page 344

ROUTE ☐ ___	CRASS ☐ ___	SLAIN ☐ ___	SADIE ☐ ___	DOORS ☐ ___	= 65
TOWER ☐ ___	CHEAT ☐ ___	ASTIR ☐ ___	TIMES ☐ ___	LATEX ☐ ___	= 65
GLARE ☐ ___	LEASH ☐ ___	LADEN ☐ ___	BLAME ☐ ___	ETHOS ☐ ___	= 65
STALE ☐ ___	DRAYS ☐ ___	CLEAR ☐ ___	CLEAN ☐ ___	SPINE ☐ ___	= 65
LAVIN 1 *ANVIL*	CAGER ☐ ___	PAGER ☐ ___	TOTER ☐ ___	RAGED ☐ ___	= 65
= 65	= 65	= 65	= 65	= 65	

1. Blacksmith's block
2. Entwiner
3. Notions
4. Educate
5. The ones there
6. Spear
7. English composer
8. Mealtime prayer
9. Aromas
10. Step
11. Fissile rock
12. Articles
13. Evergreens
14. Vine fruit
15. Exterior
16. Praise
17. Wound marks
18. Pilgrim settler
19. Smallest
20. Aquatic mammal
21. Brads
22. Rank
23. Indited
24. Stroll
25. Lawns

A																								
1	2	3	4	5	6	7	8	9	10	11	12	13	14	15	16	17	18	19	20	21	22	23	24	25

Drop-Ins

Using only the letters given in the box, fill in all the dashes to form 8-letter words. Each letter is used only once. Solution on page 344

AAAA B C D EEEE GG HH IIIII J
K NNN OOO P Q RRR S TTT UU X

1. M ___ N ___ F ___ L ___
2. S ___ R ___ I ___ H ___
3. C ___ M ___ L ___ T ___
4. P ___ I ___ T ___ N ___
5. E ___ E ___ T ___ O ___
6. S ___ I ___ M ___ S ___
7. B ___ E ___ D ___ O ___
8. J ___ D ___ P ___ R ___
9. E ___ E ___ G ___ Z ___
10. A ___ U ___ D ___ C ___

Building Blocks

Using only the letters in the word FUN, complete the words in the Building Blocks. Words read across only. Every word contains each letter of FUN at least once. Solution on page 343

Associations

You can form a chain of associated words by filling in the blanks with the letters listed on the right. Each word you make will be associated in some way with the words above and below it. The initial letters of the words are already in place. Each letter on the right will be used only once.
Solution on page 344

EARLY	AA CCC
B ___ ___ ___ ___	DD
C ___ ___ ___ ___ ___ ___ ___ ___ ___ ___	EEE
C ___ ___ ___ ___ ___ ___ ___ ___	HH II
Y ___ ___ ___ ___ ___ ___ ___ ___	KK LLL
J ___ ___ ___ ___ ___ ___ ___ ___	NN
E ___ ___ ___ ___	OOOOO
S ___ ___ ___ ___ ___ ___ ___ ___	RR TT
MASTER	WW

Tiles

Imagine that these tiles are on a table, each showing a 2-letter combination. Can you rearrange these tiles visually to form a 10-letter word? Solution on page 344

CHIPS

Place the chips of words on the dashes, one letter per dash, to discover a saying. When a word contains an even number of letters, it is split in half to form two chips. If it contains an odd number of letters, the extra letter is added to the second chip.
Solution on page 344

A ORT I UFF O MUSH T
SH LI OO ROOM S ST FE T

_ _

PULLING STRINGS

Place the answers to the clues into the squares. Squares which are connected with lines contain the same letter. Don't get tangled!
Solution on page 344

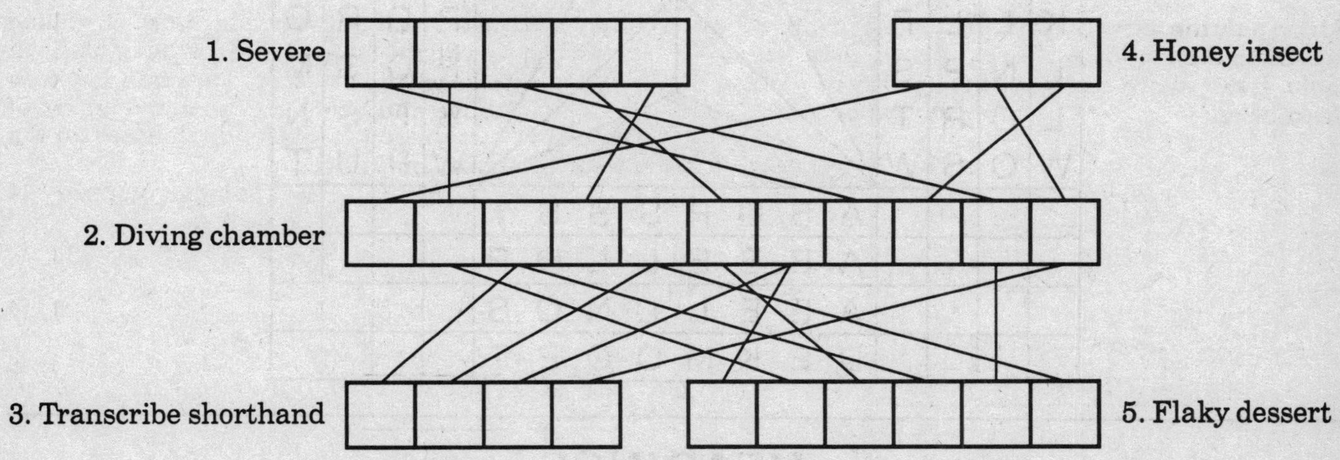

CHANGAWORD

Can you change the top word into the bottom word in each column in the number of steps indicated in parentheses? Change only one letter at a time and do not change the order of the letters. Proper names, slang, and obsolete words are not allowed.
Our solutions on page 344

1. BEEF (4 steps)	2. SOUP (4 steps)	3. HARD (5 steps)	4. COOK (5 steps)
STEW	BOWL	ROLL	MEAL

FOUR CORNERS

The letters of the four corner crossword puzzles have been alphabetized and listed across the top and bottom and down the sides of the diagram. Thus, the letters of the crossword in the upper left corner have been alphabetized with those of the upper right corner and listed in the four rows across the top. The letters from the upper left corner have also been alphabetized with those of the lower left corner and listed in the four columns on the left. Determine where the letters belong in the squares to create the four crossword puzzles. Every letter is in its proper row and column. We have inserted the letter R in its proper place by way of illustration and to get you started.

Solution on page 344

				A	F	G	L	L	P	P	U				
		R		A	E	I	L	L	O	R	S				
				A	E	E	N	N	O	P	W				
				A	E	E	E	N	R	W	W				
A	B	A	A									D	E	A	E
A	E	A	E									E	L	E	E
B	E	A	N									L	L	L	E
F	I	E	N									O	O	O	E
K	L	L	P									P	O	R	G
L	N	P	S									P	O	S	M
L	O	R	T									S	P	S	N
W	O	S	W									W	P	U	T
				A	B	O	P	S	S	S	T				
				A	B	E	E	L	L	O	P				
				A	E	E	L	L	N	O	S				
				D	E	K	M	O	O	P	T				

HEADINGS

Use the letters in each Heading to fill in the blanks to complete words related to the Heading. Cross out each letter as you use it.

Solutions on page 345

1. FINANCIAL AND BANKING TERMS

___EPO______T

CER_________IC___TE

BA_________CE

LO______

___HEC______OOK

I___TE______ST

S___V_________S

___O___EY

2. PIRATES OF THE HIGH SEAS

___R___A___URE

___R___GATE

BUCC___N___E___

S______P

S___Y___L___S___

CR___S___BONES

___YEPA___C___

___OOK

3. ITEMS OF APPAREL AND CLOTHING

___R___CK

M______K______TOS___

C___R___I___A___

___AJ___MA___

JU______E___

V___S___

___V___RA______S

SH___R___

DOUBLE OCCUPANCY

Place the letter pairs on the left into the blank squares in the diagram to form 6-letter words reading across and down. Each pair will be used only once.

Solution on page 344

AG	ED	LE	RS
AI	ED	LL	RS
AL	EE	LY	RU
AR	EL	MA	SE
AS	EL	ME	SE
BI	EN	NE	SI
BR	EP	NE	SS
BU	FE	NT	ST
CA	HO	OR	ST
DE	ID	PA	TA
DI	IG	PI	TE
EA	IN	PU	TU
ED	IN	RI	VE
ED	IT	RO	VI

	PI		CH				OX	
NI	■	ME		■		ES	■	CI
	AR				MS		AP	

IN				NG				OW
	■		DA	■	MU		■	
		ES		TE		ER		

	RE				CH		ND	
CA	■	OR		■		LS	■	CH
	FI		ES				IT	

MIND TICKLER

Every time the post office changes its rates we buy new stamps even though we still have some of the old ones on hand. Now we have a batch of 25¢ stamps and 29¢ stamps with a total value of $13.96. How many of each denomination do we have?

Solution on page 344

FAN WORDS

Place the 5-letter answers to the clues into the fan to discover an 8-letter word reading across the outlined area. As an added help, pairs of answers are anagrams (1 is an anagram of 2, 3 is an anagram of 4, etc.).

Solution on page 344

1. Multiplied by
2. Strike mightily
3. Leaves out
4. Damp
5. Take by force
6. Scatter
7. Knight's spear
8. Unsullied

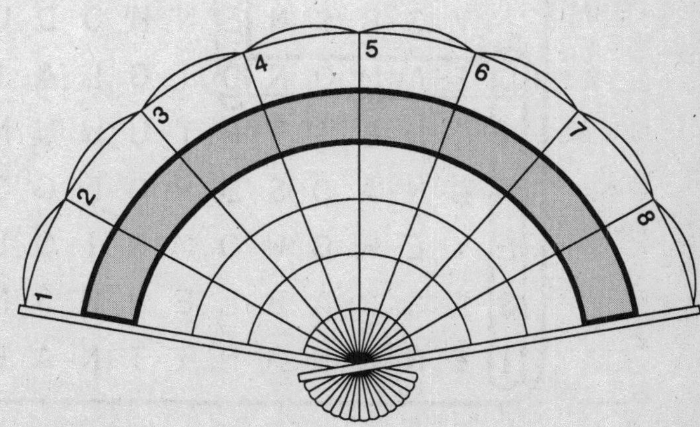

Word Seek 15

Heads & Tails

In this special Word Seek, you will form a continuous chain of looped words. The last letter of each word will be the first letter of the next. The number of letters in each word is given in parentheses. We have started you off with the first three words.

Word list on page 334

Solution on page 332

ISLAND (6)	______ (7)	______ (5)
DIAMOND (7)	______ (10)	______ (7)
DEWDROP (7)	______ (7)	______ (7)
______ (8)	______ (5)	______ (8)
______ (6)	______ (6)	______ (6)
______ (10)	______ (7)	______ (4)
______ (7)	______ (8)	______ (7)
______ (6)	______ (6)	______ (8)
______ (9)	______ (5)	______ (4)
______ (6)	______ (7)	______ (6)

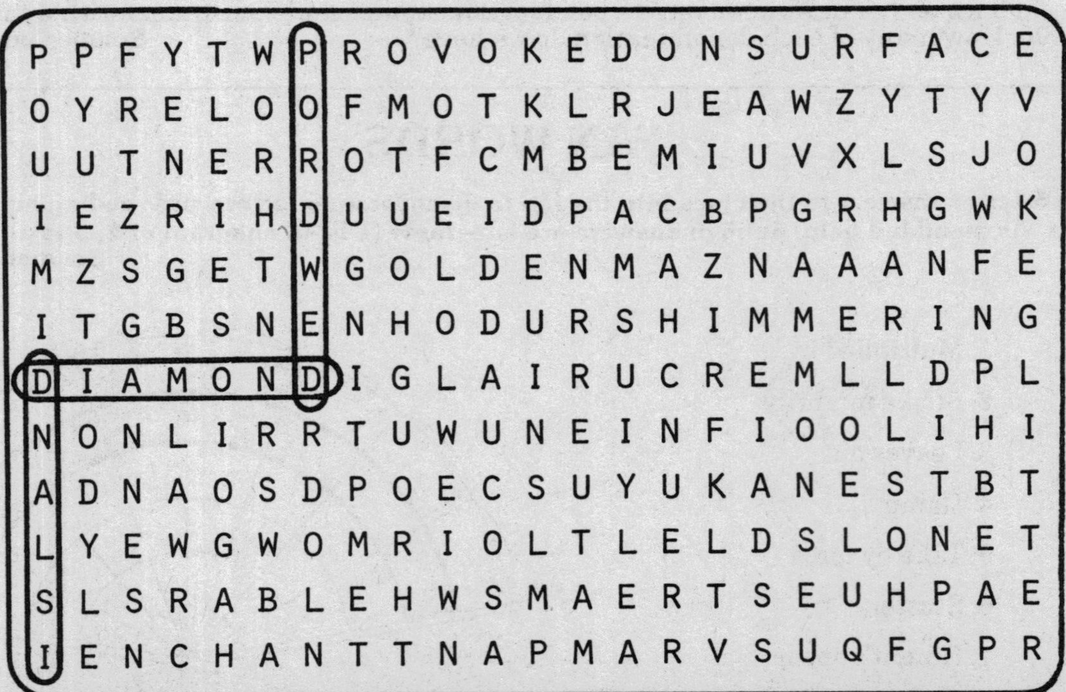

Zigzag

The entries in this Zigzag puzzle will be found in the diagram in an unusual way. They do not read in straight lines; rather, each entry has one bend in it. Circle each word when you find it in the diagram, as we did with ZIGZAG, and cross it off the list. Words often overlap, and some letters may be used more than once. Not all the letters in the diagram will be used.

Solution on page 333

Alleviate
Alliance
Attentive
Books
Christmas
Covering
Dandelion
Decibels
Delete
Elegantly
Evened
Figurine
Flange
Futuristic
Genuine
Gratifies
Hazardous
Heartthrob
Honesty
Island
Isolated
Jerusalem
Jury
Laughs
Lemonade
Misplaced
Pirate
Prelate
Purifies
Puritans
Quest
Quotation
Raised
Ruminates
Saturday
Spacious
Temporary
Traipse
Tranquility
Triton
Unopposed
Vocation
Wander
Wilderness
Zigzag ✓

O	R	H	T	T	R	A	E	H	L	S	A	M	T	S	I	R	Y	R	I	E	T	U
B	A	S	N	A	T	T	S	E	U	A	G	E	L	E	A	R	E	R	N	L	R	S
Z	F	I	E	S	E	I	F	A	N	Q	U	I	L	I	T	Y	H	I	U	E	I	A
A	I	U	E	I	F	I	R	T	O	S	H	G	S	G	E	N	U	C	J	M	T	L
R	T	G	T	G	R	T	L	U	P	T	D	E	E	D	L	I	W	S	K	O	I	E
D	A	N	Z	U	T	Y	Q	S	P	A	A	T	Y	R	A	R	O	P	N	O	N	M
O	R	A	P	R	R	D	E	S	O	C	A	T	I	O	N	N	M	A	N	B	A	E
U	G	L	L	I	A	N	C	E	V	I	L	V	I	A	T	E	D	H	O	N	T	R
S	B	F	S	N	I	P	S	E	C	O	E	E	B	O	T	E	S	E	I	E	E	E
D	A	T	T	E	N	T	I	O	I	U	R	L	V	E	N	E	D	S	L	S	S	D
E	I	G	N	I	R	E	V	M	I	S	P	L	A	C	E	P	I	R	A	T	L	N
C	I	B	E	L	S	D	E	T	A	L	O	A	Y	A	D	R	U	T	E	Y	W	A

Word Seek 17

Circular Word Seek

The listed names of animals can be found in the diagram inward, outward, clockwise, counterclockwise, and diagonally. One word has been looped as an example. **Solution on page 333**

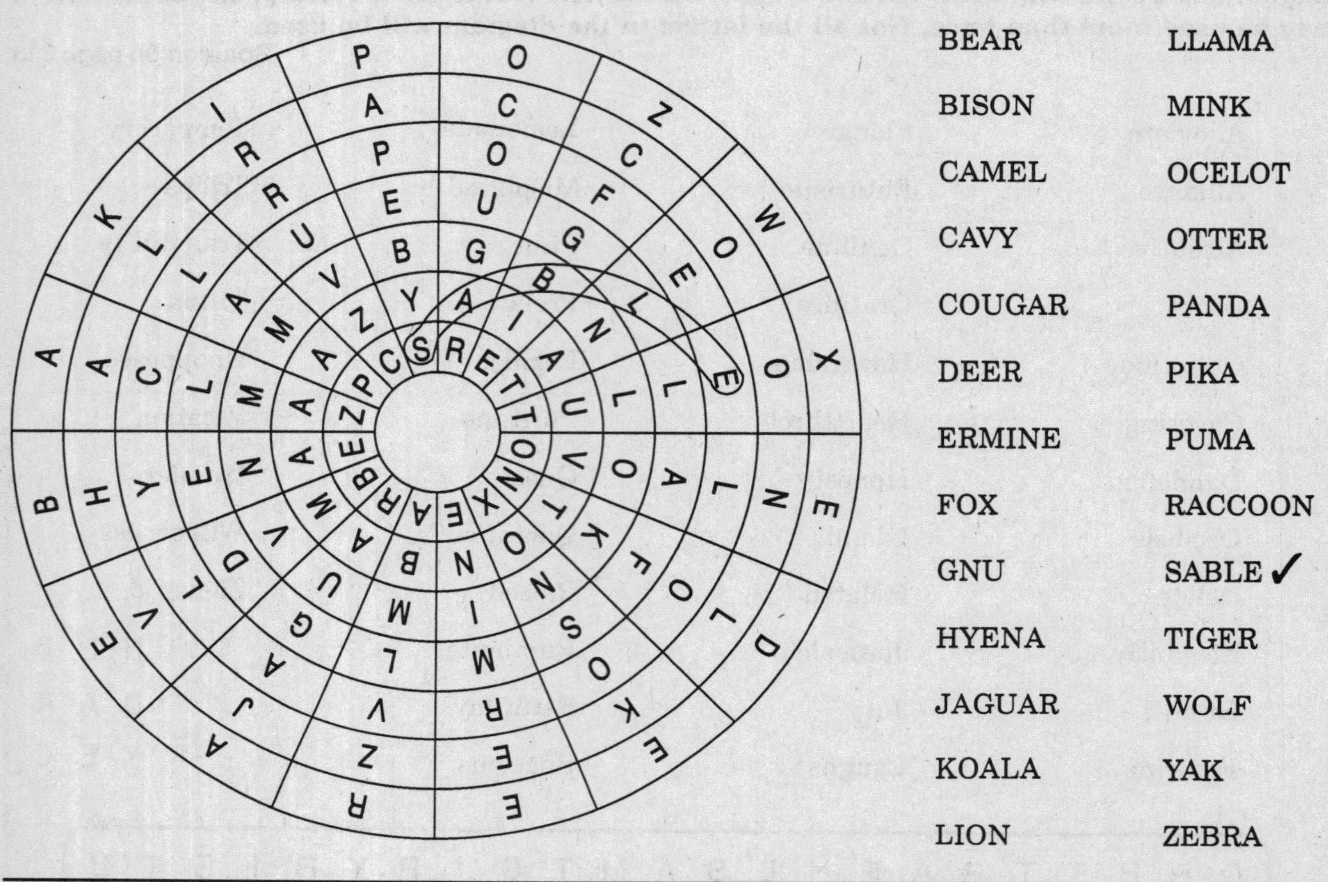

BEAR	LLAMA
BISON	MINK
CAMEL	OCELOT
CAVY	OTTER
COUGAR	PANDA
DEER	PIKA
ERMINE	PUMA
FOX	RACCOON
GNU	SABLE ✓
HYENA	TIGER
JAGUAR	WOLF
KOALA	YAK
LION	ZEBRA

CROSSBLOCKS

Insert the letters and letter groups into each diagram to form words reading across which answer the clues on the left. A bonus word will read diagonally down in the tinted blocks.

Solution on page 340

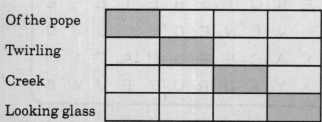

1. A AM E ING INN L
MI O P P PA R R RR
S ST

Of the pope				
Twirling				
Creek				
Looking glass				

2. A BLE CO CT DEB
E E I NG NS NT S TA
TA TRU UR

Class				
Teach				
Doubtful				
Touching				

Matching Monograms

The names of all the actors and entertainers in this puzzle have the same first and last initials. We have given you their first names; you must fill in the blanks and find their last names in the diagram. Names in the diagram read forwards, backwards, up, down, and diagonally and always in a straight line. Names overlap and not all the letters in the diagram will be used. When completed, the last names will be in alphabetical order. To start you off, we have looped (Charlie) CHAPLIN.

Word list on page 334

Solution on page 333

1. Anouk ________
2. Alan ________
3. Alan ________
4. Brigitte ________
5. Beulah ________
6. Beau ________
7. Billie ________
8. Claudia ________
9. Carol ________
10. Charlie Chaplin
11. Cyd ________
12. Chevy ________
13. Claudette ________
14. Chuck ________
15. Dan ________
16. Doris ________
17. Dom ________
18. Deanna ________
19. Dan ________
20. Greta ________
21. Greer ________
22. George ________
23. Helen ________
24. Hal ________
25. Jennifer ________
26. Kris ________
27. Louise ________
28. Loretta ________
29. Mary ________
30. Marsha ________
31. Marcello ________
32. Malcolm ________
33. Melina ________
34. Marilyn ________
35. Mary Tyler ________
36. Martin ________
37. Nick ________
38. Patti ________
39. Paula ________
40. Ronald ________
41. Robert ________
42. Rob ________
43. Ruth ________
44. Richard ________
45. Rosalind ________
46. Robert ________
47. Sylvia ________
48. Simone ________
49. Sissy ________
50. Sylvester ________
51. Stella ________
52. Susan ________
53. Susan ________
54. Sally ________
55. Vivian ________

```
O L A C H A N N I N G S V E L E P
S N I D R O F D E R T C P O G R R
H A O K L R E N I E R H I A E N V
A N I S R A N Z V O K A P N C A E
Y N T E R M Z E T N R R T M N E D
E R E A G A N O A N I I A C O A K
S E I L R S G Y L A S S E R Y E C
T D R D R O R X O S T S Y K L R C
J A E O Z N E J M R O E R L R L O
A I K O O R B L O H F T U N E U L
M L E N O M S I T N F M D B E S B
E E N O L L A T S R E E N O L T E
S Y R O T N R E E E R S R C E R R
N I L C N N T T R R S N I L S U T
N E V I O R S T R R O A A U L T T
I I O T O U D E O M N N H R L H S
B R L M O N R N G L I E G C E E I
R N A P U D N I I D N O B I S R D
U N R O A O R O R A I M E E S S N
D Y R T C H N A N I T R A M U R E
L L E W O D C M B G A R B O R I Y
```

Word Seek 19

Boxes

All the entries in the list are found in an unusual way. An entry can begin at any point and will read either clockwise or counterclockwise around the edges of a box (sometimes a square and sometimes a rectangle). BOLDNESS is boxed in the diagram.

Solution on page 333

BOLDNESS ✓
BORDER
CAMPSITE
CARAVANS
CARRYING
CIRCLE
COMRADES
CROSSING
DRIVER
EMIGRATE
ESCORT
EXPEDITION
FAMILY
FOLLOW
FRONTIER
GROUPS
GUIDES
HORSES
LEADER
MIGRATED
MILITARY
MOUNTAIN
PILGRIMS
PIONEERS
PLAINS
PROGRESS
REGION
RIVERS
ROUTES
RUGGED
SCHEDULE
SCOUTS
SETTLERS
SOLDIERS
STREAM
SUPPLIES
TERRAINS
TRAILS
TRAVELER
WAGONS
WESTWARD
WHEELS

```
C O M R S P I G G U W I A L E R T O Z A I M A
S E D A R R O E D R X N L E V A R A W R L Y F
G U I I E E N R A T I S P M A N D C T T S S B
M S E N S T R G I E C A M Y R S W E S U O C E
A T A W S Z A I M D O B I O A C O B P S M I L
E R G O N N T E E S R P L I T P E D I L G R C
S S P R B O I B S H O P B E H X H A T X S O M
W T T E D R E C H E D U S S L E N O I V P U L
E L X S B F R S E L U O F W H E H M R E Y I N
I E R S O W I R B A N M O O B S E A D R R Z G
D C S I N G V E T U T N L L O S L R E T R A C
L O S O R C W S R O A I B D N E B W S C O L Y
```

Match Words

To solve this puzzle, find two words, one in each diagram, in the same location in both diagrams, which combine to form a movie title. The first word of each answer is in the top diagram; the second word is in the bottom diagram in the same location, reading in the same direction. Words read forward, backward, up, down, and diagonally, and always in a straight line. All the letters will not be used. For example, HIGH NOON is formed by combining the word HIGH from the top diagram with the word NOON from the bottom diagram, in the same location, and reading in the same direction. The word "The" has been omitted before some titles.

Word list on page 334

Solution on page 333

YOUR WORD LIST
(31 entries)

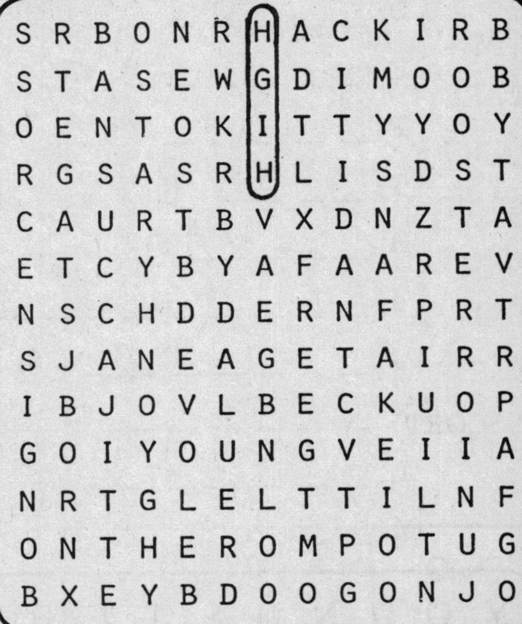

K S H I N E N A V I N C T
E V R W D P O D I N W O T
E H B A N F O Y L E W G R
R C R R W Z N N A N L B C
C A D S E E F H Y E I U J
P O C N L K M S T Z U R C
U C M H L C N O R P A N G
L E Y R E U H U L E R R Y
V F S U D L H L F K I E X
E R I L I O N S V T O N A
R E W X F E C N I R P N L
A E F A N Z A P T A H O G
H O S P I H C R M A R B E

Word Seek 21

Alphabetics

Each of the answer words starts with a different letter of the alphabet. The words are in the diagram reading forward, backward, up, down, diagonally, and always in a straight line. Words may overlap. Not all the letters in the diagram will be used. The number in parentheses is the number of letters in the word.

Word list on page 334

Solution on page 333

A A R G E N T I N A (9)
B _ _ _ _ _ _ _ (7)
C _ _ _ _ _ _ _ (7)
D _ _ _ _ _ _ _ _ (8)
E _ _ _ _ _ _ _ (7)
F _ _ _ _ _ _ (6)
G _ _ _ _ _ (5)
H _ _ _ _ _ (5)
I _ _ _ _ _ _ _ _ _ _ (10)
J _ _ _ _ _ _ _ _ (8)
K _ _ _ _ _ _ _ (7)
L _ _ _ _ _ _ _ _ (8)
M _ _ _ _ _ _ _ (7)
N _ _ _ _ _ (5)
O _ _ _ _ _ _ (6)
P _ _ _ _ _ _ _ _ _ _ (10)
Q _ _ _ _ _ _ (6)
R _ _ _ _ _ _ (6)
S _ _ _ _ _ _ (6)
T _ _ _ _ _ _ _ (7)
U _ _ _ _ _ _ _ _ _ (9)
V _ _ _ _ _ _ _ (7)
W _ _ _ _ _ _ (6)
X _ _ _ _ _ _ _ _ _ (9)
Y _ _ _ _ _ _ _ _ _ (9)
Z _ _ _ _ _ _ (6)

Y	O	U	N	G	S	T	E	R	U	D	A	R	I	C	G	I	T	S	I	C	E	R
F	P	I	N	H	O	R	F	W	S	L	R	N	H	P	R	W	T	B	B	I	R	P
E	T	G	O	A	L	I	E	P	R	J	I	A	I	O	S	Y	O	R	H	M	O	X
B	D	N	I	W	N	R	R	O	K	I	G	N	W	T	F	C	S	O	E	W	T	E
L	E	L	T	Y	U	I	T	E	K	I	T	C	H	E	N	I	H	T	A	Y	C	R
Y	J	S	A	T	N	L	M	C	T	E	G	E	M	D	R	E	I	H	A	F	E	O
E	G	S	L	G	Z	Z	I	O	X	S	N	M	R	I	C	M	G	E	O	L	P	P
L	M	U	U	V	Y	T	P	T	U	V	Y	T	O	L	A	E	Z	R	C	I	S	H
L	V	O	S	X	S	T	R	L	M	S	M	O	I	N	O	L	M	O	A	H	O	Y
O	E	L	N	P	I	A	C	A	F	S	P	T	Y	W	U	A	N	H	S	I	R	T
R	D	B	I	G	C	B	S	R	U	P	H	D	O	J	L	O	H	Q	P	O	P	E
T	O	L	Y	T	I	O	T	T	U	Q	U	O	E	Y	M	S	I	A	Y	S	S	U

Missing Vowels

Before you can loop these words about photography, you must first fill in the circles in the diagram with the missing vowels A, E, I, O, and U. Words in the diagram read forward, backward, up, down, and diagonally, and always in a straight line. Circle each word when you find it and cross it off the list. Words will often overlap, and some letters may be used more than once. Not all of the letters in the diagram will be used. We have filled in and circled ACTION as an example. Solution on page 333

PHOTOGRAPHY

~~Action~~
Amateur
Batteries
Black and white
Bulbs
Cameras
Capture
Close-ups
Color
Control
Cutoff
Developing
Distance
Film
Flash
Focus
Fun
Gear
Hobby
Hold
Inexpensive
Kits
Lens
Loading
Memories
Models
Negative
Overexpose
Pictures
Poses
Positive
Prints
Pros
Results
Rewarding
Scenic
Snapshot
Steady
Subjects
Tank
Underexpose
View

```
○ C F N ○ G ○ T ○ V ○ T ○ H W D N ○ K C ○ L B
S ○ Z ○ G N ○ D R ○ W ○ R P G M N ○ ○ ○ K K ○
○ T X Y N C S N R T C P ○ R N L T M A V N M T
P ○ S W C ○ ○ R ○ ○ S S R ○ ○ S ○ C ○ ○ ○ S T
X F N T S ○ ○ N N X ○ S ○ N D R T ○ M T T T ○
○ F ○ ○ L L P T ○ P P T ○ T ○ I W ○ ○ ○ H C R
R V P M ○ ○ R T X C Q ○ G S O D M ○ F S ○ ○ ○
○ S S C L ○ S ○ ○ P S ○ N N L ○ R ○ ○ ○ L J ○
D ○ H N L ○ R ○ T R N D B S R F C L H P D B S
N R ○ C ○ ○ F R R L ○ Y C ○ ○ ○ F G S B L ○ B
○ P T V V L P ○ C T ○ R ○ S S V M ○ D ○ L S J
Y B B ○ H T ○ C N ○ T S ○ D ○ V ○ L ○ P ○ N G
```

ALPHABET SOUP

Insert a different letter of the alphabet into each of the 26 empty boxes to form words of five or more letters reading across. The letter you insert may be at the beginning, the end, or in the middle of the word. Each letter of the alphabet will be used only once. Cross off each letter in the list as you use it. All the letters in each row are not necessarily used in forming the word.

Our solution on page 344

Example: In the first row across we have inserted the letter Q to form the word FREQUENT.

A B C D E F G H I J K L M N O P ~~Q~~ R S T U V W X Y Z

D	B	B	F	R	E	Q	U	E	N	T	A	A
E	L	E	C	T	I		N	L	I	I	T	C
A	R	S	C	U	S		S	T	E	M	C	L
O	M	R	S	U	E		A	M	P	L	E	E
R	I	S	A	U	C		T	R	A	O	K	E
R	P	E	I	D	E		L	A	L	N	N	U
R	R	A	R	R	I		E	G	G	T	O	R
U	C	H	U	R	C		M	B	L	P	R	I
U	D	N	C	H	O		E	S	T	P	E	A
A	G	T	I	O	A		J	E	C	T	S	O
P	J	U	S	T	I		Y	E	C	U	N	G
D	I	I	T	I	D		S	T	A	N	C	E
W	S	B	R	I	N		C	K	P	U	D	I
A	E	R	P	R	I		E	E	D	O	C	K
X	R	D	L	A	U		H	T	E	R	A	S
U	S	N	I	N	E		Y	N	G	E	N	U
A	J	A	T	T	O		R	I	S	T	I	O
D	I	G	T	A	B		E	C	E	A	C	K
A	I	J	A	C	U		Z	I	N	O	F	T
E	G	R	N	E	T		P	I	D	E	R	H
R	I	N	A	L	O		A	S	T	U	R	E
A	R	A	G	N	A		F	U	L	P	I	N
S	S	E	H	E	M		O	L	L	A	R	U
V	I	Y	A	M	A		E	S	T	Y	C	R
T	B	S	O	V	E		C	O	M	E	L	D
A	C	S	T	A	C		E	N	T	A	R	A

CHAIN REACTION

The answer to each clue is a word or phrase formed from two shorter words or syllables. Place the first part of the answer in the link with the corresponding number and the second part in the next link moving clockwise. Links with two numbers use the same word or syllable. The number of letters in each answer is shown in parentheses.

Solution on page 344

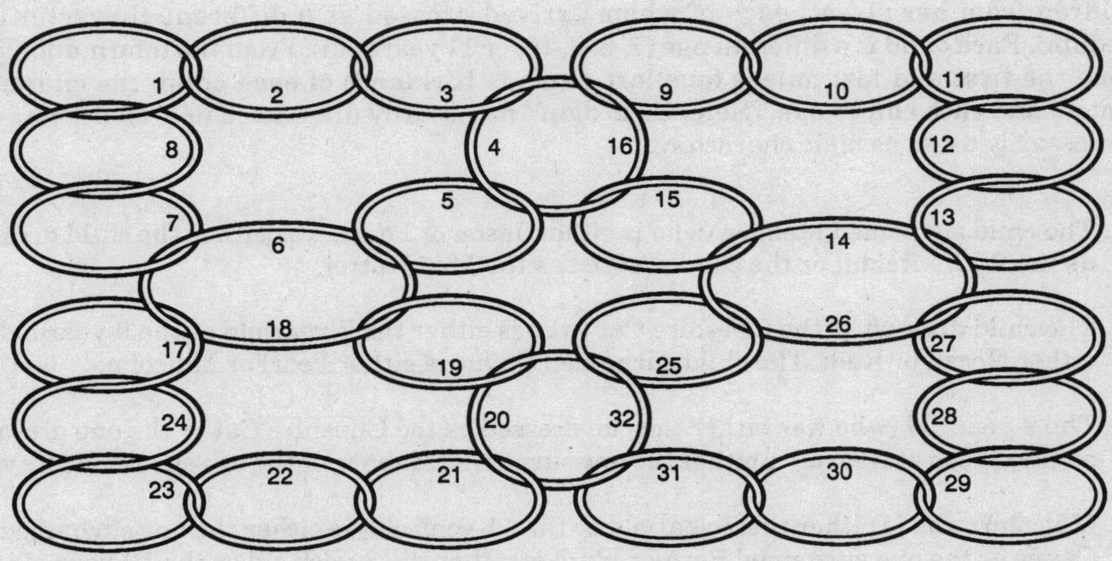

1. Kitchen closet (6)
2. Audition (6)
3. Defeated other marathon contenders (6)
4. Mr. Travis (5)
5. Fabric colorer (4)
6. Goofed (5)
7. Somewhat crimson (7)
8. Kitchen basin (7)
9. Reef material (5)
10. Mr. Trebek (4)
11. Quiz (4)
12. Sufficient (5)
13. Full assemblies (5)
14. Astronauts' agency (4)
15. Plastic wrap (5)
16. Bitter resentment (6)
17. Egg mixer (6)
18. Emerald Isle (4)
19. Tooth filling (5)
20. Temporary job reduction (6)
21. Miff (6)
22. Make precious (6)
23. Tympanum (7)
24. Percussion rhythm (8)
25. Bread from heaven (5)
26. Wealthy person (5)
27. Thread spool (6)
28. Loose-leaf notebook (6)
29. Bowler hat (5)
30. Side road (5)
31. Ambush (6)
32. Nonprofessional (6)

LOGIC PROBLEM

TEATIME

Last week, when Alice Jenkins turned 10 years old, she held a tea party and she asked all of her guests to dress up as characters from her favorite book, *Alice in Wonderland*. Included on her guest list were five children from her street, each of whom arrived dressed as a different character (one was Tweedledum). Each child is a different age (7, 8, 9, 10, or 11 years old). From the information provided, determine the first and last names (one last name is Kirkland) of each child, the character each represented, and each child's age. (Note: Girls didn't necessarily dress as female characters and boys didn't necessarily dress as male characters.)

1. The child surnamed Meharg (who is either Jason or Pearl) was either the child dressed as the White Rabbit or the child dressed as the Mad Hatter.

2. The child dressed as the Cheshire Cat (who is either the 7-year-old or the 9-year-old) is either Norah or Rudi. The child surnamed Cayne is either Pearl or Malcolm.

3. The 9-year-old (who was either the one dressed as the Cheshire Cat or the one dressed as the Queen of Hearts) is either the one surnamed Meharg or the one surnamed Cayne.

4. Malcolm (who is either the 7-year-old or the 11-year-old) is either the one surnamed Cayne or the one surnamed Bernier. Rudi is either the 8-year-old or the 10-year-old.

5. The 8-year-old (who was either the one dressed as the White Rabbit or the one dressed as the Queen of Hearts) is either the one surnamed Cayne or the one surnamed Palmer.

This chart is to help you record information from the clues as well as the facts you deduce by combining information from different clues. We suggest you use an "X" for a "no" and a "•" for a "yes."

		LAST NAME					CHARACTER					AGE				
		BERNIER	CAYNE	KIRKLAND	MEHARG	PALMER	CHESHIRE CAT	MAD HATTER	QUEEN OF HEARTS	TWEEDLEDUM	WHITE RABBIT	7	8	9	10	11
FIRST NAME	JASON															
	MALCOLM															
	NORAH															
	PEARL															
	RUDI															
AGE	7															
	8															
	9															
	10															
	11															
CHARACTER	CHESHIRE CAT															
	MAD HATTER															
	QUEEN															
	TWEEDLEDUM															
	WHITE RABBIT															

Solution on page 345

WORD MATH

In these long-division problems letters are substituted for numbers. Determine the value of each letter. Then arrange the letters in order from 0 to 9, and they will spell a word or phrase.

Solutions on page 345

1.

```
            I R A
REAP | P A R R O T
       Y C R G
       A C T Y O
       A C E E O
           O I C T
           R E A P
             G T A
```

0 __ 1 __ 2 __ 3 __ 4 __ 5 __ 6 __ 7 __ 8 __ 9 __

2.

```
           A D E
NAB | E N S I G N
      E B D S
        A E I G
        A U U B
          H D I N
          H E S N
            B I S
```

0 __ 1 __ 2 __ 3 __ 4 __ 5 __ 6 __ 7 __ 8 __ 9 __

3.

```
            A I R
AVER | V E R S E S
       M M I O
       A R Y Y E
       A A R Y Y
         C C S M S
             I R V E
             A O V C
```

0 __ 1 __ 2 __ 3 __ 4 __ 5 __ 6 __ 7 __ 8 __ 9 __

4.

```
            D I P
DIET | T O U R E D
       I E E D
       L O R T E
         E E R I
         R R C D
           U I R R
           L P T I
```

0 __ 1 __ 2 __ 3 __ 4 __ 5 __ 6 __ 7 __ 8 __ 9 __

5.

```
            O A T
HASH | S T O R M S
       H A S H
       N C N S M
       O T O C S
         H O N N S
         C I R I R
           A I C R
```

0 __ 1 __ 2 __ 3 __ 4 __ 5 __ 6 __ 7 __ 8 __ 9 __

6.

```
              L O B
FOES | N U C L E U S
       N C S E F
         E L F U U
         E N S C U
           O C N T S
           O F C C N
               L C U
```

0 __ 1 __ 2 __ 3 __ 4 __ 5 __ 6 __ 7 __ 8 __ 9 __

PUZZLE IN THE ROUND

To solve this challenging puzzle first fill in as many of the 5-letter answers next to their clues as you can. Next look for shared letters and enter each letter into its correct place in the diagram. The letter in the center will be shared by all the answer words. Look for unshared letters to help you determine the letters that will go in the outer ring to form the name of an actress and one of her roles, reading from 1 to 24.

Solution on page 345

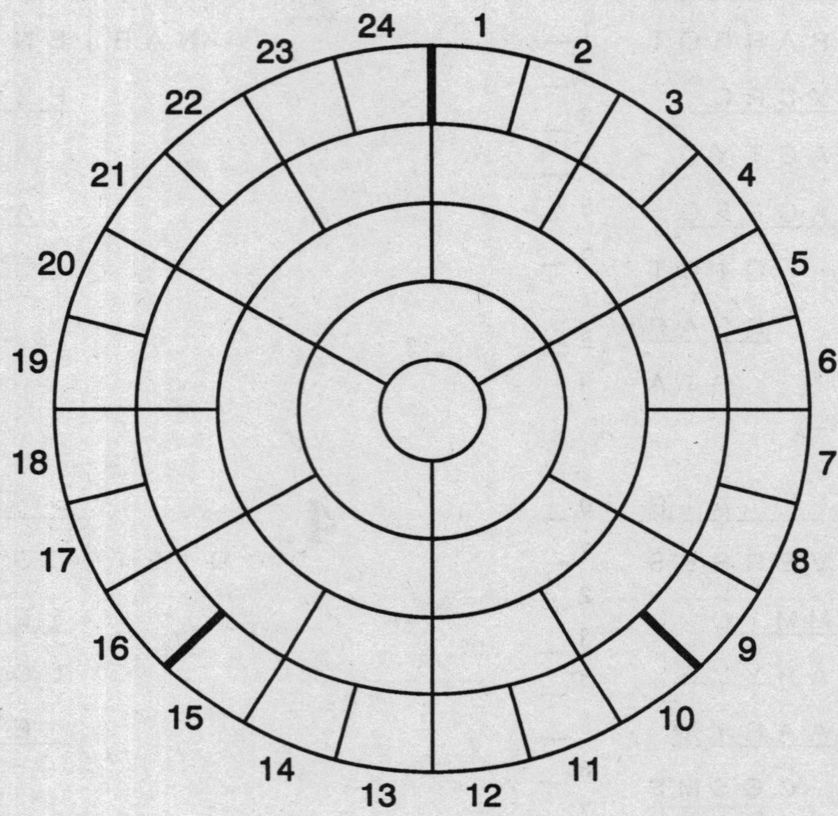

1. Delete _____
2. Noblemen _____
3. Thoughts _____
4. Stuns _____
5. African antelope _____
6. Mix _____
7. Thick _____
8. Hollows _____
9. Camouflages _____
10. Regimens _____
11. Felt ill _____
12. Harvest _____
13. Skate runner _____
14. Clay dwelling _____
15. Caliber _____
16. Penned up _____
17. Princely _____
18. Consent _____
19. Musical drama _____
20. Document _____
21. Bring up _____
22. Strives _____
23. Tower _____
24. Brown pigment _____

TO PLAY:

1. Enter the first seven LETTERBOX letters onto the first DRAWLINE and cross them off in the LETTERBOX.
2. Form a word of at least two letters across or down on the GAMEBOARD. One letter of the first word must go into the starred square.
3. Tally your score in the SCORE column.
4. Carry down all unused letters onto the next DRAWLINE. Transfer enough letters from the LETTERBOX, in the given order, so that you have seven letters to work with.
5. Build a new word or words by:
   a. adding one or more letters before and/or after words on the GAMEBOARD.
   b. adding one or more letters at right angles to words on the GAMEBOARD.
   c. adding a word parallel to one on the GAMEBOARD.

IMPORTANT: All adjoining letters must spell out complete words.

6. Continue working this way until all the letters from the LETTERBOX have been used.
7. Asterisks (*) are "wild" letters and may represent any letter you choose, but once used they cannot be changed.

NOTE: Proper names, foreign words, and abbreviations are not allowed. No word may appear twice on the GAMEBOARD.

TO SCORE:

Score every letter in each new word as follows:

1. Letters in unnumbered squares count 1 point.
2. Letters in numbered squares count the given value of the square.
3. Double the score of a word containing a circle.
4. Triple the score of a word containing two circles.
5. Add 20 points if all seven letters from a DRAWLINE are used in one play.

Can you beat our game of 344 points given on page 345?

LETTERBOX

U Y C N R W O M H I P G E A J S T A X L N E O R K I Z U * D
N T R B A Q S I E F E R I S E A * O V T O L E D T N S U O A

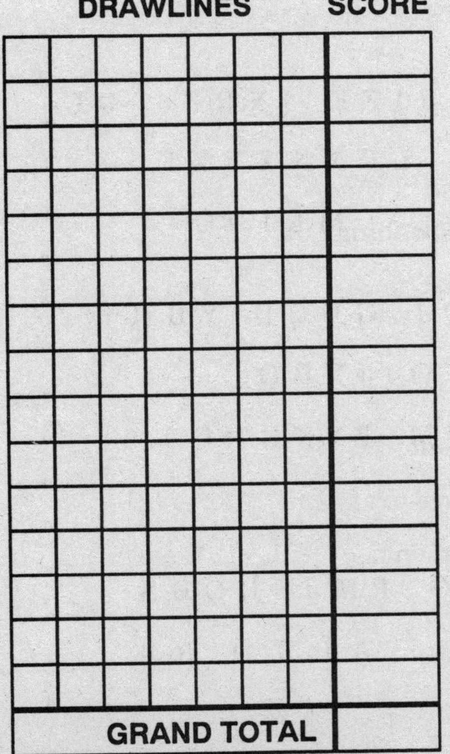

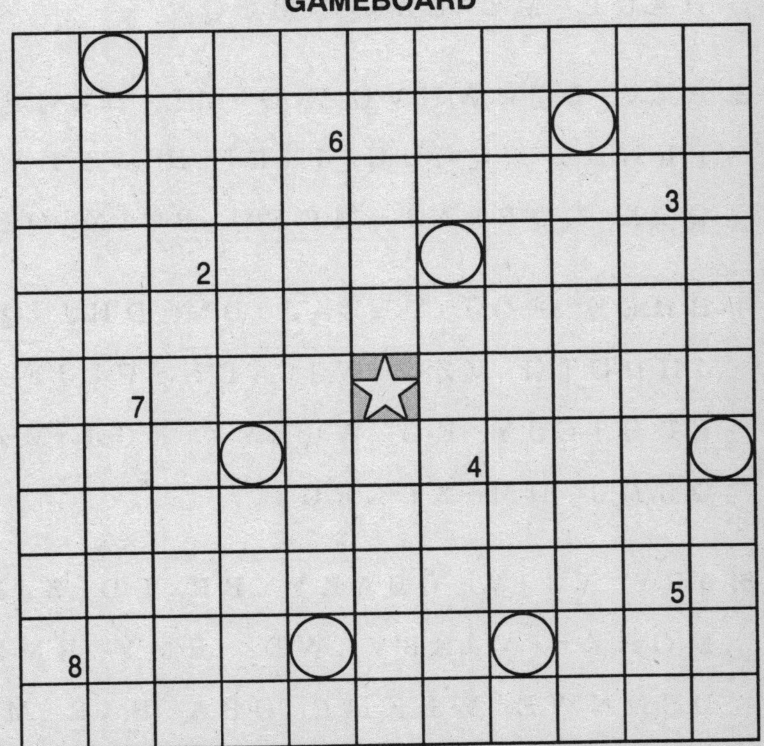

CRYPTOGRAMS

Each of these Cryptograms is a message in substitution code. THE SMART CAT might become MRX DGYUM LYM if M is substituted for T, R for H, X for E, etc. One way to break the code is to look for repeated letters. E, T, A, O, N, R, and I are the most often used letters. A single letter is usually A or I; OF, IS, and IT are common 2-letter words; try THE or AND for a 3-letter group. The code is different for each Cryptogram.

Solutions on page 345

1. MNP JZPWM UWR CX MSS SKMPR WVV SK W ICPQP; CM CX MNP VCMMVP UWR MNWM CX W DORTVP SK QSRMZWTCQMSZH PVPUPRMX. NP CX CRPANWOXMWDVP. HSO RPBPZ QSUP MS MNP PRT SK MNP XOZIZCXPX NP NWX CR XMSZP KSZ HSO.

2. ''AS UIIFP UAFT C MCQ PSIGJ YIJALE,'' PCAQ C ZIPSTPP SI C NAPASALE LTAEZMIG. ''BID ZCQ MTSSTG PSCB WIG QALLTG.'' ''LI SZCLFP,'' SZT LTAEZMIG PCAQ CMPTLSUB. ''A QIL'S SZALF AS HAUU MT SZCS MCQ.''

3. PRV DCCWHVO RQ MLIHEQPRE MRIFE IXRFJ QC PRHD: ''QLHE JXRI HQ YHVRDDJ LRNNXVXF — QLX EQRPNE MCEQ PCIX QLRV QLX MRIFE.''

4. BHED EGJ YRZAJ DM DHJ QBEEQJ GDCL YBHY JHDCTG VZO WJ ADHSCLJF CR WO JXBQ EDHTCJY ED WQZYE EGJ MZVJ DM Z KGDQJ QBMJ DM XBLECJ.

5. JBY VJJW CSAKFYBR LD ZJXRM O RMJSDOBA MODRE VJSBVLWD. RMY RMLBK RJ AJ LD RJ DSNNWE WLKMR OBA BJR MYOR.

6. ZOLY GVXK VYXZSLVXU OYQ ZYXKNBVOBD; VYWZBX GVXK GVBQJD OYQ LZBXLOVYX; BFZYQ GVXK POLZ OYQ QVBPLZXVJY; SVWZ GVXK RJU OYQ SZYZLJBVXU.

7. UIJNHI PIDICYOYNL GLE HGEYN, PRI UVOYLIOO NJ DYJI YPOIDJ ANLOVKIE KNOP NJ PRI QGZYLB RNVHO NJ GKIHYAGLO.

8. HPL UCTGNGVRVHZ HPNH BL FNZ MNVR VW HPL IHCDOORL TDOPH WTH HT KLHLC DI MCTF HPL IDUUTCH TM N YTDCIL BL GLRVLJL HT GL EDIH.

9. ZB TXBDK MIG UCPBT FGWCDS FM RJJIEIURFB EMDBW, FLBD UMMN ORJN FM FLB FCEBT ZLBD ZB LRK DMDB RDK JRUU FLBE FLB ''SMMK MUK KRWT.''

10. FQCU VUQVKU FOJJUUS AUJYOFU EZUN YIU SUFEXWUS EQ, AOE CQFE VUQVKU FOJJUUS AUJYOFU EZUN YIU SUEUICXWUS EQ.

11. TWSG W DVAOSMAATWS UWSFMZ BOA ALS FL ABWJM OS FBM DVAOSMAA DVF FBM ILHMJSTMSF DMWF BOT FL OF.

12. RPHIFBFRPT HB JG FKNSKIT DJT FV NHBLEBBHGC BEOZSLAB DS NFG'A UGFD JGTAPHGC JOFEA.

BRICK BY BRICK

Rearrange this stack of bricks to form a crossword puzzle. The clues will help you fit the bricks into their correct places. Row 1 has been filled in for you. Use the bricks to fill in the remaining spaces.

Solution on page 346

BRICKS

NNE I■R	AM■ ROV	■DI LON	MOU AST	R■A E■S
N■S G■E	EN■ ■■■	ARK T■E	ER■ R■M	GED LER
BET ER■	ATO HAR	TAR STE	N■L ■SA	E■T S■S
STA ■■■	SEW EL■	ANO BAN	P■A I■P	■LE DER
BIK ONE	ATH ■ZI	INA COT	NDI NOD	ESS NTA
MES ■■■	■EG PEE	STE ■■■	■JA GAR	REA TEW
ER■ P■M	ALE TEN	ERA AIM	R■M EMI	ERS PEE

DIAGRAM

	1	2	3	4	5	6	7	8	9	10	11	12	13	14	15
1	R	E	D	S	■	S	T	R	O	P	■	M	A	S	S
2															
3															
4															
5															
6															
7															
8															
9															
10															
11															
12															
13															
14															
15															

ACROSS

1. Warren Beatty film
   Hone a razor
   Bulk
2. Upon
   Love affair
   Zone
3. Mata ____
   Adhesive
   Ragout
4. Substitute
   Wane
5. Drowse
   Yule visitor
6. Cyclist
   Embroider
   Spurred
7. Unique person
   Honey
   Paring knife
8. Strong beer
   Tanned skin
   Epoch
9. Compassionate
   Vivacity
   Disfigure
10. Vapor
   Wager
   Actor Caan
11. Pirate
   Needlefish
12. Main meal
   Signposts
13. Actress Anderson
   Send payment
   Fencing sword
14. Soon
   Fixed gaze
   Actress Louise
15. Explosive sound
   Sen. Kefauver
   Highlander

DOWN

1. Stadium yells
   Canoes
   Science room
2. Coup d'____
   Cove
   "____ Nobis Pacem"
3. Miss Spenlow
   New Hampshire city
   A party to
4. Fishing lure
   Repairing
5. June bug
   Citrus fruit
6. Tasty
   Mal de ____
   Stanza
7. Fed
   Vast expanse
   French caps
8. Varangians
   Fizz water
   Pad
9. Bandit
   Strike
   Deep mud
10. Prettify
   Vitality
   Portals
11. Navigate
   Shake up
12. Rub
   Sells
13. "Vissi d'____"
   Brightness
   Heroic poem
14. Spotted
   Weird
   Italian river
15. Adage
   Small drinks
   Usher

SYL´´LA-CROS´TIC

The directions for solving are given on page 34. Solution on page 345

✱ SYLLABOX ✱

A A BARB BER BLOS BRA CI COUS E ENT ES FOR GEN GO GO IFF IG IM IN INE IO JIN KI LA LE LECT LI LIT LU MI MO NAL NEG NI NI NIT NUM NUM NUN O PROMP RAGL RAU RHU RIL SE SE SHER SOM SOOK TER TER TERN TION TIVE TU U U

1. Bellicose chauvinist (2) J I N G O
2. Flourish (2) _ _ _ _ _ _ _
3. Resident physician (2) _ _ _ _ _ _
4. Zodiac scales (2) _ _ _ _ _
5. Permissive (3) _ _ _ _ _ _ _
6. Extemporaneous (3) _ _ _ _ _ _ _ _ _
7. Digit (2) _ _ _ _ _ _
8. Free from hypocrisy (3) _ _ _ _ _ _ _
9. Of special quality (2) _ _ _ _ _ _
10. Large ape (3) _ _ _ _ _ _ _
11. Everlasting (3) _ _ _ _ _ _ _
12. Reverse photograph (3) _ _ _ _ _ _ _ _
13. Car starter switch (3) _ _ _ _ _ _ _ _
14. Group of soldiers (2) _ _ _ _
15. County law officer (2) _ _ _ _ _ _ _
16. Sidewalk trash (2) _ _ _ _ _ _
17. Arctic native (3) _ _ _ _ _ _
18. Lightweight metal (4) _ _ _ _ _ _ _ _
19. Baseball argument (2) _ _ _ _ _ _ _
20. Papal representative (3) _ _ _ _ _ _
21. Harem (3) _ _ _ _ _ _ _ _
22. Abandoned (2) _ _ _ _ _ _ _
23. Rough-sounding (2) _ _ _ _ _ _ _

PICTURE THIS

You do not need any special art training to produce a picture in the empty grid. Use the letter-number guide above each square and carefully draw what is shown into the corresponding square in the grid.

Solution on page 346

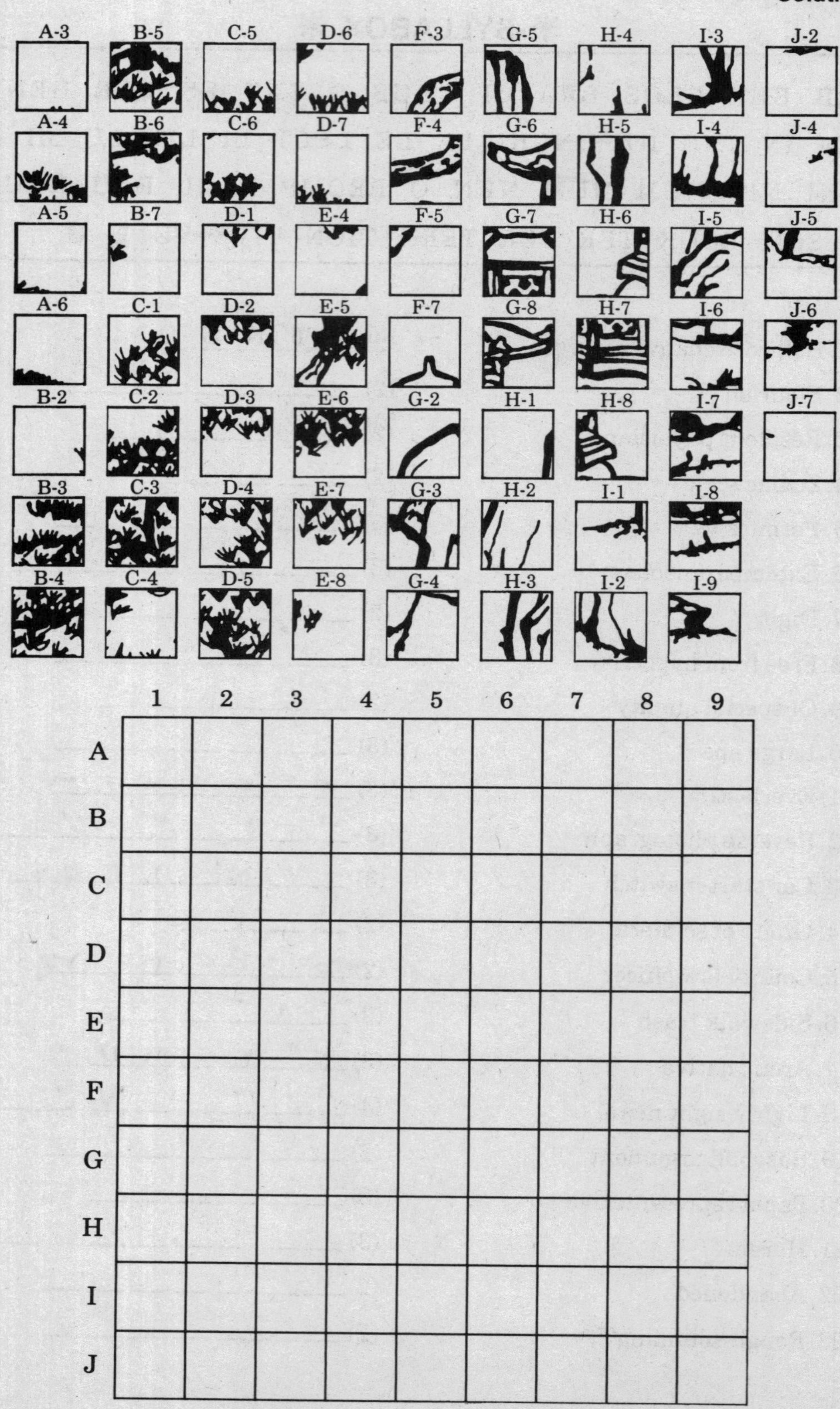

CODEWORD

The directions for solving are given on page 27.

Solution on page 344

1	14 U
2	15
3	16
4	17
5 N	18
6	19
7	20
8	21
9	22
10	23 R
11	24
12	25
13	26

16	25	20	20	24	2	23		25	5	3	24	15
25		25		5		14	23	5		25		25
10	25	12	2	18		6		9	25	15	25	18
7				24	8	6	14	2		14		18
18	4	14	25	26		15		15		2	9	17
		18		2	3	2	5	18				2
1	15	2	22		24		14		13	25	23	26
14 U				1	25	24	19	21		11		
23 R	25	11		23		5		25	15	15	17	19
5 N		21		2	22	10	2	15				24
25	10	17	23	5		2		15	25	10	2	26
10		15		20	24	12		17		14		2
2	15	2	9	13		19	17	11	2	23	2	26

A	~~N~~
B	O
C	P
D	Q
E	~~R~~
F	S
G	T
H	~~U~~
I	V
J	W
K	X
L	Y
M	Z

CODEWORD

Solution on page 345

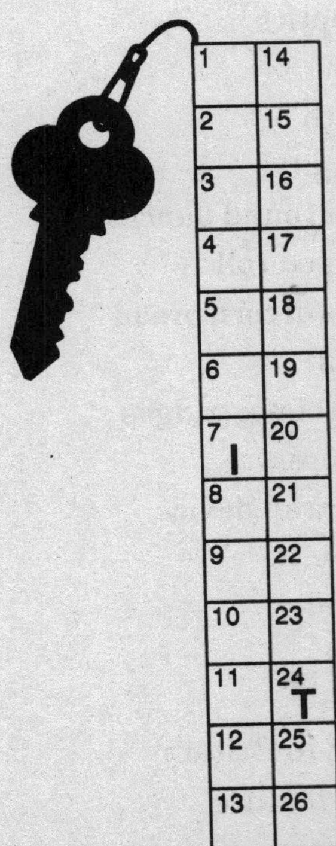

1	14
2	15
3	16
4	17
5	18
6	19
7 I	20
8	21
9	22
10	23
11	24 T
12	25
13	26

2	3	4	7 I	24 T	17		3		8		22	
1		8		11		6	13	8	15	24	8	5
8	14	24	4	3			10		21		5	
23		7		12	20	4	8		3	14	7	15
24	20	23			3		4		1		3	
17		3	21	13	24	8		9	3	13	23	24
			3		11		2		24			
9	20	13	15	24		19	20	2	8	19		5
	21		11		3		24			7	21	8
22	8	15	3		26	8	15	24		26		25
	3		26		20			3	1	7	26	7
8	23	15	1	3	25	8		14		24		21
	15		8		8		18	7	16	16	1	8

A	N
B	O
C	P
D	Q
E	R
F	S
G	~~T~~
H	U
~~I~~	V
J	W
K	X
L	Y
M	Z

FLOWER POWER

The answers to this petaled puzzle will go in a curve from the number on the outside to the center of the flower. Each number has two 5-letter words. One goes in a clockwise direction and the second in a counter-clockwise direction. Try working from both sets of clues to fill the flower.

Solution on page 345

CLOCKWISE

1. Goddesses of destiny
2. Like French vowels
3. Nostrils
4. One over par
5. Useful
6. Stupid mistake
7. Road worker
8. "____ the Barbarian"
9. Encrypted
10. Star watcher
11. Helicopter part
12. Provide food for
13. Resort building
14. Partners
15. Diminish
16. Walks back and forth
17. Designate
18. Opponent

COUNTERCLOCKWISE

1. ____ optics
2. Hubs
3. Of birth
4. Swiss city
5. Israeli round dances
6. O-shaped roll
7. Loaves of corn bread
8. Sweets
9. Group of partridges
10. Sure loser
11. Speed trap device
12. Deceive
13. Loathed
14. Engine
15. Spud
16. Father, in Britain
17. Blazer feature
18. Hastens

DOUBLE DELIGHT

Enjoy the Double Delight of solving this puzzle by placing two letters into each square. Each pair of letters in the diagram will read in the same order for both the Across and the Down words.

Solution on page 345

ACROSS

1. Summerhouse
3. Wheedle
5. Reward
7. Run aground
8. Take a chance
9. Choice
11. Elaborate
13. Chipmunk, e.g.
15. College treasurer
17. Harsh
19. Volcano feature
21. Book of prayers
22. Said
23. River embankments
25. Revised
27. Academy Awards
29. Boil
31. Steal
33. Quest
35. Nearly
36. Most peculiar
37. Wild ass
38. Some are golden
39. Engraved

DOWN

1. Horse's gait
2. Massachusetts city
3. Frankness
4. Papal representative
5. Spanish dance
6. Dictator
10. Big cats
12. Indigenous
14. Loss
15. Parcel
16. Multitudes
17. Closed securely
18. Took it easy
19. Formulas of belief
20. Blunders
24. "National ___"
26. Reflexive pronoun
28. Kind of salad
29. Fall or spring
30. Doctor
31. Gun
32. Eats away
33. Six-line stanza
34. Rang

1		2
	■	7
9	10	

3		4
	■	8
11	12	

5		6
	■	
13	14	

15		16
	■	21
23	24	

17		18
	■	22
25	26	

19		20
	■	
27	28	

29		30
	■	35
37		

31		32
	■	36
38		

33		34
	■	
39		

Changaword

Can you change the top word into the bottom word in each column in the number of steps indicated in parentheses? Change only one letter at a time and do not change the order of the letters. Proper names, slang, and obsolete words are not allowed.

Our solution on page 348

1. FARM (4 steps)	2. CORN (5 steps)	3. GROW (6 steps)	4. BARN (6 steps)
LAND	SEED	PEAS	SILO

DART GAME

Complete 5-letter words reading outward from the center by placing the given letters correctly in the diagram blanks. Each letter will be used only once. All five words begin with the center letter.

Solution on page 345

A C D E G L M N O R T

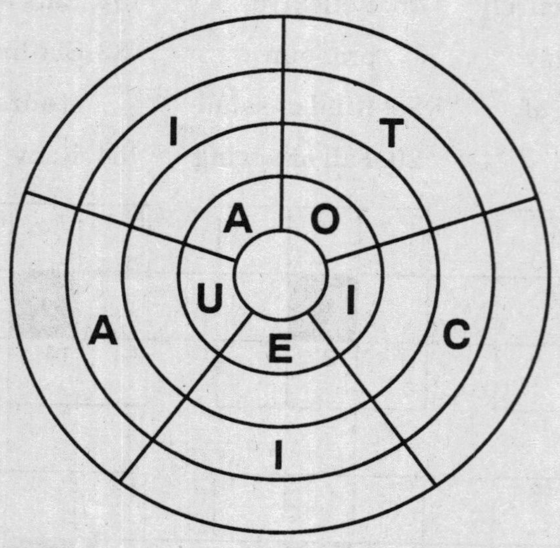

STARSPELL

How many words of five or six letters can you form by moving from letter to connected letter in the Starspell diagram? A letter may be repeated in a word, but only after leaving it and coming back. Plurals ending in S, proper names, abbreviations, contractions, and foreign words are not allowed. Our list of 36 five-letter words and 33 six-letter words is on page 345.

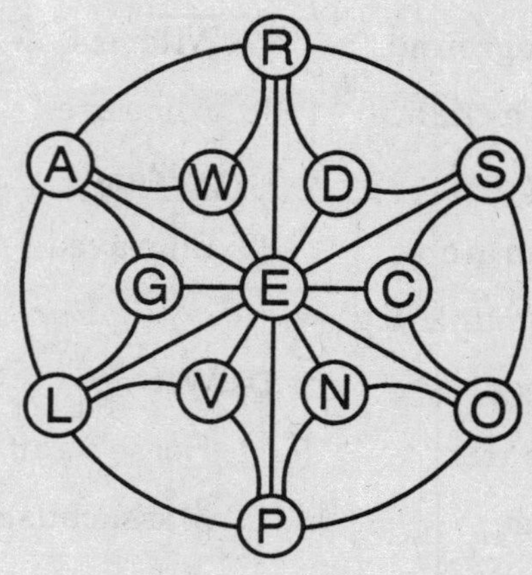

LINE 'EM UP

Line up the inner and outer rings to discover a 12-letter word. Use your imagination to rotate the rings so that the first letter of the word is opposite the number 1, the second letter opposite the number 2, and so forth. When you have lined up the first letter with number 1 correctly, the rest of the numbers will indicate the order of the letters in the word.

Solution on page 344

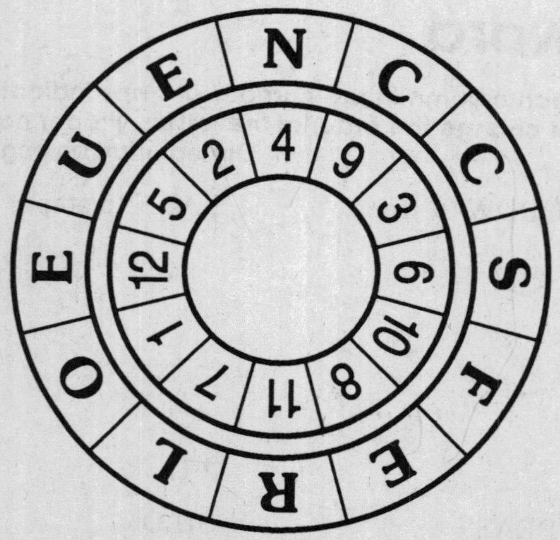

WHEEL SUMS

Using each of the numbers 1 through 13 only once, fill in the blank spaces in the wheel so that each group of three numbers from the center out totals the sum shown outside the wheel.

Solution on page 346

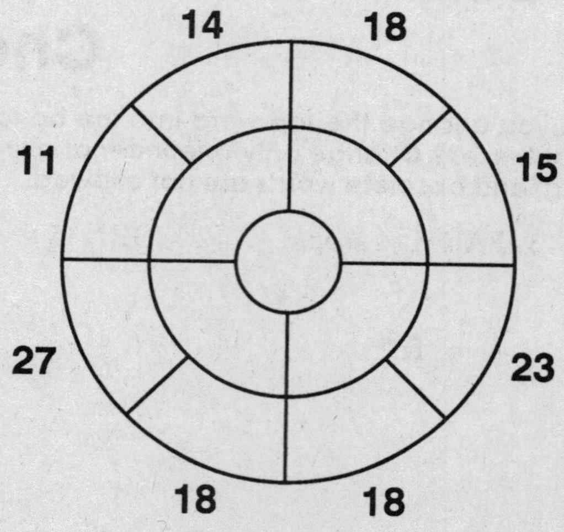

Building Blocks

Using only the letters in the word APT, complete the words in the Building Blocks. Words read across only. Every word contains each letter of APT at least once. Solution on page 346

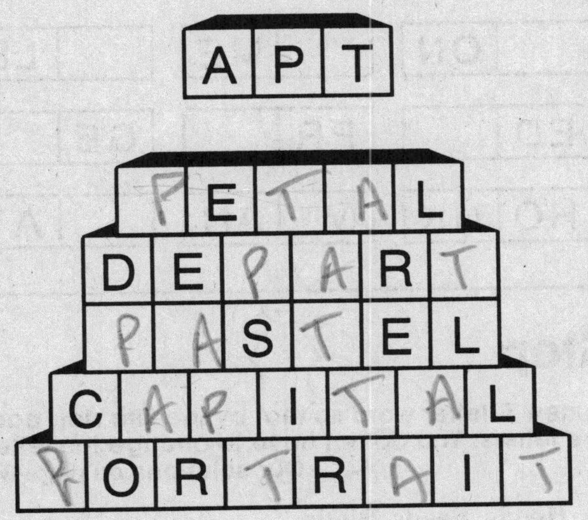

Linkwords

Add a Linkword to the end of the word on the left and the beginning of the word on the right to form two compound words or phrases. The dashes indicate the number of letters in the Linkword. For example, if the words were PEANUT _ _ _ _ _ _ FLY, the Linkword would be BUTTER (Peanut butter, Butterfly). Solutions on page 345

1. SCARE _ _ _ _ BAR
2. PAN _ _ _ _ WALK
3. HEAD _ _ _ _ STAND
4. FOOT _ _ _ _ PEEN
5. HORSE _ _ _ _ HORN
6. CRAB _ _ _ _ _ BLOSSOM
7. TEA _ _ _ HOLDER
8. TRUCK _ _ _ _ GAP
9. CHEST _ _ _ HATCH
10. HERE _ _ _ _ _ MATH

Keyword

To find the Keyword fill in the blanks in words 1 through 10 with the correct missing letters. Transfer those letters to the correspondingly numbered squares in the diagram. Approach with care—this puzzle is not as simple as it first appears. Solution on page 346

1	2	3	4	5	6	7	8	9	10

1. SHA__L
2. M__NOR
3. __IGHT
4. __RAIN
5. __UMPS
6. SN__RE
7. CHAR__
8. TI__ED
9. BL__ND
10. G__ASS

Number Sleuth

One of the numbers in the hexagons has been circled because it and the numbers in the six surrounding hexagons are all different. There are 13 others like this. Are you a sharp-eyed sleuth who can find them all? Solution on page 346

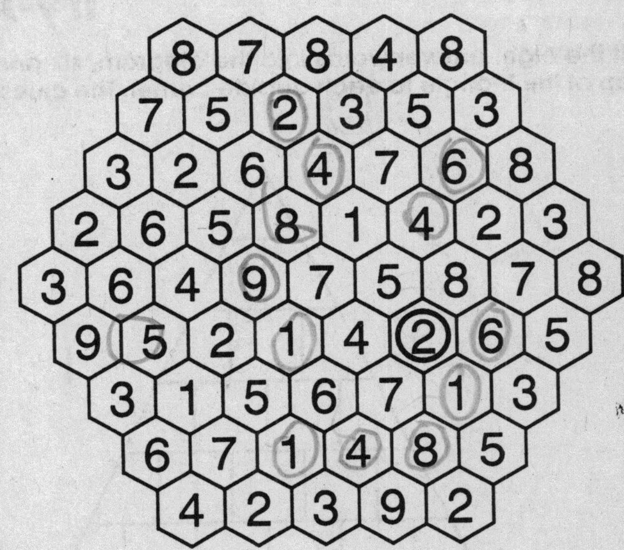

Exchange Boards

Form 4- and 6-letter words by exchanging the 2-letter groups from each set of boards to the other set. Start by taking all the pieces from the left boards and adding them to the right boards to complete 4-letter words. Then take all the pieces that were given in the right boards and add them to the left to complete 6-letter words.

Solution on page 346

LEFT BOARDS (6-Letter Words)

MO		EY	UP		
		DY			TO
	SW		SL		
FO	RM			ST	

RIGHT BOARDS (4-Letter Words)

	LD	CO	PE	ER	
	ON		ME		LE
ED		PR		GE	
HO	NK		AN		AT

Step by Step

In five steps change each word one letter at a time into a new 5-letter word so that by the fifth step each letter has been changed. Do not rearrange the order of the letters. You do not have to change the letters in order.

Our solutions on page 346

Example: Heard, Hears, Heads, Heeds, Seeds, Sleds

1. CROWN	2. SCORE	3. FAVOR	4. BLUET
______	______	______	______
______	______	______	______
______	______	______	______
______	______	______	______
______	______	______	______

Try-Angles

Fit the eight answer words into the diagram, six answers across and one answer down each side from the top of the triangle to each outside corner. The clues are given in no particular order.

Solution on page 346

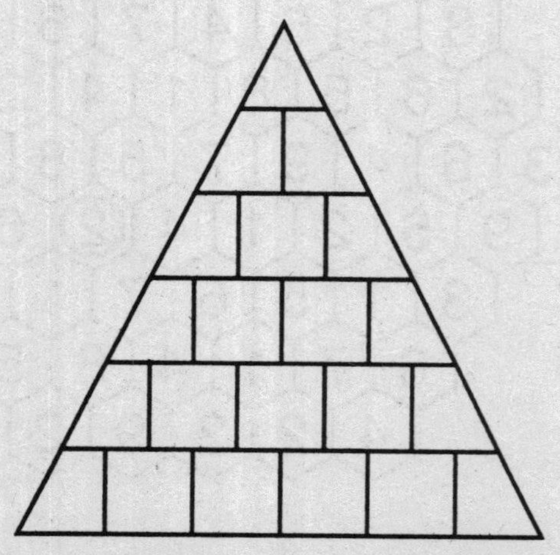

Bounce
Potential steel
Clamor
Operate
Shakespearean work
Drinking glass
Italian river
Serpentine letter

Abacus

Slide the abacus beads on the wires to form five related words reading down. All the beads will be used. Keep in mind that the beads are on wires and cannot jump over one another. An empty abacus is provided for you to work in.

Solution on page 346

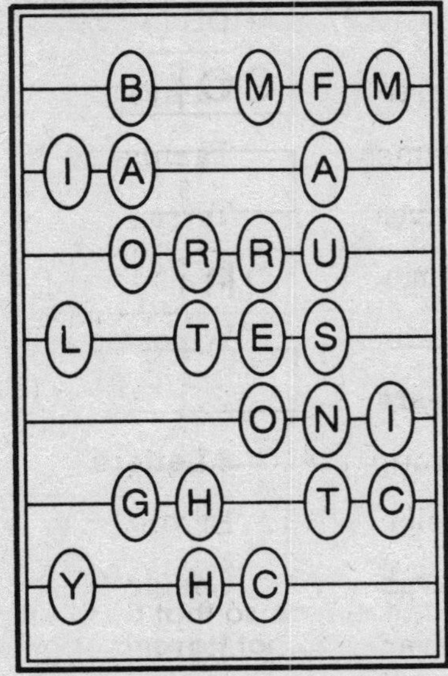

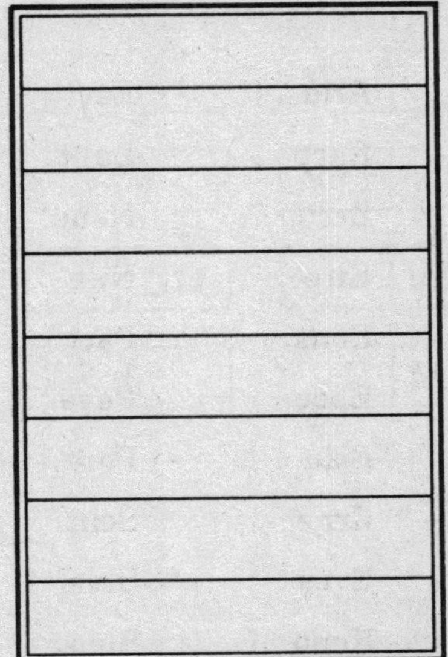

Anagram Quote

Unscramble each set of letters below the dashes to complete a humorous quotation.

Solution on page 346

A ________ is the ________ ________ between ____ ________ of ______.

ABDEET GLOSTEN CANDIETS WTO NIPSTO EVWI

Four-Fit

Without changing the order of the letters, place the 4-letter words on the dashes to form 8-letter words. Each 4-letter word will be used once.

Solution on page 347

CLAY	LOAD	MICE	RENT	SENT
FOIL	LOSE	PACE	RICH	SITE
HOSE	MART	PINT	ROSE	SOME

1. S __ __ W C A __ __
2. __ A C R __ __ S __
3. B A __ E M __ __ __
4. __ __ C O __ __ E T
5. D I S __ L __ __ __
6. C U __ T __ __ __ R
7. __ L __ T __ L __ A
8. __ __ D E S __ __ P
9. F __ __ Q U E __ __
10. T __ __ U __ __ R S
11. __ A N __ __ U R __
12. R A I __ R __ __ __
13. __ __ J O __ I __ Y
14. __ O __ G __ A N __
15. __ U __ I N __ R __

DIAGRAMLESS FILL-IN

For this fill-in puzzle we have given you all of the E's that appear in the diagram, but none of the black squares. As you solve the puzzle, remember to put a black square at the beginning and end of each answer and to balance each black square with its symmetrical counterpart on the opposite side of the diagram.

Solution on page 346

3 Letters
Ate
End
Pat
Set
Spa

4 Letters
Alai
Amah
Ames
Aria
Earp
Ecru
Eire
Eons
Epee
Erie
Erne
Eves
Keno
Lama
Levi
Lunt
Nene
Nile
Pact
Pave
Pore
Sent
Slam
Smog
Snag
Stir
Tale
Trap
Trek
Trot

5 Letters
Agora
Amend
Arrow
Avert
Carte
Dames
Eaves
Eerie
Elate
Gears
Group
Helot
Sarah
Sever
Spite
Tames
Tampa
Terra
Trait
Wipes

6 Letters
Errant
Google
Menial
Thrice

7 Letters
Aerials
Spreads

8 Letters
Adapting
Sinatras

13 Letters
United Nations

								E												
							E													
										E										
									E											
		E								E										
				E																
					E									E						
										E										
								E												
								E												
						E														E
										E										
								E			E						E			E
												E								E
										E										
													E							
											E			E						
													E		E					

WORD MERGERS

Rearrange the letters in each Word Merger to form two words using all the given letters only once. Then rearrange these same letters and merge them into one long word. You might want to form the long word first and then the pair of words. Score 5 points for each pair of words you form and 10 points for each long word. A score of 85 is good, 95 is very good, and 105 is excellent.

Our solutions with a perfect score of 120 points on page 346

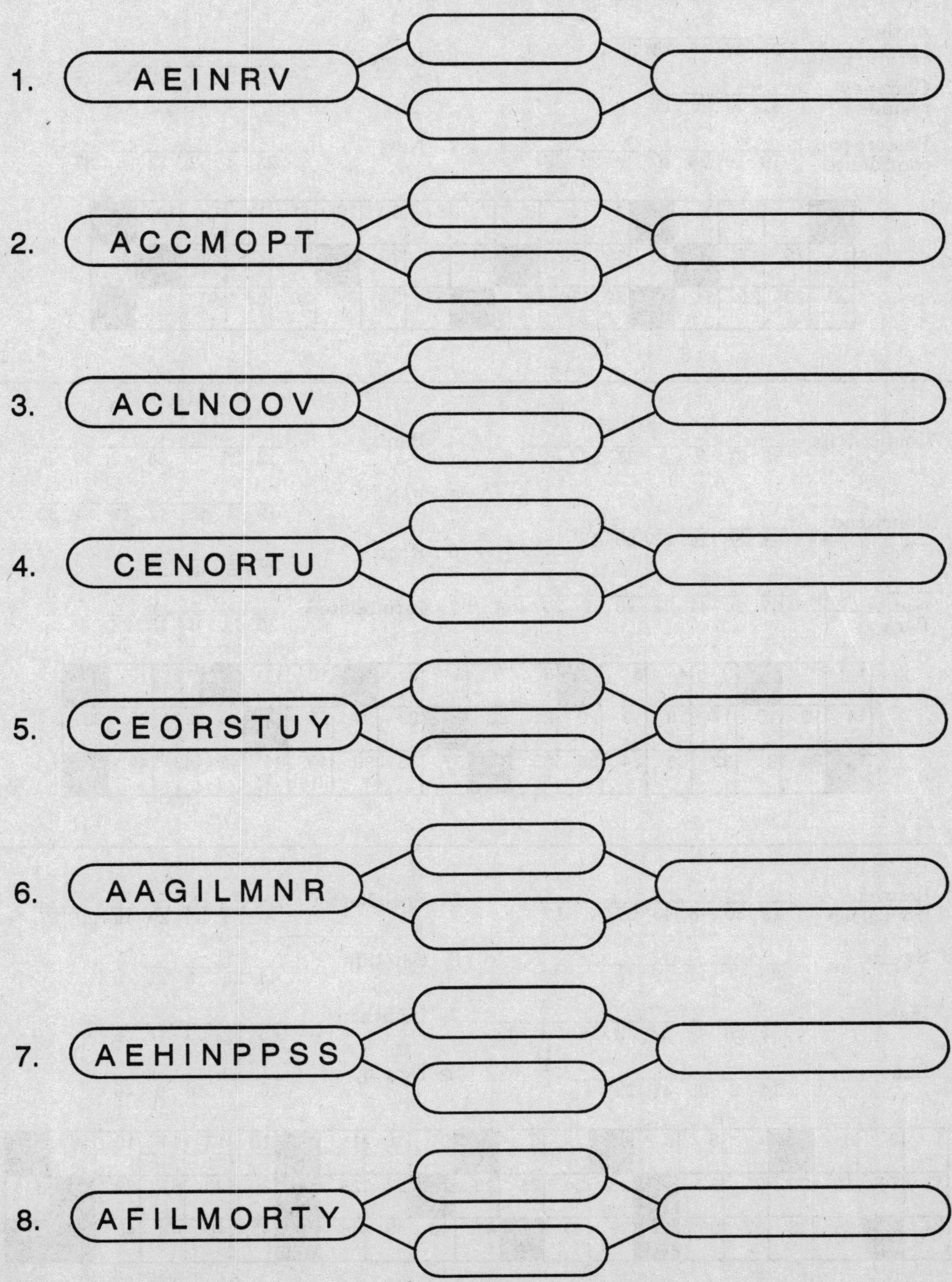

QUOTAGRAMS

Fill in the answers to the clues. Then transfer the letters to the correspondingly numbered squares in the diagrams. The completed diagrams will contain quotations.

Solutions on page 346

A.

1. Opinion — 21 34 38 10 13 18
2. Author Mark ____ — 23 27 15 12 36
3. Chimney residue — 41 24 1 11
4. Restore to confidence — 16 19 28 40 8 22 33 7
5. Mystery — 14 39 6 3 17 30
6. Reply — 32 29 9 20 35 26
7. New — 25 4 2 31 5 37

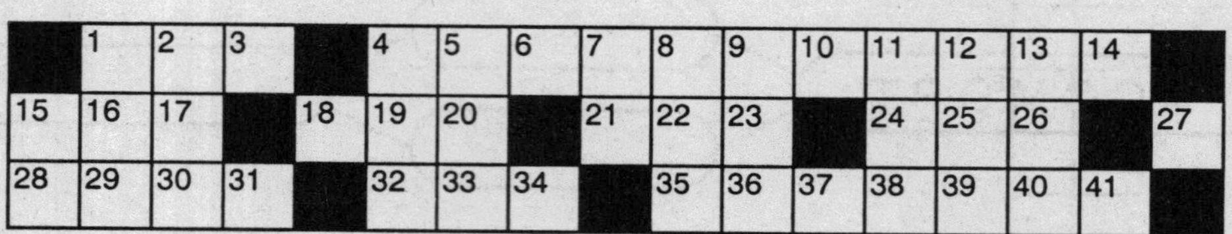

B.

1. Comic strip — 33 21 7 8 25 29 16
2. Sherwood ____ — 44 38 14 31 28 10
3. ____ National Park — 37 24 41 13 26 1 20 15
4. Pantry — 12 27 9 36 42 30 3
5. Pairs — 19 4 39 17 43 34 32
6. Rage — 2 5 40 23
7. Intimidated — 35 11 6 18 22

1	2	■	3	4	5	■	6	7	8	9	■	10	11	■	12	13	■
14	15	16	17	18	19	20	21	22	■	23	24	25	■	26	27	28	29
■	30	31	32	33	34	35	36	■	37	38	39	40	41	42	43	44	■

C.

1. Roused from sleep — 12 30 48 43 37 3 17
2. Swore — 25 7 11 19 15
3. Fist — 35 26 5 22 42 18 39 31
4. Beat — 14 2 38 41 23 4
5. Speediest — 8 24 33 29 10 20 27
6. Satellite — 44 28 13 21
7. Lighthouse — 45 32 36 47 34 6
8. Employees — 16 1 46 9 40

1	2	3	■	4	5	6	■	7	8	■	9	10	11	■	12	13	14	15	16	■
17	18	19	20	21	22	■	23	24	25	26	■	27	28	■	29	30	31	32	■	33
34	■	35	36	37	38	■	39	40	■	41	42	43	44	■	45	46	47	48	■	■

ESCALATORS

Write the answer to clue 1 in the first space. Drop one letter and rearrange the remaining letters to answer clue 2. Put the dropped letter into Column A. Drop another letter and rearrange the remaining letters to answer clue 3. Put the dropped letter into Column B. Follow this pattern for each row in the diagram. When completed, the letters in Column A and Column B, reading down, will spell related words or a phrase.

Solutions on page 346

1

1. Parish head
2. Cook, as chestnuts
3. Category
4. Small harpsichord
5. Exhausted
6. Egg holder
7. Tried to obtain
8. Yell
9. Consequently
10. Umpire's call
11. Journeys
12. Relax
13. Make angry
14. Raring
15. Equipment

	A		B	
1		2		3
4		5		6
7		8		9
10		11		12
13		14		15

2

1. Wine bottle
2. Comedy
3. Marathon, e.g.
4. Ran
5. Slight degree
6. Lean-to
7. Insist on
8. Like a horse
9. Mr. Martin
10. Texas capital
11. Components
12. Amaze
13. Biker's protection
14. Actress Merman
15. Quaker pronoun
16. Hot and humid
17. Substantive
18. Docile

	A		B	
1		2		3
4		5		6
7		8		9
10		11		12
13		14		15
16		17		18

3

1. Teeth aligners
2. Frighten
3. Burn
4. Joins
5. Beer mug
6. New Jersey team
7. "____ Dallas"
8. Minimum
9. Auction
10. Attorney
11. Track event
12. Harplike instrument
13. Passionate
14. Inclination
15. Lease
16. Prohibited
17. White or rye
18. Dull
19. Snow bits
20. Untrue
21. Secure

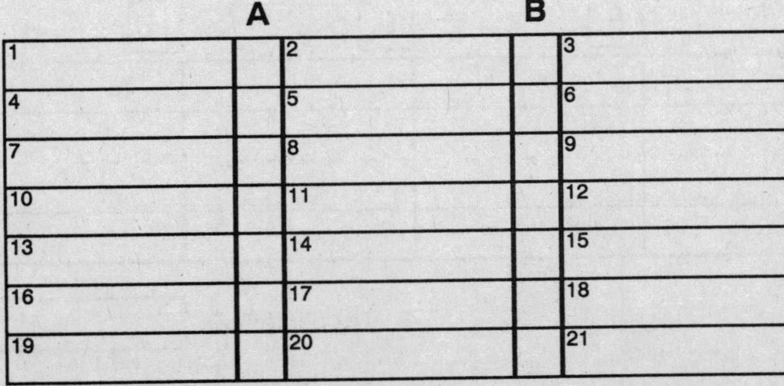

	A		B	
1		2		3
4		5		6
7		8		9
10		11		12
13		14		15
16		17		18
19		20		21

BOWL GAME

To bowl a strike (20 points) you must create a 10-letter word using all the letters in each pin. The letter on top in the pin is the first letter of the strike word. To bowl a spare (10 points) use the same 10 letters to form two words. Splits are not allowed: you may not divide the strike to form a spare. For example, SWEETHEART may not become SWEET and HEART. **Our solutions with a perfect score of 300 points given on page 346**

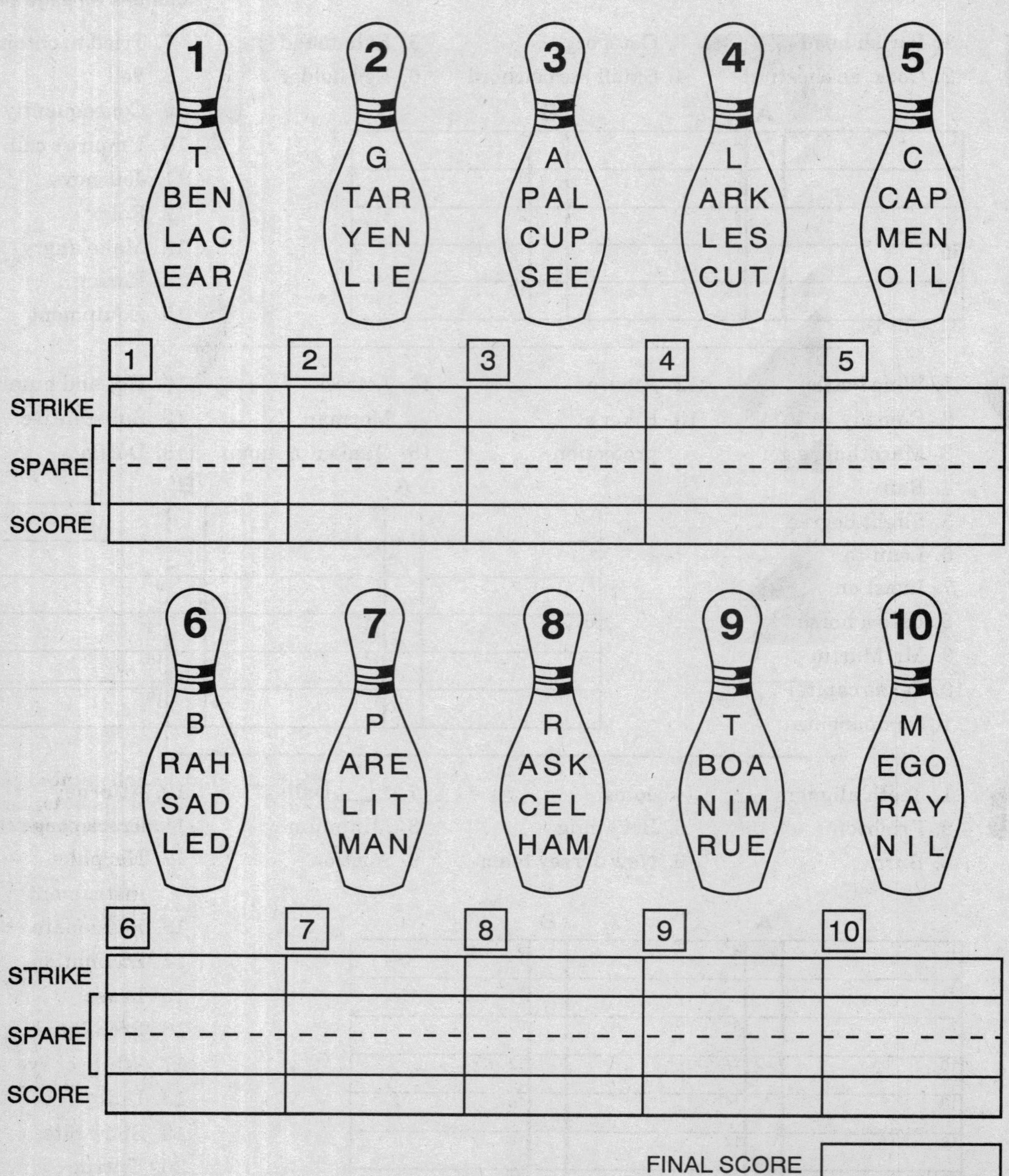

SUM TOTALS

Place one digit (1 to 9, no zeros) in each square so that the sum of the numbers in each group of squares across or down is the number given. The number below a diagonal is the sum of the numbers below it. The number to the right of a diagonal is the sum of the numbers to the right of it. IMPORTANT: No digit is used more than once in any group of squares leading to a sum. One group of digits has been given for you.

Solution on page 347

■	■	32\	6\	■	30\	8\	■	■	18\	13\	4\	19\	■
■	13\11			17\6			15\	\16					■
\39	5	3	1	9	8	7	6	14\11					24\
\9			23\9			7\16				■	\16		
■	17\3			\9			5\17			25\	37\8		
\14				24\21					6\26				
\30					16\3			\19				42\	■
■	\20					■	16\	19\10					13\
■	14\	32\21				7\17			25\19				
\18					29\24					\22			
\16			■	\13			3\3			9\15			7\
\14			12\	14\10				5\5			7\11		
■	\29					\40							
■	\22					■	\6			\9			■

DIAL-A-GRAMS

Each of the messages below is in a number code based on the familiar telephone dial. Each number represents one of the letters shown with it on the dial. You must decide which one. A number is not necessarily the same letter each time.

Solutions on page 346

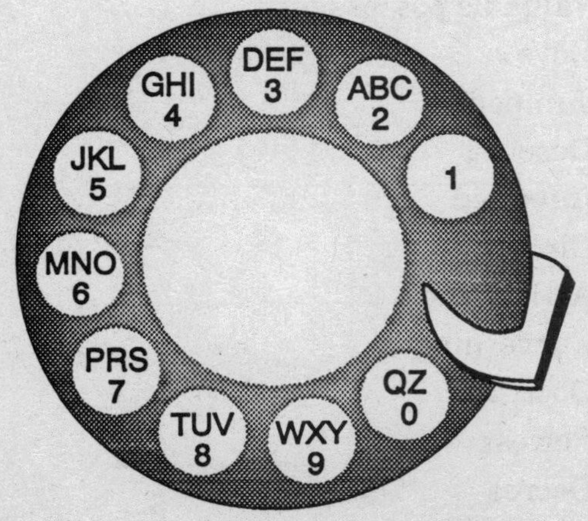

A. 843 739273 63 2 84464 9355 3663 47 86 4283 3663 48.

B. 93 2663377 76255 328587, 46 67337 86 467468283 8428 93 4283 66 47328 6637.

SPIDER'S WEB

Rearrange the 4-letter answer to each clue on the left to form a 5-letter word ending with the center letter T. Place the 5-letter word in the Spider's Web at the corresponding number, reading inward. Each 5-letter word answers one of the clues on the right. For example, the answer to the first clue is EMIR. Rearrange these letters, add the given letter T, and form the 5-letter word MERIT, which is the answer to clue J. When completed, the outer ring of the web, reading from 1 to 18, will spell out a nursery rhyme title.

Solution on page 346

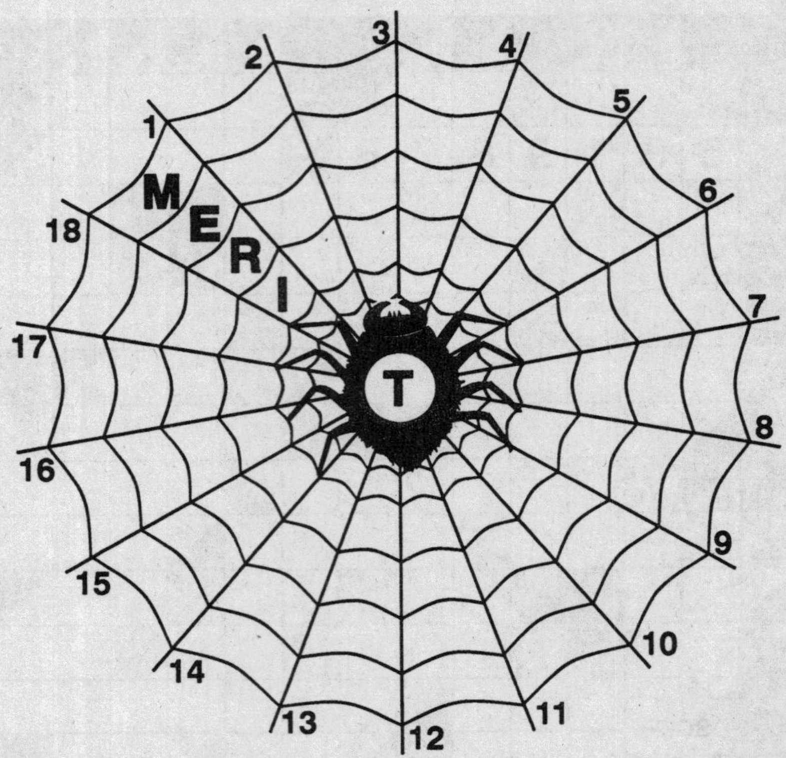

4-Letter Words

1. Arab chieftain
2. English queen
3. Bumpkin
4. Sore
5. Ostrich's kin
6. Female servant
7. Wait
8. Metrical foot
9. Store transaction
10. Queue
11. Shopping basket
12. Adolescent
13. Toll
14. Gamblers' bones
15. Actor's part
16. Oceans
17. Title
18. Malt brew

5-Letter Words

a. Automaton
b. Confess
c. Pamphlet
d. Shortcoming
e. Dormouse
f. Valentine
g. Valuable possession
h. Cove
i. Jumped
j. Deserve
k. Intended
l. Circuit
m. Artist's cap
n. Concerning
o. Doctrine
p. Fewest
q. Decree
r. Luxury ship

SCOREMASTER

TO PLAY:

1. Write the first seven LETTERS across the first line of the PLAY CHART. Indicate the last letter used.
2. Form a word of at least two letters across or down in the DIAGRAM. One letter of the first word must go into the center square.
3. Tally your score, noting any bonuses (see key at bottom).
4. Carry down all unused LETTERS to the next line of the PLAY CHART. Transfer enough LETTERS, in the given order, so that you have seven LETTERS to work with.
5. Form a new word or words from each draw by:
   a. Adding one or more letters to an existing word.
   b. Building a new word at right angles to an existing word, by adding to it or incorporating one of its letters.
   c. Setting a new word parallel to an existing word, but remember all adjoining letters must form new words in crossword fashion.
6. Continue working in this way until all the LETTERS have been used or you can no longer form any words. If you need more lines for your PLAY CHART, use a separate piece of paper.

NOTE: Proper names, foreign words, and abbreviations are not allowed.

TO SCORE:

The value of each letter is given with it. The letter has the same value every time it is used. Be sure always to include all bonuses (see key at bottom). An additional 30 points is earned when you use all seven letters in the PLAY CHART in one turn. When two words are formed in the same play, the common letter (including any bonus) is scored with each word.

Our game with a score of 601 points on page 346

LETTERS

H 5	R 2	G 3	U 1	E 1	I 1	O 1	A 1	S 2	C 5	F 3	N 2	D 2	J 7	R 2	Y 4	I 1
E 1	T 2	A 1	K 6	L 2	O 1	S 2	Q 9	B 3	I 1	M 3	E 1	Z 8	U 1	L 2	A 1	O 1
T 2	E 1	R 2	N 2	X 7	U 1	I 1	S 2	T 2	P 5	D 2	A 1	V 4	E 1	N 2	O 1	W 4

PLAY CHART **SCORE**

TOTAL

DIAGRAM

KEY: DOUBLE LETTER, TRIPLE LETTER, DOUBLE WORD, TRIPLE WORD

ALPHABET SOUP

Insert a different letter of the alphabet into each of the 26 empty boxes to form words of five or more letters reading across. The letter you insert may be at the beginning, the end, or in the middle of the word. Each letter of the alphabet will be used only once. Cross off each letter in the list as you use it. All the letters in each row are not necessarily used in forming the word.

Our solution on page 347

Example: In the first row across insert the letter F and form the word TREFOIL.

A B C D E F G H I J K L M N O P Q R S T U V W X Y Z

R	E	V	T	R	E		O	I	L	A	V	E
A	R	T	C	H	S		U	A	S	H	L	Y
B	R	A	G	R	A		E	K	E	K	N	I
A	C	I	R	C	U		T	R	I	B	L	T
O	I	R	E	F	E		E	E	I	V	E	Y
E	G	A	R	D	E		U	A	V	E	N	E
L	A	U	L	G	A		E	R	A	G	E	H
S	M	A	L	L	W		A	G	N	E	T	R
A	I	S	L	A	N		J	O	U	R	N	S
R	I	P	P	I	C		L	E	T	W	O	S
M	E	C	H	A	N		C	D	R	E	A	W
A	N	T	A	P	R		I	R	I	E	B	E
A	R	C	L	E	M		N	N	I	B	L	E
S	P	A	R	T	I		E	A	L	O	U	S
F	R	E	I	G	H		A	R	O	V	E	R
W	I	E	H	G	O		L	I	N	E	H	T
G	E	X	C	E	R		T	D	S	A	N	D
M	E	N	S	H	O		E	R	V	O	W	E
Q	U	I	Q	M	A		N	I	F	I	E	D
S	I	T	R	A	N		E	E	V	E	R	X
E	A	T	V	E	N		E	L	T	A	M	S
R	E	M	A	I	T		P	H	O	O	N	W
E	L	F	F	E	L		C	T	L	I	C	D
B	O	R	H	Y	T		M	E	M	P	Y	X
A	R	G	A	L	A		Y	G	E	N	D	Y
F	I	E	R	L	E		I	C	E	N	S	E

All at C

Framework 23

These words are listed in alphabetical order according to length. Fit them into their proper places in the Framework. This puzzle has been started for you with the entry COMPLIMENT. Now look for another 10-letter entry with a fourth letter P. Continue working this way until the puzzle is completed.

4 Letters
Chat
Chic
Cite
Clue
Coat
Coil
Cola
Cone
Copy
Cost
Cram

5 Letters
Cacti
Camel
Chalk
Chart
Chill
Cloth
Comic

6 Letters
Cached
Cachet
Caftan
Chance
Chapel
Charge
Clever
Clings
Clinic
Coffee
Cradle
Crunch
Cyclic

7 Letters
Cadence
Classes
Coconut
Collect
Concave
Contend

8 Letters
Cachucha
Cellular
Cheerful
Chivalry
Competes
Contacts
Contract
Critical
Cyclonic

9 Letters
Character
Chocolate
Classical
Commander
Component
Concocted

10 Letters
Centimeter
Chopsticks
Cloverleaf
Compliment ✓
Concurrent

Solution on page 337

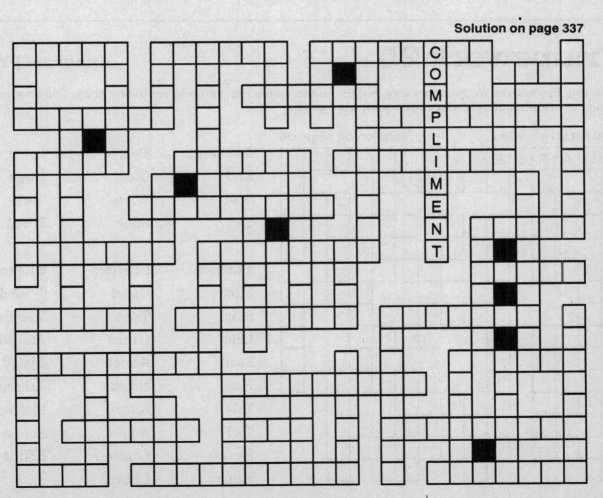

C
O
M
P
L
I
M
E
N
T

Framework 24

Martial Your Arts

First word on page 351

Solution on page 336

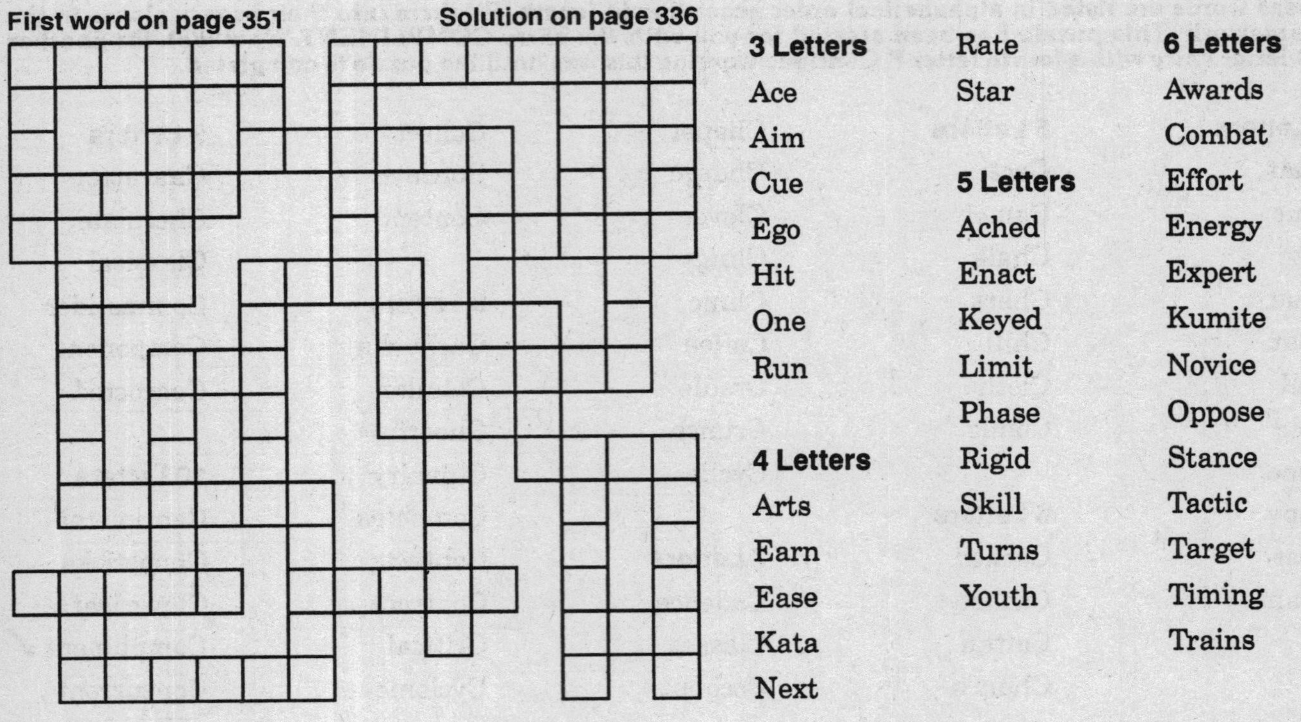

3 Letters
Ace
Aim
Cue
Ego
Hit
One
Run

4 Letters
Arts
Earn
Ease
Kata
Next
Rate
Star

5 Letters
Ached
Enact
Keyed
Limit
Phase
Rigid
Skill
Turns
Youth

6 Letters
Awards
Combat
Effort
Energy
Expert
Kumite
Novice
Oppose
Stance
Tactic
Target
Timing
Trains

Framework 25

Anagram Frame

Fill in this Framework in the usual way, but first unscramble the words to form new ones. The unscrambled words are in alphabetical order within each word group.

Word list on page 334

Solution on page 336

H O A R S E

3 Letters
End
Wed
Yap
Dent
Goat
Wane
Stew
Panel
Dirge
Taste
Wired

4 Letters
Maid
Star
Laid
Seat
Hear
Tale
Tool
Sent
Same

5 Letters
Cadet
Tacit
Caned
Armed
Neigh
Alloy
Ample
Lamed
Cheap

6 Letters
Traded
Waddle
Atoned
Dieted
Ashore ✓
Maiden
Recipe
Retina

Number Frame

Framework 26

First number on page 351 Solution on page 336

3 Digits
108
139
213
217
345
421
527
565
731
927

4 Digits
0145
0312
1054
1257
1389
1921
1986
2463
3072
3457
4352
4623
6487
6538
7448
7572
8031
8102
8768
8929
9321

5 Digits
08186
29812
30807
34694
36956
47981

6 Digits
521646
590162
697821
765432
849375
908675

Framequote

Framework 27

When this Framework has been completed, read the words in the outlined boxes in order from top to bottom to reveal a thought.

Quotation on page 334 Solution on page 336

3 Letters
Age
And
Lap
Leg
One
Sun
Thy

4 Letters
Etna
Eyes
Golf
Half
Keep
Loew
Open
Shut
Wide

5 Letters
Chase
Dress
India
Kneel
Pound
Sweep
Tiger
Trout

6 Letters
Before
Linear
Raisin
Reward
Tingle
Tragic

7 Letters
Baggage
Meander

8 Letters
Marriage
Senorita

9 Letters
Afterward
Passenger
Youngster

Framework 28

Call an Electrician

Our Framework expert needed 16 minutes to complete this puzzle. Your solving time: ______.

3 Letters
Air
Amp
Erg
Rig
Rod
Run
Tap
TLC

4 Letters
Arch
Base
Case
Easy
Glow
Glue
Hubs
Lamp
Lens
Lugs
Melt
Nuts
Plug
Rays
Ring
Seal
Sink
Span
Tape
Unit
Wing
Wire

5 Letters
Alert
Amber
Crank
Cycle
Ditch
Elbow
Exact
Globe
Guard
Latch
Lever
Motor
Plain
Rough
Shock
Therm

6 Letters
Access
Attune
Caster
Charge
Dimmer
Emerge
Energy
Ground
In-line
Outlet
Phases
Points
Radium
Remote
Single
Switch
Timing
Trench

7 Letters
Adapter
Arrange
Element
Grommet
Hot line
Mercury
Routine
Systems
Testing
Utility
Wattage

8 Letters
Antennae
Electron
Meter box
Platings
Standard

9 Letters
Cartridge
Generator

10 Letters
Attachment
Instrument
Receptacle

11 Letters
Fluorescent
Open circuit
Transformer

First word across on page 351

Solution on page 337

Framework 29

4 Letters
Amor
Ebon
Echo
Fool
Go-go
Halo
Into
Kolo
Koop
Lola
Lolo
Loop
Memo
Nook
Noon
Oahu
Oboe
Odic
Olaf
Oles
Only
Onto
Onyx
Oord
Open
Oral
Ouch
Oust
Oyer
Rhob
Rosa
Roto
Scob
Shod
Soon
Tony
Tool
Toot
Toro
Unto

5 Letters
Arbor
Bloom
Booby
Buffo
Codol
Dodge
Eloah
Elope
Error
Goner
Imago
Loner
Nonda
Notar
Ochro
Oddly
Offer
Olden
Onset
Oolak
Oolly
Oopak
Orlon
Ortho
Ovoid
Ovolo
Poker
Pooch
Senor
Sotto

6 Letters
Ashore
Boohoo
Condor
Kochia
Konker
Notary
Oenone
Oolong
Oopoda
Ormolu
Outtop
Tomato
Toroid
Vendor
Voodoo

7 Letters
Dopatta
Economy
Gorcrow
Hoecake
Laokoon
Neology
Nowroze
Ornoite
Orochon
Oronoco
Ortolan
Ouabaio
Rondout

8 Letters
Adoption
Chilopod
Foot pump
Igorrote
Korimako
Ontology
Oroonoko
Stone axe

First word across on page 351

Solution on page 338

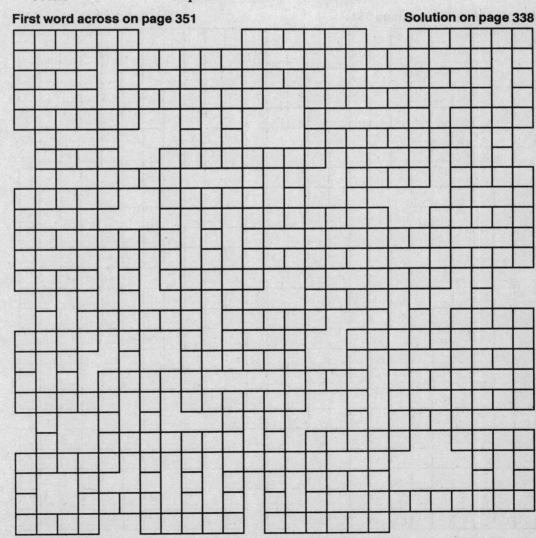

Framework 30

Authors

3 Letters
Fox
Fry
Kyd
Law
Poe

4 Letters
Agee
Ayer
Ball
Cary
Dell
Fyfe
Glyn
Hart
Hook
Lamb
Nash
Otto
Ovid
Park
Sade
Saki
Town
Webb
West

5 Letters
Aesop
Agate
Bland
Crane
Doyle
Eliot
Evans
Freud
Gibbs
Gorki
Grass
Hegel
Ibsen
Mason
Pound
Reade
Rilke
Smith
Steed
Twain
Tynan
Yates
Yonge

6 Letters
Andres
Anstey
Ascham
Barrie
Benson
Caesar
Cooper
Dryden
Evelyn
Irving
Keller
Keynes
Masson
Newman
O'Neill

7 Letters
Addison
Aquinas
Bergman
De Stael
Diderot
Emerson
Kipling
Merimee
Meynell
Oxenham

8 Letters
Anderson
Benchley
Langland
Lawrence
Montague

9 Letters
Blackwood
Euripides
Hemingway
Monsarrat
Wodehouse

10 Letters
De Bergerac
Dostoevsky
Quintilian
Richardson

First word across on page 351

Solution on page 338

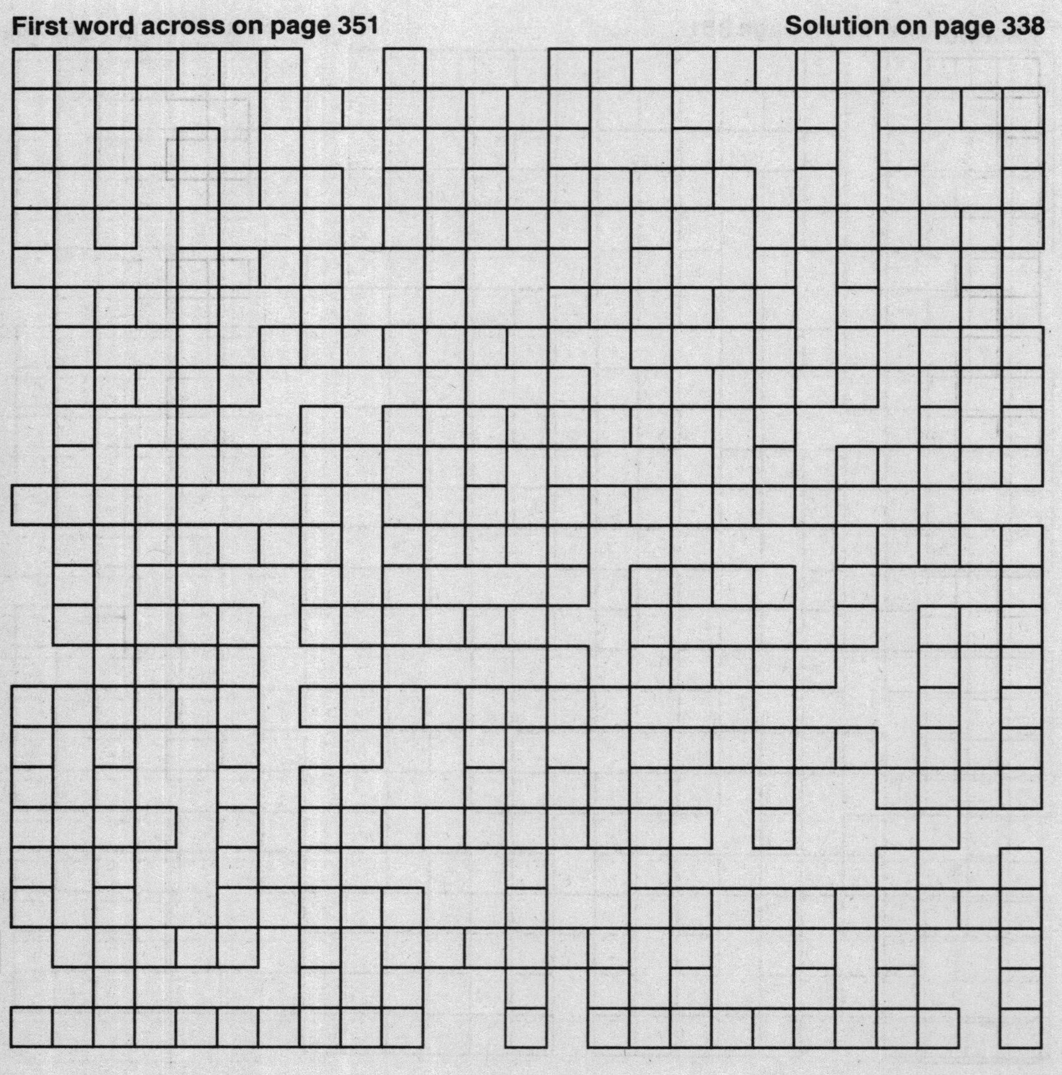

Framework 31

4 Letters
Akin
Amen
Ante
Deal
Dear
Edge
Ever
Game
Gaps
Grid
Grow
Help
Iced
Item
Make
News
Nice
Norm
Pact
Pass
Plan
Tell
Tend
Test
Unit

5 Letters
Again
Agree
Among
Brave
Break
Elate
Enter
Exact
Inert
Multi
Order
Owned
Range
Slide
Yells

6 Letters
Abides
Awards
Before
Courts
Direct
Easily
Exerts
Gamble
Gentle
Grades
Needle
Notice
Option
Picnic
Render
Temper
Trends
Wonder

7 Letters
Actions
Adverse
Assumed
Develop
Expense
Extends
Leaders
Learned
Reserve
Respond
Special
Trusted

8 Letters
Compared
Creative
Downward
Enticing
Expanded
Happened
Impulses
Listened
Mastered
Restrict
Starting
Striking
Superior

9 Letters
Abstracts
Advantage
Aggressor
Endurance
Guarantee
Memorized
Returning
Sheltered

First word across on page 351

Solution on page 338

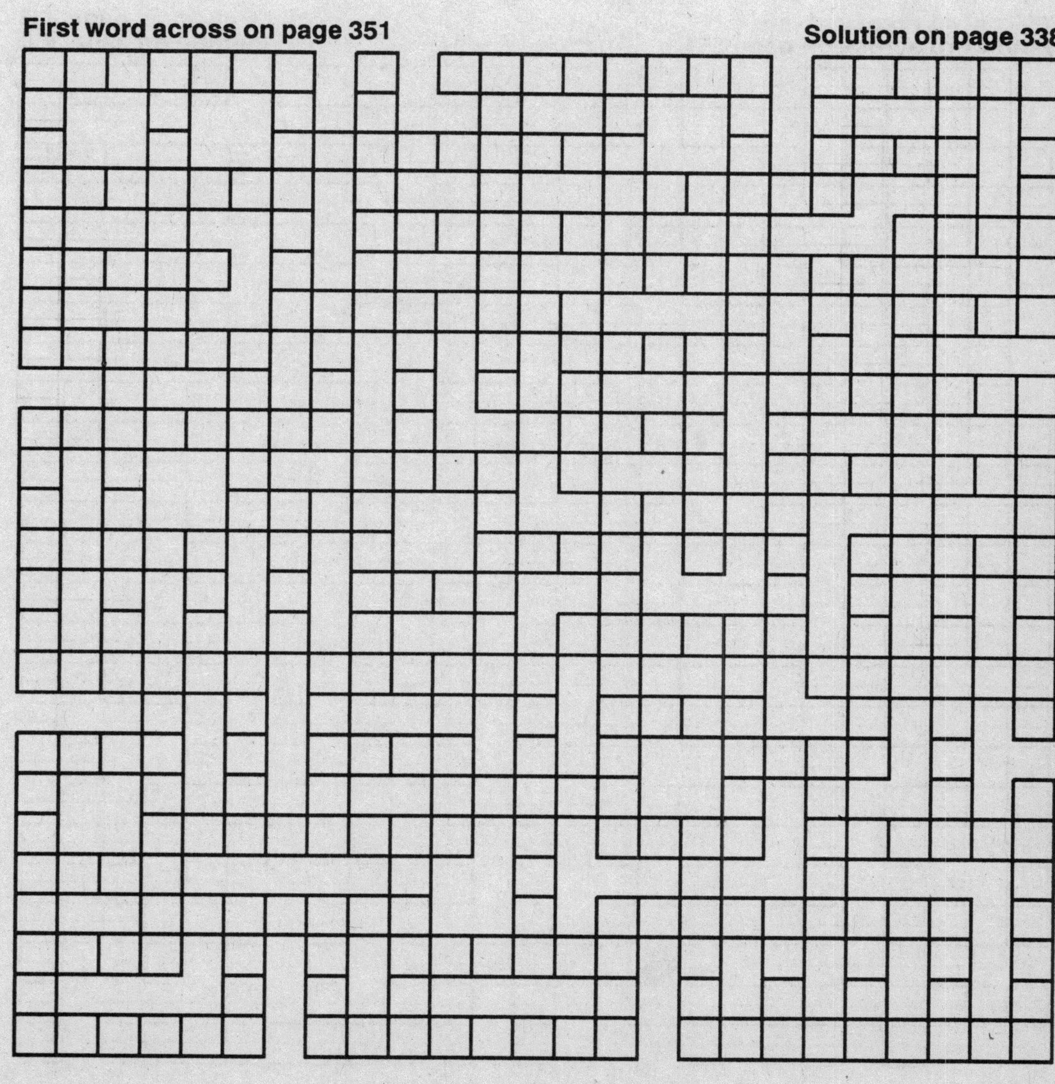

Framework 32

Career in Advertising

Our Framework expert needed 15 minutes to complete this puzzle. Your solving time: ______.

3 Letters
Air
End
Era
Men
Nod
Out
Run
Sum

4 Letters
Able
Cold
Doer
Earn
Item
Line
Near
Nice
Obey
Omni
Open
Read
Reel
Rush
Stay
Team
Text
True

5 Letters
Dream
Eager
Eclat
Erase
Essay
Ideas
Incur
Logos
Model
Noise
Spend
Stage
Theme
Users
Valid

6 Letters
Acumen
Admire
Agency
Brands
Bureau
Career
Clever
Issues
Labels
Lesson
Method
Notion
On-site
Repair
Secure
Sketch
Somber
Target
Tiring

7 Letters
Clients
Element
Insight
Leisure
Prepare
Routine
Rulings
Stories

8 Letters
Accounts
Prestige
Products
Quibbled
Research

9 Letters
Consumers
Corrected
Direction
Executive
Expedient
Originate
Sensation
Structure

10 Letters
Madison Ave.
Newspapers
Television

11 Letters
Merchandise
Reestablish

First word across on page 351

Solution on page 338

Framework 33

Sailing, Sailing

First word on page 351

Solution on page 336

3 Letters
Tan

4 Letters
Ahoy
Atop
Crew
Fore
Gull
Hull
Lake
List
Luff
Mast
Near
Prow
Rail
Roll
Ship
Spar
Stow
Tack
Tarp
Yawl

5 Letters
Craft
Hands
River
Sloop
Stern
Water
Winds
Yacht

6 Letters
Flares
Outing

7 Letters
Clipper
Pennant
Rigging

8 Letters
Foresail
Navigate

Framework 34

Patio Party

First word on page 351

Solution on page 336

3 Letters
Air
Can
Ham
Ice
Set
Sit
Sun

4 Letters
Buns
Cola
Ease
Food
Gala
Milk
Nuts
Taco

5 Letters
Apron
Cheer
Extra
Games
Grill
Music
Radio
Relax
Steak

6 Letters
Bricks
Camera
Dishes
Lounge
Screen

7 Letters
Flowers
Hammock
Iced tea
Leisure
Outside
Takeout

8 Letters
Sunshine

CRYPTO-FAMILIES

Each Crypto-Family is a list of related words in code. Each Family has its own code. When you have identified a word, use the known letters to help decode the other words in the Family.

Solutions on page 347

1. BIRDS
Example: Wren

FDWWKN
AKKGR
KWQKTR
BRWKL
TDWE
GFDWWKV
LINMWDMERW
BDVE
MBQMERL
RDATR

2. REALLY BIG
Example: Massive

HBBTGWT
JHJMGQHZ
ZVOVWWMO
BMBBVQY
QHQMGHZ
OTSHMQYMG
JMUJMGQKMG
BVKGQMHGVKW
WQKFTGAVKW
TOTFYMGQHGT

3. AFTER LIGHT
Example: Bulb

JTUC
YTEZGK
GPLNT
DCTTST
VCTUR
NGEQ
GTUCKTX
EWAUWKCJ
APPKTX
UCKEHHTCJ

4. MILITARY M's
Example: Medal of Honor

VAQQAOU
VAPUQMUUKUZ
VWHNAPU LJP
VWZAPUQ
VRZSWZ
VWCRZ
VJPASARPQ
VWZHN
VAQQARP
VUQQ NWOO

5. EATING OUT
Example: Restaurant

SOLUPF
MJEBUBPOJ
MFEEBB LQFD
SBJTBPR
XKTMQBFTBUUB
LUBJIQFKLB
UBJPFFV
DOAABPOJ
SJP JTH YPOXX
HOTBP

6. HEAVENLY BODIES
Example: Earth

ZNQCF
IKZCQIK
QXMIQU
MUCKXFLY
RQZLCKX
BMXU
WFBKC
KEKILIT UCMX
BKXWQXS
BFFI

CAMOUFLAGE

The answers to the clues can be found in the diagram, but they have been camouflaged. Their letters are in correct order, but sometimes they are separated by extra letters which have been inserted throughout the diagram. You must black out all the extra Camouflage letters. The remaining letters will be used in words reading across and down. Solve Across and Down together to determine the correct letters where there is a choice. The number of answer words in a row or column is indicated by the number of clues.

Solution on page 347

	1	2	3	4	5	6	7	8	9	10	11	12	13	14	15
1	M	N	U	G	D	G	E	A	K	P	L	H	O	M	B
2	P	E	N	S	I	L	V	C	E	G	O	I	P	A	L
3	L	O	I	T	E	K	E	R	A	L	C	U	N	P	E
4	A	P	U	A	M	R	D	T	F	O	U	P	E	R	A
5	I	Q	S	L	A	K	N	D	T	B	A	F	N	K	T
6	P	H	O	N	L	E	T	A	C	T	T	S	L	E	H
7	N	E	B	U	G	A	Q	T	E	S	E	R	E	S	K
8	I	S	N	K	M	S	U	O	R	M	I	S	B	Y	E
9	T	W	I	N	T	E	W	E	Y	E	N	E	O	T	A
10	E	T	B	E	R	N	A	L	O	A	W	T	C	H	I
11	C	R	O	W	M	G	L	A	S	R	K	D	E	X	R
12	M	U	N	D	A	H	X	I	N	E	S	O	R	E	V
13	I	K	E	R	F	A	Z	T	E	W	I	A	Z	D	N
14	Z	E	D	A	E	I	L	E	K	H	S	P	Y	M	A
15	E	F	A	B	B	B	Y	A	V	E	T	E	B	N	P

ACROSS

1. Gentle push • Poise
2. Thoughtful • October stone
3. Factual • Pool stick
4. Divided • Musical drama
5. Land mass • Gas holder
6. Pit • Blab
7. Nullify • Look for
8. Printing fluid • Conjecture
9. String • Ogle • New Jersey cager
10. Everlasting • Vow
11. Tier • Pantry
12. Boring • Achy
13. Incensed • Triumph
14. Enthusiasm • Spot
15. Recede • So long! • Decade count

DOWN

1. Obvious • List
2. Huey, to Donald • Correct
3. Agreement • Charged atom
4. Stem • Fresh • Dull
5. Jim ____ of "Murphy Brown" • Seize
6. Lubricate • Catch
7. In the end
8. Prado offering • Palm fruit • Overdue
9. Restaurant • Wallet note
10. Scheme • Blur • Pasture parent
11. Discover • Assert
12. Unsettled • Blockhead
13. Ajar • Distrustful
14. Store • Layer
15. Desolate • Marine bird

MAZE

Find your way through this maze from the arrow at the top to the one at the bottom.

Solution on page 347

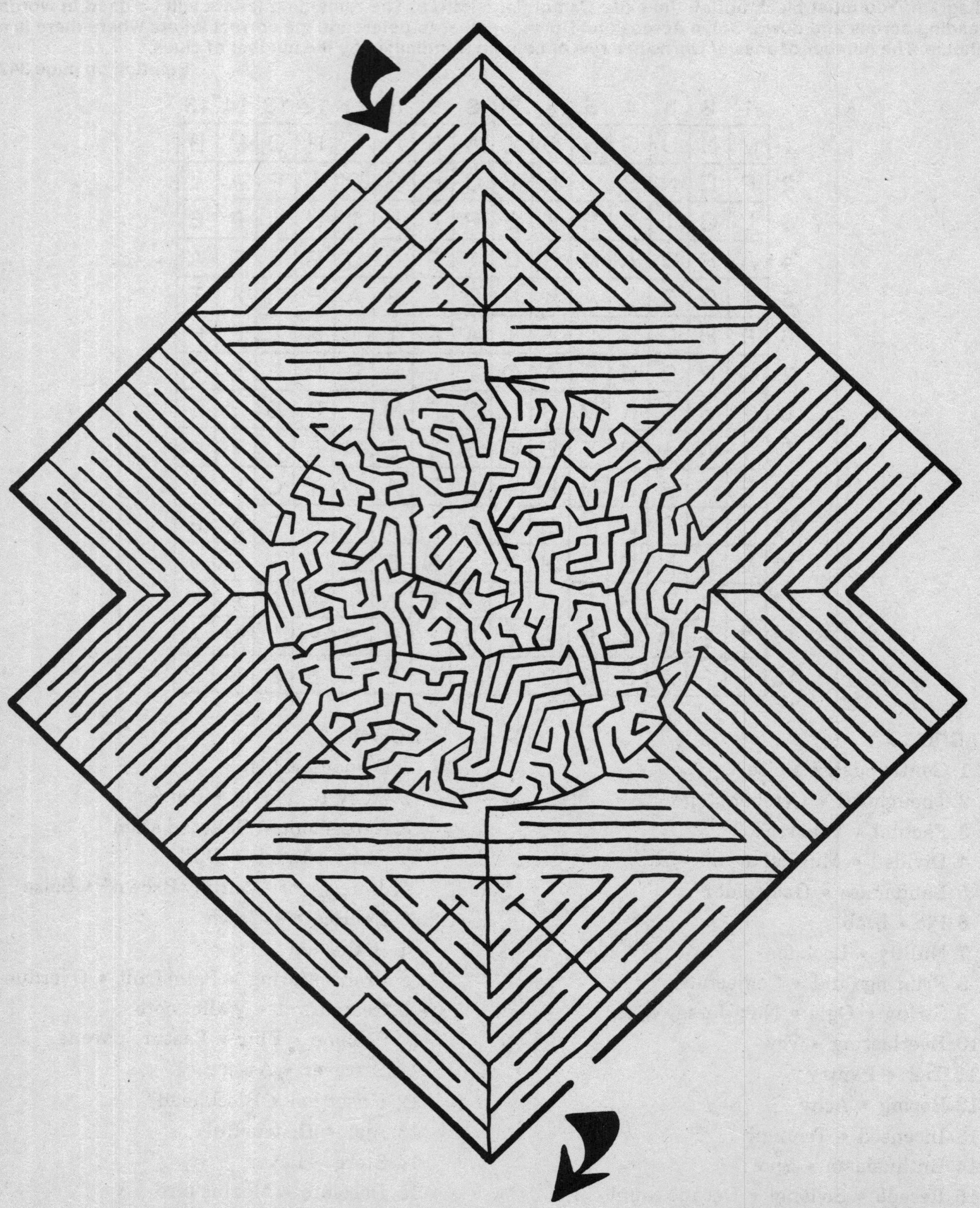

FLOWER POWER

The answers to this petaled puzzle will go in a curve from the number on the outside to the center of the flower. Each number has two 5-letter words. One goes in a clockwise direction and the second in a counterclockwise direction. Try working from both sets of clues to fill the flower. **Solution on page 347**

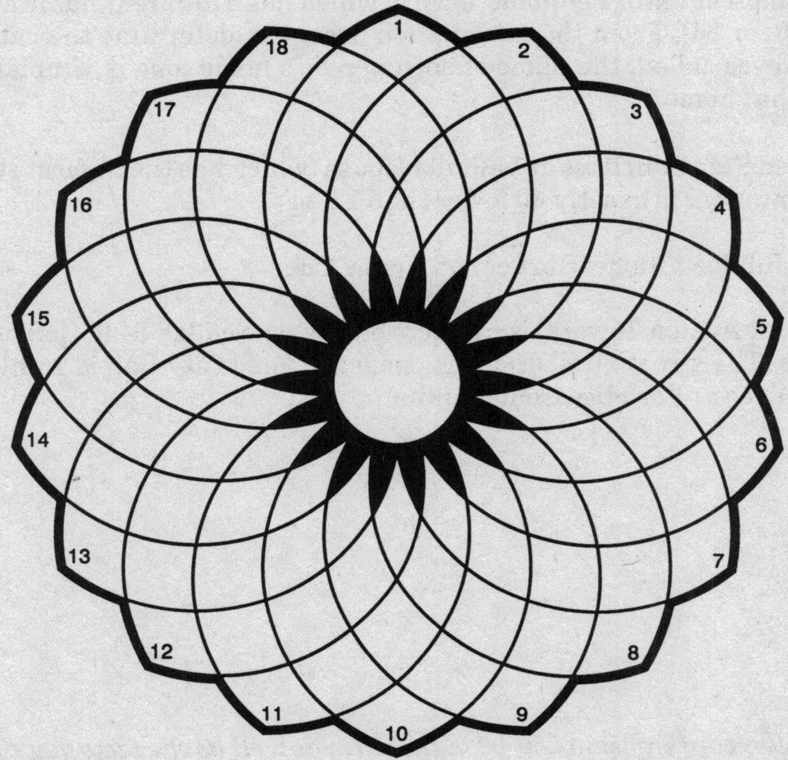

CLOCKWISE

1. Roused
2. Astute
3. Zodiac sign
4. Rich cake
5. Beef and veal
6. Beast
7. Swine
8. Respond
9. Fiber thread
10. Forest clearing
11. Edible roots
12. Blaze
13. Skier's locale
14. Eliminate
15. Previous
16. Gift receiver
17. Priest, in Puerto Rico
18. Cliques

COUNTERCLOCKWISE

1. Birch's kin
2. Conscious
3. Unaccompanied
4. Journeys
5. Watered silk
6. Cap, in Toulouse
7. Unruly youths
8. Highway
9. Stunts
10. Stare
11. Alliances
12. "Babette's ____"
13. Troikas
14. Overjoy
15. High school affairs
16. Hang loosely
17. Composure
18. Dugout

LOGIC PROBLEM

CAB CALL

It's been a long day, and Amos and four other employees of Gilbert & Co., who usually walk home, are treating themselves to cab rides. Each has requested a cab from a different company. Each person's cab will drop him or her off at his or her home, each of which has a different name and a different street number (25, 32, 44, 50, or 84). From the information provided, determine the cab company (one was Quick Cab) each employee called, the name of each person's home (one is Utopian Apartments), and the street number of that home.

1. Ellen (who called Star Cab) lives at Valhalla House (which has the highest street number). Gloria's street number is exactly 40 lower than Ellen's.

2. Gloria lives in Jubilee Village. Burt called Arrow Cab.

3. Jack (who lives at Avalon Towers) is neither the one who called Blue Cab nor the one who called City Cab. The street number of the one who called City Cab is 25 higher than that of the one who lives at Paradise Condominiums.

This chart is to help you record information from the clues as well as the facts you deduce by combining information from different clues. We suggest you use an "X" for a "no" and a "•" for a "yes."

		COMPANY					HOME					NUMBER				
		ARROW CAB	BLUE CAB	CITY CAB	QUICK CAB	STAR CAB	AVALON TOWERS	JUBILEE VILLAGE	PARADISE CONDOMINIUMS	UTOPIAN APARTMENTS	VALHALLA HOUSE	25	32	44	50	84
EMPLOYEE	AMOS															
	BURT															
	ELLEN															
	GLORIA															
	JACK															
NUMBER	25															
	32															
	44															
	50															
	84															
HOME	AVALON TOWERS															
	JUBILEE VILLAGE															
	PARADISE COND.															
	UTOPIAN APART.															
	VALHALLA HOUSE															

Solution on page 348

PICTURE THIS

You do not need any special art training to produce a picture in the empty grid. Use the letter-number guide above each square and carefully draw what is shown into the corresponding square in the grid.

Solution on page 347

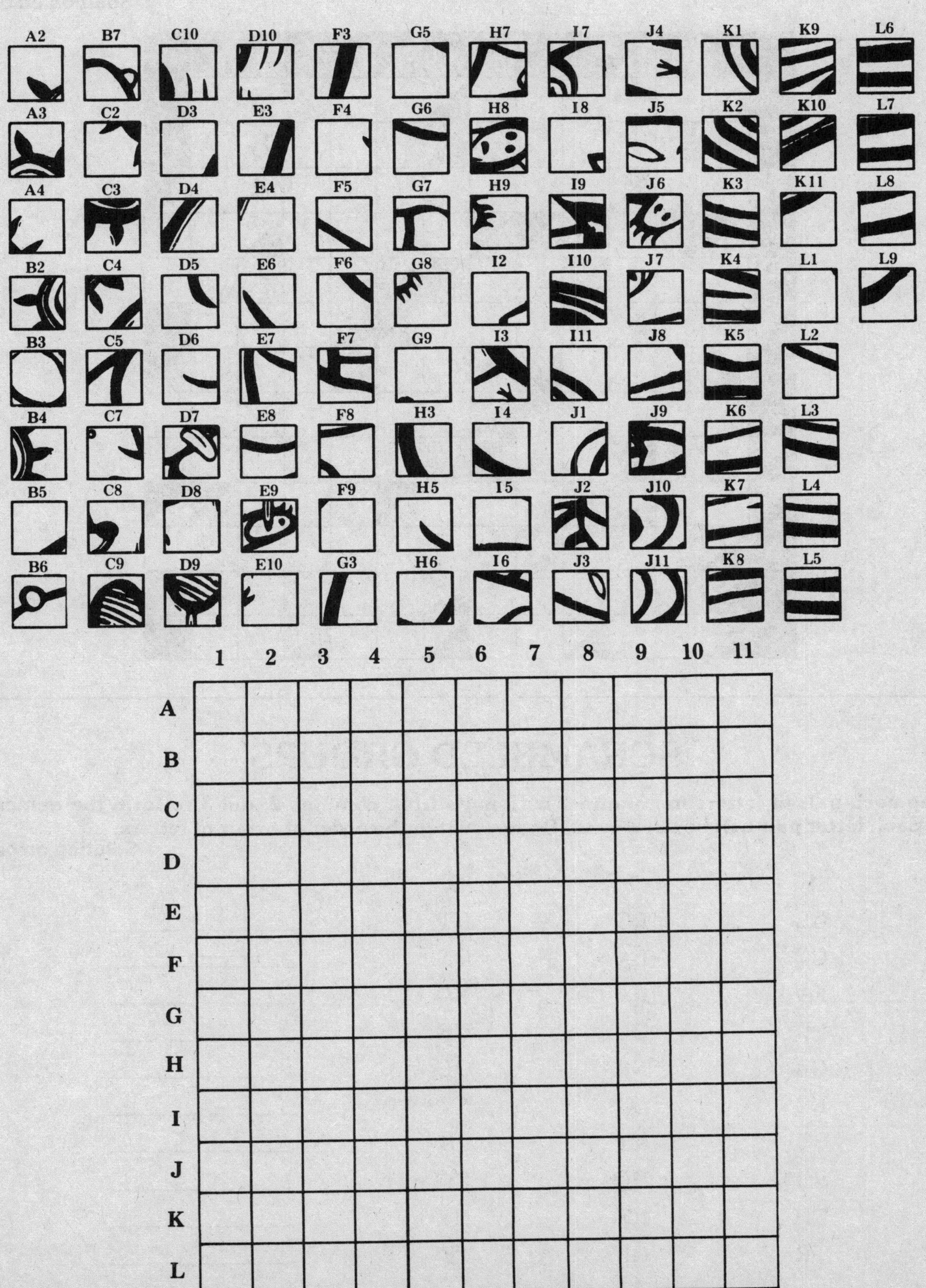

SUM TOTALS

Place one digit (1 to 9, no zeros) in each square so that the sum of the numbers in each group of squares across or down is the number given. The number below a diagonal is the sum of the numbers below it. The number to the right of a diagonal is the sum of the numbers to the right of it. IMPORTANT: No digit is used more than once in any group of squares leading to a sum. One group of digits has been given for you.

Solution on page 349

SCRAMBLED GROUPS

Match up each pair of letters in column 1 with pairs from columns 2 and 3 to form the names of ten groups. Each letter pair will be used once. Do not switch the order of a pair of letters.

Solution on page 347

1	2	3	
CL	RO	HT	FLIGHT
CO	LA	ON	CLIQUE
FA	IG	NG	
FL	OU	UE	
GA	NA	OL	
LE	LO	XY	
SC	MI	PE	
SE	HO	LY	
TH	IQ	NY	
TR	GI	TE	

DIAGRAMLESS FILL-IN

For this fill-in puzzle we have given you all of the E's that appear in the diagram, but none of the black squares. As you solve the puzzle remember to put a black square at the beginning and end of each answer and to balance each black square with its symmetrical counterpart on the opposite side of the diagram.

Solution on page 347

3 Letters
Ade
Ale
Are
Bin
Chi
Cup
Dee
Dry
Dye
Gap
Gem
Gum
Has
Hut
Ira
Kip
Mud
Nee
Oar
Ohm
Oho
Red
See
Tad
Tan
The
Tic
Tun

4 Letters
Alma
Atom
Aura
Avid
Bury
Dean
Dine
East
Edna
Ella
Font
Ford
Gosh
Hate
Here
Hogs
Hurt
Mere
Navy
Omar
Ones
Pave
Said
Sand
Sten
Sulk
Syne
Tart
Tiny
Utah
Worn
Yard

5 Letters
Drain
Green
Kenya
Moves
Norma
Omaha
Trial
Wordy

6 Letters
Ravels
Travel

8 Letters
Encroach
Kentucky

9 Letters
Outranked
Sentiment

								E								
							E		E			E				
			E					E						E		
															E	E
					E	E										
							E								E	
		E	E													
													E			
												E				
									E	E						

BOWL GAME

To bowl a strike (20 points) you must create a 10-letter word using all the letters in each pin. The letter on top in the pin is the first letter of the strike word. To bowl a spare (10 points) use the same 10 letters to form two words. Splits are not allowed: you may not divide the strike to form a spare. For example, SWEETHEART may not become SWEET and HEART.

Our solutions with a perfect score of 300 points on page 348

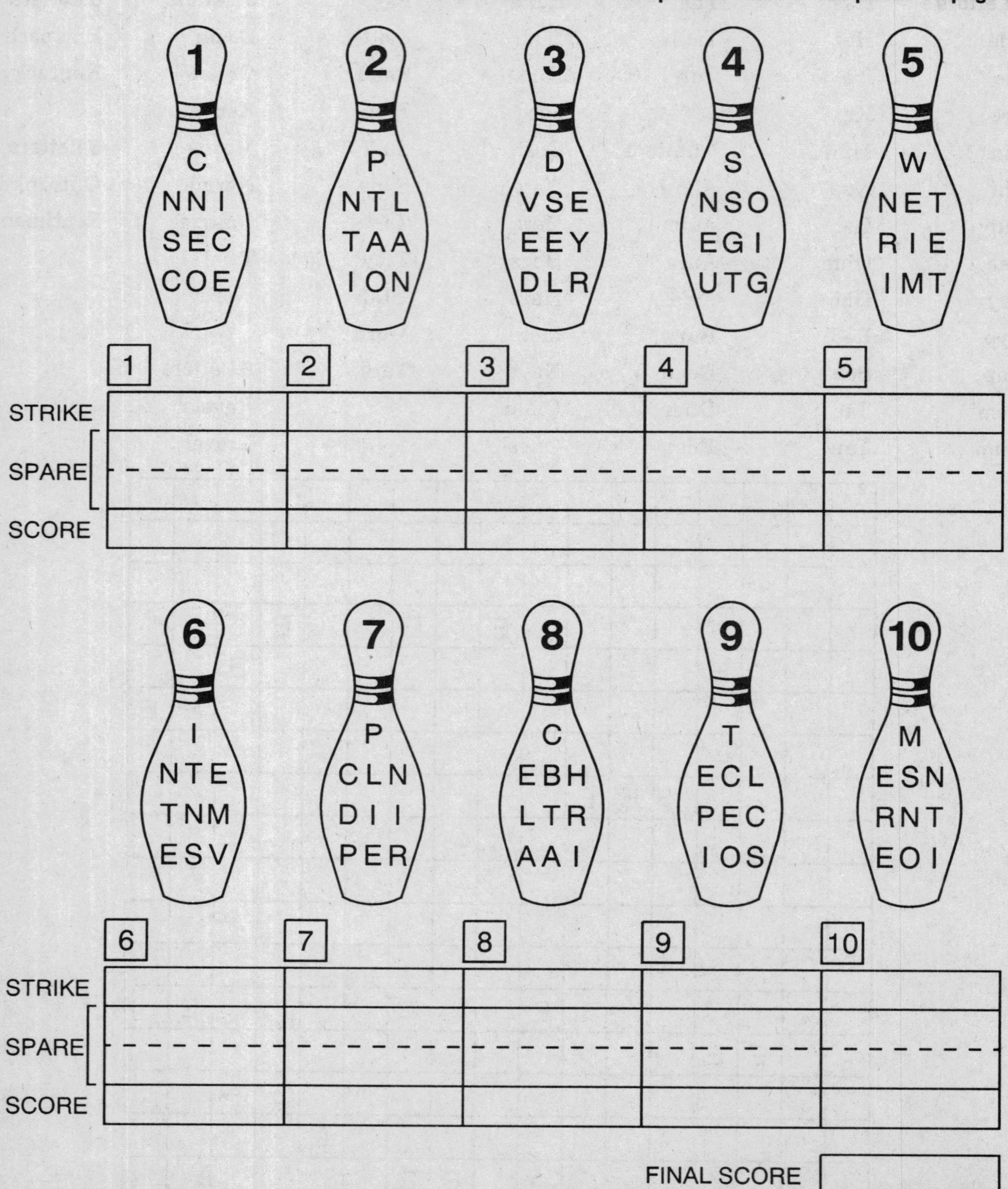

DOUBLE DELIGHT

Enjoy the Double Delight of solving this puzzle by placing two letters into each square. Each pair of letters in the diagram will read in the same order for both the Across and the Down words.

Solution on page 347

1 2 3 4 5 6 7 8 9 10 11 12 13 14 15 16 17 18 19 20 21 22 23 24 25 26 27 28 29 30 31 32 33 34 35 36 37 38 39

ACROSS

1. Montana's capital
3. Garbage
5. Kind of cat
7. Tortoise
8. Magnificent
9. Sports official
11. Derides
13. "____, Christian Soldiers"
15. Bath alternative
17. Road
19. Aunt's daughter
21. Sleeve type
22. Kind of necklace
23. Despot
25. Ended
27. Concrete ingredient
29. Burn
31. Vulture's relative
33. ____ butter (jelly's companion)
35. Source
36. Charge
37. Counting device
38. Palatable
39. Slender candles

DOWN

1. Balloon gas
2. Essence
3. Strike out
4. Emerges
5. Duplicate
6. Playwright Noel ____
10. Kind of talk
12. Guarantee
14. "I Am the ____"
15. Sly
16. Roving
17. Position
18. Carved
19. Compel
20. Baby
24. Enmity
26. Climb
28. Midpoint
29. Beetle
30. Musical group
31. Invented
32. Prophet
33. Spanish monetary unit
34. Speaks

RINGMASTER

Place the letter groups in the diagram to form 24 five-letter words as indicated by arrows. The two-letter groups go in the circles in the outer ring, the three-letter groups in the inner ring. Two words have been given to start you off.

Solution on page 348

OUTSIDE RING

AG	QU
BU	RI
CH	SC
CR	SM
DR ✓	TE
PH	TR

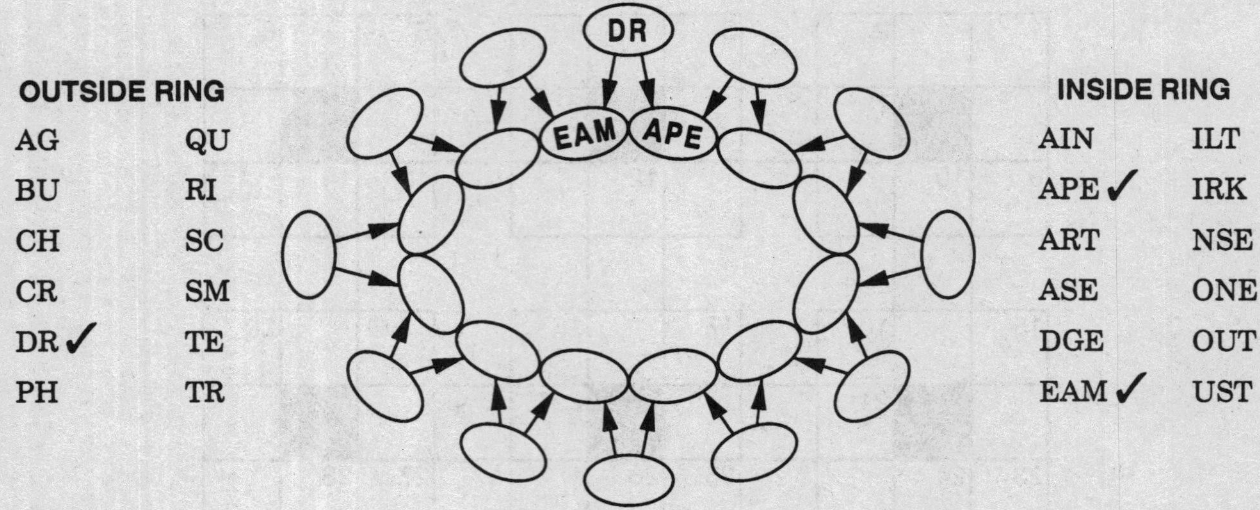

INSIDE RING

AIN	ILT
APE ✓	IRK
ART	NSE
ASE	ONE
DGE	OUT
EAM ✓	UST

KEYWORD

To find the Keyword, fill in the blanks in words 1 through 10 with the correct missing letters. Transfer those letters to the correspondingly numbered squares in the diagram. Approach with care—this puzzle is not as simple as it first appears.

Solution on page 349

1	2	3	4	5	6	7	8	9	10

1. C R A __ E
2. S T A R __
3. S P A __ K
4. T R A I __
5. S P O __ L
6. S T A __ E
7. S M __ L L
8. __ O O T H
9. S C __ R E
10. S T E E __

CIRCLE SUMS

Each circle, lettered A through H, has its own number value from 2 to 9. No two circles have the same value. The numbers shown in the diagram are the sums of the circles which overlap at those points. For example, 15 is the sum of circles B and D. Can you find the value of each circle?

Solution on page 346

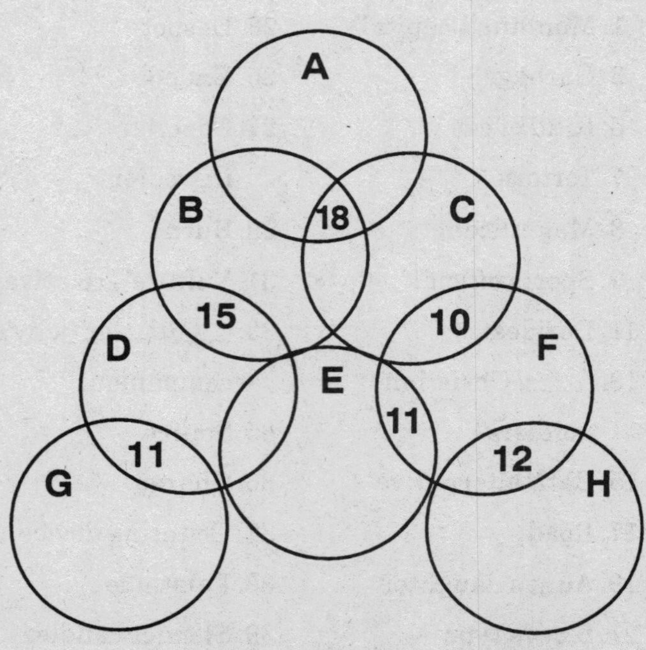

ANAGRAM QUOTES

Unscramble each set of letters below the dashes to complete the quotations.

Solutions on page 347

1. ________ were ________ to make ________ ________ by
SPRETAN EVITNEDN HERLNDIC PAHYP
________ them ________ to ________.
GINVIG MEHISTNOG ERIGON

2. ________ the ________ ________ : its ________ ________ in
DRONSEIC OTEGPAS MAPTS SELNUSUSFE NISTCSOS
the ________ to ________ to one ________ till it ________ ________.
BLYAITI KCSIT HIGNT TEGS HETER

3. ________ loves ________, but ________ does not ________.
SIREMY MANOPCY PACYMON PIAORCTRECE

4. ________ ________ is ________ a ________ ________ and a ________
FRITS VOLE LOYN TILTEL LSONSISOFHE TOL
of ________.
YUTROICIS

Stars and Arrows

Start at the square marked "S" and move through the diagram to the square marked "F." An arrow in a square indicates the direction you must take; a star allows you to move in any direction horizontally or vertically, but not diagonally. No turns are allowed in the blank squares. You do not have to pass through all the squares.

Solution on page 347

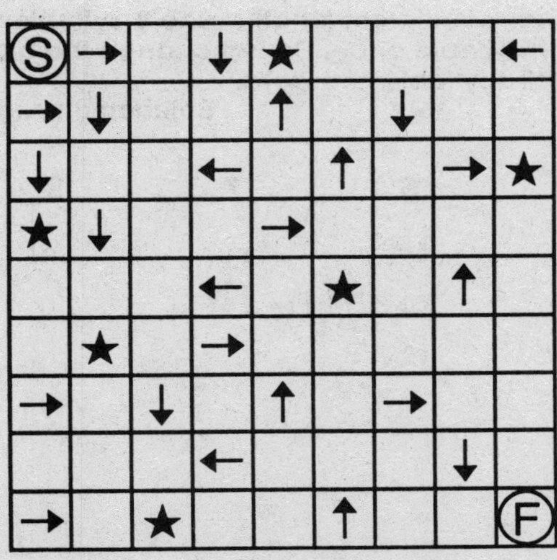

Little Puzzler

Put the answers to the clues into the diagram reading across and down in crossword fashion using only the letters given in the LETTERBOX.

Our solution on page 347

Rent payment
Adjust a lens
Extra tire
Female sheep
Espied
Cleo's snake
Zodiac lion

Not at work
Needle hole
Up in years
Transfer design
Sunbeam
Utilize
Lawyer's charge

LETTERBOX

A	A	A	C	D
E	E	E	E	E
E	F	F	L	L
O	O	P	R	S
S	S	U	W	Y

FOUR CORNERS

The letters of the four corner crossword puzzles have been alphabetized and listed across the top and bottom and down the sides of the diagram. Thus, the letters of the crossword in the upper left corner have been alphabetized with those of the upper right corner and listed in the four rows across the top. The letters from the upper left corner have also been alphabetized with those of the lower left corner and listed in the four columns on the left. Determine where the letters belong in the squares to create the four crossword puzzles. Every letter is in its proper row and column. We have inserted the letter J in its proper place by way of illustration and to get you started.

Solution on page 347

J				C	E	H	I	J	N	S	T				
				A	A	B	E	L	L	N	Y				
				C	N	O	O	P	R	S	U				
				B	E	E	E	K	N	S	T				
A	A	E	E									A	A	A	D
B	B	I	E									B	E	B	E
C	D	L	L									C	G	E	E
C	E	N	P									C	H	I	E
I	E	O	P									L	L	K	G
J	L	O	T									S	R	N	N
K	N	R	T									T	U	N	S
R	O	S	Y									U	Y	S	T
				B	C	C	E	I	L	P	U				
				A	A	D	E	E	G	R	R				
				A	D	G	I	L	L	O	S				
				B	E	E	K	N	T	T	Y				

Syllability

Unscramble these eight columns of syllables to form eight words of different lengths: one 8-syllable word, one 7-syllable word, etc., down to a 1-syllable word. Use each syllable once. Do not change the order of the syllables; if the syllable appears in column 3, it will be the third syllable of a word.

Solution on page 347

1	2	3	4	5	6	7	8
Lu	eant	ni	bil	ca	ty	ry	cal
Gig	tempt	nes	path	i	to	i	
Phys	a	mu	cence	tion	log		
Mech	com	ry	ni	o			
Ring	i	i	za				
Ex	gle	o					
Con	mi						
Pag							

Mixed Sixes

Place each of the 6-letter words onto one of the sets of six dashes so that, when you transfer the letters into the correspondingly numbered squares in the diagram, a quotation is revealed.

Solution on page 347

CROUCH	POTION	THATCH
DETEST	POTTED	THREAT
FAMOUS	SIMMER	TROPHY

__ __ __ __ __ __
20 34 52 43 6 12

__ __ __ __ __ __
38 51 5 23 44 24

__ __ __ __ __ __
48 2 16 25 36 14

__ __ __ __ __ __
4 13 31 41 19 28

__ __ __ __ __ __
1 40 8 15 49 10

__ __ __ __ __ __
32 27 11 46 17 37

__ __ __ __ __ __
47 30 26 53 50 9

__ __ __ __ __ __
42 21 35 54 22 29

__ __ __ __ __ __
39 33 45 7 3 18

■	1	2	3	■	4	5	6	7	8	9
10	■	11	12	13	14	■	15	16	17	18
19	20	21	22	■	23	24	25	■	26	27
28	29	■	30	31	32	33	34	35	36	37
38	■	39	40	41	42	43	44	45	■	46
47	■	48	49	50	■	51	52	53	54	■

Hexagrams

One of the letters in the hexagons has been circled because it and the letters in the six surrounding hexagons can be unscrambled to form a seven-letter word (in this case BAGPIPE). We were able to form 12 other words in this manner.

Solutions on page 344

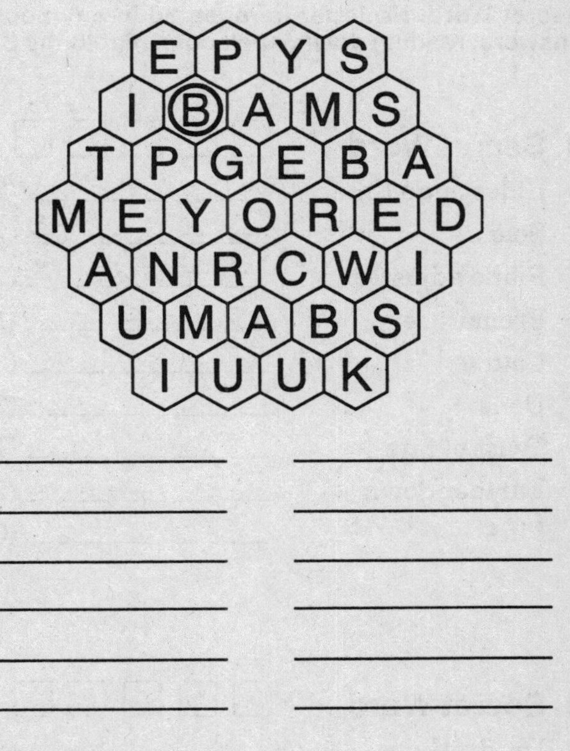

__________ __________

__________ __________

__________ __________

__________ __________

__________ __________

__________ __________

____

Throwbacks

You have to throw your mental gears into reverse to play this game. Reading backward there are at least three 4-letter words to be found in each of the longer words. You can skip over letters, but don't change the order of the letters. For example, in the word DECLARE you can find the word RACE reading backward by starting with the next-to-last letter and skipping over the L, but you can't find the word READ without changing the order of the letters.

Our solutions on page 348

1. ENWRAP ________ ________ ________
2. GERUNDS ________ ________ ________
3. REWRITE ________ ________ ________
4. UNTRUTH ________ ________ ________
5. WONDERED ________ ________ ________
6. NECKLINES ________ ________ ________
7. PARAMEDIC ________ ________ ________
8. EIDERDOWN ________ ________ ________

Secret Word

Discover the 5-letter Secret Words by the process of elimination and deduction. Fill in the blanks with the 5-letter answers to the clues. The number in parentheses next to each answer tells you how many of the letters in that word are also in the Secret Word. A zero next to an answer indicates that none of the letters in that word is in the Secret Word. After you have determined the correct five letters, rearrange them to form the Secret Word. No letter is repeated in any Secret Word or within any answer word. The first letters of the answers, reading down, spell out a hint to the Secret Word.

Solutions on page 348

1. Secret Word ☐☐☐☐☐

Bides one's time WAITS (2)
Solo ALONE (2)
Piano adjuster TUNER (2)
Premature EARLY (1)
Course _____ (3)
Dens _____ (2)
Twist of fate _____ (1)
Further down LOWER (2)
Pine _____ (0)

2. Secret Word ☐☐☐☐☐

Trim _____ (2)
Deduce _____ (3)
Katmandu's site _____ (0)
T.S. ____ _____ (2)
Subsequently _____ (3)
Cost _____ (2)
Veranda _____ (1)
Of the moon _____ (2)
"____ Frome" _____ (1)

3. Secret Word ☐☐☐☐☐

Dr. Brothers _____ (2)
Make amends _____ (3)
Restaurants _____ (3)
Switchblade _____ (0)
Relish _____ (1)
Subway coin _____ (2)
Beer mug _____ (2)

4. Secret Word ☐☐☐☐☐

Stomach malady _____ (2)
Scandinavian _____ (3)
Witch's spell _____ (2)
Else _____ (2)
Bank safe _____ (2)
Cowgirl Dale _____ (3)
Cattleman's stead _____ (0)

5. Secret Word ☐☐☐☐☐

Place to ski _____ (2)
Sharpens _____ (0)
Landlord _____ (1)
As _____ (2)
Merits _____ (2)
Incites _____ (3)
Pickpocket _____ (2)

6. Secret Word ☐☐☐☐☐

Wall painting _____ (2)
Confess _____ (2)
Dominates _____ (2)
Travels _____ (0)
Nonreactive _____ (3)
Relating to sound _____ (2)
Bellini opera _____ (2)

LIST-A-CROSTIC

Solve this puzzle as you would solve a crostic, by answering the clues and transferring the letters to the diagram. When the puzzle is completed, thirteen names will appear in the diagram reading horizontally, and one additional name will read down, starting in box 8. The first letters of the answer words will reveal what these names have in common.

Solution on page 348

A. Night wear — 23 154 79 45 96 29 5

B. Doubtful — 150 126 106 37 91 4 119 75

C. Unreasonable delay, in law — 47 61 109 140 116 101

D. Underwriter — 143 21 73 121 56 15 30

E. Public announcement maker: 2 wds. — 38 12 104 54 122 153 86 141 99

F. Actress Stephanie ___ — 13 70 142 88 127 63 100 44 111

G. Creator of "Nana": 2 wds. — 132 36 62 68 89 14 152 50 108

H. Meet again in competition — 118 137 60 71 158 11 81

I. On the ground — 128 58 43 9 134 103

J. Unchangeably — 25 3 57 46 92 147 131 69 159

K. Paired — 90 93 22 115 51 34 10

L. Acrobat — 84 8 72 120 42 124 135

M. Lou Gehrig's nickname: 2 wds. — 67 114 97 87 28 2 136

N. At work: 3 wds. — 102 144 35 112 64 1 80 48

O. Buffalo's state: 2 wds. — 94 113 66 148 52 65 26

P. Cover up faults — 155 40 95 74 85 53 110 17 20

Q. Disregard — 105 6 78 55 133 41

R. Decreases in width — 16 117 33 130 77 146 83

S. Nude — 59 32 123 149 24

T. Chinese dish: 2 wds. — 49 145 31 98 19 157 107

U. Rebuff — 76 156 18 129 39 139

V. Saturated — 138 7 151 125 27 82

1 N	2 M	3 J	4 B	5 A	6 Q	7 V	8 L	9 I	10 K	11 H	12 E	13 F	14 G	15 D	16 R	17 P
18 U	19 T	20 P	21 D	22 K	23 A	24 S	25 J	26 O	27 V							
28 M	29 A	30 D	31 T	32 S	33 R	34 K	35 N	36 G	37 B	38 E	39 U	40 P	41 Q	42 L	43 I	
44 F	45 A	46 J	47 C	48 N	49 T	50 G	51 K	52 O	53 P							
54 E	55 Q	56 D	57 J	58 I	59 S	60 H	61 C	62 G	63 F	64 N	65 O					
66 O	67 M	68 G	69 J	70 F	71 H	72 L	73 D	74 P	75 B	76 U	77 R	78 Q				
79 A	80 N	81 H	82 V	83 R	84 L	85 P	86 E	87 M	88 F	89 G	90 K	91 B				
92 J	93 K	94 O	95 P	96 A	97 M	98 T	99 E	100 F	101 C	102 N	103 I					
104 E	105 Q	106 B	107 T	108 G	109 C	110 P	111 F	112 N	113 O	114 M						
115 K	116 C	117 R	118 H	119 B	120 L	121 D	122 E	123 S								
124 L	125 V	126 B	127 F	128 I	129 U	130 R	131 J	132 G	133 Q							
134 I	135 L	136 M	137 H	138 V	139 U	140 C	141 E	142 F	143 D	144 N	145 T	146 R	147 J	148 O		
149 S	150 B	151 V	152 G	153 E	154 A	155 P	156 U	157 T	158 H	159 J						

QUOTAGRAMS

Fill in the answers to the clues. Then transfer the letters to the correspondingly numbered squares in the diagram. The completed diagram will contain a quotation. **Solutions on page 347**

A.

1. Customary ___ ___ ___ ___ ___ ___ ___ ___ 13 28 8 17 1 31 5 24
2. Account book ___ ___ ___ ___ ___ ___ 25 3 11 6 14 32
3. Easy thing ___ ___ ___ ___ ___ 22 33 15 18 2
4. Filter ___ ___ ___ ___ ___ ___ 21 35 16 23 20 10
5. Cast a ballot ___ ___ ___ ___ 4 9 29 26
6. Follow secretly ___ ___ ___ ___ ___ ___ 34 19 7 27 30 12

1	2	3	■	4	5	6	7	8	9	10	11	■	12
13	14	15	■	16	17	18	19	■	20	21	■	22	23
24	25	26	27	■	28	■	29	30	31	32	33	34	35

B.

1. Cartoon bear ___ ___ ___ ___ 22 33 7 20
2. Author of "The Virginian" ___ ___ ___ ___ ___ ___ 1 38 19 41 31 15
3. Instants ___ ___ ___ ___ ___ ___ ___ 10 14 34 17 39 4 43
4. Sea travels ___ ___ ___ ___ ___ ___ ___ 30 26 45 29 40 11 32
5. Genuine ___ ___ ___ ___ ___ ___ ___ 12 23 6 8 35 2 16
6. Part of a river ___ ___ ___ ___ ___ 13 42 27 36 28
7. Greasy ___ ___ ___ ___ 9 5 21 25
8. Israeli port ___ ___ ___ ___ ___ 37 18 3 24 44

1	2	3	4	5	6	7	■	8	9	10	11	12	■	13	14	15	16
■	17	18	19	20	21	22	■	23	24	■	25	26	27	■	28	29	30
31	■	32	33	34	35	36	37	38	39	40	■	41	42	■	43	44	45

C.

1. Atomic merging ___ ___ ___ ___ ___ ___ 23 56 29 65 17 4
2. Short-tempered one ___ ___ ___ ___ ___ ___ ___ 37 55 62 11 47 34 28
3. Aristocracy ___ ___ ___ ___ ___ ___ ___ ___ 13 63 16 30 52 5 35 68
4. Crass ___ ___ ___ ___ ___ ___ ___ 64 51 18 44 6 46 39
5. Majestic ___ ___ ___ ___ ___ ___ ___ 61 1 41 19 26 59 54
6. Amaze ___ ___ ___ ___ ___ ___ ___ ___ 48 8 32 58 27 12 67 40
7. Might ___ ___ ___ ___ ___ ___ ___ ___ 31 9 24 3 20 14 70 33
8. Erased ___ ___ ___ ___ ___ ___ ___ 50 43 53 7 36 66 60
9. Critic's work ___ ___ ___ ___ ___ ___ 49 38 42 25 69 22
10. Menace ___ ___ ___ ___ ___ ___ 10 2 57 21 15 45

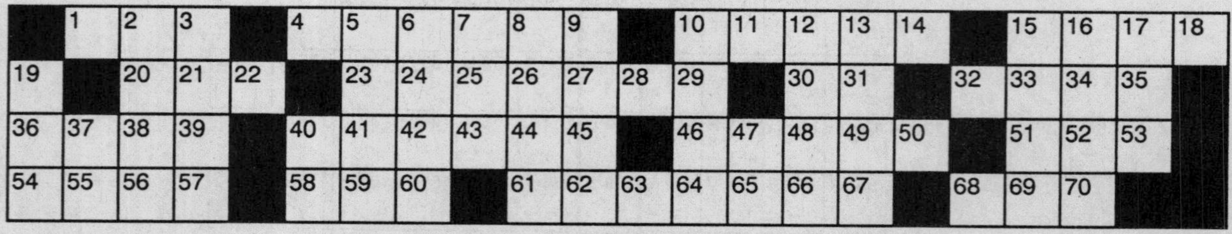

SCOREMASTER

TO PLAY:

1. Write the first seven LETTERS across the first line of the PLAY CHART. Indicate the last letter used.
2. Form a word of at least two letters across or down in the DIAGRAM. One letter of the first word must go into the center square.
3. Tally your score, noting any bonuses (see key at bottom).
4. Carry down all unused LETTERS to the next line of the PLAY CHART. Transfer enough LETTERS, in the given order, so that you have seven LETTERS to work with.
5. Form a new word or words from each draw by:
   a. Adding one or more letters to an existing word.
   b. Building a new word at right angles to an existing word, by adding to it or incorporating one of its letters.
   c. Setting a new word parallel to an existing word, but remember all adjoining letters must form new words in crossword fashion.
6. Continue working in this way until all the LETTERS have been used or you can no longer form any words. If you need more lines for your PLAY CHART, use a separate piece of paper.

NOTE: Proper names, foreign words, and abbreviations are not allowed.

TO SCORE:

The value of each letter is given with it. The letter has the same value every time it is used. Be sure always to include all bonuses (see key at bottom). An additional 30 points is earned when you use all seven letters in the PLAY CHART in one turn. When two words are formed in the same play, the common letter (including any bonus) is scored with each word.

Our game with a score of 559 points on page 348

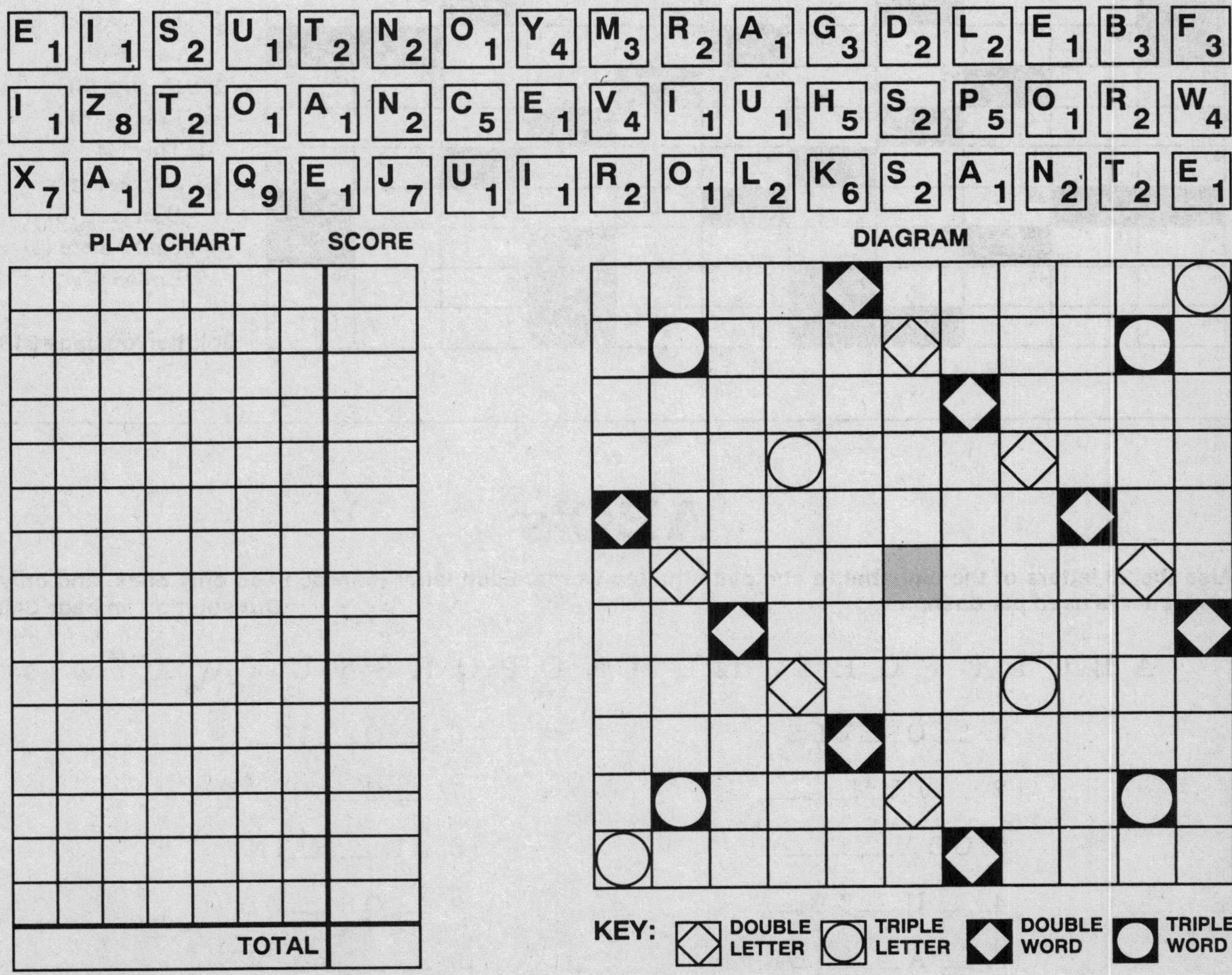

DOUBLE TROUBLE

Not really double trouble, but double fun! Solve this puzzle as you would a regular crossword, EXCEPT place one, two, or three letters in each box. The number of letters in each answer is shown in parentheses after its clue.

ACROSS
1. Recoil (5)
4. Discharge (4)
6. Building addition (5)
9. Turn upside down (6)
10. Torte (4)
11. Excuse (7)
12. Pekoe or Darjeeling (3)
13. Rage (7)
15. Watch over (4)
16. Curl (7)
18. Prank (5)
20. Molten rock (4)
21. Soon (4)
23. Snake (7)
26. Hanker (4)
28. Frolic (4)
30. Subsequently (5)
31. Scabbard (6)
33. Building clay (5)
35. Carry on (4)
36. Spice (6)
38. Driver's need (7)
40. Barrie's Peter (3)
42. Tell (7)
44. Night before (3)
45. Comments (7)
47. Skirt edge (3)
48. Tried (6)
50. Spin (6)
51. Sprinted (3)
52. Ogle (4)

DOWN
1. Come in first (3)
2. Habitual (10)
3. Sure (7)
4. Onlooker (9)
5. Rouse (5)
6. Tiny colonist (3)
7. Following (4)
8. Stretch (6)
11. Basis (7)
14. School skipper (6)
17. Collect (5)
19. Skill (5)
20. Generous (6)
22. Wanderer (5)
24. Endure (9)
25. Contestant (7)
27. Pursue (5)
29. Badge carrier (9)
32. Gratitude (6)
34. Honey maker (3)
37. Navigation device (5)
39. Cuddle (6)
40. Repeat (6)
41. Tidy (4)
43. Journalist Dan ___ (6)
46. Foal's mom (4)
49. Ended (4)

1	2	3	■	4	5	■	■	6	7	8
9			■	10		■	11			
■	12		■	13		14		■	15	
■	16		17		■	18		19	■	■
20		■	21		22	■	23		24	25
26		27	■	28		29	■	30		
31			32	■	33		34	■	35	
■	■	36		37	■	38		39		■
40	41	■	42		43		■	44		■
45		46		■	47		■	48		49
50			■	■	51		■	52		

Solution on page 348

ABC's

Use the 26 letters of the alphabet to complete the ten words. Each letter is to be used only once, and only one letter is used per dash.

Our solution on page 348

A B C D E F G H I J K L M N O P Q R S T U V W X Y Z

1. __O__ELS
2. __LUM____
3. COA__E__
4. __U__TL__
5. __A____ER
6. __O__IE__
7. __C__U__T
8. AD____IN
9. __OR__ED
10. ____N__EL

WORD MATH

In these long-division problems letters are substituted for numbers. Determine the value of each letter. Then arrange the letters in order from 0 to 9, and they will spell a word or phrase. **Solutions on page 347**

1.

```
         TON
ONLY | DELAYS
       DNSE
        OSEY
        ONLY
         GELS
         NEOA
          YAD
```

0 __ 1 __ 2 __ 3 __ 4 __ 5 __ 6 __ 7 __ 8 __ 9 __

2.

```
         FEE
ROLE | TRIFLE
       FLAB
       ROBAL
       RRAPR
        RRABE
        RRAPR
           BL
```

0 __ 1 __ 2 __ 3 __ 4 __ 5 __ 6 __ 7 __ 8 __ 9 __

3.

```
         OPT
TREE | PERSON
       TREE
       NYOUO
       NSUTC
        OPPON
        OPRUC
          OYN
```

0 __ 1 __ 2 __ 3 __ 4 __ 5 __ 6 __ 7 __ 8 __ 9 __

4.

```
        MID
EON | MAROON
      RNMN
       NEDO
       NHZH
        ERON
        ZIHN
         IOH
```

0 __ 1 __ 2 __ 3 __ 4 __ 5 __ 6 __ 7 __ 8 __ 9 __

5.

```
         HAL
RICH | SCHOOL
       RICH
        IUHRO
        IAUCA
         VVRVL
         VHCCL
          IRVC
```

0 __ 1 __ 2 __ 3 __ 4 __ 5 __ 6 __ 7 __ 8 __ 9 __

6.

```
         ELS
VANE | LEARNS
       UNVY
       ALLAN
       ASANN
        AUSRS
        AORRA
         ASRU
```

0 __ 1 __ 2 __ 3 __ 4 __ 5 __ 6 __ 7 __ 8 __ 9 __

CRYPTOGRAMS

The directions for solving are given on page 98.
Solutions on page 348

1. G J M I X U J X D X P M Z Y I L S W T X Q Q M W O J Y Q Z W O B V X S X P D W Q U W T U J X Z J M I P J W W P P M Q X Y Q X Q, F W C Q Y O P R M S I Q Q X X D U W F X Y T T I M Z U X P Y Q D V Z J Y Q X H X S G M U J G J Y U X H X S M U M Q U J Y U L S X H X O U Q U J X D T S W D F X M O R Q I X X L C Y U F X P U M D X.

2. U B I D O S I U Z H R O E U W C U N G, ''N W I B I D C U S U W O H R N W Y N T P V Z G Q V O A P D U G P Z Z U D H R U H U F F I U Z I G H P E I U C E V T R U C H R I G P Z Z U D N H C I Z A.''

3. M K C Z R V E R O E R S V M A R B S C K C U B M A S K E Q M O D R V. L Q R O M X C F O D M K F Z G S V Y R G L R R O G Q R M D R V C U G L R Z I R M O K V R I R O G R R O, U C B R H M T A Z R, M A M B R O G M D R V M V T F E Q M V G L R O G X X R M B V.

4. A C E V M E W P U M D T V D C O T P V K V M D T M H W G T P N T C U D T M A C E V W N L W V Y A E R W K P U E K Z K G C N A C V. A C E H W T J P W V V K V M D T M H W D T L W M A Z A K M V A A Y M W P.

5. Q X Q B Z Y Q P I O I C K G R K G R Y P D P G R Y A G D Q X H Q X M F I J Q X Z Q X Y Q U P; R Y P I O H P B G Y P C P R G, R Y P J I B P K X R P B P G R P H Y P K G K X Y P B. (Q C Q R Y Q Z Y B K G R K P)

6. XIMJ EV YEEO XWAAFBZ LZ WKEIN TAERLAY RJFA NE CBFNFAO NJWN RJWN'Z JWCCFALAY LZA'N JWCCFALAY.

7. JGO VOUJ THR JF YOHBD GFT JF ZF WJ RFLBUOYE WU JF QBWJWQWKO JGO THR JGO QFCCWJJOO WU PFWDP JF ZF WJ.

8. NGKU XYA QKFYDK PMDYAE, XYA FMU'S PYLBKS YVH PLOKUHE. YG, XYA FMU SLX, QAS SGKX NYU'S VKS XYA. (LYHUKX HMUBKLPOKVH)

9. BIWXIN QP O HLOKQBJ BCOB OB O GNQBQGOK WVWITB BITZP BV IKQGQB BCI UIPB QT PBIIK OTZ BCI RVNPB QT XIVXKI.

10. DXQ GYTYPE AOTD SQ BPCCPMQF SL DXQ GQEDOJQ. YD YT EPD QEPOUX DP TDZJQ OH DXQ TDQHT — MQ AOTD TDQH OH DXQ TDZYJT.

11. CF ZPWA PU UF UCIYCZPSL PC ZAIWAU ZPCCZA CPRA TFY ISXCKPSL AZUA. (ARPZX JPMHPSUFS)

12. MXGZPIAU ZM LZSU, OIP RXI SUUA MXWUXSU PX PUGG RXI PVQP MXGZPIAU ZM LZSU. (VXSXKU AU OQGYQH)

13. RXHSIXC HXCGRHL XIG CFJG RXHSIXC ACXRHL; HUGE RGGT OXIGPSCCE ACXRRGT AISRFRZ.

14. ''QJ QI YVW XGHF IK EVSZ V YXVHF HVI UKXXKO NKG?'' ''IEVI WZBZTWJ, VAZ NKG V RVT KA RKGJZ?''

QUOTEFALLS

The letters in each vertical column go into the squares directly below them, but not necessarily in the order they appear. A black square indicates the end of a word. When you have placed all the letters in their correct squares, you will be able to read a quotation across the diagram from left to right.

Solutions on page 348

1.

2.

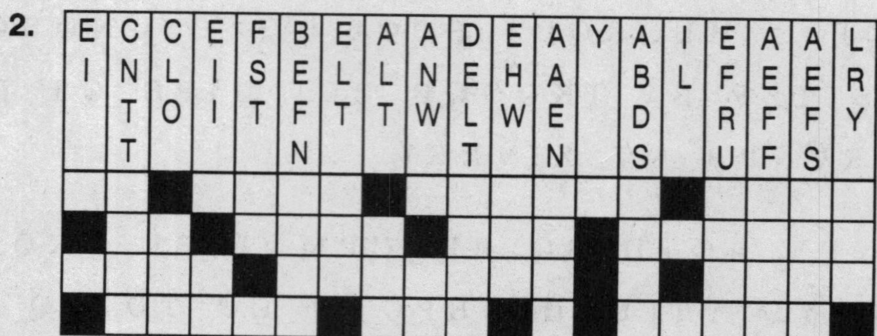

3.

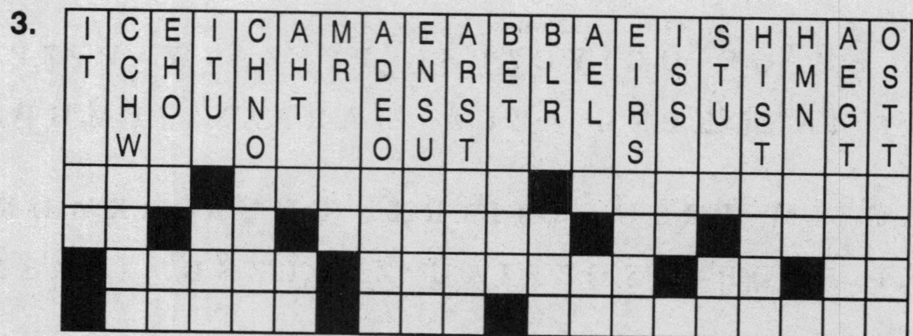

4.

A I O S	F L T	E U W	D O T	A A I U	L O R	C D N W	A I	B N N W	A E S	O S	A P T	B C E H	E L N O	E E O R	R R R	E T Y	B C O	O T Y	F O	C N P	A E E O	R T V W
		■								■							■			■		
							■				■								■			
	■						■			■					■			■				
			■		■				■							■			■			

FILL-IN

The entries for this puzzle are given to you, listed alphabetically according to length. Across and Down words are all mixed together, and you are to find their proper places in the diagram.

Solution on page 349

2 Letters
Dr.
IV
OE
On

3 Letters
And
Boy
Dun
Ere
Gin
Lot
Met
Moa
Ore
Owe
Own
Pod
Rio
Sip
Sop
Spa
Spy
Tar
Toy
Ups
Use
Yes

4 Letters
Aloe
Asia
Gate
Mews
Neon
Peer
Rate
Sere
Ship
Spud

5 Letters
Aline
Areas
Aspen
Asset
Chore
Cider ✓
Climb
Harts
Heaps
Hovel
Motto
Never
Odors
Steed
Stere
Tooth
Topic
Vases
Wagon

6 Letters
Besets
Modest
Spigot
Wanted

7 Letters
Asserts
Blasted
Edition
Shiners
Stretch
Tropics
Waiters

C I D E R

Bubbles

In each of the circles is the name of a U.S. city minus one letter! Find that missing letter to complete the city's name. Then arrange the missing letters to spell the name of the bonus city.

Solution on page 348

1.

2.

3.

4.

5.

6.

1. ______

2. ______

3. ______

4. ______

5. ______

6. ______

Bonus: ______

Crostic Puzzle 13

Use the CLUES on the left to fill in the WORDS column. Then transfer each letter to the correspondingly numbered square in the diagram. (We have inserted WORD A as an example.) It is not necessary to know all the words to start solving. Work back and forth from the diagram to the WORDS column until both are filled. A black square indicates the end of a word. The completed diagram will contain a quotation, and the first letter of each word in the WORDS column, reading down, will spell the author's name and the source of the quotation.

CLUES	WORDS
A. Patted gently	D A B B E D 143 22 52 72 7 129
B. Alerts	114 38 94 126 15
C. Branch	59 3 75 51 115 61 133 16
D. Minded	98 88 131 74 105 113
E. Fit together	10 158 28 108 70 139 142 60
F. Watered down	91 151 56 97 124 90 132
G. Female fowl	66 93 112 135
H. Rub out	29 8 11 96 127
I. Jane's mate	34 45 68 41 17 102
J. Scaler of Mt. Everest	24 101 89 39 145 65 12
K. Belgian seaport	76 86 117 134 140 55
L. Defends	165 18 100 71 161 120 9
M. African animal	63 81 149 1 154 13 79
N. Pounded	118 116 47 82 37 144 33 109
O. Finished	5 92 36 21 73 103 147
P. Dry	137 6 40 20 150 146 48
Q. Held in esteem	78 31 54 152 156 25 162
R. Mountain on Chalcidice	160 43 49 84 26
S. Window dividers	141 164 67 159 80 155 32 85
T. Hewed	30 104 35 167 83 64 69
U. Like Sills's voice	121 153 107 77 4 163 87 23
V. Abandoned	50 62 138 111 58 125 95 157
W. Titles	106 14 166 128 123
X. Actors	46 130 42 2 19 27 53 136 110
Y. Boil	57 148 122 99 44 119

Solution on page 354

				1 M	2 X		3 C	4 U	5 O	6 P	7 A E	8 H	9 L		10 E	11 H	12 J				
	13 M	14 W	15 B	16 C		17 I	18 L	19 X	20 P	21 O	22 A A	23 U	24 J	25 Q	26 R		27 X	28 E	29 H		30 T
31 Q	32 S	33 N		34 I	35 T		36 O	37 N	38 B	39 J	40 P	41 I	42 X		43 R	44 Y	45 I	46 X		47 N	48 P
	49 R	50 V	51 C	52 A B	53 X	54 Q	55 K		56 F	57 Y		58 V	59 C		60 E	61 C	62 V	63 M	64 T	65 J	
66 G	67 S	68 I	69 T		70 E	71 L		72 A B	73 O	74 D		75 C	76 K	77 U		78 Q	79 M	80 S		81 M	82 N
83 T	84 R	85 S	86 K	87 U	88 D	89 J	90 F		91 F	92 O	93 G	94 B	95 V	96 H		97 F	98 D	99 Y	100L	101J	102I
103O		104T	105D		106W	107U	108E	109N	110X		111V	112G	113D		114B	115C	116N	117K		118N	119Y
	120L	121U	122Y	123W	124F	125V		126B	127H	128W	129A D		130X	131D		132F	133C	134K	135G	136X	137P
	138V	139E	140K	141S		142E	143A D		144N	145J	146P	147O	148Y	149M		150P	151F	152Q	153U		154M
			155S	156Q		157V	158E	159S	160R	161L	162Q		163U	164S	165L	166W	167T				

Crostic Puzzle 14

A. Private feud
163 39 194 15 87 9 108 116

B. Intellectual
14 156 43 7 118 52 160

C. Audience dubbing: 2 wds.
17 191 150 93 56 29 165 23 82 107

D. Extinct elephant
117 85 139 53 19 69 38

E. Wonderful
8 33 132 133 148 96 173

F. Very tidy
48 109 35 10 192 94 124 149 134

G. Pleasure skipper
57 30 13 34 178 78 62 138 184

H. Be aware of: 2 wds.
171 68 183 46 4 49 26 63 119

I. Found
106 64 55 143 180 113 186 103 120

J. Exhibitionist: hyph.
188 37 89 67 71 101 136

K. Mystery story
1 22 41 185 72 28 166 151

L. Bushman
70 152 65 169 16 167 59 176 187

M. Hailing cry: hyph.
54 145 164 179 66 193

N. Sorry
129 79 174 61 32 51 91 146 21

O. Ames university: 2 wds.
31 170 60 47 144 95 155 88 161

P. Coffee dunker
126 11 102 123 83 90 42 99

Q. Entrance
121 159 73 81 172 40 111

R. Professional driver
36 131 80 27 114 153 18 177 141

S. Utility
92 98 112 127 5 135 20 181 189 77

T. Spectacles
3 58 122 104 158 137

U. Upper canines
142 182 2 130 110 157 45 74

V. Arrogant
44 162 50 6 75 24 175

W. Actuality: 2 wds.
76 125 140 154 25 190 84 147

X. Ichneumon
86 128 12 168 97 100 115 105

Solution on page 354

			1 K	2 U		3 T	4 H	5 S	6 V	7 B		8 E	9 A		10 F	11 P	12 X	13 G			
		14 B		15 A	16 L		17 C	18 R	19 D	20 S		21 N	22 K	23 C	24 V		25 W	26 H	27 R		
28 K	29 C	30 G	31 O	32 N		33 E	34 G	35 F	36 R	37 J		38 D	39 A		40 Q	41 K	42 P	43 B	44 V	45 U	
46 H	47 O	48 F		49 H	50 V	51 N		52 B		53 D	54 M	55 I	56 C		57 G	58 T	59 L		60 O	61 N	
62 G	63 H	64 I	65 L		66 M	67 J	68 H		69 D	70 L	71 J	72 K	73 Q	74 U		75 V	76 W	77 S		78 G	79 N
80 R	81 Q	82 C	83 P		84 W	85 D	86 X	87 A		88 O	89 J		90 P	91 N	92 S	93 C	94 F	95 O		96 E	97 X
98 S	99 P		100 X	101 J		102 P	103 I		104 T	105 X	106 I	107 C		108 A	109 F	110 U		111 Q	112 S	113 I	114 R
—	115 X	116 A	117 D	118 B		119 H	120 I	121 Q	122 T	123 P		124 F	125 W	126 P		127 S	128 X	129 N		130 U	131 R
132 E		133 E	134 F	135 S	136 J	—	137 T	138 G	139 D	140 W		141 R	142 U	143 I	144 O	145 M	146 N		147 W	148 E	
149 F	150 C	151 K		152 L	153 R	154 W		155 O	156 B	157 U		158 T	159 Q	160 B	161 O	162 V	163 A	164 M	165 C	166 K	167 L
		168 X		169 L	170 O		171 H	172 Q	173 E	174 N		175 V	176 L	177 R	178 G	179 M		180 I	181 S		
			182 U	183 H	184 G	185 K		186 I	187 L	188 J		189 S	190 W	191 C	192 F	193 M	194 A				

Crostic Puzzle 15

A. Personal driver — 127 113 82 55 25 38 149 65 110

B. Native of Ireland — 61 78 67 129 96 6 109 9 42

C. Showing warmth — 92 108 184 52 124 89 80

D. Come forth again — 17 185 174 46 107 32 7 168

E. Concocted a story — 167 145 87 179

F. Activity — 72 130 44 100 104 2 27 157 171 120

G. Hone — 111 71 31 88 33 57 153

H. European linden — 85 28 13 98

I. Respond — 95 64 164 41 16 158

J. Household appliance — 141 19 116 162 182 21 192 53 178 148

K. Toni Morrison, e.g. — 147 154 10 144 118 173

L. Computer transmitting device — 146 54 169 136 66

M. Finish — 133 121 74 189 163

N. Interpret — 103 101 119 143 70 3 77 11

O. Dismal — 29 132 102 115 156 35 188 159 152 138

P. Miller's Willy — 176 193 180 139 93

Q. Lack of mastery — 183 22 34 175 142 166 60 23 97 117

R. Herman's Hermits' lead singer — 160 63 40 99 47

S. Constitution addition — 45 155 134 24 81 91 68 73 123

T. Reduction — 4 43 165 59 83 48 39 137 126 20

U. Foot feature — 170 1 131 106

V. Gauge — 150 26 12 86 18 186 177 79 128

W. Theater producer — 56 187 50 58 135 122 75

X. Ingenuity — 8 30 15 191

Y. Branch of metaphysics — 37 62 36 114 125 76 94 181

Z. Perry King series — 69 140 49 112 5 172 84

a. Kind of address — 190 14 90 51 151 105 161

Solution on page 354

1 U	2 F	3 N	4 T	5 Z	6 B	7 D		8 X	9 B	10 K	11 N	12 V		13 H	14 a	15 X	16 I	17 D	18 V		19 J
20 T		21 J	22 Q		23 Q	24 S	25 A	26 V	27 F	28 H	29 O	30 X	31 G	32 D		33 G	34 Q	35 O	36 Y		37 Y
38 A		39 T	40 R	41 I	42 B		43 T		44 F	45 S	46 D	47 R		48 T	49 Z	50 W	51 a		52 C		53 J
54 L	55 A	56 W	57 G		58 W	59 T	60 Q	61 B		62 Y	63 R		64 I	65 A	66 L	67 B	68 S	69 Z		70 N	71 G
72 F	73 S		74 M		75 W	76 Y	77 N	78 B	79 V	80 C	81 S		82 A	83 T		84 Z	85 H	86 V	87 E	88 G	89 C
90 a		91 S	92 C	93 P		94 Y	95 I	96 B	97 Q	98 H	99 R	100 F	101 N	102 O		103 N	104 F		105 a	106 U	107 D
	108 C	109 B	110 A	111 G	112 Z		113 A	114 Y	115 O	116 J	117 Q		118 K	119 N		120 F	121 M	122 W	123 S		124 C
125 Y	126 T	127 A	128 V		129 B	130 F	131 U	132 O	133 M	134 S		135 W	136 L		137 T		138 O	139 P	140 Z	141 J	
142 Q	143 N		144 K	145 E	146 L		147 K	148 J	149 A		150 V	151 a	152 O		153 G	154 K	155 S	156 O	157 F	158 I	
159 O	160 R	161 a		162 J	163 M		164 I	165 T	166 Q	167 E	168 D	169 L		170 U	171 F	172 Z		173 K	174 D	175 Q	176 P
177 V	178 J	179 E		180 P	181 Y		182 J	183 Q	184 C	185 D		186 V	187 W	188 O	189 M	190 a	191 X		192 J	193 P	

Crostic Puzzle 16

A. Black-tongued dog: 2 wds. 49 24 91 163 109 40 30 20

B. Rough calculation 25 15 84 66 171 97 72 141

C. Swiss river 63 47 136 139 82

D. Glitzy 76 190 113 131 182 127

E. Honks 93 161 116 130 148

F. Alternates 74 128 65 122 57 105 28

G. Sigh 143 54 13 70 135 164 32 102 176 83

H. Pennsylvania sect 168 23 111 45 58

I. Added honey 137 37 120 147 80 87 9 167 123

J. Full-length 129 39 1 179 126 17 12 188 183 159

K. Prepared 155 59 8 99 165

L. Plutocrat's pastime 180 185 6 21 46 172 11 150

M. Authorized 55 18 43 51 106 7 36 186

N. Perfect 187 104 189 16 79 95 90 144

O. Obie and Edgar 3 29 138 108 121 170

P. Looter 145 184 132 68 71

Q. Horse 89 34 27 119

R. General survey 160 153 118 166 101 107 134 81

S. Altered 61 157 124 92 140 154 178

T. Prohibited 14 42 142 73 4 88 173

U. Scorched 22 96 158 67 94 19 75 181 48 133

V. Final proposal 110 177 33 149 2 10 156 77 52

W. Wrapped 35 26 53 62 146 64 169

X. Actress Bergen 117 152 103 50 86

Y. Certain Slav 98 174 162 60 38 151 125 44 114

Z. Peachy 31 5 56 112 85

a. Cowpoke's need 175 41 69 115 78 100

Solution on page 354

		1 J		2 V	3 O	4 T	5 Z	6 L	7 M	8 K	9 I		10 V	11 L	12 J		13 G	14 T	15 B		
	16 N	17 J	18 M	19 U		20 A	21 L	22 U	23 H		24 A	25 B		26 W	27 Q	28 F		29 O	30 A	31 Z	32 G
	33 V	34 Q		35 W	36 M	37 I		38 Y	39 J		40 A	41 a	42 T	43 M		44 Y	45 H		46 L	47 C	48 U
	49 A	50 X	51 M	52 V	53 W	54 G		55 M	56 Z		57 F	58 H	59 K		60 Y	61 S	62 W		63 C	64 W	65 F
66 B	67 U	68 P	69 a		70 G	71 P	72 B	73 T	74 F		75 U		76 D	77 V	78 a	79 N		80 I	81 R	82 C	83 G
84 B	85 Z		86 X	87 I	88 T	89 Q	90 N		91 A	92 S		93 E	94 U	95 N		96 U	97 B	98 Y	99 K	100 a	101 R
102 G	103 X	104 N	105 F		106 M	107 R	108 O	109 A	110 V	111 H	112 Z		113 D	114 Y	115 a		116 E	117 X	118 R	119 Q	120 I
121 O		122 F		123 I	124 S	125 Y	126 J	127 D		128 F	129 J	130 E	131 D	132 P	133 U	134 R		135 G	136 C	137 I	
138 O	139 C	140 S	141 B	142 T	143 G	144 N		145 P	146 W	147 I		148 E	149 V	150 L	151 Y		152 X	153 R	154 S	155 K	
156 V	157 S	158 U		159 J	160 R	161 E	162 Y	163 A	164 G	165 K		166 R	167 I	168 H	169 W	170 O		171 B	172 L	173 T	174 Y
	175 a	176 G	177 V	178 S		179 J	180 L		181 U	182 D	183 J		184 P	185 L	186 M	187 N		188 J	189 N	190 D	

Crostic Puzzle 17

A. Early Palace Theatre offering
179 50 175 96 26 81 91 3 44 156

B. Correctly
94 146 112 99 106 153

C. Journal or gazette
86 35 1 138 65 69 38 60 23

D. Hindu garment
97 167 29 154 158

E. Frequently
47 28 144 149 89 102 170 126 76 67

F. Verse
27 52 24 108 152

G. Messenger
6 21 80 41 32 161 48 173

H. Occasionally: 3 wds.
77 85 164 178 95 55 12 172 45 132

I. Willowy
157 88 166 116 180 40 105 13 10

J. Authorization
137 15 127 64 98 49 11 78 90 160

K. Consomme
43 73 125 176 34

L. Study of causation
114 133 130 39 181 22 79 18

M. Quotient
9 128 139 135 151

N. Counselor
7 115 57 145 30 129 123 103

O. Minimum
54 131 168 82 75 87

P. High regard
2 136 61 20 14 31

Q. Thin coins
71 101 19 63 83

R. Large indeterminate ordinal number
143 37 150 68 74 141 70 104 155

S. Variable
124 140 53 25 72 93

T. Unassailable
109 165 177 147 4 8 134 121

U. Sparing
33 62 17 42 46 92 163

V. Of waves below the audio-frequency range
119 100 113 162 66 56 16 110 117 171

W. City on Lake Winnebago
58 120 169 5 174 118 122

X. Entertainment spot
51 36 59 148 142 84 111 107 159

Solution on page 354

1 C	2 P		3 A	4 T	5 W	6 G		7 N		8 T	9 M	10 I	11 J	12 H		13 I	14 P	15 J	16 V	17 U	18 L
	19 Q	20 P	21 G	22 L	23 C	24 F		25 S	26 A	27 F	28 E	29 D	30 N	31 P	32 G		33 U	34 K	35 C		36 X
37 R	38 C	39 L	40 I	41 G	42 U	43 K	44 A	45 H		46 U	47 E	48 G		49 J	50 A	51 X		52 F	53 S	54 O	55 H
56 V		57 N	58 W	59 X	60 C	61 P	62 U	63 Q	64 J		65 C	66 V	67 E	68 R		69 C	70 R	71 Q		72 S	73 K
74 R	75 O	76 E	77 H	78 J		79 L	80 G	81 A	82 O	83 Q		84 X	85 H	86 C	87 O	88 I	89 E	90 J	91 A	92 U	93 S
	94 B	95 H	96 A		97 D	98 J	99 B	100 V	101 Q	102 E	103 N		104 R	105 I		106 B	107 X	108 F	109 T	110 V	
111 X	112 B	113 V	114 L		115 N	116 I	117 V	118 W		119 V	120 W		121 T	122 W	123 N		124 S	125 K	126 E	127 J	128 M
129 N	130 L	131 O	132 H		133 L	134 T	135 M	136 P		137 J	138 C		139 M	140 S	141 R		142 X	143 R	144 E	145 N	146 B
	147 T	148 X	149 E		150 R	151 M	152 F	153 B		154 D	155 R	156 A		157 I	158 D	159 X	160 J	161 G	162 V	163 U	
164 H	165 T	166 I	167 D		168 O	169 W	170 E	171 V	172 H		173 G	174 W	175 A		176 K	177 T	178 H	179 A	180 I	181 L	

Crostic Puzzle 18

A. Rickety — 222 206 160 193 167 152 93 108 213 175

B. Of unknown origin — 8 149 27 216 126 205 82 67 47

C. Game with looped string: 2 wds. — 110 183 77 7 96 143 135 9 42 24

D. Unsettled: 4 wds. — 23 69 113 162 153 53 214 173 120 74

E. Heat control device — 121 58 95 38 50 75 64 154 165 15

F. Plaid — 63 98 226 52 101 169

G. Represent — 79 212 89 60 158 196 30 99 16

H. Demand — 102 200 130 62 190 181 87

I. Rumored — 148 66 54 19 132 224

J. Charles Kuralt show — 5 208 170 204 46 133 117 43 48 221

K. Rapids: 2 wds. — 159 78 168 20 3 28 161 199 85 156

L. Abilities — 56 147 11 36 127

M. Exotic — 218 29 73 124 125 12 192 118 220 4

N. Boundlessness — 6 31 114 223 207 21 198 92

O. Kitchen aid — 184 14 171 157 80 106 139 57 134

P. Heighten — 155 194 2 186 90 41 103

Q. Puccini opera — 172 115 137 91 68

R. Upset — 150 86 10 97 83 202 51 191 145

S. Profit-producer — 76 49 187 210 65 17 70 174 180 116

T. Idiosyncrasy — 211 84 217 122 45 40

U. Hot drink — 128 182 188 142 163

V. Vitality — 177 35 151 219 138

W. Sunday entree — 71 195 104 227 178

X. Particular — 166 179 203 37 185 18

Y. Maine seaport — 100 33 81 164 26 140 176 189

Z. Levantine sailing vessel — 39 197 44 22 131 109

a. Dormant — 141 111 72 215 55 25

b. Unbiased — 107 34 61 146 201 136 129 119 94

c. Italian port — 13 59 209 112 144 123

d. Chaps — 32 225 88 1 105

Solution on page 354

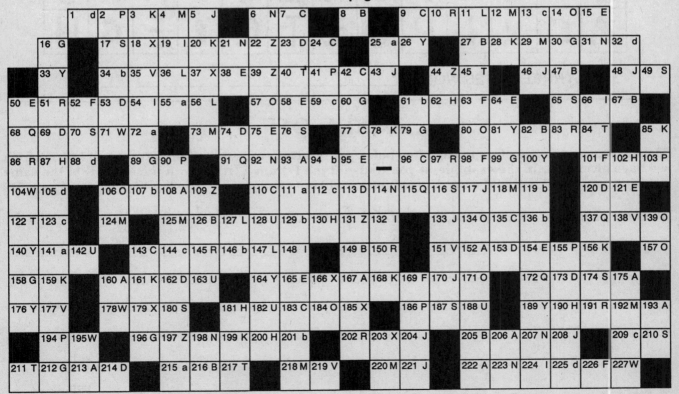

		1 d	2 P	3 K	4 M	5 J	■	6 N	7 C	■	8 B	■	9 C	10 R	11 L	12 M	13 c	14 O	15 E		
	16 G	■	17 S	18 X	19 I	20 K	21 N	22 Z	23 D	24 C	■	25 a	26 Y	■	27 B	28 K	29 M	30 G	31 N	32 d	
■	33 Y	■	34 b	35 V	36 L	37 X	38 E	39 Z	40 T	41 P	42 C	43 J	■	44 Z	45 T	■	46 J	47 B	■	48 J	49 S
50 E	51 R	52 F	53 D	54 I	55 a	56 L	■	57 O	58 E	59 c	60 G	■	61 b	62 H	63 F	64 E	■	65 S	66 I	67 B	■
68 Q	69 D	70 S	71 W	72 a	■	73 M	74 D	75 E	76 S	■	77 C	78 K	79 G	■	80 O	81 Y	82 B	83 R	84 T	■	85 K
86 R	87 H	88 d	■	89 G	90 P	■	91 Q	92 N	93 A	94 b	95 E	—	96 C	97 R	98 F	99 G	100 Y	■	101 F	102 H	103 P
104 W	105 d	■	106 O	107 b	108 A	109 Z	■	110 C	111 a	112 c	113 D	114 N	115 Q	116 S	117 J	118 M	119 b	■	120 D	121 E	■
122 T	123 c	■	124 M	■	125 M	126 B	127 L	128 U	129 b	130 H	131 Z	132 I	■	133 J	134 O	135 C	136 b	■	137 Q	138 V	139 O
140 Y	141 a	142 U	■	143 C	144 c	145 R	146 b	147 L	148 I	■	149 B	150 R	■	151 V	152 A	153 D	154 E	155 P	156 K	■	157 O
158 G	159 K	■	160 A	161 K	162 D	163 U	■	164 Y	165 E	166 X	167 A	168 K	169 F	170 J	171 O	■	172 Q	173 D	174 S	175 A	■
176 Y	177 V	■	178 W	179 X	180 S	■	181 H	182 U	183 C	184 O	185 X	■	186 P	187 S	188 U	■	189 Y	190 H	191 R	192 M	193 A
■	194 P	195 W	■	196 G	197 Z	198 N	199 K	200 H	201 b	■	202 R	203 X	204 J	■	205 B	206 A	207 N	208 J	■	209 c	210 S
211 T	212 G	213 A	214 D	■	215 a	216 B	217 T	■	218 M	219 V	■	220 M	221 J	■	222 A	223 N	224 I	225 d	226 F	227 W	■

THREESOMES

Locate in the diagram all the letters that appear exactly alike three times. A letter may appear many times in different styles, but you want only those that are exact triplicates. Rearrange the Threesomes letters to spell a common word.

Solution on page 348

T	J	E	B	E	A	N	E	D	X	E	M	G
J	O	R	N	A	W	Y	G	A	O	Q	F	P
S	O	C	S	P	E	O	L	R	S	Y	T	F
T	G	I	A	O	S	U	W	O	T	O	I	A
N	E	A	H	E	I	S	J	Y	U	I	J	L
E	U	I	E	Q	G	T	Q	S	S	P	R	W
A	W	Y	S	F	I	S	E	O	N	A	C	A
I	G	A	D	T	E	B	S	T	O	I	M	E
O	F	U	Q	S	O	N	E	S	P	N	A	O
A	R	X	L	P	O	E	T	C	I	E	G	H

THREESOMES WORD: ______________________

TRADE-OFF

The answers to the two clues in each line below are 6-letter words that differ by only one letter, which we have given you. In the example, if you trade off the P from STRIPE with the letter K in the same position, you get STRIKE. The order of the letters will not change.

Solutions on page 349

Example: Chevron S T R I P E — S T R I K E Hit

1. Large wasp H _ _ _ _ _ — C _ _ _ _ _ Instrument
2. Haven _ _ _ _ G _ — _ _ _ _ S _ Deny
3. Marvel _ O _ _ _ _ — _ A _ _ _ _ Ramble
4. Shocking effect _ _ _ _ C _ — _ _ _ _ R _ Make known
5. Surrender _ _ _ V _ _ — _ _ _ T _ _ Garcon
6. Menace _ _ _ _ _ T — _ _ _ _ _ D Filament

WORD CALCULATOR

Each of the letters in the diagram has a numerical value which you can calculate by adding the number of the row (across) and the column (down) in which the letter is shown. For example, a Y is in the 2nd row and the 3rd column of the diagram and therefore has a value of 5. Other Y's will have different values. Each 5 may represent a different letter. Each letter in the diagram will be used only once.

Each number chart below the diagram represents a 6-letter word. The numbers are in correct order. You must determine the correct letter for each number. It is a good idea to try to calculate the letters with the highest and lowest values first.

Solution on page 349

	1	2	3	4	5	6	7	8
1	O	N	E	F	A	N	L	S
2	D	O	Y	H	T	D	T	K
3	I	D	E	L	Y	I	P	A
4	H	I	W	G	P	B	O	O
5	O	D	C	R	S	T	R	A
6	T	F	A	D	I	I	E	N

1.

6	10	12	4	8	7

2.

9	6	8	10	13	7

3.

3	13	5	8	9	11

4.

12	10	7	9	3	5

5.

10	6	5	11	14	8

6.

5	11	7	8	4	9

7.

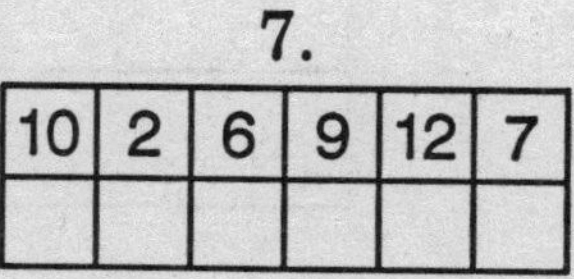

10	2	6	9	12	7

8.

7	4	9	11	6	8

You Know the Odds

Six dog breeds are spelled out, but they are missing every other letter. It shouldn't be too difficult to fill in the even letters now that You Know the Odds!

Solutions on page 349

1. B ___ A ___ L ___
2. C ___ C ___ E ___ S ___ A ___ I ___ L
3. S ___ I ___ Z
4. C ___ I ___ U ___ H ___ A
5. S ___ Y ___ T ___ R ___ I ___ R
6. D ___ L ___ A ___ I ___ N

THREE'S COMPANY

This alphabetical list of seemingly unrelated words actually contains 15 groups of three related items. Your job is to sort them out into those 15 groups using each item only once. The trick is that some of the items could be used in more than one list, but only one arrangement of all the items will work. Remember, use each item only once and have exactly three items in each group.

Solution on page 349

Alder	Cheers	Larch	Rome	Stevenson
Alter	Danson	M*A*S*H	Sacrifice	Swing
Amend	Delicious	Mound	Sandbox	Tam-o'-shanter
American	Doyle	Orange	Sandburg	Tomato
Base	Fairway	Pine	Shelley	Transform
Bonanza	Fez	Pfennig	Shilling	Turner
Bowler	Franc	Prune	Slide	Twain
Brown	Green	Qantas	Southwest	Whitman
Bunker	Koppel	Rainbow	Speckled	Winesap

1. On the playground ____________ ____________ ____________

2. Teds ____________ ____________ ____________

3. On the links ____________ ____________ ____________

4. Trees ____________ ____________ ____________

5. Baseball terms ____________ ____________ ____________

6. Airlines ____________ ____________ ____________

7. TV shows ____________ ____________ ____________

8. Apple varieties ____________ ____________ ____________

9. Authors ____________ ____________ ____________

10. Change ____________ ____________ ____________

11. Juice ____________ ____________ ____________

12. Poets ____________ ____________ ____________

13. Trout ____________ ____________ ____________

14. Hats ____________ ____________ ____________

15. Foreign coins ____________ ____________ ____________

BULL'S-EYE SPIRAL

This is a new target for those who can think in circles. The game works two ways, outward and inward. If you're outward bound, guess the word that fits clue 1-3. Then go on to clue 4-6 and so on. If you're stuck with an outward-bound word, try the inward clues. Work both ways to hit the Bull's-Eye.

Solution on page 349

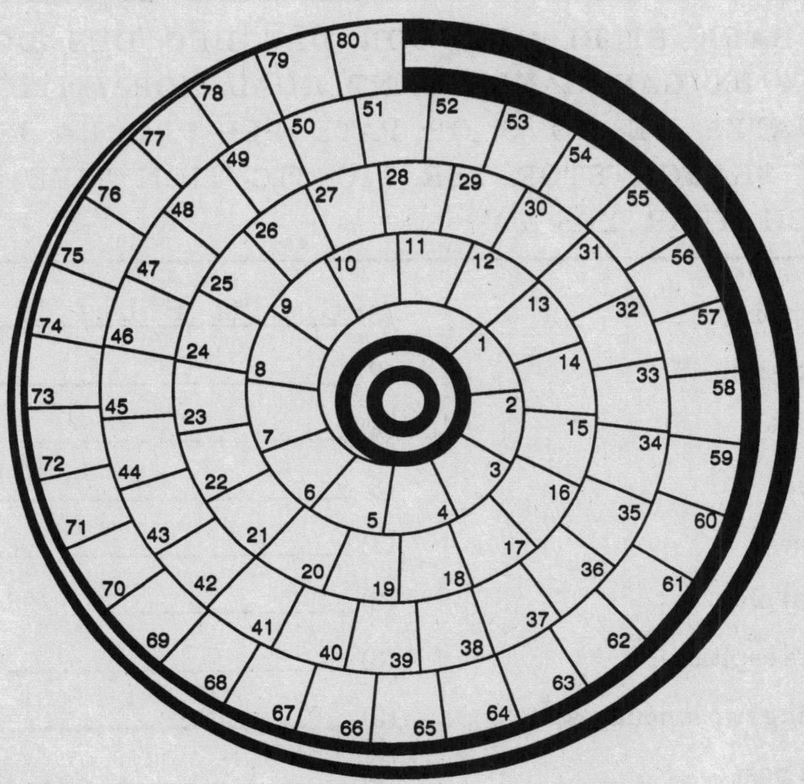

OUTWARD

1-3. Give silent consent
4-6. Arrest
7-15. Reticence
16-21. Overjoyed
22-25. Fury
26-30. Tubers
31-35. Aviator
36-39. Smooth
40-43. Confederate
44-48. Mutineer
49-51. Egyptian cobra
52-54. High card
55-59. Intelligible
60-62. Great anger
63-66. Healthy
67-71. Cognizant
72-75. Ceremonial staff
76-80. Chopped finely

INWARD

80-75. Determine
74-69. Photog's instrument
68-65. Room side
64-62. Female sheep
61-54. Make fun of
53-51. Bottle top
50-47. Auction
46-42. Green mineral
41-38. Country road
37-34. President's refusal
33-30. Mouth border
29-27. Also
26-21. Consider
20-18. Greek letter
17-12. Abate
11-8. Dunce
7-1. Leave high and dry

SYL´´LA-CROS´TIC

Fill in the answers to the clues by using all the syllables in the Syllabox. The number of syllables to be used in each answer is shown in parentheses. The number of letters in each answer is indicated by the dashes. Each syllable will be used once. When the words are correctly filled in, their first and last letters, reading down, will reveal an epigram preceded by its author's name.

Solution on page 349

✱ SYLLABOX ✱

A A AN AR BARK BI BI ~~COM~~ COR DAT DEC DES DOR E EC ED EL EM ER EX EX GAN GANCE GANT GUAL HOP I I IG LA LIN LO ~~MENT~~ NAI NATES NE NO O OP PATE ~~PLI~~ PRO RA RE RI RO RO RUS SCOTCH SEARCH STOP TER TIC TIC TION TIVE TRAV U VAL VEL VO WATCH YEAR YES ZA

1. Give praise (3) C O M P L I M E N T
2. Child's game (2) ____________
3. Foresee (4) ____________
4. Specifies (3) ____________
5. Ornament (4) ____________
6. Musical play (3) ____________
7. Kenya's capital (3) ____________
8. Speaking two languages (3) ____________
9. Recent past (3) ____________
10. Italian cheese (4) ____________
11. Spectacular show (5) ____________
12. Rural (2) ____________
13. Race timer (2) ____________
14. Administrator (4) ____________
15. Confirmed (4) ____________
16. Tasteful (3) ____________
17. Investigate (2) ____________
18. Overbearing manner (3) ____________
19. Short prose work (3) ____________
20. Hallway (3) ____________
21. Board ship (2) ____________

WORD MERGERS

Rearrange the letters in each Word Merger to form two words using all the given letters only once. Then rearrange these same letters and merge them into one long word. You might want to form the long word first and then the pair of words. Score 5 points for each pair of words you form and 10 points for each long word. A score of 85 is good, 95 is very good, and 105 is excellent.

Our solutions with a perfect score of 120 points on page 349

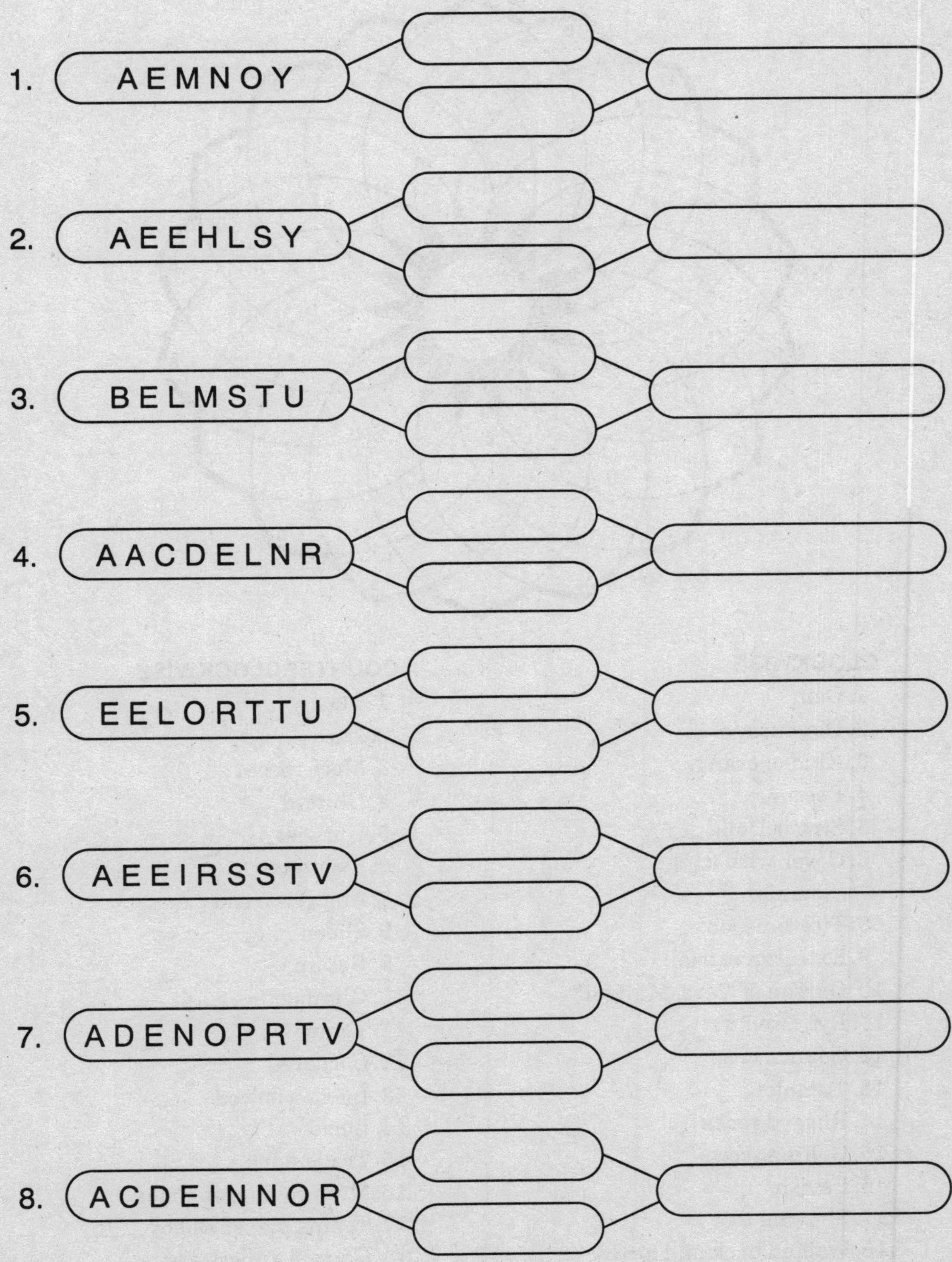

FLOWER POWER

The answers to this petaled puzzle will go in a curve from the number on the outside to the center of the flower. Each number has two 5-letter words. One goes in a clockwise direction and the second in a counterclockwise direction. Try working from both sets of clues to fill the flower. **Solution on page 349**

CLOCKWISE

1. Gem
2. Discourage
3. Kind of orange
4. Rescues
5. Singer Della ____
6. Cover with icing
7. Slammer
8. Tiresome job
9. Extraterrestrial
10. Garson of "Mrs. Miniver"
11. Rye or white
12. Council city
13. Tumbler
14. Rugged rocks
15. Golfing score
16. Lavish
17. Shaving tool
18. Walked back and forth

COUNTERCLOCKWISE

1. Flashy
2. Lure
3. More recent
4. Glutted
5. Untwist
6. Excitement
7. Angler's basket
8. Sheen
9. Get up
10. Glimmer
11. Verge
12. Cornered
13. Inexperienced
14. Lucid
15. Trademark
16. Main course, at times
17. Tennis player Bobby ____
18. Certain appetizers

ALPHABET SOUP

Insert a different letter of the alphabet into each of the 26 empty boxes to form words of five or more letters reading across. The letter you insert may be at the beginning, the end, or in the middle of the word. Each letter of the alphabet will be used only once. Cross off each letter in the list as you use it. All the letters in each row are not necessarily used in forming the word.

Our solution on page 349

Example: In the first row across we have inserted the letter Z to form the word VAPORIZED.

A B C D E F G H I J K L M N O P Q R S T U V W X Y ~~Z~~

V	A	P	O	R	I	**Z**	E	D	W	A	R	D
A	M	E	L	I	A		H	R	I	L	L	E
B	A	R	A	N	C		N	A	N	C	E	E
A	L	I	C	E	S		U	R	G	E	O	N
P	A	R	E	C	D		A	G	O	N	A	L
G	I	M	M	I	C		D	E	N	N	I	S
P	A	U	L	P	U		D	L	E	L	E	E
N	O	R	M	A	M		M	O	R	Y	O	U
T	A	L	L	E	A		N	A	N	C	E	E
E	S	T	H	E	R		U	G	G	L	E	E
I	N	T	E	R	I		M	A	R	G	O	T
R	E	D	D	D	E		S	E	W	A	R	D
B	E	A	U	T	I		Y	L	I	N	D	A
A	D	A	M	E	E		C	I	T	E	D	Y
M	A	U	D	D	O		B	L	E	T	O	M
D	A	I	S	Y	L		I	N	D	O	W	E
A	L	E	C	O	U		H	A	R	O	L	D
A	L	E	X	C	L		W	N	J	O	H	N
W	E	N	D	Y	A		U	R	D	E	N	E
D	O	N	N	A	C		E	P	T	O	D	D
E	B	B	A	R	O		U	E	D	W	I	N
B	A	R	B	B	A		L	O	O	N	E	D
H	E	R	M	A	N		U	T	H	O	R	V
G	A	P	P	R	O		R	I	A	T	E	Z
A	N	N	U	I	T		R	O	G	E	R	S
L	A	U	R	A	D		A	N	C	E	L	L

DOUBLE TROUBLE

Not really double trouble, but double fun! Solve this puzzle as you would a regular crossword, EXCEPT place one, two, or three letters in each box. The number of letters in each answer is shown in parentheses after its clue.

ACROSS

1. Nick and Nora's dog (4)
3. Provide refreshments (5)
6. Guarantees (9)
11. Designer Chapman (4)
12. Sweet wine (7)
14. Meadow newborns (5)
15. High-minded (5)
17. ____ Pan Alley (3)
18. Choir recess (4)
19. Actress Barrymore (4)
20. Candid (6)
22. Periphery (4)
24. Prayer book (6)
25. Change (5)
27. Hot tub (3)
29. Decorate (7)
32. Prim (6)
33. Surgeon's stitch (6)
34. Clad (7)
35. Guide (5)
36. Present (7)
37. Bound (4)
38. Publishing tycoon (6)
39. Military eating hall (4)
40. Writer Bombeck (4)
41. Excuse (6)
42. Gray matter (5)
44. Bank clerk (6)
46. Chivalrous (7)
48. Endure (4)
51. Blake of "Gunsmoke" (6)
53. Fate (3)
54. Windbag (8)
55. Idealist (7)
57. Finagle (6)
59. Golfer Sutton (3)
60. Captivated (9)
61. Like some windshields (6)
62. Smart (5)

DOWN

1. Go up (6)
2. Suit maker (6)
3. Arrived (4)
4. Shreds (5)
5. Logical (8)
6. Applaud (4)
7. Expunged (6)
8. Used a stopwatch (5)
9. White lie (3)
10. Double curve (3)
13. Narrow road (4)
16. Wafted (4)
20. Gander's warning (4)
21. Hem and haw (7)
23. Body English (8)
24. Moped (6)
26. Accustom (5)
28. Mom and pop (7)
29. Plumper (6)
30. Ballpark figure (8)
31. All in (5)
32. Abhor (6)
33. Unwavering (4)
35. Tahiti garb (6)
36. Curry seasoning (5)
38. Got wind of (5)
41. Perpetual (9)
42. Out and out (7)
43. Carry on (4)
45. Andes animal (5)
47. Sanction (5)
48. Dawdle (3)
49. Horrified (6)
50. Unnerving (9)
52. Ventured (5)
54. Strain (5)
55. Reading room (3)
56. Achieve (5)
58. Sparkle (5)

Solution on page 349

1	2	■	3	4	5	■	■	6	7	8	9	10
11		■	12			13	■	14				
15		16		■	17		■	18			■	■
19			■	20			21	■	22		23	■
■	■	■	24			■	25	26		■	27	28
29	30	31		■	■	32			■	33		
34				■	35			■	36			
37			■	38			■	■	39			
40		■	41			■	42	43		■	■	■
■	44	45		■	46	47			■	48	49	50
■	■	51		52	■	53		■	54			
55	56				■	57		58		■	59	
60					■	■	61			■	62	

BOWL GAME

To bowl a strike (20 points) you must create a 10-letter word using all the letters in each pin. The letter on top in the pin is the first letter of the strike word. To bowl a spare (10 points) use the same 10 letters to form two words. Splits are not allowed: you may not divide the strike to form a spare. For example, SWEETHEART may not become SWEET and HEART.

Our solutions with a perfect score of 300 points on page 350

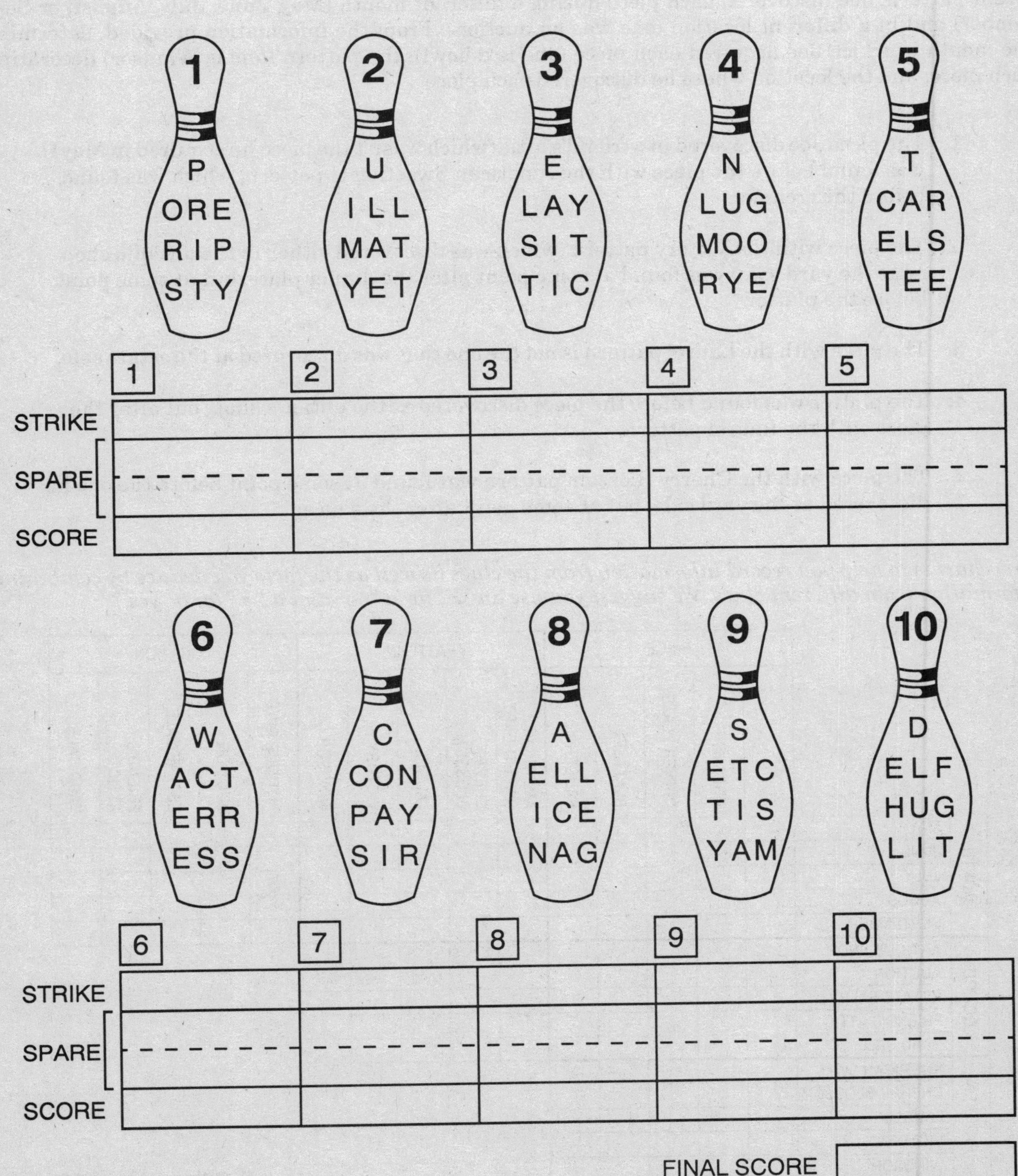

LOGIC PROBLEM

GLASS PATTERNS

Joe, an avid collector of Depression glass, is always on the lookout for pieces to add to his collection. This year, Joe acquired five different pieces of Depression glass, each of which is decorated with a different pattern. Joe discovered each piece during a different month (May, June, July, August, or September) and in a different location (one was an auction). From the information provided, determine the month in which Joe acquired each piece (one is a bowl), the pattern (one is Windsor) decorating each piece, and the location where he discovered each piece.

1. The piece Joe discovered in a friend's attic (which wasn't the piece he acquired in May) was found before the piece with the American Sweetheart pattern, which was found before the creamer.

2. The piece with the Victory pattern (which was discovered either in the antique shop or at the yard sale) was found at some point after the dinner plate, but at some point before the platter.

3. The piece with the Laurel pattern is not the one that was discovered at the estate sale.

4. The platter was found before the piece discovered at the antique shop, but after the piece with the Laurel pattern.

5. The piece with the Cherry Blossom pattern was found at some point before the one he discovered at the yard sale, but at some point after the saucer.

This chart is to help you record information from the clues as well as the facts you deduce by combining information from different clues. We suggest you use an "X" for a "no" and a "•" for a "yes."

		PIECE					PATTERN					LOCATION				
		BOWL	CREAMER	DINNER PLATE	PLATTER	SAUCER	AMERICAN SWEETHEART	CHERRY BLOSSOM	LAUREL	VICTORY	WINDSOR	ANTIQUE SHOP	AUCTION	ESTATE SALE	FRIEND'S ATTIC	YARD SALE
MONTH	MAY															
	JUNE															
	JULY															
	AUGUST															
	SEPTEMBER															
LOCATION	ANTIQUE SHOP															
	AUCTION															
	ESTATE SALE															
	FRIEND'S ATTIC															
	YARD SALE															
PATTERN	AMERICAN SW.															
	CHERRY BLOSSOM															
	LAUREL															
	VICTORY															
	WINDSOR															

Solution on page 350

BRICK BY BRICK

Rearrange this stack of bricks to form a crossword puzzle. The clues will help you fit the bricks into their correct places. Row 1 has been filled in for you. Use the bricks to fill in the remaining spaces.

Solution on page 349

ACROSS

1. Secular
   Slumber
   Person's nature
2. Redolence
   Analyze grammatically
   Esau's grandson
3. Cadence
   Fit to be tied
   Al Hirschfeld's daughter
4. Word before room
   Blathers
5. American Indian
   Bar measure
6. Variety shows
   Freeloader, at sea
7. Encourages
   Negotiates
   French land mass
8. Band singer Stafford and namesakes
   Twilled fabric
   Zip
9. Emmet
   Small yeast cakes
   Kind of point
10. Affecting the whole body
    Constraint
11. Musical symbol
    Funny one
12. Steep slope
    Weapons storage
13. Fashionable
    Asunder
    "Arrivederci, ____"
14. Abhor
    Italian poet
    Flat
15. Is indebted
    Finished
    Unpleasantly humid

DOWN

1. Yuletide leaper
   Indian rulers
   Lover of Narcissus
2. Month before Nissan
   Lustrous black
   Artie or Irwin
3. Jot
   Doublets
   French municipality
4. Mohawk's kin
   Vestiges
5. Incenses
   Porter's cousin
6. Book parts
   Humphrey Bogart role
7. Gargantuan
   Liability
   Forest deity
8. Geologic division
   Glacial ice mass
   Conjunction
9. Erhard's prog.
   Parties for grooms
   ____ blanche
10. Door aperture
    Scrambled
11. Propels a bireme
    Hairy coats
12. Musical composition
    Commanded
13. Issue forth
    Flinch
    TV science show
14. "Penny ____"
    Assumed moniker
    Sherman Hemsley vehicle
15. Monks
    Cheers
    Gaunt

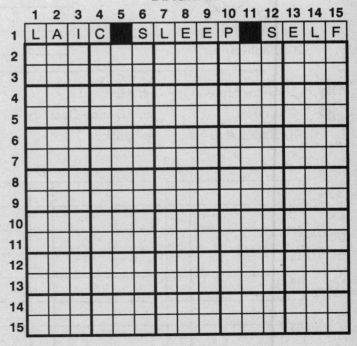

BRICKS

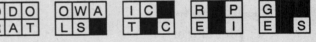

ERG / BAS — ■■S / ■BA — NIL / CAL — HAT / OWE — ESC / CHI

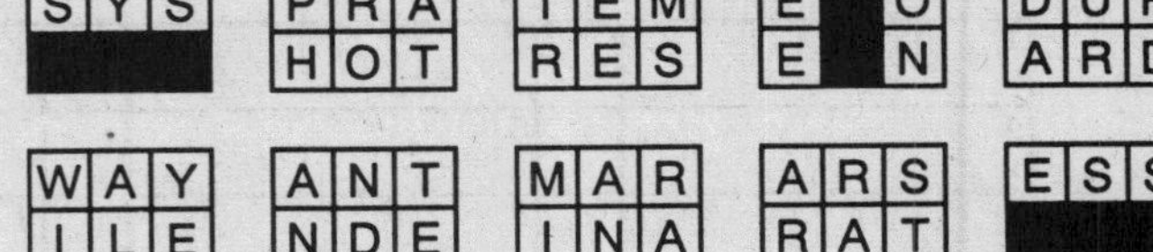

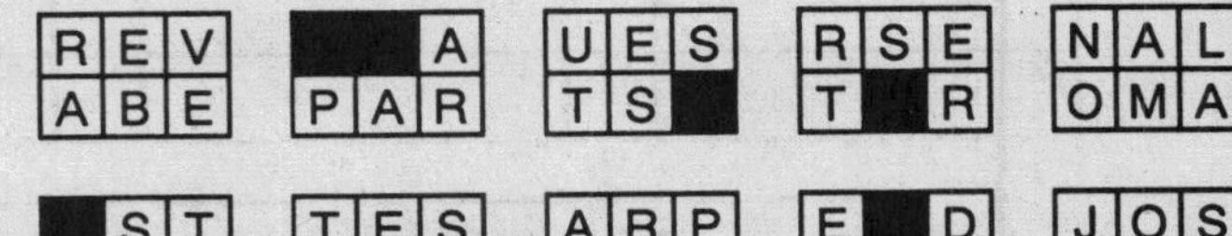

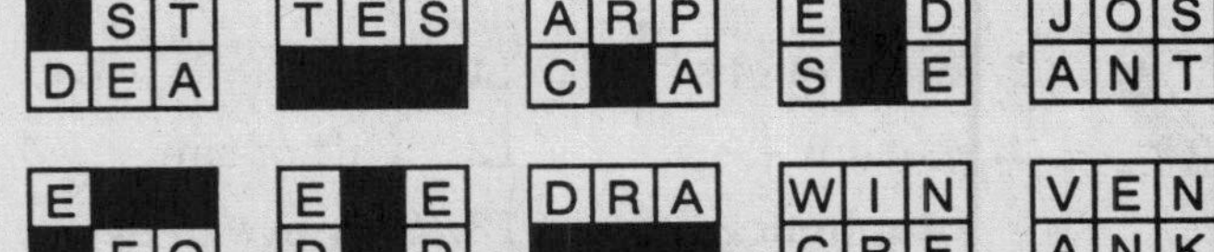

ODO / RAT — OWA / LS■ — IC■ / T■C — R■P / E■I — G■■ / E■S

DIAGRAM

	1	2	3	4	5	6	7	8	9	10	11	12	13	14	15
1	L	A	I	C	■	S	L	E	E	P	■	S	E	L	F
2															
3															
4															
5															
6															
7															
8															
9															
10															
11															
12															
13															
14															
15															

ESCALATORS

Write the answer to clue 1 in the first space. Drop one letter and rearrange the remaining letters to answer clue 2. Put the dropped letter into Column A. Drop another letter and rearrange the remaining letters to answer clue 3. Put the dropped letter into Column B. Follow this pattern for each row in the diagram. When completed, the letters in Column A and Column B, reading down, will spell related words or a phrase.

Solutions on page 349

1

1. Grave
2. Presages
3. Alaskan seaport
4. Or's partner
5. In that place
6. Clothes hanger
7. Drenched
8. Beseeched
9. Secretary
10. Usual
11. Grinding tooth
12. Fertile soil
13. Upright piano
14. Clumsy
15. Quantity of ale

	A		B	
1		2		3
4		5		6
7		8		9
10		11		12
13		14		15

2

1. Bizet opera
2. Author Stephen ____
3. Teen's bane
4. Acclimate
5. Met singer
6. Budget item
7. Fellow headliner
8. Fur trader
9. Part of BA
10. Fashioning
11. Pixie
12. "Gift of the ____"
13. Saw eye to eye
14. Stormed
15. Pull
16. Australian city
17. Force units
18. Excite greatly

	A		B	
1		2		3
4		5		6
7		8		9
10		11		12
13		14		15
16		17		18

3

1. Grew crops
2. Vision
3. Expensive
4. Give
5. "Divine Comedy" author
6. Mind
7. Restore
8. Radio part
9. Faithful
10. Debates
11. Sucrose
12. Carpets
13. Iron
14. Gather
15. Highway section
16. Nappy
17. Lion family
18. Plumber's problem
19. Intense
20. Commerce
21. Palm fruit

	A		B	
1		2		3
4		5		6
7		8		9
10		11		12
13		14		15
16		17		18
19		20		21

MASTERWORDS

Using only the ten letters shown, fill in the diagram by forming words across and down to achieve the highest possible score. Each letter has a given value, so try to use the high-value letters as much as possible. You may repeat letters as often as you wish, even within words. Do not repeat words in the diagram. Foreign words, abbreviations, and words starting with a capital letter are not allowed.

When the diagram is completely filled, add up your score. Count each letter, line by line, going across only. Put the total for each line in the boxes at the right.

Our solution with a score of 354 on page 350

D	E	G	I	M	P	R	S	T	W
1	4	1	5	4	5	3	3	2	2

SCORE

TOTAL

CRYPTO-FAMILIES

Each Crypto-Family is a list of related words in code. Each Family has its own code. When you have identified a word, use the known letters to help decode the other words in the Family.

Solutions on page 350

1. HANG UPS
Example: Laundry

WTCUGXTF

BTCCLTLUF

LIDPDAFTLI

BZGX WIZHUM

PUCULIDGU

LTZGPZGA

WCDPIZGA

LUGGTGP

HZFFDF

HDRZCU

2. VOCALISTS
Example: Songster

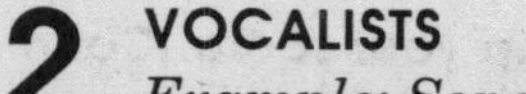

OUJJUSXXB

KBTTZXB

MXBXZUSXB

MTZIOFBS

TWXBU MFZIXB

SFLU

FQWBTLFMUCTB

KUZCTB

KUBTJXB

QFZMCBXJ

3. THINGS TO CUT
Example: Class

LPMSDV

TBEYV

SBPXV

OMEYDPEBMAV

LMD SPZVC

SGPEDPV

TZXYDC

OAGHDPV

LBLDP XGAAV

YPBVV

4. NOT REAL
Example: Artificial

KZTO-AOPLOUO

QHZMSMPOCW

JLKMPZWLBC

QZAHLRZWLBC

RBMCWOHQOLW

KZC-KZSO

ABDMJ

QZPJO

QLRWLWLBMJ

LKLWZWLBC

5. INNER "K" CITIES
Example: Akron

ZQEQTMHM

QUTEQUT

XQRFEM

ZQWEFYU

TFIUSWES

URQEMWF

PMDEUQW

NYMWENOYX

XQEZQ

PMEMYXM

6. JUST DUCKY
Example: Canvasback

VUBVL

ZGKKGLB

ZVLFGTJVL

HUTIGUK

IVGK

AUBFVCT

PSDDKVYVGB

YGLKVXSUT

CKBJXSGA

JMCIVL

WORDBENDERS

The answers for this crossword puzzle might be just around the bend! Solve the puzzle as you would a regular crossword. The clues for the words which bend in the diagram are listed under the heading BENDERS.

BENDERS

1. Organic compound
2. Red gem
8. PBS science program
9. Fact
17. Church musician
18. Unlawful act
28. Mouthpieces
29. Like some decks
30. Influenced
32. Heedful
43. Xanadu
49. Frosted

ACROSS

1. Reclusive actress
6. Extra compensation
10. Scold
13. Type of quark
14. Eccentric wheel
19. Fore's counterpart
21. Freud's concern
22. "The ____" (Chaplin film)
23. Waikiki present
24. Pivot
25. Produces
26. Dry ____
33. Sweetheart letter?
34. Locust tree
36. Say from memory
38. Electrified particle
39. Hillary Clinton, ____ Rodham
40. ____ up to
41. Sign of assent
42. Negative word
44. Fashionable
50. Floods
51. Ecclesiastical council
52. Angled block

DOWN

3. School transport
4. Select
5. Precambrian, e.g.
6. ____ Bird
7. Sonnet's relative
11. Go-betweens
12. Painkiller
15. In the past
16. Native country
19. Share
20. ____ up (disgusted)
27. Provo's state
29. Public disgrace
31. Andiron
35. Bill's partner
37. Cardinal number
44. Brouhaha
45. Was in the vanguard
46. Drinking cup
47. Defense line acronym
48. Compass pt.

Solution on page 350

Secret Word

Discover the 5-letter Secret Words by the process of elimination and deduction. Fill in the blanks with the 5-letter answers to the clues. The number in parentheses next to each answer tells you how many of the letters in that word are also in the Secret Word. A zero next to an answer indicates that none of the letters in that word is in the Secret Word. After you have determined the correct five letters, rearrange them to form the Secret Word. No letter is repeated in any Secret Word or within any answer word. The first letters of the answers, reading down, spell out a hint to the Secret Word. **Solutions on page 349**

1. Secret Word ☐☐☐☐☐

Group of bees _____ (3)
Cord _____ (1)
Flexible _____ (2)
Certain candies _____ (0)
Bangor's site _____ (1)
Merits _____ (2)
Crest _____ (2)
Thoughts _____ (2)
Hammer targets _____ (2)
Skate _____ (2)

2. Secret Word ☐☐☐☐☐

Windshield blade _____ (2)
Paragon _____ (1)
Disperse _____ (1)
On a par _____ (2)
Felt concern _____ (0)
Stones _____ (1)
Greek fabulist _____ (2)
Glass bottle _____ (1)
Highland wear _____ (2)
Patrol _____ (3)

3. Secret Word ☐☐☐☐☐

Abrade _____ (3)
Songs of praise _____ (2)
Imply _____ (1)
Chop finely _____ (0)
Christens _____ (2)
Foyer _____ (1)
Luxury boat _____ (3)

4. Secret Word ☐☐☐☐☐

Location _____ (0)
Theater guide _____ (2)
Mandolins' kin _____ (1)
Cavalry sword _____ (2)
Approximate _____ (3)
Tiny bit _____ (2)
Era _____ (2)

5. Secret Word ☐☐☐☐☐

Visitor _____ (3)
Dark _____ (2)
Articles _____ (3)
Courtroom event _____ (2)
Cherub _____ (0)
Kingdom _____ (2)

6. Secret Word ☐☐☐☐☐

"The Golden ____" _____ (2)
Radiant _____ (3)
Colonist Standish _____ (1)
Free-for-all _____ (3)
Branches _____ (0)
Arm joint _____ (2)

SCOREMASTER

TO PLAY:

1. Write the first seven LETTERS across the first line of the PLAY CHART. Indicate the last letter used.
2. Form a word of at least two letters across or down in the DIAGRAM. One letter of the first word must go into the center square.
3. Tally your score, noting any bonuses (see key at bottom).
4. Carry down all unused LETTERS to the next line of the PLAY CHART. Transfer enough LETTERS, in the given order, so that you have seven LETTERS to work with.
5. Form a new word or words from each draw by:
   a. Adding one or more letters to an existing word.
   b. Building a new word at right angles to an existing word, by adding to it or incorporating one of its letters.
   c. Setting a new word parallel to an existing word, but remember all adjoining letters must form new words in crossword fashion.
6. Continue working in this way until all the LETTERS have been used or you can no longer form any words. If you need more lines for your PLAY CHART, use a separate piece of paper.

NOTE: Proper names, foreign words, and abbreviations are not allowed.

TO SCORE:
The value of each letter is given with it. The letter has the same value every time it is used. Be sure always to include all bonuses (see key at bottom). An additional 30 points is earned when you use all seven letters in the PLAY CHART in one turn. When two words are formed in the same play, the common letter (including any bonus) is scored with each word.

Our game with a score of 550 points on page 350

LETTERS

I 1	N 2	R 2	K 6	A 1	T 2	B 3	E 1	U 1	D 2	I 1	G 3	S 2	O 1	Z 8	L 2	V 4
E 1	Q 9	A 1	W 4	C 5	T 2	I 1	R 2	H 5	U 1	D 2	E 1	O 1	S 2	N 2	L 2	A 1
F 3	I 1	E 1	U 1	O 1	J 7	Y 4	S 2	R 2	T 2	P 5	X 7	A 1	E 1	M 3	N 2	O 1

PLAY CHART **SCORE**

TOTAL

DIAGRAM

KEY: DOUBLE LETTER, TRIPLE LETTER, DOUBLE WORD, TRIPLE WORD

Word Ways

Hidden in each diagram are five 5-letter words beginning with the same letter. Draw a continuous line through the letters as you spell each word by moving in any direction from letter to adjoining letter without crossing your line. Each puzzle has a different starting letter.

Solutions on page 350

1.

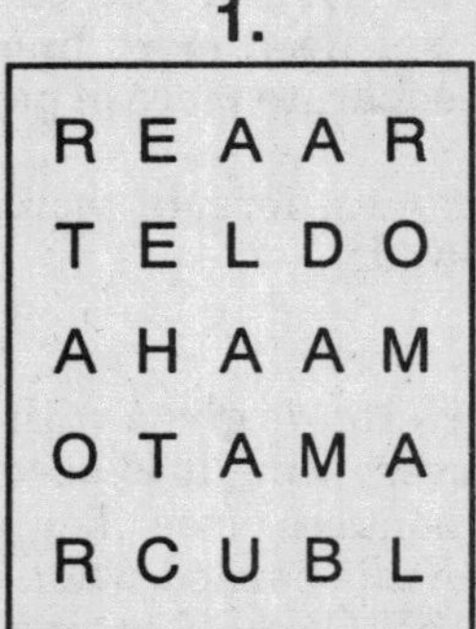

R	E	A	A	R
T	E	L	D	O
A	H	A	A	M
O	T	A	M	A
R	C	U	B	L

2.

O	D	A	L	K
S	U	K	A	O
K	A	K	N	E
A	Y	Y	A	D
K	T	T	I	K

3.

E	E	N	G	V
G	R	L	O	E
A	G	E	G	G
N	I	R	U	A
T	G	A	C	E

Changaword

Can you change the top word into the bottom word in each column in the number of steps indicated in parentheses? Change only one letter at a time and do not change the order of the letters. Proper names, slang, and obsolete words are not allowed.

Our solutions on page 352

1. HUNT (4 steps)	2. MAKE (4 steps)	3. TYPE (4 steps)	4. SEND (5 steps)
PECK	TYPO	WORD	NOTE

Mix and Mingle

The letters to the right of each row when unscrambled and placed in the correct squares will spell out nine compound words or phrases. In addition the initial letters of the answers can be rearranged to form a bonus compound word or phrase.

Solutions on page 349

1.	O		F	S		R		N		FIGP
2.			N		W		G		N	ADOBA
3.		Y		S		A			W	HEODE
4.	W		L		P		W			ROILE
5.		U	T		K	I		T		ROSS
6.	R		D	C		R			T	EPAE
7.			U	S		T			P	ROMEA
8.		O		K			I	T		SHMCL
9.	O			R		H	R		W	TOVE

BONUS: ___________________

Lucky Clover

Fit the 8 words into the four-leaf clover. Each word starts in a circle and may go in either direction. Words sometimes overlap. Solution on page 349

Along Lavish Optimist Sentence

Enough Neutral Popular Slept

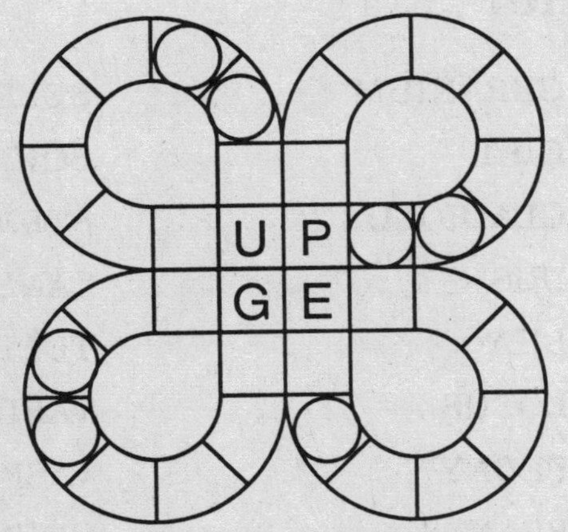

Number Sleuth

One of the numbers in the hexagons has been circled because it and the numbers in the six surrounding hexagons are all different. There are 12 others like this. Are you a sharp-eyed sleuth who can find them all? Solution on page 349

Hop, Skip, and Jump

What is the longest word you can find starting with any letter, moving only from left to right? You may Hop, Skip, and Jump over any number of letters, but once you choose a letter you may not backtrack. A word with 10 letters is excellent. Our 10-letter word on page 349

T S A E C R Y P R O E W L N T U D I N R E

Three to One

Starting with each word in Column A, add a word from Column B and then one from Column C to build eight longer words. For example, CORN plus ERST plus ONE is CORNERSTONE. Each small word will be used only once. Solution on page 349

A	B	C	
1. KNOW	A	GALE	1. ______
2. CAB	IN	BACK	2. ______
3. RUN	PA	ABLE	3. ______
4. PAST	PER	ON	4. ______
5. NIGHT	LEDGE	ATE	5. ______
6. SAND	I	ROUND	6. ______
7. PA	DRAG	PER	7. ______
8. SNAP	OR	NET	8. ______

Word Seek 23

Missing Vowels

Before you can loop these words about a florist shop, you must first fill in the circles in the diagram with the missing vowels A, E, I, O, and U. Words in the diagram read forward, backward, up, down, and diagonally, and always in a straight line. Circle each word when you find it and cross it off the list. Words will often overlap, and some letters may be used more than once. Not all of the letters in the diagram will be used. We have filled in and circled AROMA as an example.

Solution on page 333

IN A FLORIST SHOP

AROMA ✓
ARRANGEMENT
ASTER
BABY'S-BREATH
BEGONIA
BLOOM
BLOSSOM
BOUQUET
BUDS
BULBS
CANNA

CARD
CORSAGE
CROCUS
DAHLIA
DELIVERY
DISPLAY
FERN
FERTILIZER
FLORAL
FLOWERS
FRAGRANCE

GERANIUM
GIFT
GLADIOLUS
IRIS
LILY
LOTUS
PEONY
PLANTS
PRETTY
ROSES
SEEDS

SELECTION
SOIL
STEM
TANSY
TULIP
VARIETY
VASE
VINE
VIOLET
ZINNIA

Z M Q V C P V C ○ R D Z R G W T M ○ S S ○ L B
○ F C S ○ R C ○ W Y M ○ ○ L B B S D ○ B N S F
N C R ○ C ○ S N S R S N L Y T ○ ○ R ○ V ○ A ○
N S N ○ R R ○ N G ○ M ○ N T T S S B N L S M R
○ Y T ○ G S F ○ S V T ○ L ○ P ○ Y ○ ○ L ○ O T
○ T ○ N D R ○ N ○ ○ T C ○ L ○ S ○ ○ ○ ○ T R ○
R V L ○ ○ V ○ G F L ○ R ○ L B L D Q N L ○ A L
L C ○ G H L P N ○ ○ L Y S R W ○ R ○ ○ Y L D ○
D Q ○ ○ L V P M C D F F ○ T L S R ○ W ○ L F Z
P F V B ○ M G N R ○ F ○ ○ G ○ ○ S B L ○ B N ○
T Y S N ○ T P R ○ T T Y D V G M T C ○ S T ○ R
C N ○ D P G S M R H Q L S ○ R ○ C M C M C P F

Match Words

To solve this puzzle, find two words, one in each diagram, in the same location in both diagrams, which combine to form the title of a song. The first word of each song title is in the top diagram; the second word is in the bottom diagram in the same location, reading in the same direction. Words read forward, backward, up, down, and diagonally, and always in a straight line. Not all the letters will be used. For example, "AUTUMN LEAVES" is formed by combining AUTUMN from the top diagram with LEAVES from the bottom diagram, in the same location and reading in the same direction.

Word list on page 334

Solution on page 333

YOUR WORD LIST
(34 entries)

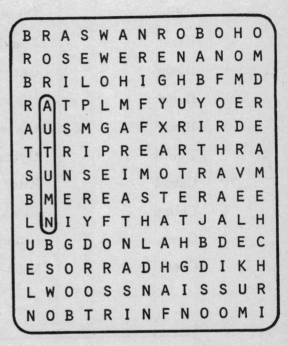

B R A S W A N R O B O H O
R O S E W E R E N A N O M
B R I L O H I G H B F M D
R A T P L M F Y U Y O E R
A U S M G A F X R I R D E
T T R I P R E A R T H R A
S U N S E I M O T R A V M
B M E R E A S T E R A E E
L N I Y F T H A T J A L H
U B G D O N L A H B D E C
E S O R R A D H G D I K H
L W O O S S N A I S S U R
N O B T R I N F N O O M I

R A I L A K E E R F A S T
O D A Y M U S T R A S I L
B O Y D R N O O N C Y C L
T L O O O E N I L E O K O
S E U L W L G H N O U N V
U A P E R E A N G E L I E
D V R M S N A M S I V V R
R E E R P A R A D E I A E
O S I W Y I Z I Z J H L W
O H G T N R D O T A D C Y
M O O R Y A B U L D A T A
O W O O T M Y B A L L U L
N E W E R T S F W O L G O

Word Seek 25

Zigzag

The 5-letter animals in this puzzle will be found in the diagram in an unusual way. They do not read in straight lines; rather each entry has one bend in it. Loop each word when you find it in the diagram, as we did with ADDAX, and cross it off the list. Words overlap, and some letters may be used more than once. All the letters in the diagram will not be used.

Solution on page 333

ANIMAL FIVES

~~Addax~~	Dingo	Moose	Sloth
Beast	Eland	Mouse	Steed
Bison	Gator	Okapi	Steer
Bongo	Hippo	Otter	Swine
Boxer	Horse	Panda	Tapir
Bunny	Hyena	Puppy	Tiger
Camel	Kitty	Rhino	Zebra
Chimp	Koala	Sable	
Civet	Lemur	Sheep	
Coati	Llama	Skunk	

```
R H C W T I A L U N C A B Y I X M Y R E E C H
T I B A N O R L L O M O D X A O Y O V S A Y S
V N P I K S K P A A X E B D U D H C O M E D K
R E F A O G I H C I P U L K N S N M O R S N T
A H T N B A N B P O X U V A S D E G U V U B A
R U I N T U S T P V A Y P R E L A B O R I K E
I W A N Y H N P O T S P B E L T R Y V E I T S
S L V R E A R K I K Y E L A T L O O K T H E Y
T A K L O E P G U H A T V N A S L R T I T A B
N O B X E A P R E N E S T O X S I B T H I Y G
G E A R I T R I I R G A T O G E O B U H N M C
Z D F H A M S D R A K O B I S N R X C N E R P
```

Alphabetics

Each of the answer words starts with a different letter of the alphabet. The words are in the diagram reading forward, backward, up, down, and diagonally, and always in a straight line. Words may overlap. Not all the letters in the diagram will be used. The number in parentheses is the number of letters in the word.

Word list on page 334 **Solution on page 333**

A ____________ (5)
B ____________ (9)
C ____________ (8)
D ____________ (5)
E ____________ (6)
F ____________ (8)
G ____________ (6)
H ____________ (8)
I ____________ (8)
J ____________ (7)
K ____________ (7)
L ____________ (7)
M ____________ (8)
N ____________ (8)
O ____________ (6)
P ____________ (9)
Q ____________ (7)
R ____________ (6)
S ____________ (5)
T ____________ (6)
U ____________ (8)
V ____________ (7)
W ____________ (6)
X ____________ (5)
Y ____________ (6)
Z ____________ (6)

```
R E S T E W N V J N O I N G E H I H A N N A R
B P H L Y O K T O L E C O U D R R T L A I R F
A O K D S T N O A L I L I O N N I A L L I V E
R C L G T H R M E L Y X S I O D N R N T B C O
N S N C E O A E E G S E U L H E E Y H S A R N
S I M I A C A R B N N I L E V A J R E C O E Y
T R R U K N N P Y I C V L Y E A O W D U M M Y
O E O E L O N O N H L O I L L N O H G O L O E
R P R F T W L I E T P Q R I G R G P E I G C M
M E S N U R U T B R U E B E R T G E H B D W M
L V A V I Q A A S A U I Z A W O H W O N K E Y
R W O J W O E G R F L O Y X G R A Z G I U N U
```

Word Seek 27

Heads & Tails

In this special Word Seek, you will form a continuous chain of looped words. The last letter of each word is the first letter of the next. The number of letters in each word is given in parentheses. We have started you off with the first three words.

Word list on page 334

Solution on page 333

GLOVE (5)	______ (5)	______ (4)
ERMINE (6)	______ (4)	______ (4)
EARN (4)	______ (4)	______ (6)
______ (6)	______ (6)	______ (7)
______ (4)	______ (4)	______ (6)
______ (7)	______ (5)	______ (4)
______ (4)	______ (6)	______ (5)
______ (5)	______ (7)	______ (5)
______ (6)	______ (6)	______ (6)
______ (5)	______ (5)	______ (6)

```
M A E R D O D O N A P N O R T H U R G L O V E
A A N I O N R E E D L O P U R I N A E U N R S
S T S L E M U R C E I O G T I D E N S A M I T
T R O T L C B O N A P N V L A D O R O I S N E
E A U H R L U N B R N U E R T E V A N R E A P
R O S E A E R P L A H T H P A N M E A L M R A
R A I R L S A L W Y O E R G M I N U L H E A E
I O A E E U N T O R N D A L E A O I A T E L L
N E R M Y P R A M O A E L E K E D L E R A D S
S H E R L I E E A S V L P A E L T N R I P T E
T A N O E L N A E E A O R I Z E D O O M I N G
O N E D N T A R T O L D E A R R E B U E N A S
```

Boxes

All the names of the singers in the list below can be found in the diagram in an unusual way. Instead of reading in a straight line, an entry will read either clockwise or counterclockwise in a box shape (sometimes a square and sometimes a rectangle). AL JOLSON has been boxed as an example for you.

Solution on page 333

~~Al Jolson~~
Andy Gibb
Anne Murray
Bing Crosby
Bobby Darin
Dean Martin
Dinah Shore
Doris Day
Ed Ames
Elvis Presley
Frank Sinatra
Grace Moore
Helen Reddy
Jo Stafford
Kay Starr
King Cole (Nat)
Mac Davis
Mario Lanza
Mary Ford
Mary Martin
Nelson Eddy
Pat Boone
Peggy Lee
Red Foley
Sammy Davis
Tommy Sands

A S I R O B C G N I D Y R A M E G N O M E D D
J D A Y D E R O X B I F O R D E R N L A N N Y
B A T B I Y O S B Y A F C D D E G E J H O I N
E P J O N K H L M P N A P J Y H E L O L S L E
G E N O A H S S A M O T S O Q U Y X F R T I N
G E Y E L V I S U M O N D Y O B R E D A N V D
Y L O I S I V A D Y S A N N I S K S E M N A E
A S E R P S O D A B O B B A R V N E B B I N E
B A B R Y M A C G N O W Y T W R A Y A I G A C
O I R A D A R O L I R A D R A F R O N D Y S T
L A V M N I T L E K B G R A C E R W N T A X A
A N Z A X E W O R I N E R O O M U M E R K R R

ROULETTE

A guaranteed winner! Fill in the 6-letter answers to clues 1 to 12 radially, from the outside ring to the center. The 3- and 5-letter answers to clues 13-24 read in a clockwise direction. When all the clues are answered, add the 12 letters given below to the outermost ring and you will discover the name of an author and the title of one of his novels.
Solution on page 352

C E E H I I K M N O U Y

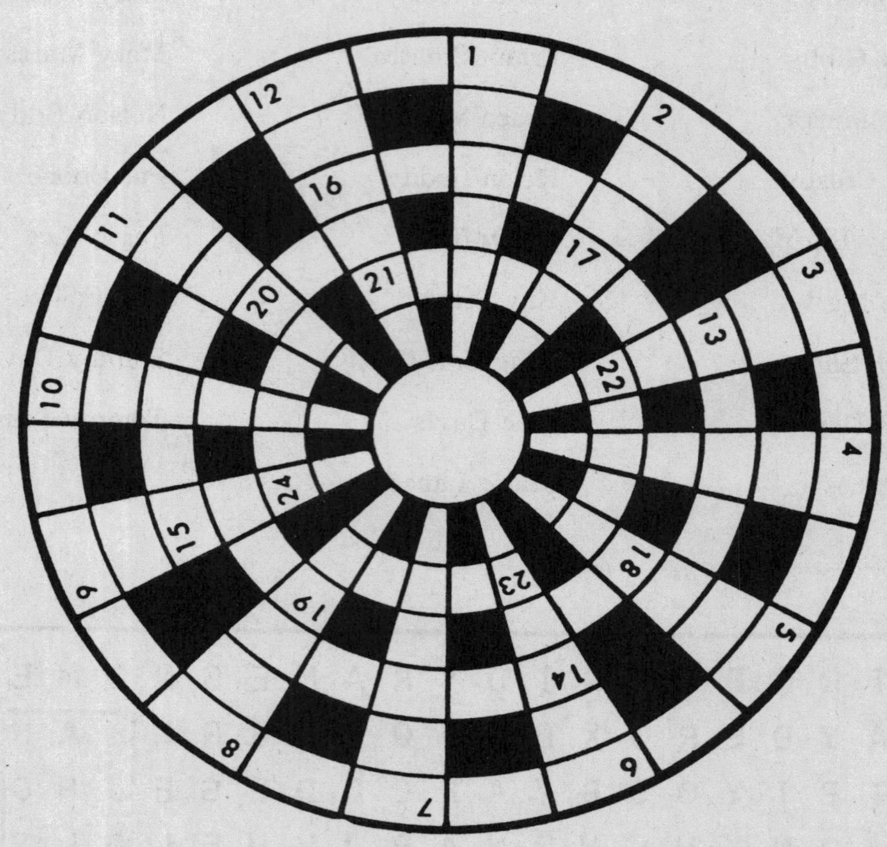

RADIALLY (Out to in)

1. Messenger
2. Automatons
3. Aphrodite's love
4. Smite mightily
5. Like a snob
6. Dutch blooms
7. Kind of account
8. Allocate
9. Maidens of myth
10. Movement
11. African fly
12. ____ State (Connecticut)

AROUND (Clockwise)

13. Yellow primrose
14. Shoestrings
15. Photo finish
16. Pulse
17. Admit
18. Here: Fr.
19. Wee devil
20. Highland hat
21. Brilliance
22. False gods
23. Tine
24. Barrel binders

QUOTEFALLS

The letters in each vertical column go into the squares directly below them, but not necessarily in the order they appear. A black square indicates the end of a word. When you have placed all the letters in their correct squares, you will be able to read a quotation across the diagram from left to right.

Solutions on page 352

1.

F	A	E	B	C	C	N	M	E	E	E	F	A	A	L	A	B	M
I	C	H	H	E	H	O	N	H	S		F	H	A	T	A	S	T
O	M	S	I	I	O	U	T	I	S		R	O	N	T			Y
	W		N	T				I	V		T	S	R				
							■			■					■		
■						■				■							
		■								■				■		■	
					■										■	■	■

2.

A	H	B	A	D	O	C	A	D	E	D	G	A	A	E	A	L	E	E
A	L	E	E	N	T	C	A	N	L	E	H	A	C	M	A	T	O	
L		M	E	T	U	E	L	T	N	O	T	F	L	Y	I	V	W	
T				W		R	R			T			N				Y	
	■				■							■						■
	■							■							■			■
			■						■					■		■		
		—									■							■

3.

B	I	C	A	B	E	D	I	A	E	E	A	E	D	H	I	A	G	E	H
E	L	E	H	N	E	G	I	F	G	R	G	I	H	O	O	E	K	W	R
O	M	E	M	O	U	R		N	O		W	N	T	T	S	N	T		
W		T	S	S		T		V	R			T	T		T	U			
							■				■						■		
	■				■					■								■	
										■				■					■
							■											■	■

4.

A	N	N	E	E	E	E	B	H	E	H	E	E	E	E	E	L	L	N	E	E	I
I	O	T	O	F	F	I	C	I	O	N	K	E	E	F	P	L	O	O	E	H	S
S	S		O	N	H		W	O	T		N	R	V	M	R		O	T	W	P	
				T	S			U	T		T			P	S		S	Y		S	
		■										■									■
		■				■				■						■			■		
	■					■				■						■					
■			■				■						■								■

Secret Word

Discover the 5-letter Secret Words by the process of elimination and deduction. Fill in the blanks with the 5-letter answers to the clues. The number in parentheses next to each answer tells you how many of the letters in that word are also in the Secret Word. A zero next to an answer indicates that none of the letters in that word is in the Secret Word. After you have determined the correct five letters, rearrange them to form the Secret Word. No letter is repeated in any Secret Word or within any answer word. The first letters of the answers, reading down, spell out a hint to the Secret Word.

Solutions on page 351

1. Secret Word ☐☐☐☐☐

Kitchen clock _____ (2)
Harangue _____ (2)
Telegraph inventor _____ (0)
Group of bees _____ (2)
Rebelled _____ (1)
Reagan's first wife _____ (3)
Leavening _____ (2)
Works to get _____ (2)
Disturbs the peace _____ (2)

2. Secret Word ☐☐☐☐☐

Square of ice cream _____ (0)
Tolerate _____ (2)
Cradles _____ (1)
Pottery ovens _____ (2)
Oil spill _____ (2)
Merry adventures _____ (3)
Peruvian Indians _____ (2)
Faucet leaks _____ (2)
Sagas _____ (3)

3. Secret Word ☐☐☐☐☐

TV knobs _____ (2)
Brandish _____ (2)
Hawkeye _____ (3)
Viking _____ (3)
Tendency _____ (0)
Hoists _____ (1)
Cape elk _____ (3)
Insinuating _____ (3)

4. Secret Word ☐☐☐☐☐

Fetch _____ (2)
Correct _____ (3)
Aids in wrong _____ (2)
Wall recess _____ (1)
Wading bird _____ (0)
Door joint _____ (2)
"Dallas" name _____ (3)
Take an oath _____ (2)

5. Secret Word ☐☐☐☐☐

Subsequently _____ (2)
Hawk's claw _____ (3)
Wheel cushions _____ (2)
Deduce _____ (1)
Was concerned _____ (0)
Chastise _____ (3)

6. Secret Word ☐☐☐☐☐

Political power _____ (2)
Something else _____ (3)
Bicker _____ (3)
Irks _____ (1)
Vision _____ (2)
Brilliance _____ (0)

PLACES, PLEASE

Fill the diagram with all the words in the word list. The words from each group start on their matching number, and they will read in all directions —forward, backward, up, down, and diagonally. Words from different groups sometimes overlap; therefore, some letters will be used more than once. When the puzzle is completed, all the squares will be filled.

Solution on page 351

1. SATED
   SKY
   SOLE
2. SECONDS
   STAND
3. RADAR
   RIND
   ROBOT
4. PAIN
   PIE
   PILL
   PIN
5. THE
   TRAIN
   TROTS
6. SANER
   SILO
   SITS
   SLEIGH
   SLOT
7. PELT
   PILOT
   PIT
8. BALLAD
   BAN
   BARD
   BILL
   BLAST
   BLINK
   BROWN
9. RAMP
   REALITY
   REED
   ROB
   RUT
10. OBJECT
    OBLIGATED
    OFFERING
    OLD
    OMITTED
    OPERATE
    ORCHESTRA
11. LAMP
    LOUDER
12. DAD
    DEED
    DEN
    DOLL
    DRY
    DUE
    DUST
13. HERDS
    HUB
14. GAIN
    GATE
    GEL
    GENT
    GIRL
    GRIP
    GROWL
15. OARS
    ODD
    OINK
    OUT
    OWL
16. LEAP
    LEARNING
    LEMON
    LESS
    LIE
17. GAS
    GRIM
18. OAT
    OPENED
    OPERA
    OTHERWISE
    OUTBOARD
19. DEAR
    DOT
    DRUM

1							2							
												3		
						4								5
					6									
		7												
				8								9		
								10						
													11	
			12											13
							14		15					
16											17			
				18							19			

QUOTAGRAMS

Fill in the answers to the clues below. Then transfer the letters to the correspondingly numbered squares in each diagram. Each completed diagram will contain a quotation. **Solutions on page 350**

A.

1. Oil and ____ — 35 14 28 8 43 9 24
2. Drone's home — 19 30 36 13 41 7 20
3. Not loose — 5 34 16 26 39
4. Sermon subject — 3 17 37 10 4 29 31
5. Conceited — 18 15 2 38 21 11
6. "____ Girl" — 12 40 27 33
7. Long-suffering — 1 32 25 6 23 42 22

1	2	3	4	5	6	7	8	■	9	10	11	12	13	14	15	16
■	17	18	■	19	20	21	22	23	24	■	25	26	27	28	■	29
30	31	32	33	34	35	36	■	37	38	39	40	41	42	43	■	■

B.

1. Firedogs — 12 42 20 5 11 46 19 6
2. Identification tag — 4 38 23 37 18 24 39
3. Of delicate beauty — 14 43 2 13 9 29
4. Bull's-eye — 36 41 17 10 22 26
5. Generally known — 7 27 44 31 28 45 8 16 33
6. Confiscate — 1 15 25 3 32
7. Sinew — 21 40 34 30 35 47

1	2	3	4	■	5	6	■	7	8	9	■	10	11	12	13	14	15	16
17	■	18	19	20	■	21	22	23	24	25	26	27	28	29	■	30	31	32
33	■	34	35	36	■	37	38	39	40	■	41	■	42	43	44	45	46	47

C.

1. Brutus's wife in "Julius Caesar" — 4 11 37 14 19 32
2. Beacon tower — 9 23 43 15 30 25 34 45 3 28
3. Protective — 22 5 12 48 42 52 39 50 16
4. Pursues — 35 2 49 10 13 31 20
5. Lightness of movement — 38 8 17 41 27 51 40 24
6. Impudent — 47 6 29 18 33
7. Shared — 36 21 46 1 44 26 7

1	2	■	3	4	5	6	7	■	8	9	10	■	11	12	■	13	14	15	16	17
18	■	19	20	■	21	■	22	23	24	25	26	27	28	29	30	■	31	32	33	■
34	35	■	36	37	38	39	40	41	42	43	■	44	45	46	47	48	49	50	51	52

CODEWORD

The directions for solving are given on page 27.

Solution on page 350

1	14 R
2	15
3	16
4	17
5	18
6 P	19
7	20
8	21 O
9	22
10	23
11	24
12	25
13	26

9	16	7	15	14	5	16	20		16	6	18	11
4			9		26		5	11	20			5
9	10	15	7		21	17	11		5	2	13	15
25			15	14	14		2	18	15			19
5	14	21	11		8	15	16		14	9	24	15
11		23		22		13		4		10		
24	9	10	13	15		21		9	17	21	20	15
		21		17		6		14		26		12
1	9	17	16		6 P	15	6		10	15	9	18
9			3	15	14 R		15	14	9			15
18	24	13	8		21 O	26	9		16	6	18	14
11			15	24	21		14		5			14
7	21	18	14		22	15	13	5	19	5	7	8

A	N
B	~~O~~
C	~~P~~
D	Q
E	~~R~~
F	S
G	T
H	U
I	V
J	W
K	X
L	Y
M	Z

CODEWORD

Solution on page 351

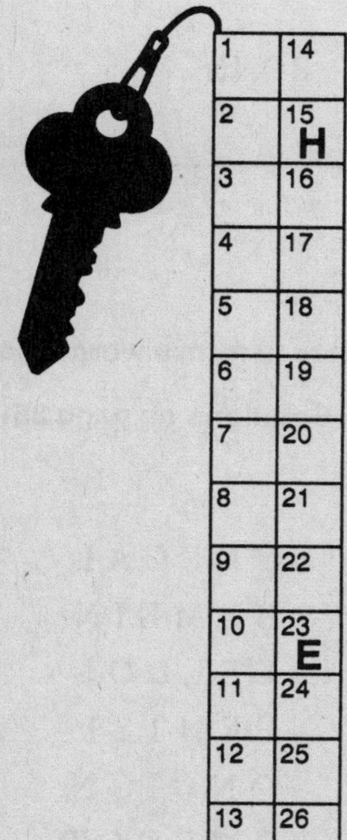

1	14
2	15 H
3	16
4	17
5	18
6	19
7	20
8	21
9	22
10	23 E
11	24
12	25
13	26

2	1	5	15	6	25		19	5	11	6	3	24
1		17		10				10		3		23
6	1	12	18	16	18		11	16	13	12	23	11
12				18		3		6				11
23	11	21		16	18	16	6	26		22	6	6
18		7		8		17				23		20
	19	6	9	23		9		4	5	7	24	
20		14				23		23		12		14
5	21	12		22	5	12	6	13		15 H	23 E	26
14				5		14		12				16
15	5	8	5	7	18		2	1	16	4	23	7
23		6		25				7		16		17
18	7	6	4	23	7		18	23	12	5	17	15

A	N
B	O
C	P
D	Q
~~E~~	R
F	S
G	T
~~H~~	U
I	V
J	W
K	X
L	Y
M	Z

Top to Bottom

Place the letters given below each diagram into the squares to form eight 4-letter words reading from top to bottom from square to connected square. The top letter is the first of all eight words, each letter in the second row is the second letter of four words, and so on.

Solutions on page 352

Example:

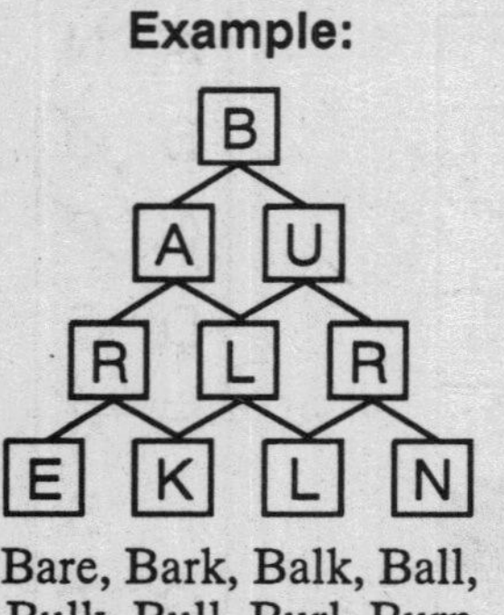

Bare, Bark, Balk, Ball, Bulk, Bull, Burl, Burn

1.

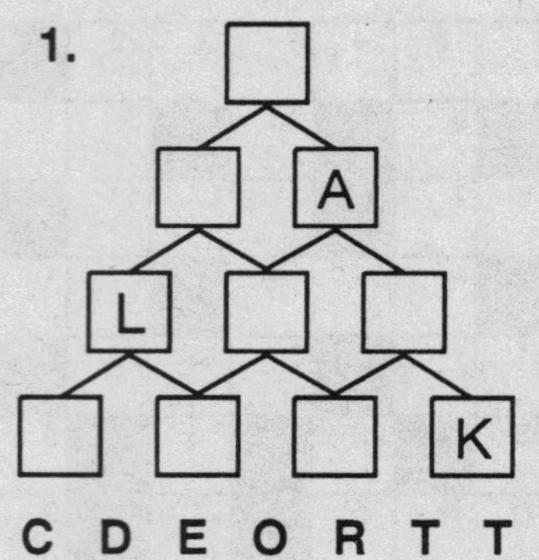

C D E O R T T

2.

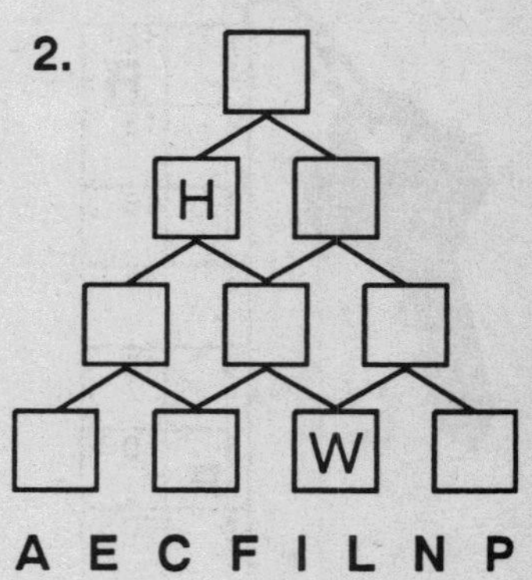

A E C F I L N P

Changaword

Can you change the top word into the bottom word in each column in the number of steps indicated in parentheses? Change only one letter at a time and do not change the order of the letters. Proper names, slang, and obsolete words are not allowed.

Our solutions on page 353

1. SLIP (4 steps)	2. FIRE (4 steps)	3. EAST (5 steps)	4. TAIL (5 steps)
KNOT	SALE	WIND	BONE

Crisscross

Beside each diagram are six groups of scrambled letters. Rearrange each group of letters to form a word, and then fit the words into the diagrams to read across or down in crossword fashion.

Solutions on page 351

1.

KYLIEL
IVLRIE
HIVRET
NEACRV
OKEERV
CALKET

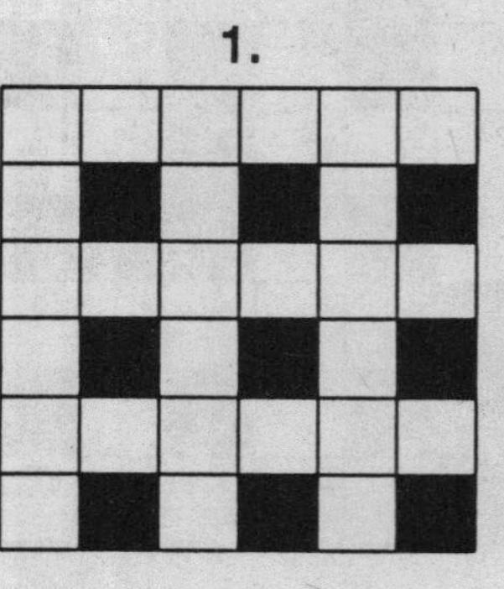

2.

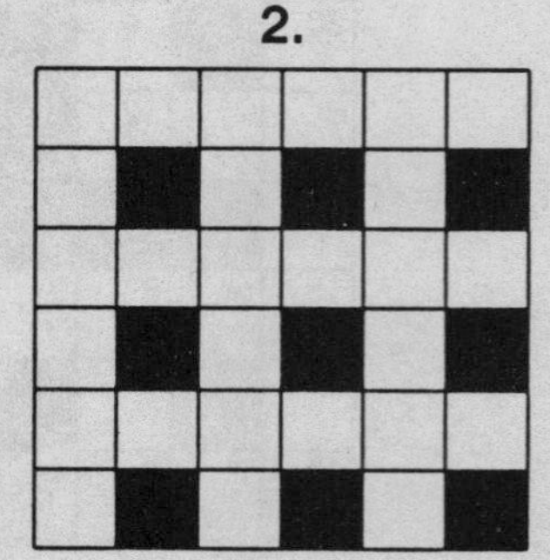

YDFGAL
BEMLIN
LELDOL
PENTSI
ONGIGN
SMEDOT

PERFECT FIT

Fit the words in the list into the diagram reading forward, backward, up, down, and diagonally, always in a straight line. The words cross as indicated. **Solution on page 351**

Bleach
Brief
Catcher
Cypress
Dancer
Farrier
Feature
Funnel
Mayor
Reserve
Surf
Terry

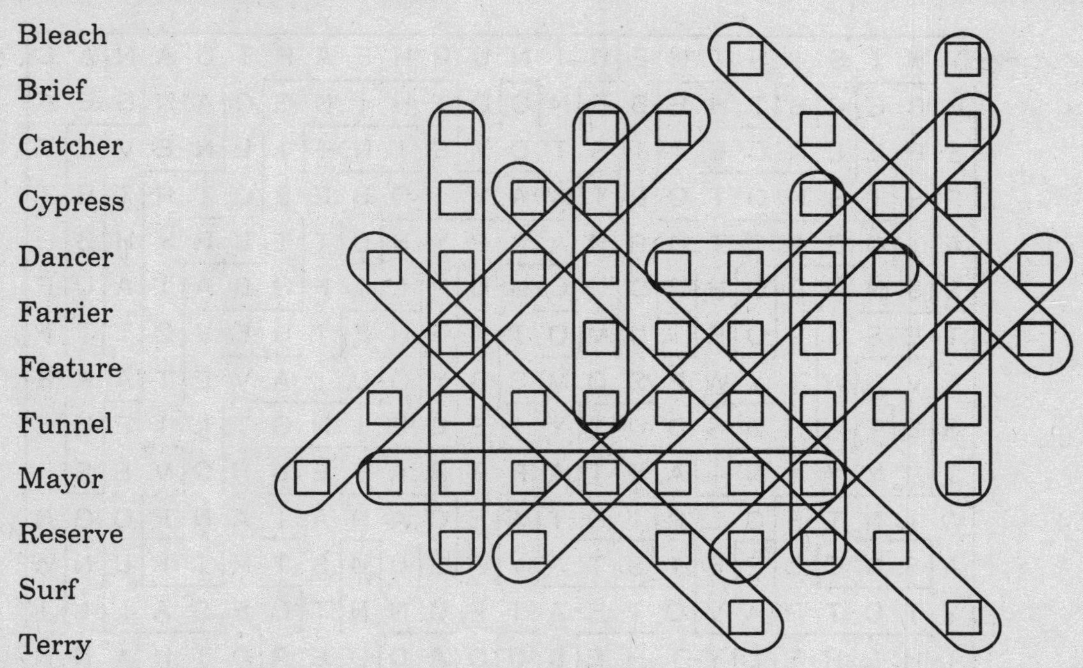

PUZZLER

I am a word of eight letters.

My 2, 5, 6, 3, 2, 1 is a lacquer.
My 3, 8, 7, 6, 1 is an award.
My 5, 4, 3, 6, 7 is a wanderer.
My 3, 4, 7, 8, 1 is an example.
My 7, 2, 6, 1 is an agreement.
My 7, 4, 3, 8 is a curved roof.
My 6, 1, 4, 5, 2 is solitary.

Solution on page 351

TRIANGLE SUMS

The two diagonals divide the diagram on the right into four large triangles. Place the nine squares on the left into the diagram so that the sums of the four numbers in those triangles are equal. If a square is divided, place it in the diagram in a square that is divided the same way. **Solution on page 351**

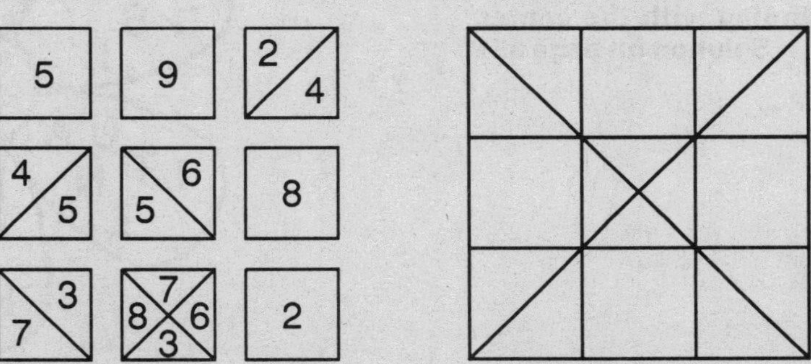

TURN A PHRASE

Find your way through the maze to discover the hidden quotation.

Solution on page 350

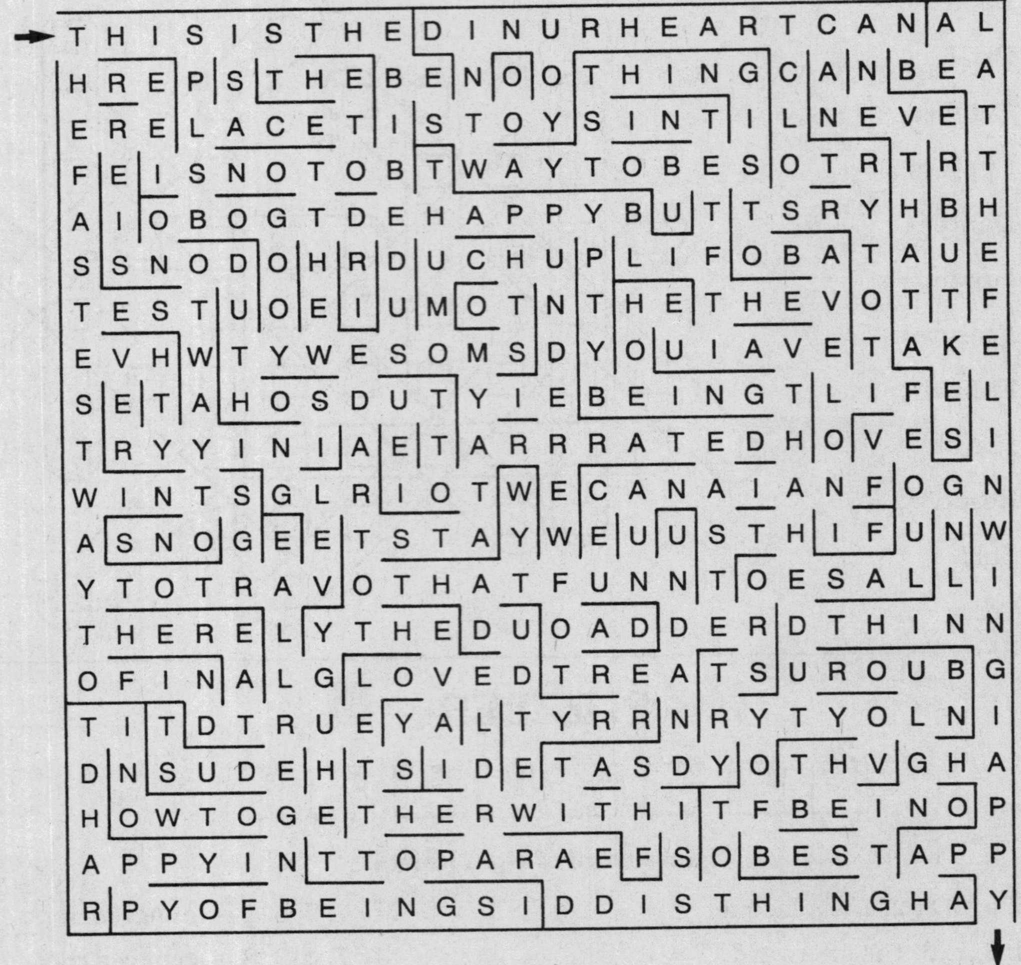

DAISY

Form six 7-letter words using the letters in each Daisy petal PLUS the letter in the Daisy center, P. The P may not be used as the first letter of these words. Next, form a bonus 7-letter word using the first letters of these words and beginning with the center letter P.

Solution on page 351

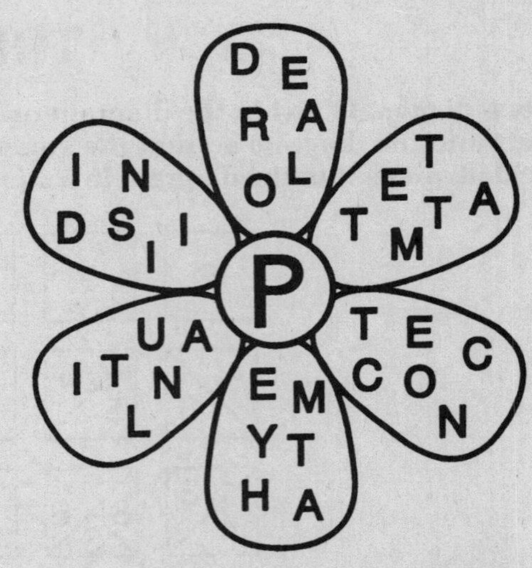

DOUBLE TROUBLE

Not really double trouble, but double fun! Solve this puzzle as you would a regular crossword, EXCEPT place one, two, or three letters in each box. The number of letters in each answer is shown in parentheses after its clue.

ACROSS

1. Erode (4)
4. Happen by fate (6)
7. King or emperor (7)
8. Ceramic planter (9)
10. Singing group (5)
11. Thus (9)
13. Main point (4)
15. With no pattern (6)
17. Short race (4)
18. Task (5)
19. Breakfast pastry (6)
21. Renter (6)
23. Tit for ____ (3)
24. Most occupied (7)
26. Dull (4)
28. Out of (4)
30. "In vino ____" (7)
32. Crane (7)
35. Additional (5)
37. Creates (5)
39. Othello, for one (4)
40. Rim (4)
41. News (7)
43. Moving truck (3)
44. Spanish friend (5)
46. Classifier (7)
48. High-schooler (4)
49. Written composition (5)

DOWN

1. Was victorious (3)
2. Soil (5)
3. Curved (6)
4. In advance (10)
5. Run smoothly (4)
6. Averse (8)
7. Carmen ____ (7)
9. Haphazard try (7)
10. Musical harmony (5)
12. Attach again (8)
14. Pay for (5)
16. All-encompassing (7)
20. Tremble with cold (6)
22. Barterer (6)
25. Educated guess (10)
27. Hat visor (4)
28. Foamed (7)
29. Ω (5)
31. Gave work to (6)
33. Lid (5)
34. Islamic bible (5)
36. Send money (5)
38. One-base hit (6)
42. Back talk (4)
45. Gosh! (3)
47. Secure a rope (5)

Solution on page 350

■	■	1	2	3	■	4	5	6	■	■
■	7				■	8			9	■
10		■	11		12		■	13		14
15		16	■	17			■	18		
19			20	■	21		22	■	23	
■	■	24		25	■	26		27	■	■
28	29	■	30		31	■	32		33	34
35		36	■	37		38	■	39		
40			■	41			42	■	43	
■	44		45		■	46		47		■
■	■	48			■	49			■	■

WHIRLY WORDS

This diagram has been divided into sections, numbered 1 to 6. Each section contains spaces for four letters. The answer to each clue is a 4-letter word whose letters fit into the corresponding section so that the inner ring, middle ring, and outer ring all spell words reading clockwise beginning in section 1.

Solution on page 351

CLUES

Section 1: Cut short
Section 2: Appear
Section 3: Bursts
Section 4: Enameled metalware
Section 5: Kite streamer
Section 6: What Jack Sprat ate

Inner Ring: Mortar and ____
Middle Ring: Annul, as a tax
Outer Ring: Sophisticated

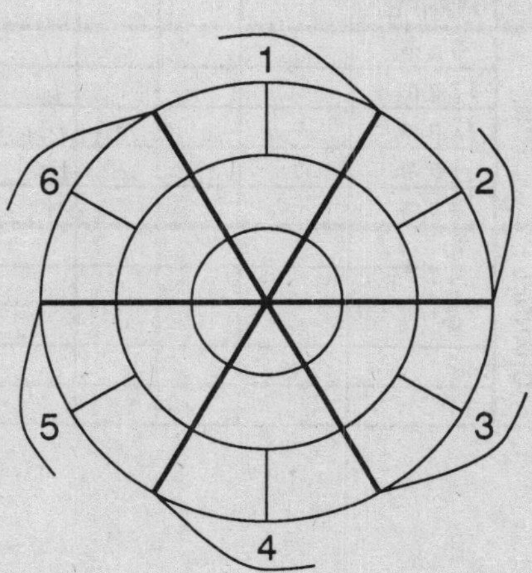

LOGIC PROBLEM

TASTEFUL TELEVISION

Ovens are heating up as new cooking shows pop up on daytime television. Each of five new cooking shows, including "Smart Cooking," airs at a different time (9 a.m., 11 a.m., 12 p.m., 1 p.m., or 3 p.m.) on a different channel (4, 7, 9, 12, or 14) and is hosted by a different culinary genius. Match each chef, including Henri, with his show and determine the channel on which it airs, as well as the time it airs.

1. "Kitchen Topics" airs at 12 p.m.
2. "Food Feasts" is broadcast on a channel two higher than the one featuring Antone.
3. The 11 a.m. show is on a channel three higher than the one airing "Eating Healthy."
4. Franco creates culinary masterpieces on "Culinary Delights," which airs later in the day than "Eating Healthy."
5. Pierre's show starts sometime after 12 p.m., as does the show on channel 7.
6. Charles's show airs earlier than the show on channel 9 but later than "Food Feasts."

This chart is to help you record information from the clues as well as the facts you deduce by combining information from different clues. We suggest you use an "X" for a "no" and a " • " for a "yes."

		SHOW					CHANNEL					TIME				
		CULINARY DELIGHTS	EATING HEALTHY	FOOD FEASTS	KITCHEN TOPICS	SMART COOKING	4	7	9	12	14	9 a.m.	11 a.m.	12 p.m.	1 p.m.	3 p.m.
CHEF	ANTONE															
	CHARLES															
	FRANCO															
	HENRI															
	PIERRE															
TIME	9 a.m.															
	11 a.m.															
	12 p.m.															
	1 p.m.															
	3 p.m.															
CHANNEL	4															
	7															
	9															
	12															
	14															

Solution on page 351

SYL´´LA-CROS´TIC

Fill in the answers to the clues by using all the syllables in the Syllabox. The number of syllables to be used in each answer is shown in parentheses. The number of letters in each answer is indicated by the dashes. Each syllable will be used once. When the words are correctly filled in, their first and last letters, reading down, will reveal an epigram preceded by its author's name. **Solution on page 353**

✻ SYLLABOX ✻

A AG BEL BLE ~~BO~~ BOU CAB CAL CIENT CRO CUS DY EF EM ER ER FI FLA FORM GEN GLE GRANT HAR HIS I I IM IN INE IOUS ~~JUM~~ LISH MAR MIE NI NIB PEDE RAM SNICK STAM STY TAX TOR U UV WOLF WRAN

1. Larger than average (2) J U M B O
2. Distinctive attire (3) _ _ _ _ _ _ _
3. Take small bites (2) _ _ _ _ _ _
4. Productive (3) _ _ _ _ _ _ _ _ _
5. Slightly stifled laugh (2) _ _ _ _ _ _ _
6. Adjutant stork (3) _ _ _ _ _ _ _
7. Think up (3) _ _ _ _ _ _ _
8. Vehicle for hire (3) _ _ _ _ _ _ _
9. Weather-resistant (2) _ _ _ _ _
10. Deliberately shocking (2) _ _ _ _ _ _ _ _
11. Decorate (3) _ _ _ _ _ _ _ _ _
12. Bicker noisily (2) _ _ _ _ _ _ _
13. Tungsten (2) _ _ _ _ _ _ _
14. Very clever (3) _ _ _ _ _ _ _ _ _
15. Cattle riot (2) _ _ _ _ _ _ _ _
16. Based on actual events (4) _ _ _ _ _ _ _ _ _ _
17. Symbolic Sabbath boundary (2) _ _ _ _
18. Thwart (2) _ _ _ _ _ _
19. Spring flower (2) _ _ _ _ _ _

BOWL GAME

To bowl a strike (20 points) you must create a 10-letter word using all the letters in each pin. The letter on top in the pin is the first letter of the strike word. To bowl a spare (10 points) use the same 10 letters to form two words. Splits are not allowed: you may not divide the strike to form a spare. For example, SWEETHEART may not become SWEET and HEART. **Our solutions with a perfect score of 300 points on page 353**

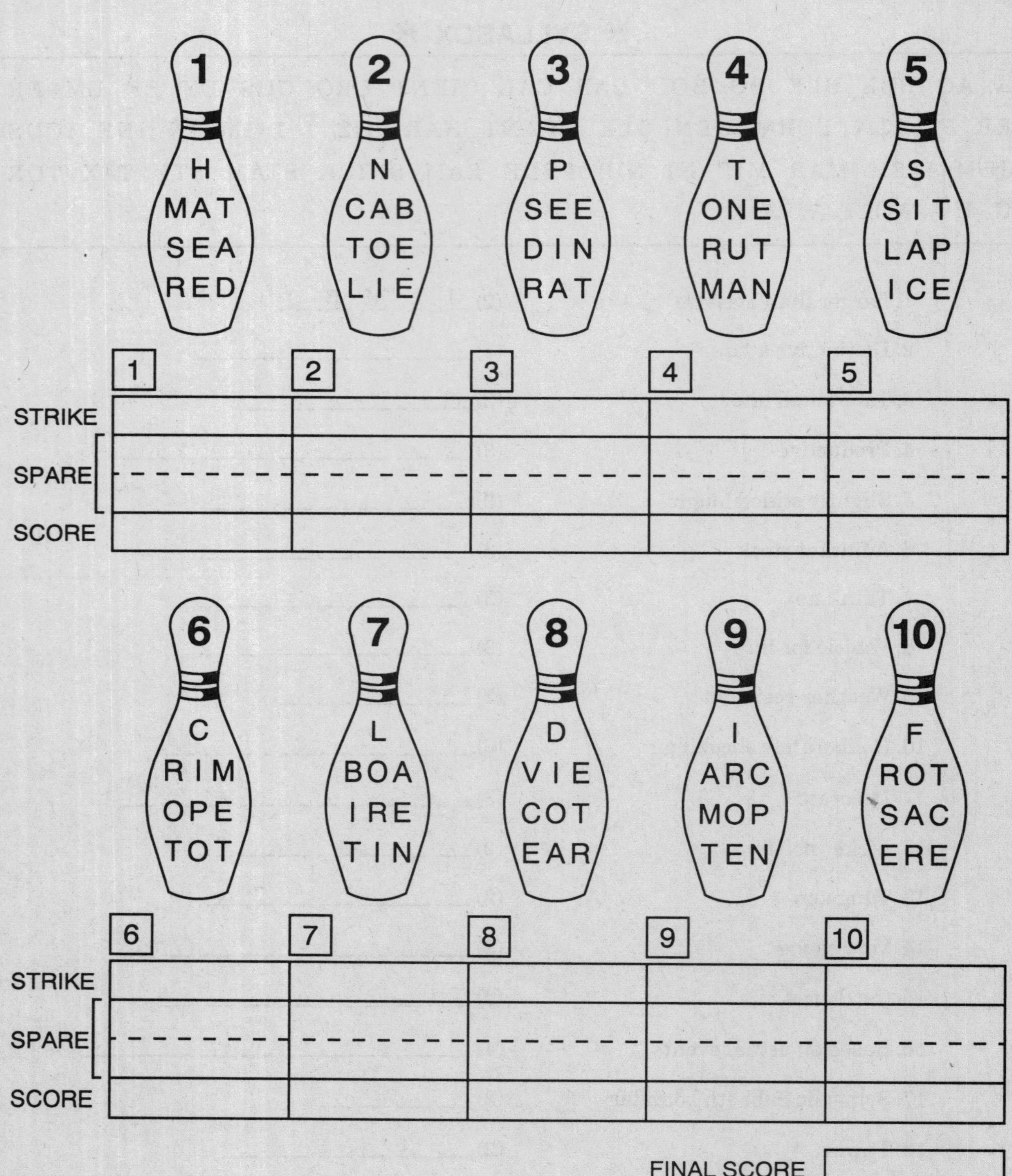

FINAL SCORE

CRYPTO-FAMILIES

The directions for solving are given on page 15.
Solutions on page 352

1. NOTIONS DEPARTMENT
Example: Pins

GKOJITL
ALHJ BOXXLB
GKBLHZ
XHGGLBEA
AWOAAPBA
IOHA GHXL
LTHAGOW
ELLZTLA
ISGGPE
AEHXA

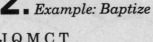

2. SOAK IT
Example: Baptize

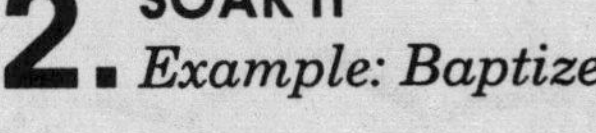

JQMCT
DMTZIN
KZMZJYBT
CQMCT
CXYAW
JHQXZ
OUQQJ
KAATHCT
JHTZIN
CMRATHST

3. SUPERBOWL MVP'S
Example: Joe Montana

RKTJ UTXXU
NLIIW VIQAUKQG
DTX RJCYPLNN
SNNTU QYALIUSY
VQIN UNQII
ASCZ GTJJTQXU
JWYY UGQYY
JQIIW FUSYPQ
DSL YQXQNK
JLY AQGUSY

4. ANGRY WORDS
Example: Row

BYNN
OIFZSVMB
THOB
GZOIIVP
TGZOJJPV
LVJOBV
LYTOFIVVSVMB
OPBVIQOBYAM
LYTHZBV
JYQEVIYMF

5. YELLOW ____
Example: Sea

OVOIYE
MKENYH
UYESINE
IWCTK
GVQELYIWMX
ONEFT
GYFHNK
OYCNM
EWSSVL
OWLN

6. TYPES OF ORANGES
Example: Jaffa

DKESNC
YMEVSM
CKAMS
IMANSSM
DJEJIJIIK
AKSMCRNK
VKTIJC
IY. ENRDKMS
VNCMKVVSM
MCYMTVTNIM

FLOWER POWER

The answers to this petaled puzzle will go in a curve from the number on the outside to the center of the flower. Each number has two 5-letter words. One goes in a clockwise direction and the second in a counterclockwise direction. Try working from both sets of clues to fill the flower. **Solution on page 352**

CLOCKWISE

1. Dodge
2. Spotted pony
3. Chew
4. Duck's call
5. Trademark
6. Rips
7. Madrid museum
8. Trepidations
9. Rush
10. Tremor
11. Stiffened, as a corset
12. Cheerful
13. Discovered
14. English poet
15. Pert
16. Bridge seat
17. Veranda
18. Parody

COUNTERCLOCKWISE

1. Social gathering
2. Desiccate
3. Sousa work
4. Paper measure
5. Rabbit
6. Pamphlet
7. Summer fruit
8. Open
9. Listened to
10. Certain leg muscles
11. Pack animal
12. Flies high
13. Offbeat
14. Gift recipient
15. Noise
16. Child's attendant
17. British money
18. Power

BRICK BY BRICK

Rearrange this stack of bricks to form a crossword puzzle. The clues will help you fit the bricks into their correct places. Row 1 has been filled in for you. Use the bricks to fill in the remaining spaces.

Solution on page 351

ACROSS

1. Gaze rudely
   Involved with
   Title for Hess
2. Law's partner
   Close-by
   Verve
3. Reneges on a promise
   Tough spot
4. Homily: abbr.
   Invent
   Gluts
5. Shirt fastener
   Encourage
6. Aureole
   Having keen vision
7. Gazettes
   Gather in
   Roe
8. Arthurian lady
   Used a lever
   Made do
9. Long time period
   Pegs for Palmer
   Seniors
10. Very stubborn
    Simple
11. Requests
    Susa's land
12. Forewarnings
    God of love
    Young fellow
13. Promenade
    Put on the back burner
14. Word of a threat
    Islands off Galway
    Ghostly
15. Headliner
    Boutique
    Great fear

DOWN

1. Female swine
   Hatchery sound
   Is in the red
2. Clothes hanger
   Asian capital
   Beer ingredient
3. Sixth Hebrew month
   Mimicking
   Ms. Maxwell
4. Legal thing
   Luge
   Yearn
5. Certain muscle
   Roman
   Polanski film
6. Actor Gossett
   Utter
   Jack of clubs
7. Private
   Lipstick colors
   Certain pension fund: abbr.
8. Las Vegas light
   Rebel
   Algae derivative
9. Part of ZBT
   Crooked
   Make crazy
10. Leftover morsel
    Dashing young man
    Card game, of old
11. Ooze
    Jurist Hand
12. Formal argument
    Netherlands town
    "And I Love ___"
13. Deplaned
    Couples
    Traditional knowledge
14. Lion's pride?
    Each and ___
    Inter ___
15. Termini
    Papas
    Property document

BRICKS

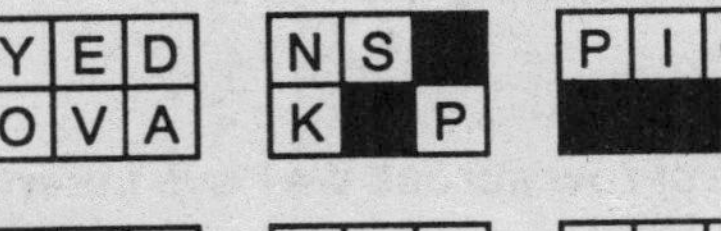
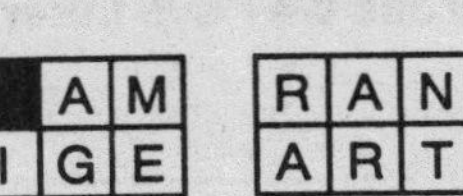
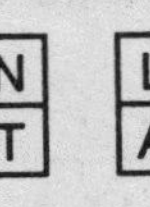

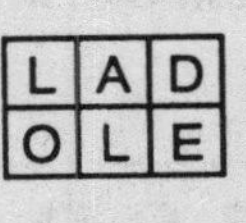

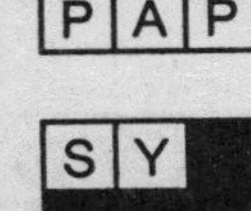

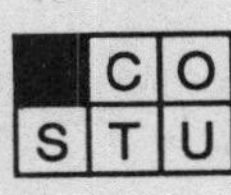

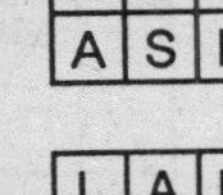
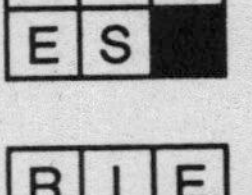
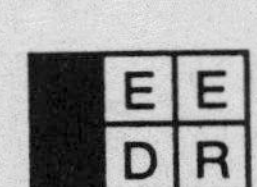
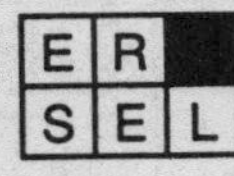
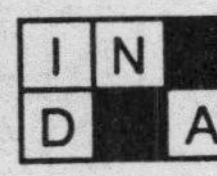

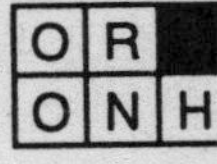

DIAGRAM

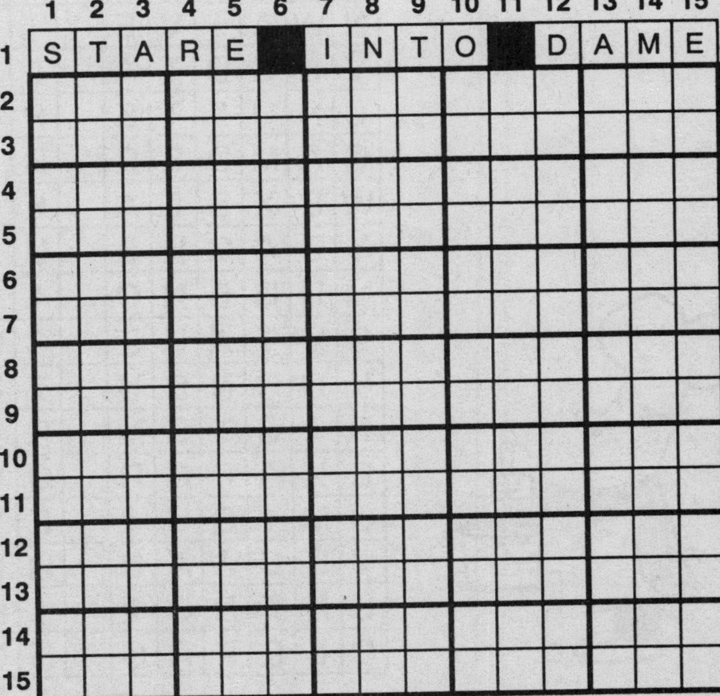

ALPHABET SOUP

Insert a different letter of the alphabet into each of the 26 empty boxes to form words of five or more letters reading across. The letter you insert may be at the beginning, the end, or in the middle of the word. Each letter of the alphabet will be used only once. Cross off each letter in the list as you use it. All the letters in each row are not necessarily used in forming the word.

Our solution on page 351

Example: In the first row across we have inserted the letter F to form the word AFTER.

A B C D E ~~F~~ G H I J K L M N O P Q R S T U V W X Y Z

M	C	A	W	O	A	**F**	T	E	R	U	V	X
A	B	I	O	B	E		I	E	N	C	E	M
C	H	U	M	U	R		L	T	S	A	Z	E
I	N	S	U	R	A		C	E	F	O	G	Y
Z	E	A	P	L	U		U	R	I	O	U	S
O	W	T	H	R	O		Z	V	E	K	A	N
D	Y	R	G	U	L		I	B	L	E	B	D
A	Q	F	O	R	G		T	I	M	P	O	L
G	A	I	S	T	O		T	L	S	H	E	U
V	E	Y	X	I	D		N	A	M	I	T	E
M	O	B	L	U	C		Y	C	O	S	P	H
N	W	A	I	V	E		I	E	M	D	Q	U
V	E	G	D	T	A		L	E	K	M	A	S
C	R	U	F	T	E		P	O	H	O	I	N
G	A	M	D	E	R		R	A	V	I	T	Y
W	E	X	B	L	A		E	R	F	A	E	G
Y	O	A	G	H	S		U	A	T	K	F	I
M	U	R	E	N	O		A	T	E	M	Z	W
B	V	T	A	U	E		C	O	R	T	Y	O
K	C	O	N	D	U		T	U	Q	L	A	I
D	I	S	T	S	M		R	K	F	O	A	N
E	X	A	F	G	R		O	V	E	X	L	B
O	M	I	Q	U	I		E	Y	S	A	T	M
V	S	U	W	A	P		R	E	H	E	N	D
U	N	F	R	O	T		I	P	R	U	V	S
C	L	E	P	R	O		E	C	T	L	H	E

The entries for this puzzle are given to you, listed alphabetically according to length. Across and Down words are all mixed together, and you are to find their proper places in the diagram.
Solution on page 351

3 Letters
Aft
Arf
Eli
End
Era
Fig
Gag
Hoe
Hut
Mad
Nap
Nat ✓
Ore
Pat
Pin
Sly
Tea
Urn

4 Letters
Ally
Amid
Anew
Anna
Char
Deed
Eats
Echo
Ecru
Ekes
Ella
Etna
Have
Idea
Inca
Lake
Lion
Neil
Newt
Pest
Seat
Tact
Thaw
Turn

5 Letters
Arena
Cigar
Crane
Crony
Gunny
Inner
Loved
Owing
Rules
Stare
Steel
Tulip

6 Letters
Acting
Fossil
Gauged
Linnet
Pierce
Sonata

8 Letters
Invested
Nearness

9 Letters
Marmalade
Navigator

Split Personalities

The names of ten flowers have been split into 2-letter segments. The letters in each segment are in order, but the segments have been scrambled. For each group can you put the pieces together to identify the flowers?
Solutions on page 354

1. TH AC HY IN ______
2. IA NN ZI ______
3. ET VI OL ______
4. RA GE UM NI ______
5. DA IA HL ______
6. IN MO RY GG RN LO ______
7. OR ID CH ______
8. LD MA GO RI ______
9. ON AG AP DR SN ______
10. RI LE PE NK WI ______

SCOREMASTER

TO PLAY:

1. Write the first seven LETTERS across the first line of the PLAY CHART. Indicate the last letter used.
2. Form a word of at least two letters across or down in the DIAGRAM. One letter of the first word must go into the center square.
3. Tally your score, noting any bonuses (see key at bottom).
4. Carry down all unused LETTERS to the next line of the PLAY CHART. Transfer enough LETTERS, in the given order, so that you have seven LETTERS to work with.
5. Form a new word or words from each draw by:
   a. Adding one or more letters to an existing word.
   b. Building a new word at right angles to an existing word, by adding to it or incorporating one of its letters.
   c. Setting a new word parallel to an existing word, but remember all adjoining letters must form new words in crossword fashion.
6. Continue working in this way until all the LETTERS have been used or you can no longer form any words. If you need more lines for your PLAY CHART, use a separate piece of paper.

NOTE: Proper names, foreign words, and abbreviations are not allowed.

TO SCORE:

The value of each letter is given with it. The letter has the same value every time it is used. Be sure always to include all bonuses (see key at bottom). An additional 30 points is earned when you use all seven letters in the PLAY CHART in one turn. When two words are formed in the same play, the common letter (including any bonus) is scored with each word.

Our game with a score of 603 points on page 353

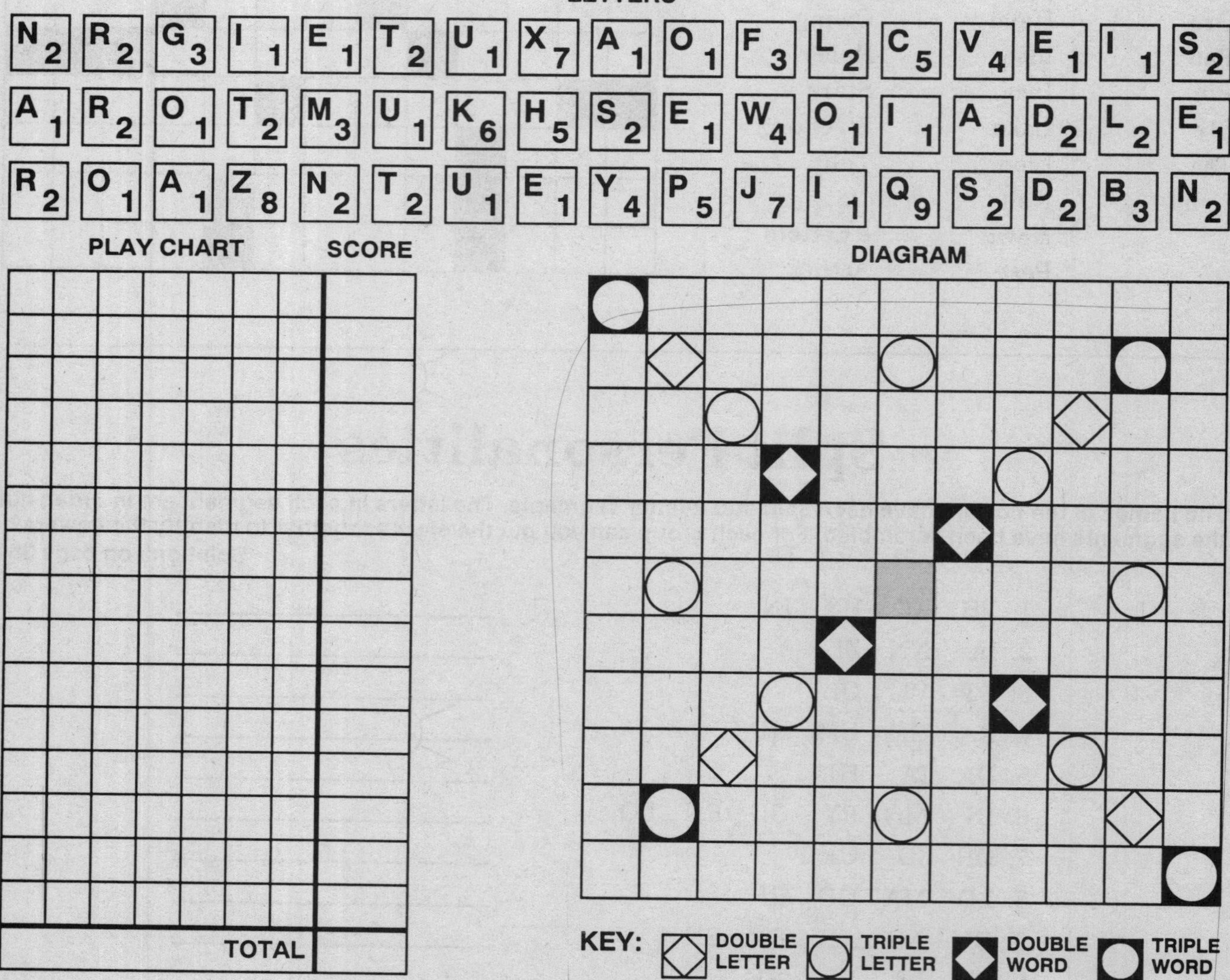

WORD MERGERS

Rearrange the letters in each Word Merger to form two words using all the given letters only once. Then rearrange these same letters and merge them into one long word. You might want to form the long word first and then the pair of words. Score 5 points for each pair of words you form and 10 points for each long word. A score of 85 is good, 95 is very good, and 105 is excellent.

Our solutions with a perfect score of 120 points on page 351

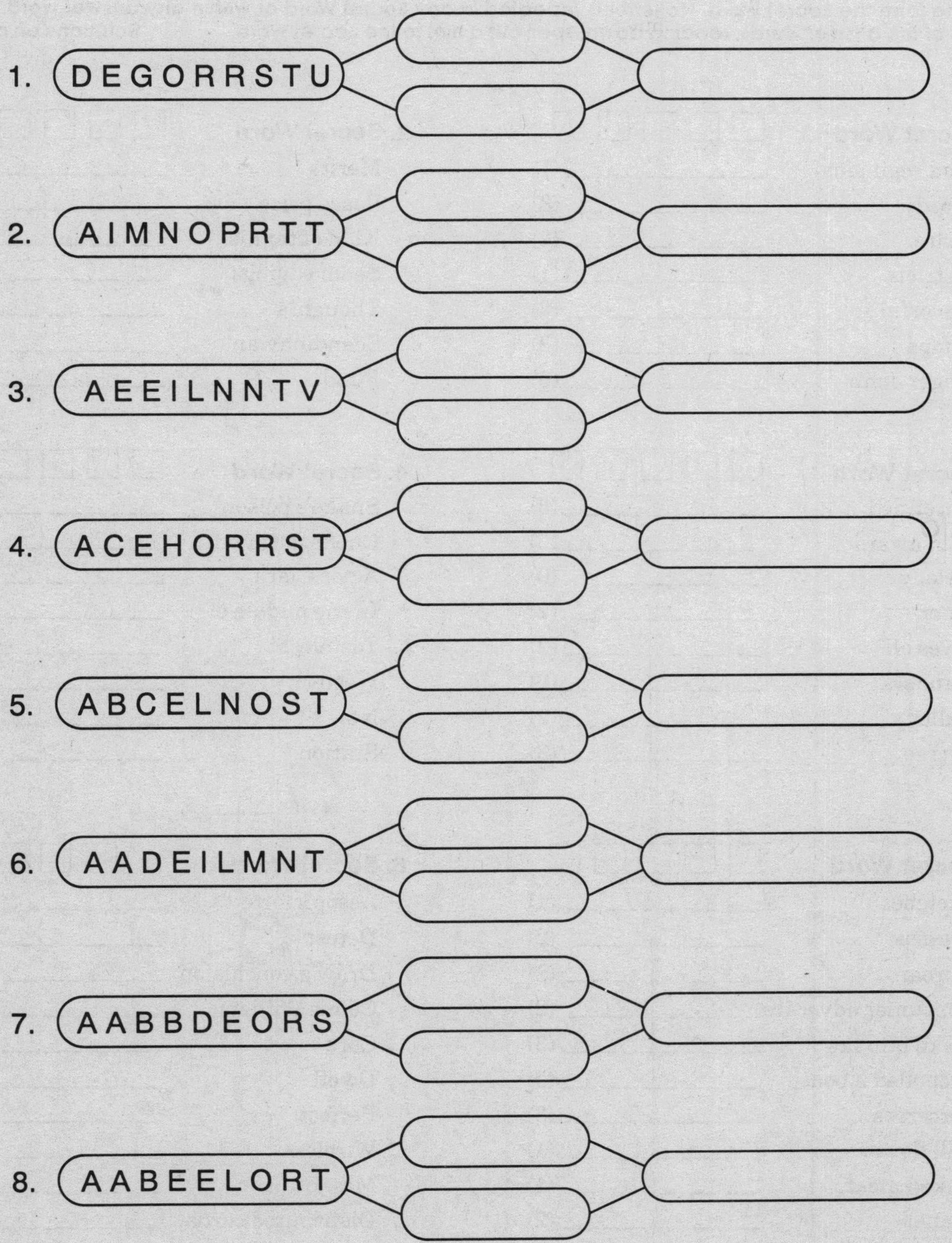

Secret Word

Discover the 5-letter Secret Words by the process of elimination and deduction. Fill in the blanks with the 5-letter answer words to the clues. The number in parentheses next to each answer word tells you how many of the letters in that word are also in the Secret Word. A zero next to an answer word indicates that not one of the letters in that word is also in the Secret Word. After you have determined the correct 5 letters, rearrange them to form the Secret Word. No letter is repeated in any Secret Word or within any answer word. The first letters of the answer words, reading down, spell out a hint to the Secret Word. **Solutions on page 353**

1. Secret Word ☐☐☐☐☐

Food regimens _____ (1)
Speedy _____ (3)
Satire _____ (2)
Districts _____ (1)
Flavorful _____ (2)
Jumps _____ (3)
Singer John _____ (0)

2. Secret Word ☐☐☐☐☐

Merits _____ (2)
Peace prize _____ (1)
Kind of tennis _____ (2)
Seam edgings _____ (0)
Thoughts _____ (3)
Scandinavian _____ (1)
Fund _____ (1)

3. Secret Word ☐☐☐☐☐

Unrefined _____ (3)
Film award _____ (2)
Melody _____ (0)
Piker _____ (2)
Gives off _____ (2)
Wanders _____ (2)
Halley's ____ _____ (2)
Decree _____ (3)

4. Secret Word ☐☐☐☐☐

Snake's poison _____ (1)
Chef's garment _____ (3)
Actor Clark _____ (1)
In the middle of _____ (2)
Tasteless _____ (1)
Western _____ (3)
New _____ (0)
Station _____ (2)

5. Secret Word ☐☐☐☐☐

Sketches _____ (1)
Presses _____ (2)
Uproar _____ (2)
Consumer advocate _____ (2)
Make into law _____ (3)
Propelled a boat _____ (0)
Sorceress _____ (3)
Fall flower _____ (1)
Baked meat _____ (1)
Planet _____ (2)

6. Secret Word ☐☐☐☐☐

Aesop's forte _____ (2)
Detest _____ (2)
Draw a conclusion _____ (1)
Comic Williams _____ (3)
Core _____ (0)
Dwell _____ (2)
Perfect _____ (2)
Wireless _____ (2)
Mrs. Bunker _____ (1)
Distributed cards _____ (2)

SUM TOTALS

Place one digit (1 to 9, no zeros) in each square so that the sum of the numbers in each group of squares across or down is the number given. The number below a diagonal is the sum of the numbers below it. The number to the right of a diagonal is the sum of the numbers to the right of it. IMPORTANT: No digit is used more than once in any group of squares leading to a sum. One group of digits has been given for you.

Solution on page 351

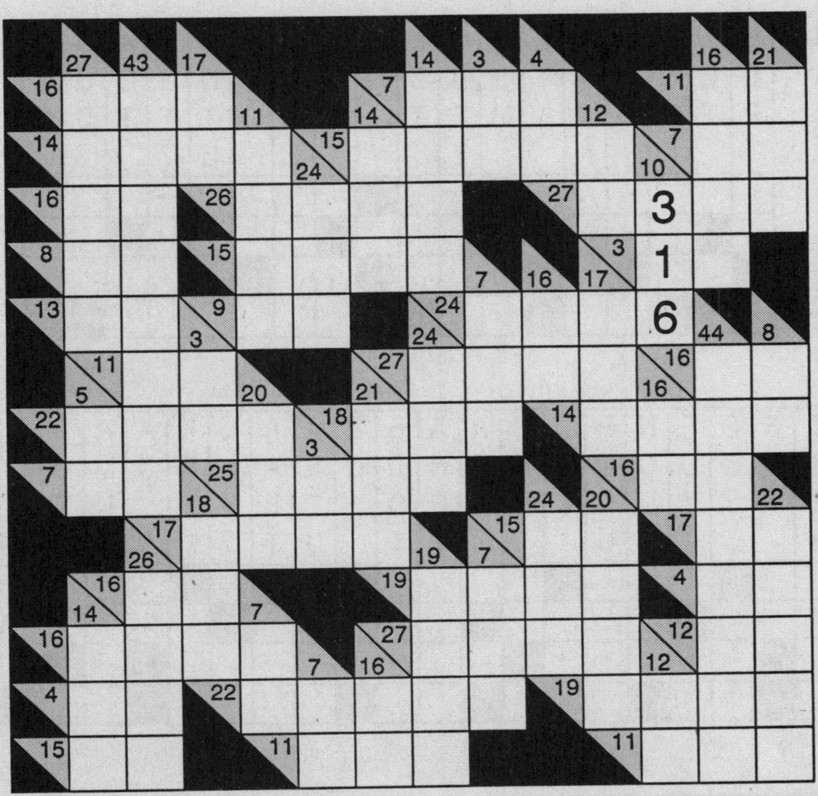

SUM WORDS

This puzzle adds words instead of numbers, which makes it sumwhat different. Answer the top two clues in each problem with words containing the number of letters indicated in parentheses. Then rearrange these letters to find the Sum Word answer. If the math-od eludes you, try working backward.

Solutions on page 354

1.

	Clue	Letters
	Jackets	(5)
+	Departed	(4)
=	Covered wagon	(9)

2.

	Clue	Letters
	Hollow grass	(4)
+	Rational	(4)
=	Lover's song	(8)

3.

	Clue	Letters
	Full-length	(5)
+	Baby's seat	(3)
=	On time	(8)

4.

	Clue	Letters
	Currency	(5)
+	Leading actor	(4)
=	Abbot's domain	(9)

QUOTEFALLS

The letters in each vertical column go into the squares directly below them, but not necessarily in the order they appear. A black square indicates the end of a word. When you have placed all the letters in their correct squares, you will be able to read a quotation across the diagram from left to right. **Solutions on page 354**

1. 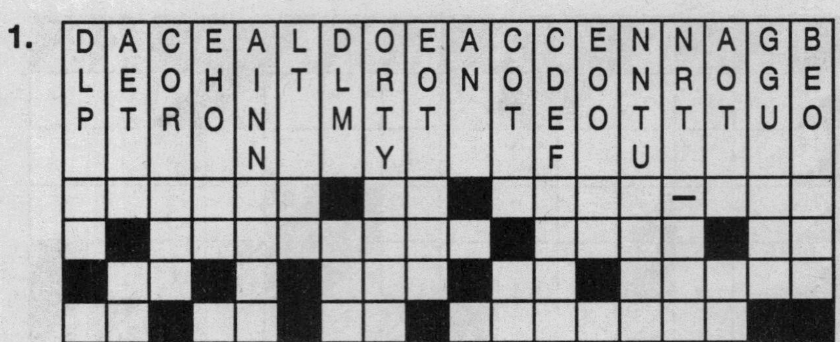

2. 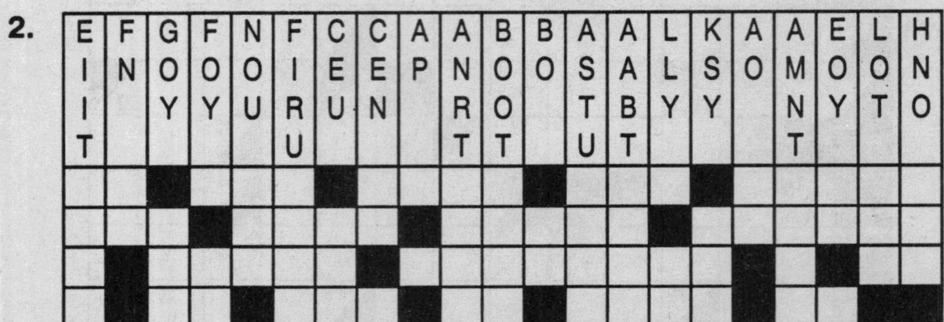

3. 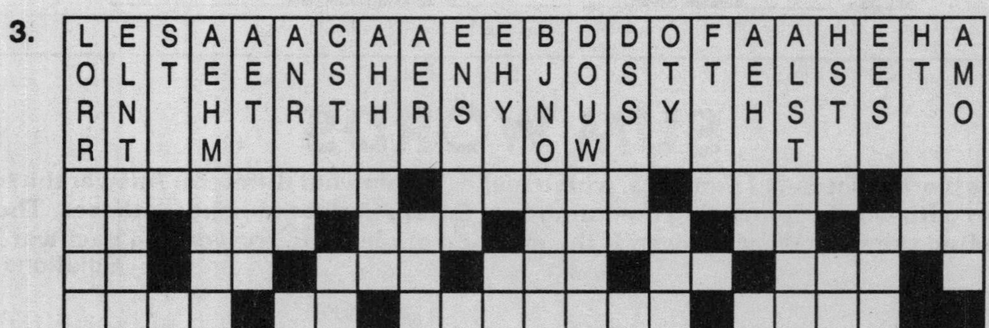

4. 

TO PLAY:

1. Enter the first seven LETTERBOX letters onto the first DRAWLINE and cross them off in the LETTERBOX.
2. Form a word of at least two letters across or down on the GAMEBOARD. One letter of the first word must go into the starred square.
3. Tally your score in the SCORE column.
4. Carry down all unused letters onto the next DRAWLINE. Transfer enough letters from the LETTERBOX, in the given order, so that you have seven letters to work with.
5. Build a new word or words by:
   a. adding one or more letters before and/or after words on the GAMEBOARD.
   b. adding one or more letters at right angles to words on the GAMEBOARD.
   c. adding a word parallel to one on the GAMEBOARD.

IMPORTANT: All adjoining letters must spell out complete words.

6. Continue working this way until all the letters from the LETTERBOX have been used.
7. Asterisks (*) are "wild" letters and may represent any letter you choose, but once used they cannot be changed.

NOTE: Proper names, foreign words, and abbreviations are not allowed. No word may appear twice on the GAMEBOARD.

TO SCORE:

Score every letter in each new word as follows:

1. Letters in unnumbered squares count 1 point.
2. Letters in numbered squares count the given value of the square.
3. Double the score of a word containing a circle.
4. Triple the score of a word containing two circles.
5. Add 20 points if all seven letters from a DRAWLINE are used in one play.

Can you beat our game of 347 points given on page 354?

LETTERBOX

C A T D F O I L R E Z U S N A X G E T Y R O P * I E U N S A
H Q E O J T S R I V N A W * K L E U M O B I R E D A S T O N

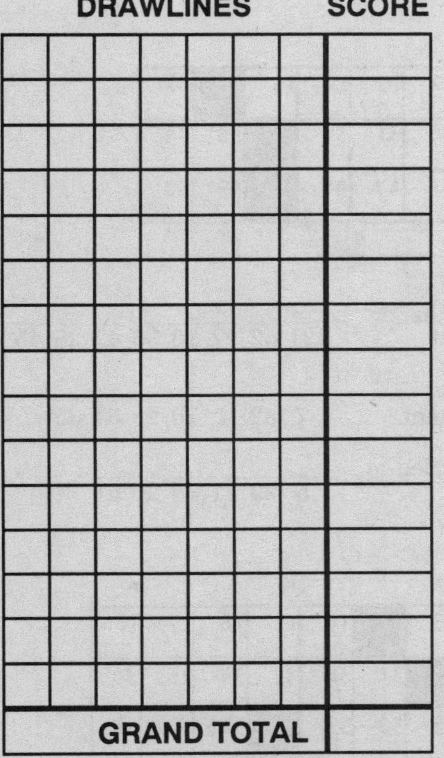

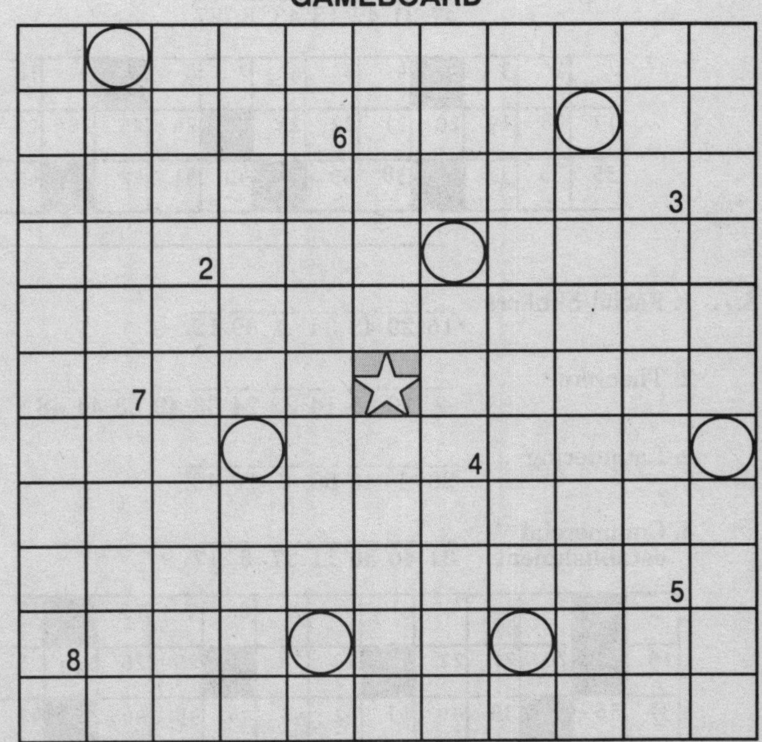

QUOTAGRAMS

Fill in the answers to the clues below. Then transfer the letters to the correspondingly numbered squares in each diagram. Each completed diagram will contain a quotation. **Solutions on page 354**

A.

1. Illegal whiskey — 1 21 14 38 8 34 32 37 12
2. Instructor — 4 17 30 33 9 39 29
3. Evidence — 19 27 20 24 6
4. Take an oath — 15 35 26 18 40
5. Guided trip — 11 2 7 31
6. Seaman — 25 10 36 23 5 22
7. Foot digits — 13 28 16 3

1	2	3	4	■	5	6	■	7	8	■	9	10	11	12	■	13	14
■	15	16	17	■	18	■	19	20	21	22	■	23	24	25	26	27	■
28	29	■	30	■	31	32	33	34	■	35	36	37	38	39	40	■	■

B.

1. Extremely large — 50 17 21 12 3 28 48 41 33 15
2. Inquire into — 36 14 26 6 22 20 46 16 10 35 39
3. Gloss over — 9 45 24 1 18 4 19 11 38
4. Distinguished — 47 31 42 13 43 8 27
5. Flax fabric — 37 49 32 7 25
6. Camp shelter — 23 44 34 29
7. Lofty — 2 30 40 5

1	2	3	■	4	5	6	7	8	■	9	10	11	■	12	13	14	15	■	16
17	18	19	20	21	22	23	■	24	25	26	27	28	29	30	31	32	■	33	34
35	36	37	■	38	39	■	40	41	42	■	43	44	45	46	47	48	■	49	50

C.

1. Facial blinkers — 15 29 43 34 8 39 12
2. Theorem — 2 16 18 14 22 24 33 49 53 44 48
3. Laundering — 20 1 46 50 6 19 42
4. Commercial establishment — 31 40 30 11 37 3 17 9
5. Honolulu resident — 21 52 27 13 36 47 25 45
6. Hot-dog condiment — 7 32 4 10 28 54 35
7. Unmarried — 5 23 41 38 26 51

1	■	2	3	4	5	6	7	8	9	10	■	11	12	■	13	■	14	15	16	17	18
19	■	20	21	22	■	23	24	■	25	26	27	28	29	30	■	31	32	33	34	35	36
37	38	■	39	40	41	42	43	44	45	46	■	47	48	■	49	50	51	■	52	53	54

WORD MATH

In these long-division problems letters are substituted for numbers. Determine the value of each letter. Then arrange the letters in order from 0 to 9, and they will spell a word or phrase. **Solutions on page 353**

1.

```
             SOP
ALSO ) INFANT
       OHFN
       LSTHN
       LANLO
        LLSAT
        LFONF
          OHT
```

0 __ 1 __ 2 __ 3 __ 4 __ 5 __ 6 __ 7 __ 8 __ 9 __

2.

```
             REB
MARE ) NUMBER
       IEIL
       AARBE
       ALUME
         UALR
         QRBE
          QQN
```

0 __ 1 __ 2 __ 3 __ 4 __ 5 __ 6 __ 7 __ 8 __ 9 __

3.

```
             OUT
LIAR ) RARITY
       LIAR
       OTOOT
       OLCRT
        UTAJY
        UTJLT
          LRO
```

0 __ 1 __ 2 __ 3 __ 4 __ 5 __ 6 __ 7 __ 8 __ 9 __

4.

```
             EAR
VOTE ) NATIVE
       AHER
       ETRRV
       ERNVR
        HOCNE
        HRERI
          IRR
```

0 __ 1 __ 2 __ 3 __ 4 __ 5 __ 6 __ 7 __ 8 __ 9 __

5.

```
             URN
ERAS ) ASTRAY
       ERAS
       UIERA
       UETSS
        ZARAY
        ZRUAS
         UESY
```

0 __ 1 __ 2 __ 3 __ 4 __ 5 __ 6 __ 7 __ 8 __ 9 __

6.

```
             EAU
QUAY ) TITTLE
       LYOT
       OTICL
       OIEYA
        OUOOE
        OQTQL
          EIL
```

0 __ 1 __ 2 __ 3 __ 4 __ 5 __ 6 __ 7 __ 8 __ 9 __

LETTER POWER

SAMPLE:

P	L	A	Y					
1	1	1	1					4

L	E	T	T	E	R			
2	1	1	2	2	1			9

P	O	W	E	R				
2	1	1	3	2				9

TOTAL 22

Use your Letter Power to earn the highest score by repeating letters in each answer and from one answer to another as often as you can. There are many possible choices, so we suggest you pencil in your words lightly. Use a maximum of eight letters for each answer.

SCORING: Do not add your score until you have all your answers, since you may want to make changes. A letter is worth 1 point the first time it is used in your answers, 2 the second, 3 the third, etc. Add the points earned in each answer and put the total in the box at the right. Then compare your total score with ours.

1. American state
2. Beverage
3. Mammal
4. Opera heroine
5. European city
6. Board game
7. Musical term
8. Biblical king
9. Horse
10. Flowering shrub

Our solutions with a score of 478 points on page 354

TOTAL

ALPHABET SOUP

EMERALD
MANDOLIN
SQUASH
TURNIP
FABRIC
OYSTER
PLASTIC
MUSHROOM
PHRASE
PATIENCE
POWDER
AVOCADO
EXCUSE
ACROBAT
VISITOR
PIGEON
SHRIEK
CHALLENGE
NURTURE
ENJOY
ABSENT
RAZOR
UNIFORM
CAMERA
TRIANGLE
ROWBOAT

SUM TOTALS

9	8			9	1	8		2	1	7	8	3
7	6	2		6	2	5	1	4	3	8	9	7
	1	3	4	8		9	6			9	5	
8	9		1	5	3			3	9			
5	7	6	9		6	7		1	2		9	3
		9	7			6	4	5			8	1
6	9	8			7	9	8			1	5	4
2	7			9	6	8			6	3		
5	8		9	8		1	8		8	7	6	9
			4	7			4	5	7		1	5
	1	6			1	3		6	9	1	8	
1	4	9	5	3	2	8	6	7		2	9	7
2	7	8	1	4		4	1	9			5	9

LETTERBOXES

E	L	E	M	M	O	R	T	E	M	I	A	L	C
P	A	Y	D	I	R	T		L	T			O	M
O	M	O	T	H	E	R	L	O	D	E	L	I	
T	P	M	A	D	E	K	O	H	C	L	N		T
S	T	R	I	K	E	H		E	A	E	R	F	E
	D	E	P	O	S	I	T	R	B		A	S	L
E	X	C	A	V	A	T	I	O	N	H	L	M	D
A	I	R	W	A	Y		N	B	S	O	L	E	D
T	R	E	P	A	N	A	T	C		R	I	L	I
S	T	I	P	D	N	E	I	U		E	P	T	R
E	A		R	Z	K		D	P	N	E	C	A	F
A	M	I	A	C			A	E		N	I	E	V
M	L		O	E	G	D	E	L	R	E	E	F	
L		P	R	O	S	P	E	C	T	O	R	L	

JIGSAW PUZZLE

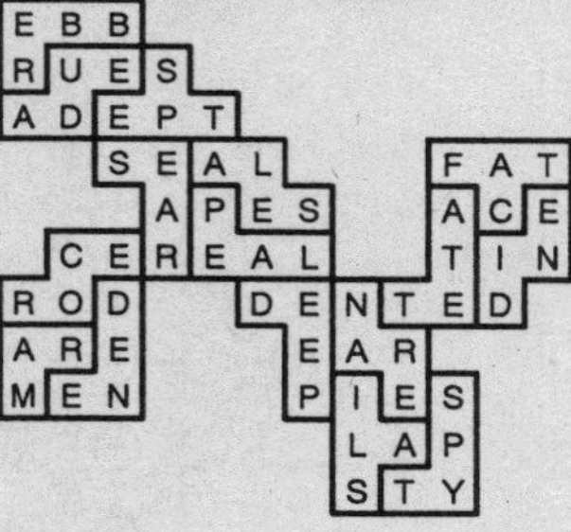

PICTURE THIS

AROUND THE BLOCK

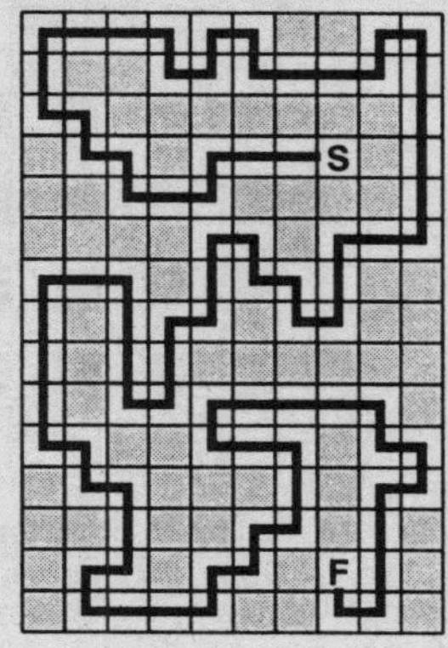

MATCH-UP

2 and 7 match. (Differences: 1. No bow in hair, 3. Diamonds on dress, 4. Squares on tablecloth, 5. Not licking ice cream, 6. Larger drink, 8. Thermometer temperature, 9. Two scoops on cone.)

A FEW CHOICE WORDS

1. Flower, 2. Wonder, 3. Meddle, 4. Pretty, 5. Uproar, 6. Sultan, 7. Auburn, 8. Yogurt.

MAZE

PICTURE SLEUTH

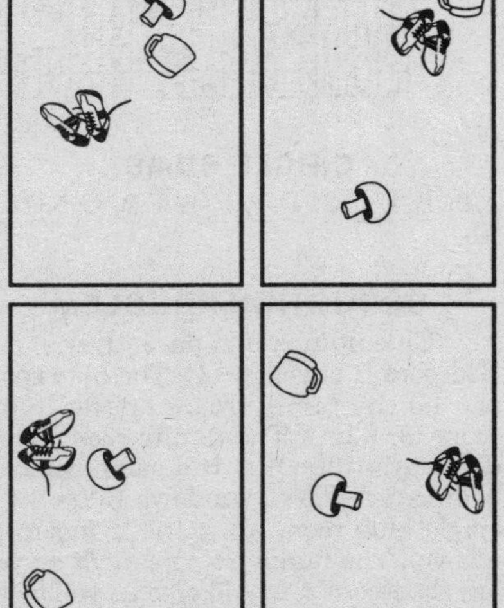

FLOWER POWER

C: 1. Dizzy, 2. Mazes, 3. Hilts, 4. Plant, 5. Aries, 6. Bones, 7. Jones, 8. Mates, 9. Cadet, 10. Carol, 11. Japan, 12. Began, 13. Decoy, 14. Rests, 15. Patty, 16. Jeans, 17. Jewel, 18. Korea.

CC: 1. Downy, 2. Mires, 3. Hazel, 4. Pizza, 5. Alley, 6. Brats, 7. Joins, 8. Monet, 9. Canes, 10. Cates, 11. Jades, 12. Bares, 13. Depot, 14. Regal, 15. Pecan, 16. Jason, 17. Jetty, 18. Keats.

JIGSAW SQUARES

An office manager needed to reach one of his employees elsewhere in the building. In his haste he accidentally dialed his secretary. The secretary answered the phone and, motioning to him, held up the receiver. "Is it for me?" he asked. "No," came the reply, "it IS you."

ANAGRAM MAGIC SQUARE

1. Horde, 2. Angle, 3. Lodge, 4. Feast, 5. Anger, 6. Lotus, 7. Onset, 8. Acres, 9. Float, 10. Inset, 11. Sheik, 12. Brief, 13. Elbow, 14. Tribe, 15. Taste, 16. Early, 17. Ridge, 18. Tuber, 19. Hears, 20. Adept, 21. North, 22. Nurse, 23. Outer, 24. Never, 25. Easel.

SAYING: Half a loaf is better than none.

COMMON COMBOS

1. Roll, 2. Square, 3. Head, 4. Drop, 5. Bird, 6. Piece, 7. Play, 8. Hand, 9. Foot, 10. Band.

CLASSIFIED ADDS

1. Salmon, Network, Kuwait, (John) Travolta, Azalea.
2. Mussel, Laptop, Portugal, (Jack) Lemmon, Narcissus.
3. Scallop, Program, Mexico, (Laurence) Olivier, Rose.
4. Crab, Byte, Ecuador, (Robert) Redford, Daffodil.
5. Haddock, Keyboard, Denmark, (Boris) Karloff, Fuchsia.
6. Sushi, Input, Thailand, (Robert) De Niro, Orchid.

WHEELS

A: 1. Spinet, 2. Severe, 3. Aliens, 4. Fewest, 5. Basset, 6. Candle, 7. Mystic, 8. Agenda.

MESSAGE: A spider spins its web strand by strand.

B: 1. Action, 2. Ladled, 3. Climax, 4. Edison, 5. Elijah, 6. Stance, 7. Burden, 8. Hiatus.

MESSAGE: Rain falls alike on the just and unjust.

FANCY FIVES

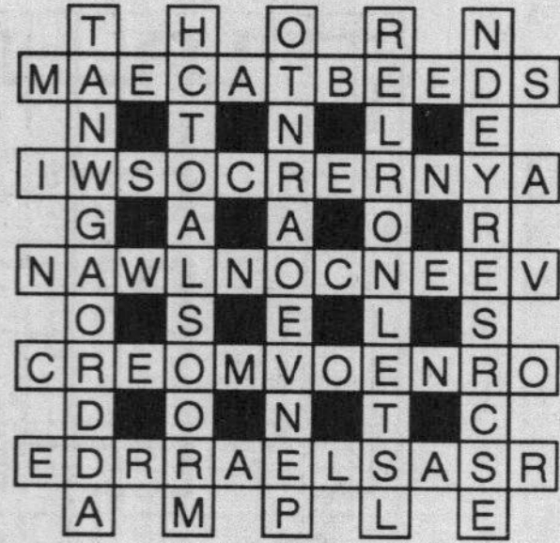

1. Meant, 2. Teach, 3. Baton, 4. Rebel, 5. Dense, 6. Swing, 7. Tacos, 8. Crane, 9. Enrol, 10. Yearn, 11. Wagon, 12. Lawns, 13. Ocean, 14. Clone, 15. Verse, 16. Credo, 17. Moose, 18. Venom, 19. Elton, 20. Scorn, 21. Dread, 22. Armor, 23. Plane, 24. Stall, 25. Scare.

A PERFECT TEN

1. Shape, 2. Erode, 3. Error, 4. Rhyme, 5. Easel, 6. Longs.

TELEVISION CHARACTER: Perry Mason

THE SHADOW

7 matches. (Differences: 1. No parsley at bottom left, 2. Holes in cheese, 3. Ladle on left side of pot, 4. Longer pot handle, 5. Mushroom missing stem, 6. Small onion, 8. Larger container behind pot.)

BULL'S-EYE SPIRAL

OUT: 1. Lad, 4. Epee, 8. Petrel, 14. Warbles, 21. Severe, 27. Vernal, 33. Garret, 39. Tilde, 44. Mantel, 50. Lapse, 55. Uneven, 61. Anise, 66. Dice, 70. Denim, 75. Regard.

IN: 80. Drag, 76. Ermine, 70. Decides, 63. Inane, 58. Venues, 52. Pallet, 46. Named, 41. Litter, 35. Raglan, 29. Revere, 23. Vessel, 17. Brawler, 10. Tepee, 5. Pedal.

SIMON SAYS

1. PLUMBER
2. RAINBER
3. NIARBER
4. NIARREB
5. NIARSURE
6. ONNIARSURE
7. ONNIARSURGE
8. NNRSRG
9. NANARASARAGA
10. NANARDSARAGA
11. NARDSARAGA
12. NIARDSARAGA
13. NIARDSARAGAON
14. NIARDSARGAON
15. NIARDSARGAEON
16. NIARDSARGEON
17. DRAINSARGEON
18. DRAIN SURGEON

CIRCLES IN THE SQUARE

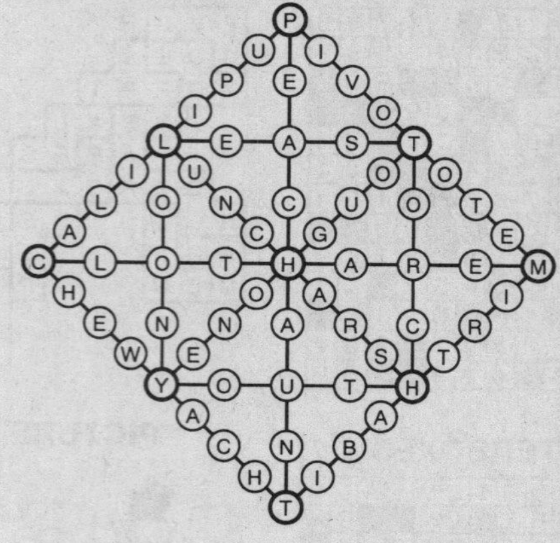

SHARE-A-LETTER

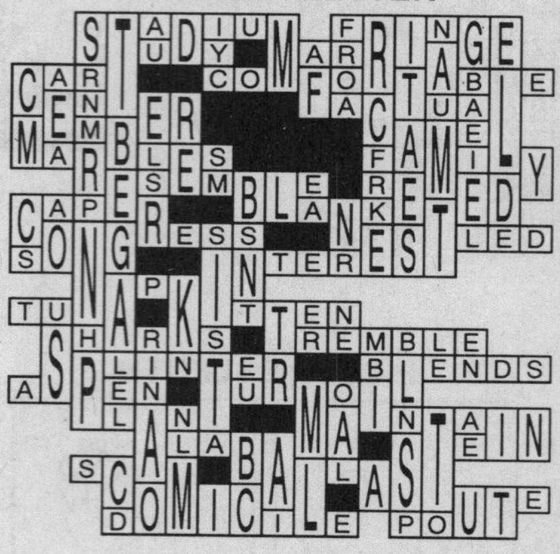

CIRCLE SUMS

A-9, B-4, C-3, D-7, E-1, F-2, G-5, H-6, I-8.

DEDUCTION PROBLEM

(Clue numbers in parentheses)

Bedroom B is yellow (1). The blue room can be the family room or the living room (3, illus.). The family room [most doorways (illus.)] is the same color as bedroom A [most windows (illus.)] (2); single blue room (3) is the living room (above). The family room cannot be yellow [bedroom A would also be yellow (2, above), so 3 rooms would be yellow] (1) or gray (4); the family room and bedroom A are white (2, above). The kitchen [2 windows (illus.)] isn't yellow (1), white [family room and bedroom A] (2), or blue (3, illus.); it's gray. The dining room isn't white [family room and bedroom A] (2), blue (3, illus.), or gray [kitchen] (5); it's yellow. Bedroom C isn't yellow [bedroom A and dining room] (1), white [family room and bedroom A] (2), or blue (3, illus.); it's gray.

In summary:
Kitchen, gray
Dining room, yellow
Living room, blue
Family room, white
Bedroom A, white
Bedroom B, yellow
Bedroom C, gray

CODEWORD

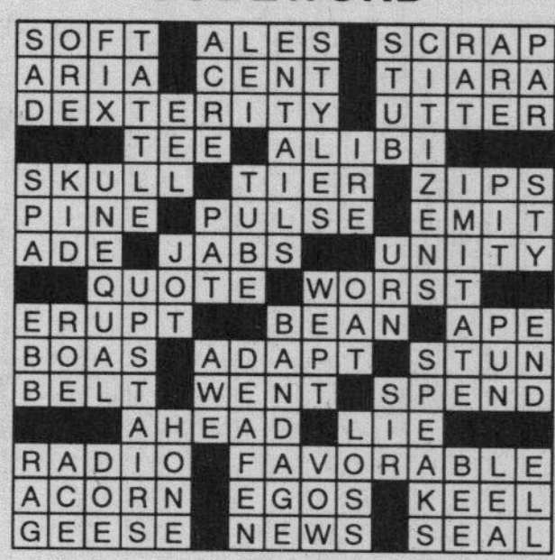

1-N, 2-A, 3-Y, 4-G, 5-S, 6-X, 7-I, 8-R, 9-C, 10-H, 11-V, 12-D, 13-F, 14-L, 15-B, 16-Z, 17-M, 18-O, 19-W, 20-J, 21-Q, 22-U, 23-E, 24-T, 25-K, 26-P.

PLUS ONE

1. Chiefly, 2. Explain, 3. Quart, 4. Civic, 5. Though, 6. Carbon.

BONUS WORD: Flavor

WINDOW BOXES

1-d Club, 2-j Work, 3-f Ugly, 4-c Kilt, 5-e Draw, 6-i Stop, 7-a Vine, 8-g Able, 9-h Text, 10-b Join.

BITS AND PIECES

1. Hubert Humphrey, 2. Lyndon Johnson, 3. Walter Mondale, 4. Gerald Ford, 5. Richard Nixon, 6. George Bush, 7. Spiro Agnew, 8. Harry S. Truman.

SPELLBOUND

1. Torque (6), Clamp (5), Justify (7), Blaze (5), Mouth (5), Slave (5), Dowry (5), Knight (6), Flame (5), Curd (4), Toxin (5).
TOTAL: 58 + 10 = 68

2. Cavity (6), Dozen (5), Slick (5), Hexagon (7), Fluid (5), Therapy (7), Jonquil (7), Swarm (5), Blond (5), Script (6), Lunge (5).
TOTAL: 63 + 10 = 73

CRYPTO-FAMILIES

1. SHAPE UP!: Rectangle, Diamond, Triangle, Ellipse, Pentagon, Pyramid, Cylinder, Circle, Cone, Oval.

2. IN THE MAIL: Package, Invitation, Newspaper, Circular, Postcard, Leaflet, Catalog, Letter, Check, Bill.

3. SHOW ____: Business, And tell, Window, Place, Stopper, Boat, Case, Piece, Tune, Down.

4. GET BETTER: Amend, Progress, Revise, Enhance, Improve, Correct, Develop, Advance, Reform, Enrich.

5. COMIC RELIEF: Hi and Lois, Beetle Bailey, The Far Side, Blondie, Andy Capp, Li'l Abner, Nancy, Peanuts, Doonesbury, Cathy.

6. WATCH YOUR DIET: Protein, Calories, Cholesterol, Calcium, Fiber, Niacin, Potassium, Fat, Amino acid, Iodine.

RINGMASTER

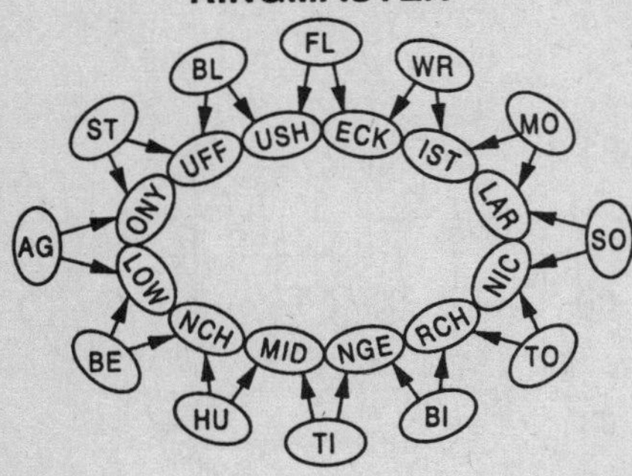

CROSSED NAMES

1. Jerry Lewis, 2. Tina Turner, 3. Stephen King.

RINGERS

1. Forty, Paint, Drama, Stock; 2. Diary, Vault, Twine, Loyal; 3. Tempt, World, Kazoo, Punch; 4. Yearn, Waltz, Torch, Blimp; 5. Swift, Delta, Baton, Vowel.

SPELLBOUND

1. Hazel (5), Minor (5), Jacket (6), Proxy (5), Making (6), Croquet (7), Spawn (5), Moved (5), Swan (4), Profit (6), Bash (4).
TOTAL: 58 + 10 = 68

2. Squelch (7), Topaz (5), Glued (5), Swift (5), Only (4), Raved (5), Minks (5), Project (7), Swab (4), Nightly (7), Boxers (6).
TOTAL: 60 + 10 = 70

THREE'S COMPANY

1. Exhibitionist, Grandstander, Hotshot; 2. Pursue, Shadow, Trail; 3. Azure, Royal, Sky; 4. Gleam, Glow, Shimmer; 5. Fall, Locked, Mark; 6. Derrick, Hoist, Pulley; 7. Hasty, Quick, Speedy; 8. Bacon, Ham, Sausage; 9. Girl, Lady, Woman; 10. Crane, Hardy, Swift; 11. Collar, Sleeve, Tail; 12. Beam, Joist, Rafter; 13. Noble, Princely, Regal; 14. Army, Marines, Navy; 15. Seesaw, Slide, Swing.

WORD GAMES

WHAT'S MY NAME?: 1. Jennings, 2. Whitcomb, 3. Boothe, 4. Greenleaf.

ANIMAL FARM: 1. Sheepskin, 2. Trojan horse, 3. Chicken feed, 4. Goose bumps.

COLOR CHART: 1. Gray matter, 2. Pink lady, 3. Ivory tower, 4. Blue Grotto.

THREE + THREE = ONE: 1. Tomato, 2. Yogurt, 3. Napkin, 4. Donate.

VERSE: The proper way to leave a room
Is not to plunge it into gloom;
Just make a joke before you go,
And then escape before they know.

ACROSS AND DOWN

A

W	A	S	T	E
A	C	T	O	R
S	T	O	N	E
T	O	N	I	C
E	R	E	C	T

B

C	L	E	A	R
L	E	A	V	E
E	A	V	E	S
A	V	E	R	T
R	E	S	T	S

STRETCH LETTERS

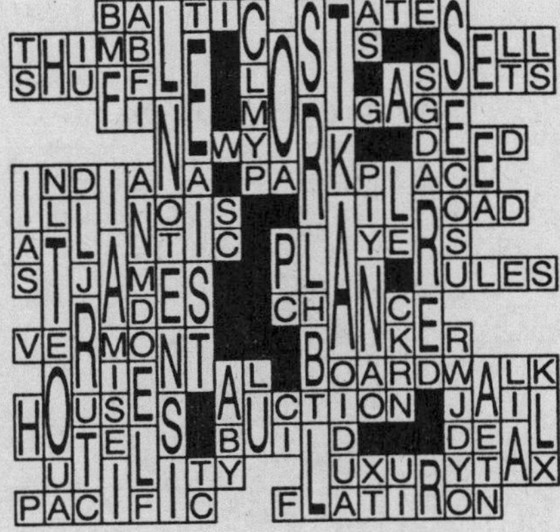

LETTER POWER

1. Mushroom (10), 2. Solomon (19), 3. Blue Moon (25), 4. Teaspoon (28), 5. Onondaga (37), 6. Monmouth (49), 7. Coronado (61), 8. Homeroom (78), 9. Doubloon (83), 10. Tom Jones (77).

SYLLACROSTIC

(Richard Henry) Horne: 'Tis always morning somewhere in the world.

1. Hamburg, 2. Oasis, 3. Romano, 4. Narcissism, 5. Elite, 6. Tomorrow, 7. Irish, 8. Serene, 9. Alligator, 10. Lettuce, 11. Waikiki, 12. Abdomen, 13. Yogurt, 14. Stylish, 15. Magazine, 16. Overflow, 17. Rodeo, 18. Nectar, 19. Illegal, 20. Noted.

ESCALATORS

1

SMOOTH	M	HOOTS	T	SHOO
SONATA	O	SANTA	A	ANTS
NORMAL	N	MOLAR	L	ROAM
RACKET	E	TRACK	K	CART
YEARNS	Y	SNARE	S	NEAR

2

PILFER	P	FLIER	F	RILE
DONATE	O	ANTED	A	TEND
TARGET	T	GREAT	R	GATE
CAMERA	A	CREAM	M	ACRE
CARPET	T	RECAP	E	CARP
ROUGHS	O	SHRUG	R	HUGS

3

STREAM	M	RATES	T	SEAR
SUITOR	I	TOURS	O	RUST
ASSERT	S	STARE	R	SATE
LAPSED	S	PLEAD	P	DEAL
ASPIRE	I	REAPS	E	SPAR
FILLED	L	FIELD	D	FILE
ORATES	E	ROAST	O	STAR

PLACES, PLEASE

C	I	T	R	E	K	A	M	Y	A	H	O	A	R	D
Y	I	I	H	L	Y	O	A	A	A	A	A	G	A	A
R	R	N	A	I	M	D	O	L	I	R	Y	S	E	P
N	A	T	A	L	R	A	H	C	E	M	E	N	T	Y
A	S	L	U	E	A	T	R	A	O	O	S	O	E	E
M	O	E	T	M	C	E	E	V	O	N	O	M	I	K
O	M	S	O	D	A	O	T	E	A	I	T	R	N	R
E	E	S	D	T	N	U	S	R	N	O	K	E	I	Y
Y	O	G	U	R	T	O	E	N	Y	U	E	S	X	P
E	N	R	O	E	H	R	U	O	A	S	U	E	R	T
A	E	O	L	O	U	P	B	U	I	R	R	A	O	O
S	T	A	C	O	S	M	O	S	M	A	T	U	R	N
T	R	O	O	A	I	H	P	I	T	H	Y	X	R	I
Y	R	I	L	K	K	O	S	S	E	R	P	S	E	T
D	I	M	A	L	T	E	R	N	A	T	O	R	S	E

MISSING TRIOS

1. Legible, Boxing, Bingo, Glib, Big.
2. Refrain, Inform, Fairy, Rift, Fir.
3. Pattern, Napkin, Paint, Plan, Pan.
4. Flowing, Yellow, Below, Wolf, Low.
5. Defense, Endure, Denim, Dune, End.
6. Hopeful, Patrol, Spool, Loop, Lop.
7. Average, Allege, Grape, Gear, Age.
8. Theater, Rather, Shore, Hire, Her.

ANAGRAM MAGIC SQUARE

1. Crate, 2. Otter, 3. Nears, 4. Dowel, 5. Earls, 6. Meant, 7. Norse, 8. Trove, 9. Hires, 10. Ethan, 11. Satin, 12. Irate, 13. Notes, 14. Never, 15. Oaths, 16. Treed, 17. Tress, 18. Heals, 19. Errol, 20. Spray, 21. Incur, 22. Names, 23. Nolte, 24. Easel, 25. Raced.

SAYING: Condemn the sin, not the sinner.

WHEELS

A: 1. Notion, 2. Spoken, 3. Shrewd, 4. Thread, 5. Leaden, 6. Listen, 7. Helmet, 8. Strike.

MESSAGE: No one knows what he can do till he tries.

B: 1. Infant, 2. Sketch, 3. Nearly, 4. Cinema, 5. Hustle, 6. Polite, 7. Pastry, 8. Market.

MESSAGE: Man is the only animal that plays poker.

CRYPTO-FAMILIES

1. ON YOUR FEET: Cowboy boots, Docksiders, Moccasins, Wingtips, Galoshes, High heels, Sneakers, Slippers, Sandals, Pumps.

2. WEATHER FORECAST: Cloudy, Sunny, Snow, Humid, Windchill, Front, Blizzard, Flurries, Storm, Breezy.

3. "CROSS" WORDS: Section, Country, Bar, Current, Stitch, Cut, Wind, Road, Bow, Bones.

4. BRITISH POETS: Byron, Keats, Shelley, Tennyson, Pope, Spenser, Lear, Burns, Donne, Auden.

5. GRAMMAR LESSON: Noun, Sentence, Object, Pronoun, Adverb, Conjunction, Passive, Clause, Preposition, Plural.

6. WALK ON: Stroll, March, Amble, Saunter, Strut, Promenade, Plod, Tread, Trudge, Stride.

MASTERWORDS

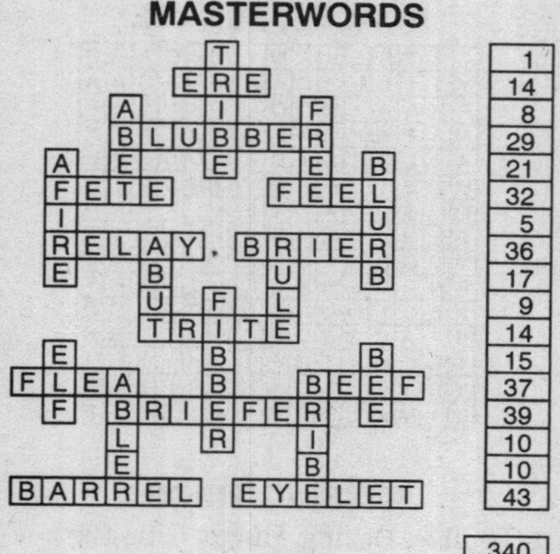

FAN WORDS

1. Aster, 2. Tears, 3. Onset, 4. Stone, 5. Yemen, 6. Enemy, 7. Scare, 8. Cesar.
8-LETTER WORD: Sentence

SPECULATION

1. Lease, 2. Wage, 3. Lords, 4. Told, 5. Alter, 6. Hostage.
QUOTATION: All the world's a stage.

THREE FROM NINE

1. Fathoms, Manor, Air; 2. Parable, Unlit, Inn; 3. Doubles, Train, Ice; 4. Congeal, Grind, Ire; 5. Impress, Visor, Emu; 6. Apricot, Epoch, Sir.

CHANGAWORD

1. Moat, Molt, Mole, Mote.
2. Pain, Pail, Pall, Pale, Pane.
3. Bear, Bead, Bend, Band, Bane, Bare.
4. Fare, Fire, File, Fill, Fall, Fail, Fair.

HEADINGS

1. Fable, Riddle, Definition, Song, Report, Myth, Story, Review.
2. Drum, Violin, Trumpet, Bassoon, Cello, Guitar, Harp, Samisen.
3. Vehicle, Flag, Banks, Rapid, Victory, Steer, Track, Course.

PUZZLE DERBY

1. Facs*imile*, 2. Bull*finch*, 3. Vine*yard*, 4. Dia*meter*, 5. Col*league*, 6. Bare*foot*, 7. Wise*acre*, 8. Nim*rod*, 9. Short*hand*, 10. *O*micron.
Win: I; Place: E; Show: A.
All words end in a measurement.

BIG QUESTION

1. Palace, 2. Center, 3. Erode, 4. Escapade, 5. Adept, 6. Trombone, 7. Onerous, 8. Usher, 9. Heritage, 10. Agent, 11. Entrance, 12. Ancestors, 13. Scatter, 14. Terse, 15. Senator, 16. Ornament, 17. Entrust, 18. Strum, 19. Umpire, 20. Reduce, 21. Cello, 22. Lode.
RIDDLE ANSWER: Stampede

SPLIT AND SPLICE

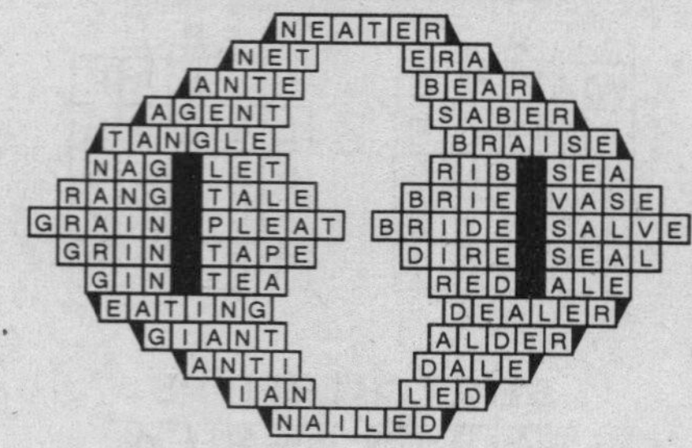

STRETCH LETTERS

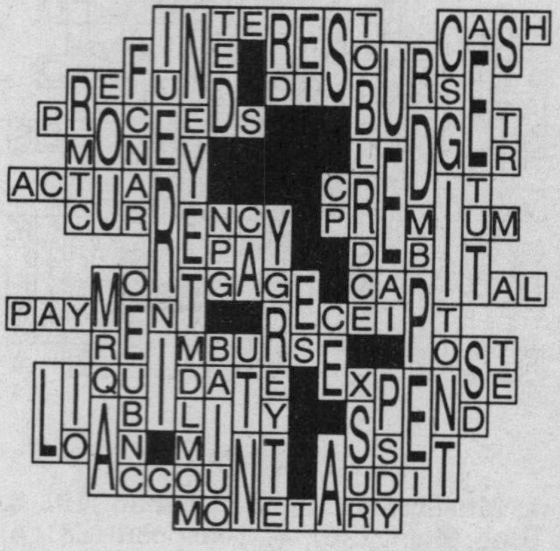

BLIPS

Ade, Ado, Adz, And, Ant, Any, Are, Ark, Arm.

LOGIC PROBLEM

Days were Mon. through Fri., and nos. of points of excellence were 1, 4, 5, 8, and 12 (intro.). Belle [Mon. (1)], who gave 3 points more than the one who went to Amberblack's on Fri. (2), didn't give 1, 5 [no one gave 2 points], 12 [no one gave 9 points], or 4 [1 point given by one who went Thurs. (2)]; Belle gave 8 points, and the one who went to Amberblack's gave 5 points. Edmund [4 points more than one who went to Taj Mahal (4)] didn't give 1, 4, or 12 points [Carlo (3)]; he gave 5 points, and the one who went to Taj Mahal gave 1 point. The one who went to Taj Mahal [1 point] wasn't Belle [8 points], Carlo [12 points], or Dixie [Pasta Kitchen (3)]; he was Angel. Dixie gave 4 points. Dixie didn't go on Tues. (3); Carlo did. Dixie went on Wed. Belle didn't go to Don Carlo's (1); Carlo did. Belle went to Cafe Christine.

In summary:
Angel, Taj Mahal, Thurs., 1
Belle, Cafe Christine, Mon., 8
Carlo, Don Carlo's, Tues., 12
Dixie, Pasta Kitchen, Wed., 4
Edmund, Amberblack's, Fri., 5

CIRCLES IN THE SQUARE

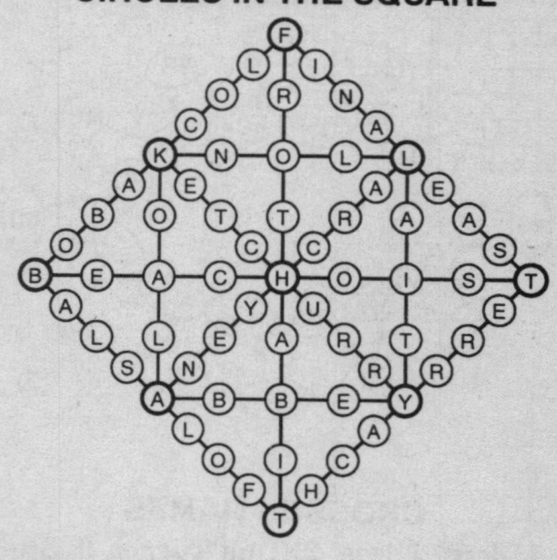

INSERT-A-WORD

1. Pirate, 2. Pardonable, 3. Pitcher, 4. Reverend, 5. Predicament, 6. Knowing, 7. Practice, 8. Recreational, 9. Pleasure, 10. Sparkled, 11. Frighten, 12. Absently.

ALPHABET PLUS

Senate, Belong, Escort, Thread, Height, Inform, Magnet, Shaker, Valise, Jangle, Strike, Revolt, Custom, Fender, Onward, Carpet, Squint, Insert, Slogan, Trowel, Pursue, Gravel, Answer, Extent, Argyle, Blazer.

WHICH WAY WORDS

1. Egret, 2. Ammunition, 3. Portico, 4. Makeshift, 5. Notched, 6. Totem, 7. Prune, 8. Update, 9. Seances, 10. Giggle, 11. Battery, 12. Stellar.
RELATED WORDS: Committee, President, Amendment, Secretary, Legislate.

WORDFINDER

ACROSS: Lukewarm, Whitecap, Fortune, Plaudit, Skyward, Jasmine, Nadir, Organize, Brimful, Divulge, Vocalist.
DOWN: Gems, Unsteady, Know, Hemlock, Yolks, Rightful, Quad, Ahoy, Triumph, Certify, Melody.

ACCORDION WORDS

1. Forget, Forge, Fore, For, Or.
2. Heaviest, Heavies, Heaves, Heave, Eave, Eve.
3. Flattery, Flatter, Latter, Later, Late, Ate, At, A.
4. Stolid, Solid, Slid, Lid, Id, I.
5. Manager, Manger, Mange, Mane, Man, An, A.
6. Crumble, Rumble, Ruble, Rule, Rue, Re.
7. Scream, Cream, Ream, Ram, Am, A.
8. Couplet, Couple, Coupe, Coup, Cup, Up.
9. Howled, Holed, Hole, Hoe, He.
10. Maligned, Aligned, Alined, Lined, Lied, Lid, Id, I.

ALPHABET SOUP

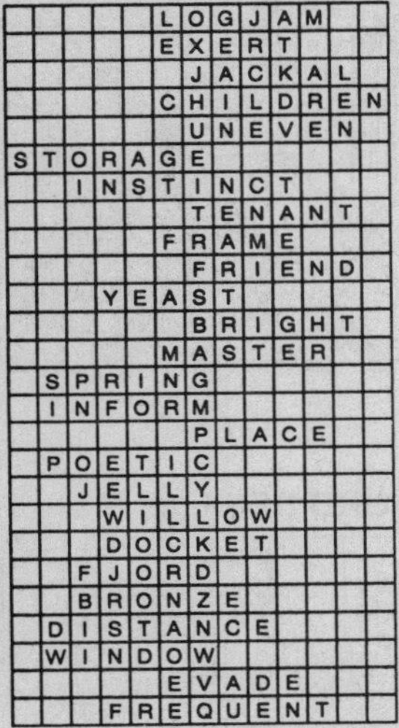

JIGSAW PUZZLE

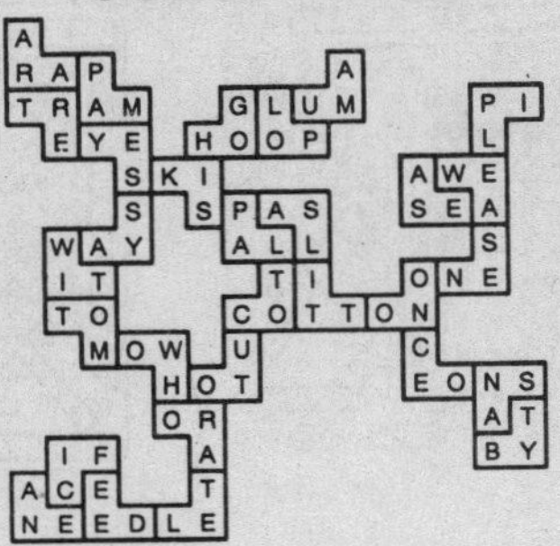

PLACE YOUR NUMBER

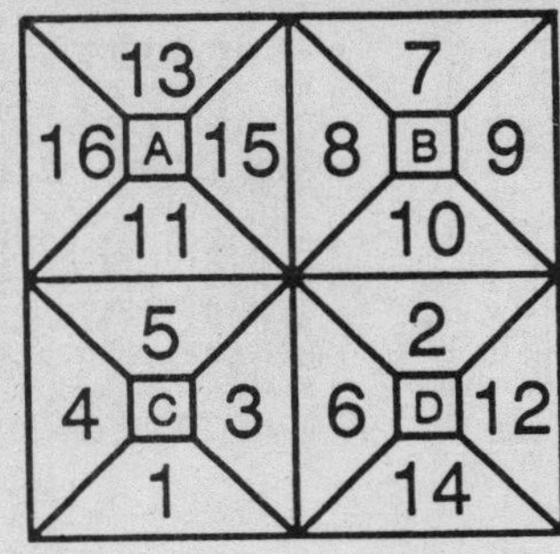

ABACUS

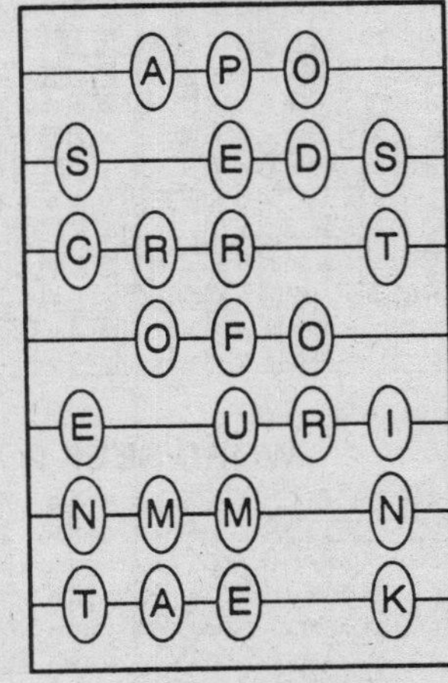

CRISSCROSS

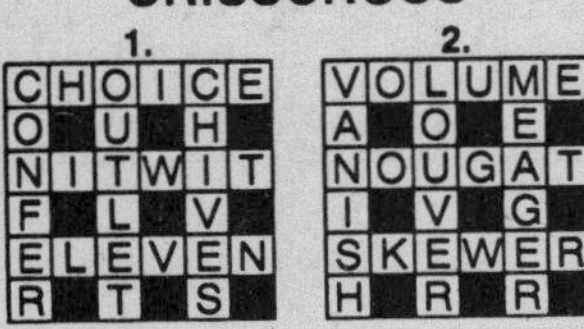

JACKPOT

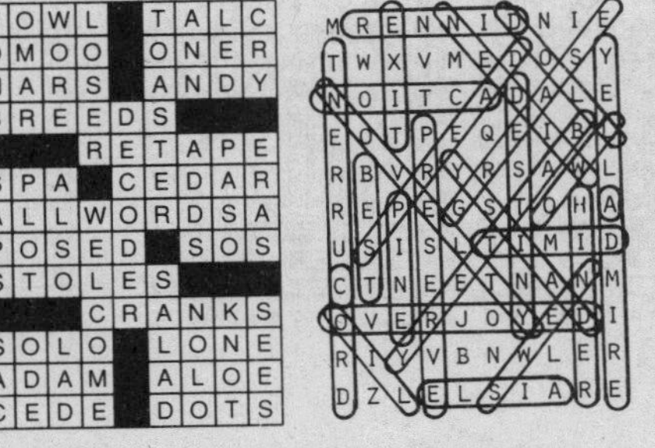

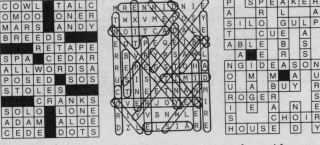

JACKPOT QUOTE: All words are pegs to hang ideas on.

BUILD-A-PYRAMID

A
AT
TAP
PART
TAPER
PATTER
SPATTER
PATTERNS

SUM TOTALS

CRYPTO-FAMILIES

1. POWER: Boat, Plant, Steering, Line, Station, Shovel, House, Train, Play, Base.

2. SECRET IDENTITIES: Superman, Mr. Terrific, Lone Ranger, Green Hornet, Wonder Woman, Captain Marvel, Spider-Man, The Hulk, Robin, Batman.

3. BEWARE!: Peril, Risk, Danger, Hazard, Menace, Emergency, Pitfall, Exposure, Threat, Uncertainty.

4. MIDDLES: Delano, Baines, Milhous, David, Howard, Wilson, Abram, Henry, Alan, Gamaliel.

5. CARIBBEAN: Barbados, Anguilla, Guadeloupe, St. Lucia, Nevis, Jamaica, Antigua, Barbuda, Trinidad, Montserrat.

6. IN THE FUTURE: By and by, Later, Anon, Erelong, Hereafter, Upcoming, In due time, Henceforth, Ultimately, Someday.

PICTURE PAIRS

QUOTAGRAM

Bees that have honey in their mouths have stings in their tails.

1. Thirty
2. Everest
3. Alive
4. Shams
5. Heath
6. Though
7. Inhibit
8. Anise
9. Sonnet

IN AND AROUND

1. Swim, 2. Hone, 3. Once, 4. Room, 5. Tome, 6. Sips, 7. Ivan, 8. Garb, 9. Heal, 10. Tubs, 11. Ella, 12. Deep.
OUTER RING: Shortsighted
THIRD RING: Incomparable

THREE'S COMPANY

1. Frost, Keats, Tennyson; 2. Court, Lob, Serve; 3. Chicory, Cotton, Mustard; 4. Atlanta, Denver, Lincoln; 5. Emperor, Pharaoh, Queen; 6. Kyoto, Osaka, Tokyo; 7. Cinnamon, Ginger, Nutmeg; 8. Hail, Sleet, Snow; 9. Candy, Cusack, O'Hara; 10. Bogus, Ersatz, Imitation; 11. Cool, Great, Swell; 12. Akita, Beagle, Dalmatian; 13. Cashmere, Denim, Taffeta; 14. Brinkley, Carradine, Niven; 15. Basket, Foot, Volley.

CODEWORD

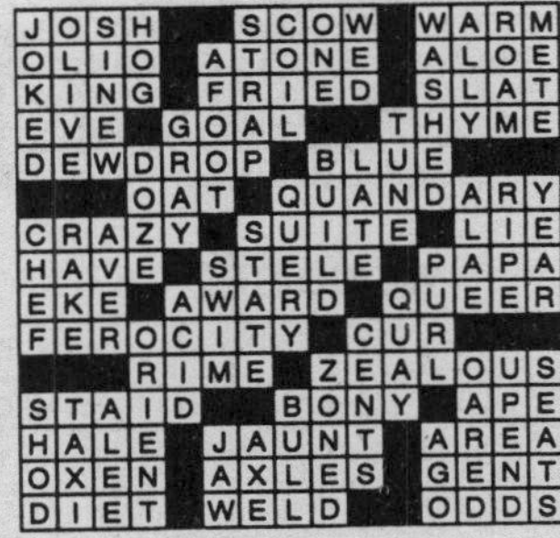

1-N, 2-D, 3-W, 4-H, 5-U, 6-S, 7-I, 8-J, 9-M, 10-E, 11-C, 12-O, 13-K, 14-T, 15-A, 16-Q, 17-Z, 18-G, 19-P, 20-L, 21-V, 22-X, 23-Y, 24-B, 25-F, 26-R.

JIGSAW SQUARES

An office worker on his noon hour picked up a phone and dialed his home, where his wife and daughter were. There was a phone in the kitchen and an extension upstairs. Two female voices answered simultaneously, "I've got it," followed by two clicks as both hung up.

BOWL GAME

STRIKES: 1. Calibrated, 2. Dogcatcher, 3. Ladyfinger, 4. Midwestern, 5. Podiatrist, 6. Tenderfoot, 7. Segregated, 8. Wanderlust, 9. Balustrade, 10. Girlfriend.
SPARES: 1. Braid, Cleat; 2. Torch, Caged; 3. Fling, Ready; 4. Write, Mends; 5. Spirit, Toad; 6. Roof, Netted; 7. Greed, Stage; 8. Trued, Lawns; 9. Beads, Ultra; 10. Grind, Rifle.

WORD SEEK 1

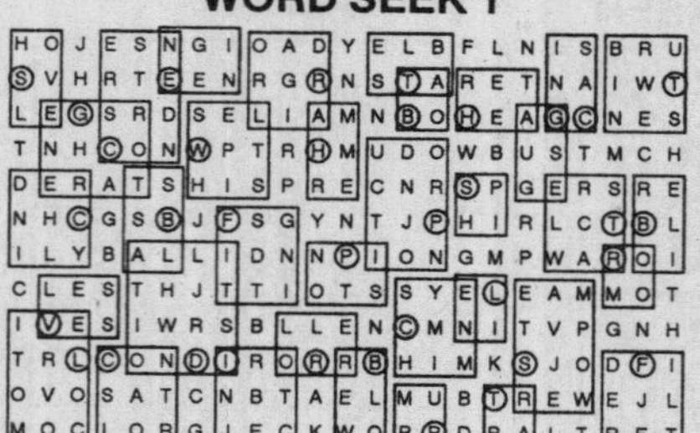

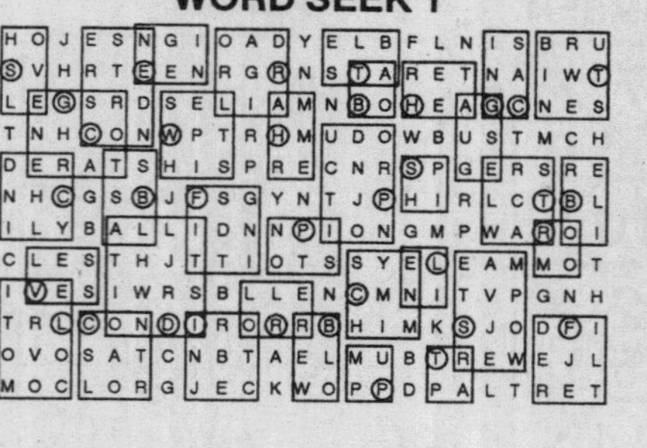

WORD SEEK 6

B F C M N H G F V P V G N I L R E G N I F J F
M P S H P B A U Q S V R F T E N G Y C B T R G
N R P H U O E A G L E T E P M Q G B R C M R N
V G G N P L U O W L E T P F F N H S T A I A I
H K N Q P T W L T Y E A R L I N G Q Y L Y P L
G Y I I Y I T T T T L D V L E E W U S F P E G
M H L T L N G E L F A P D S Q R H E O N V R D
G K S L T K G L V O I O T V E C E A T E W N E
B Q O O R E C L E L C L H V F F L K R N J A L
R P G M D R N U Q T I E L S F Y P E C J D K F
Y D V S R H Q P D N R E T Y S Q T R J O E Y P
Q R D F S P R A G M T V M M P T K C I H C V C

WORD SEEK 11

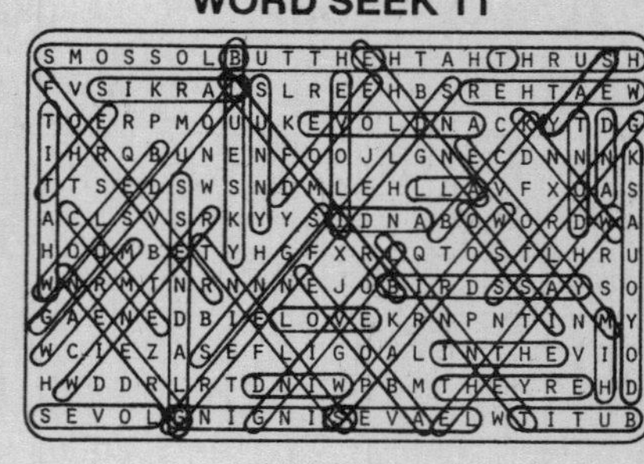

WORD SEEK 2

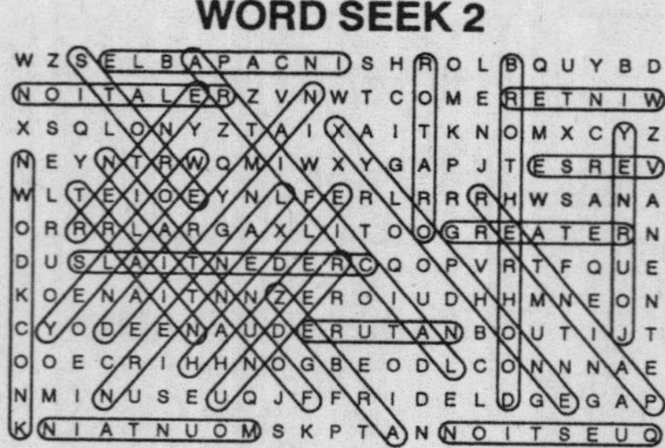

WORD SEEK 7

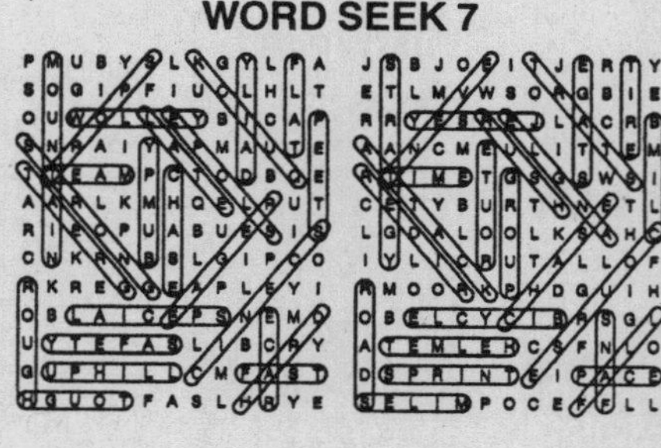

WORD SEEK 12

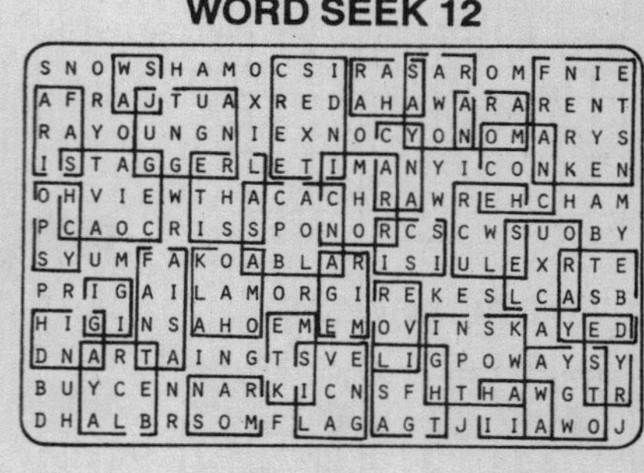

WORD SEEK 3

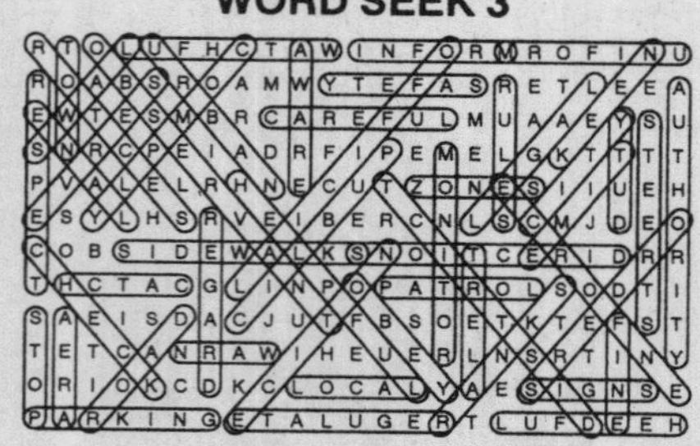

WORD SEEK 8

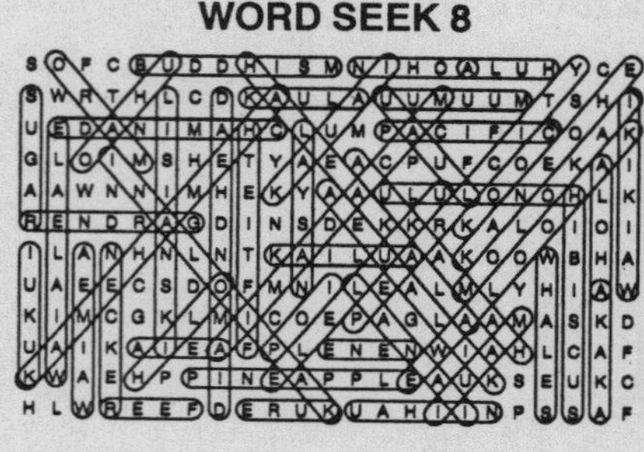

WORD SEEK 13

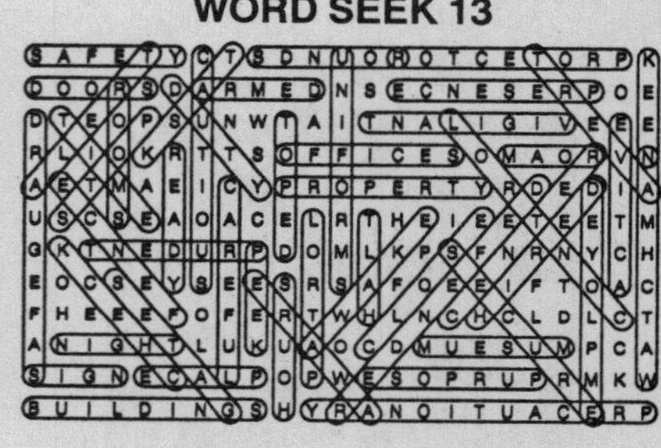

WORD SEEK 4

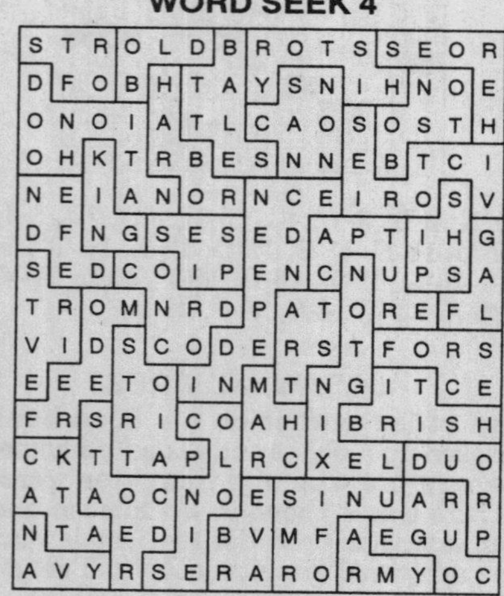

WORD SEEK 9

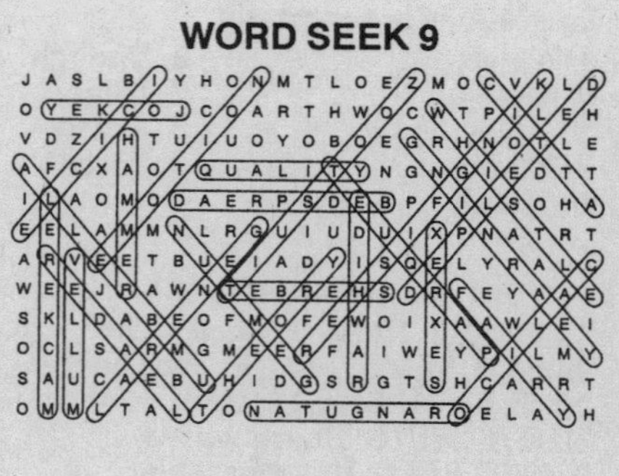

WORD SEEK 14

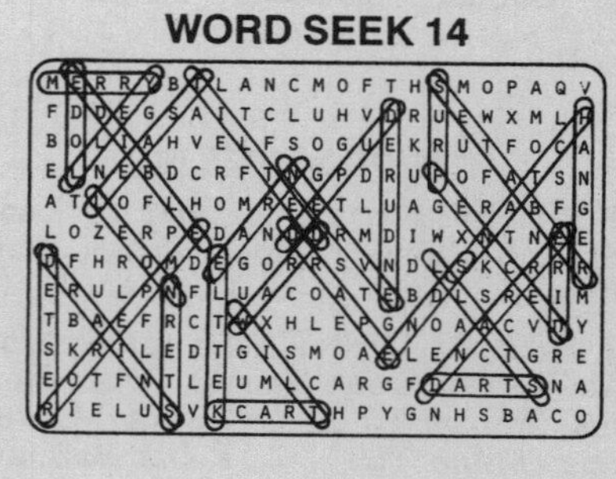

WORD SEEK 5

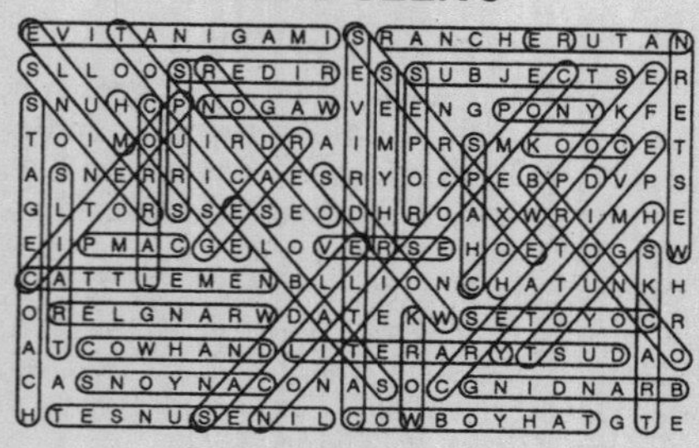

WORD SEEK 10

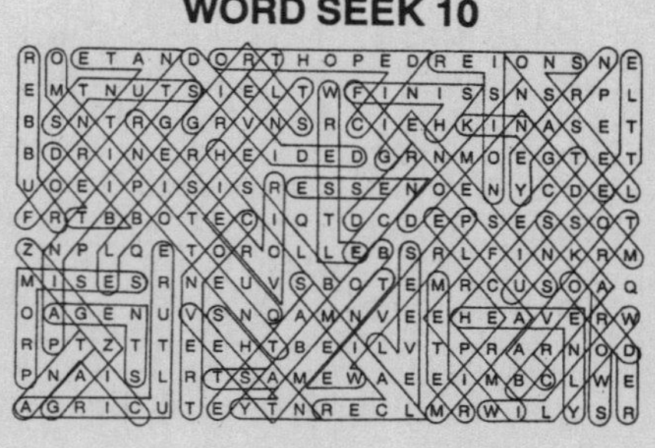

WORD SEEK 15

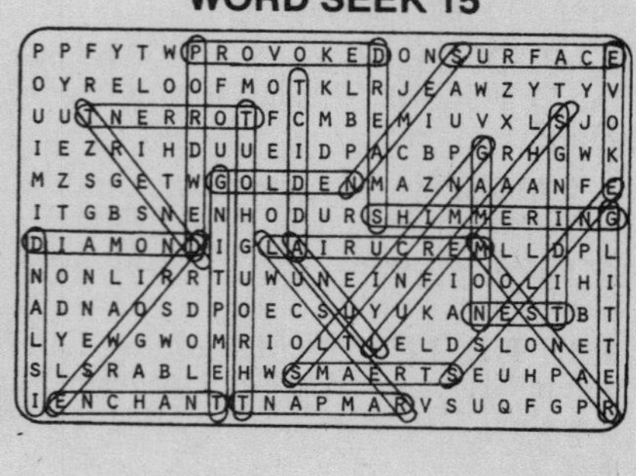

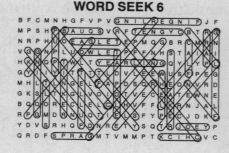

WORD SEEK 16

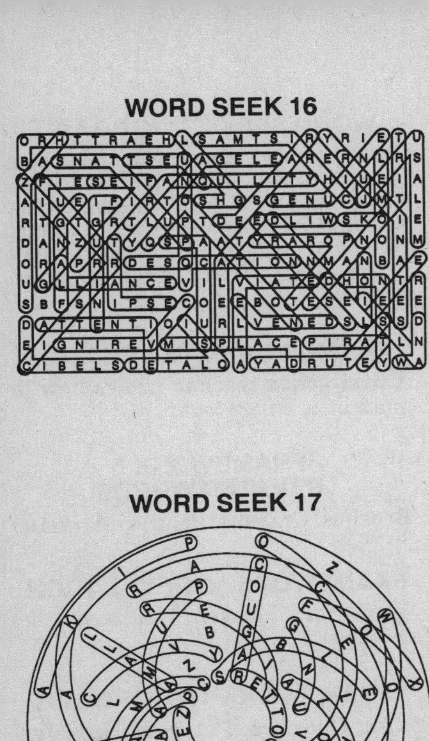

WORD SEEK 17

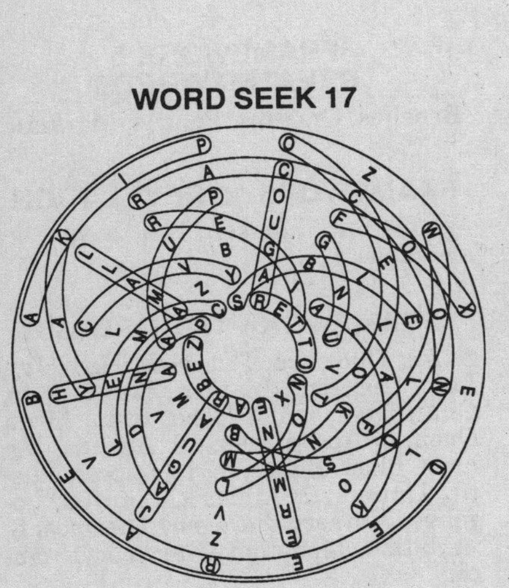

WORD SEEK 18

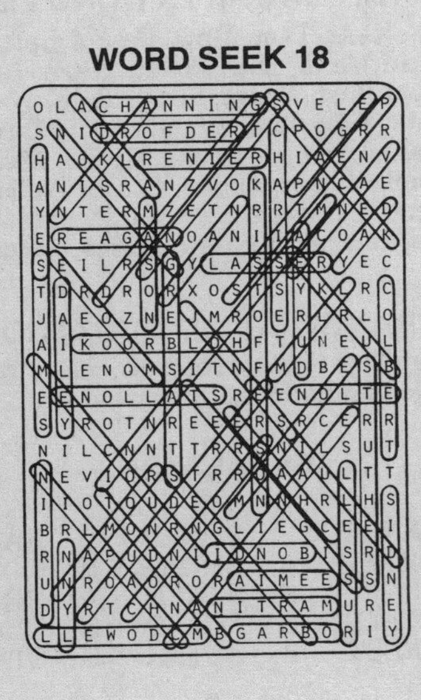

WORD SEEK 19

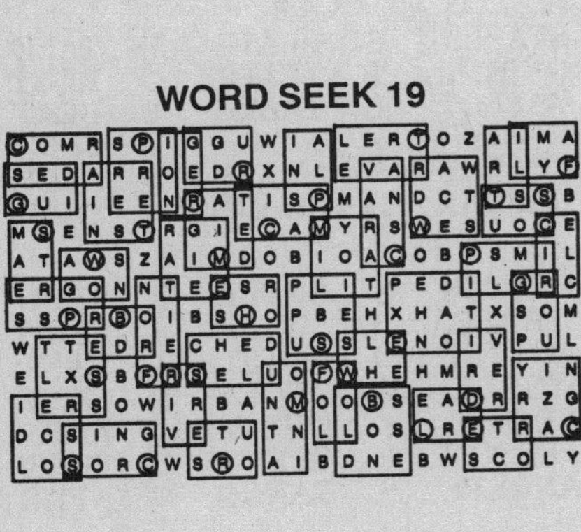

WORD SEEK 20

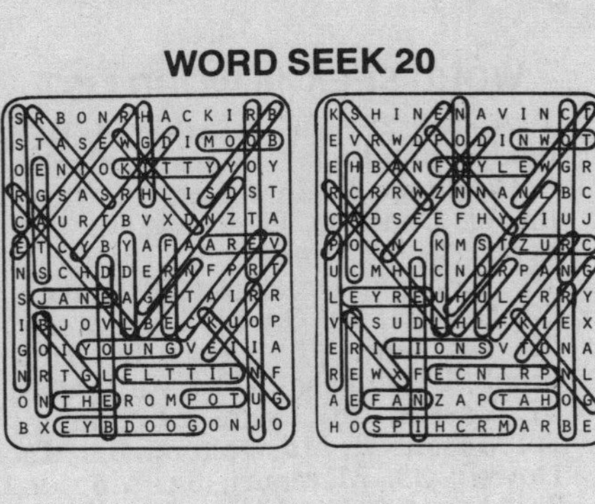

WORD SEEK 21

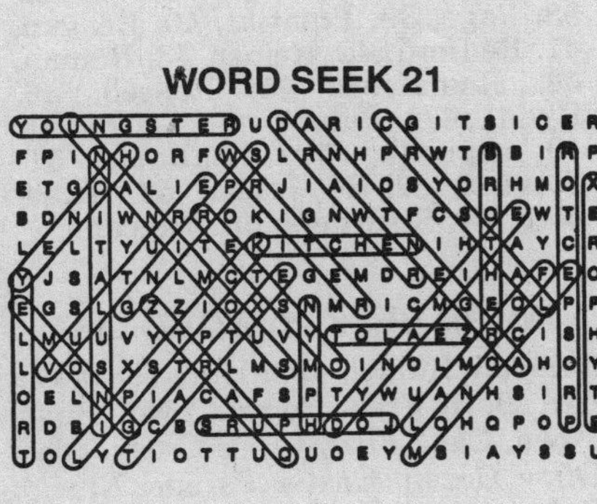

WORD SEEK 22

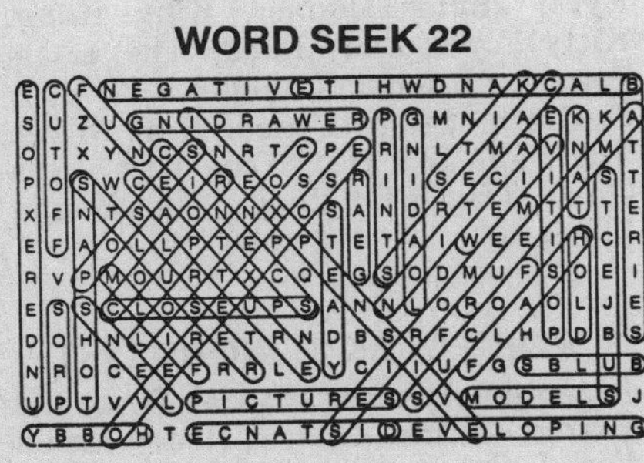

WORD SEEK 23

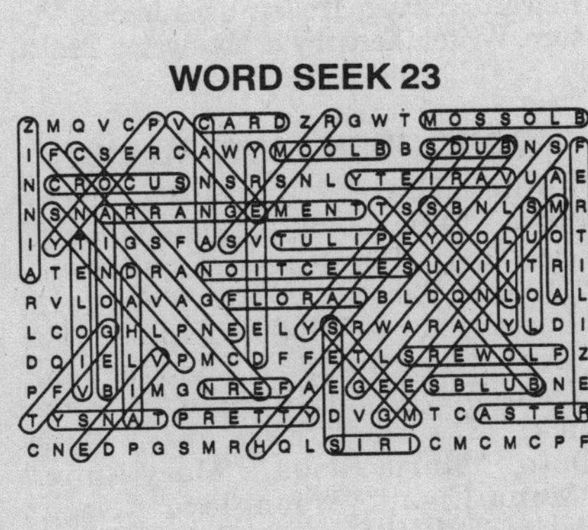

WORD SEEK 24

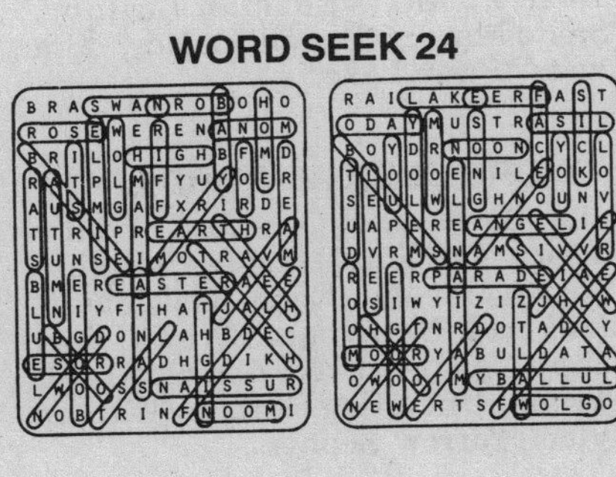

WORD SEEK 25

WORD SEEK 26

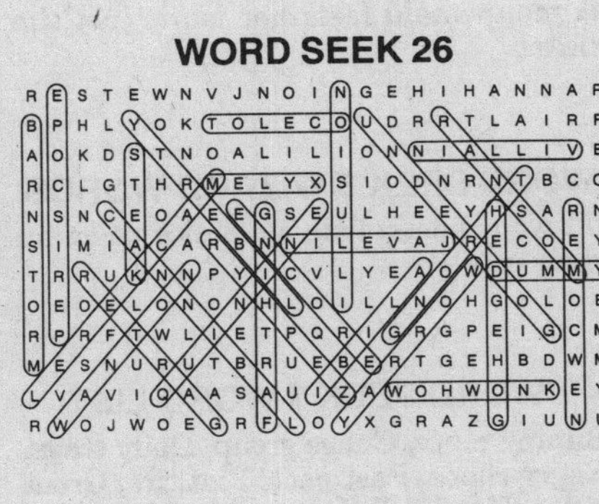

WORD SEEK 27

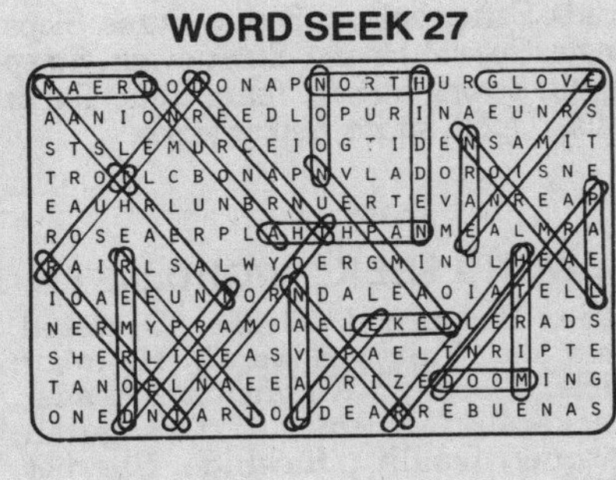

WORD SEEK 28

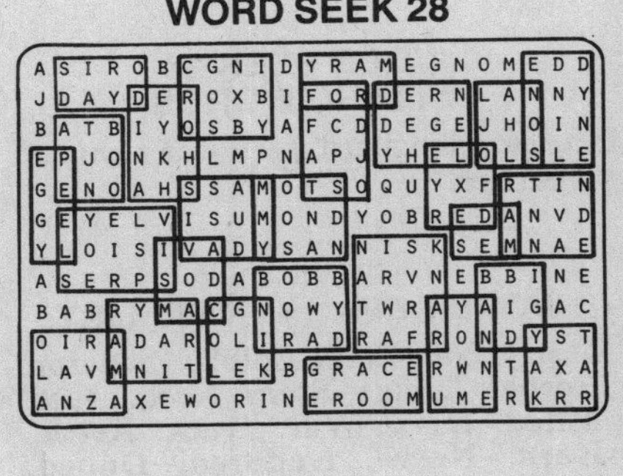

SPLIT AND SPLICE

WORD SEEK 2 WORD LIST

Artificial, Brotherhood, Credentials, Dairyman, Enter, Fountain, Greater, Handle, Incapable, Journey, Knockdown, Lantern, Mountain, Nature, Orator, Painter, Question, Relation, Store, Train, Under, Verse, Winter, Xylophone, Yellow, Zebra.

WORD SEEK 3 SECRET MESSAGE

A meter maid feels her job is just the ticket.

WORD SEEK 5 WIZARD WORDS

(Cowboy poets) long for a nice poem on the range!

WORD SEEK 7 WORD LIST

Bumpy route, Chase group, Daily stage, Eager chase, Fast pace, Flat tire, Great rider, Hard fall, Late rush, Mountain strategy, Quick start, Race fans, Rough roads, Safety helmet, Scenic course, Slope angle, Special bicycle, Sport event, Steep climb, Strong attack, Team time, Tough miles, Uphill sprint, Yellow jersey.

WORD SEEK 9 WORD LIST

Attic, Bedspread, Calico, Depleted, Emotion, Fairy, General, Hammer, Icicle, Jockey, Kingfisher, Leader, Mackerel, Nutmeg, Orangutan, Parquet, Quality, Rawhide, Sherbet, Theory, Umbrella, Vellum, Whistle, Xerxes, Yearning, Zoot suit.

WORD SEEK 13 WIZARD WORDS

(The security guard's) son was a chip off the old lock!

WORD SEEK 14 WORD LIST

Merry, Yell, Lode, Edible, Emperor, Rested, Drains, Stern, Noel, Least, Tilted, Draw, Wilt, Track, Kettle, Earn, Nerve, Endured, Duped, Drape, Ends, Snatch, Hanger, Rebates, Surf, Fenced, Dire, Errand, Darts, Stall.

WORD SEEK 15 WORD LIST

Island, Diamond, Dewdrop, Provoked, Dreams, Shimmering, Glitter, Ransom, Mercurial, Luster, Rampant, Throughout, Torrent, Trend, Drowse, Enchant, Tempting, Golden, Names, Surface, Evoke, Endless, Streams, Sluicing, Gammon, Nest, Tidings, Shameful, Luna, Addict.

WORD SEEK 18 WORD LIST

1. Aimee, 2. Alda, 3. Arkin, 4. Bardot, 5. Bondi, 6. Bridges, 7. Burke, 8. Cardinale, 9. Channing, 10. Chaplin, 11. Charisse, 12. Chase, 13. Colbert, 14. Connors, 15. Dailey, 16. Day, 17. DeLuise, 18. Durbin, 19. Duryea, 20. Garbo, 21. Garson, 22. Grizzard, 23. Hayes, 24. Holbrook, 25. Jones, 26. Kristofferson, 27. Lasser, 28. Lynn, 29. Martin, 30. Mason, 31. Mastroianni, 32. McDowell, 33. Mercouri, 34. Monroe, 35. Moore, 36. Mull, 37. Nolte, 38. Page, 39. Prentiss, 40. Reagan, 41. Redford, 42. Reiner, 43. Roman, 44. Roundtree, 45. Russell, 46. Ryan, 47. Sidney, 48. Signoret, 49. Spacek, 50. Stallone, 51. Stevens, 52. St. James. 53. Strasberg, 54. Struthers, 55. Vance.

WORD SEEK 20 WORD LIST

Beloved Infidel, Ben-Hur, (The) Big Fix, Born Free, Boom Town, Boys' Town, Cape Fear, Cross Creek, (The) Dirty Dozen, Easter Parade, Ensign Pulver, (A) Free Soul, Goodbye, Mr. Chips, Grand Hotel, High Noon, Jane Eyre, Junior Bonner, King Kong, Kitty Foyle, Lady Luck, (The) Little Prince, Rachel, Rachel, Rooster Cogburn, Stage Coach, Star Wars, The Fan, Top Hat, True Grit, Vera Cruz, (The) Wild Pony, (The) Young Lions.

WORD SEEK 21 WORD LIST

Argentina, Brother, Crystal, Dynamite, Extract, Formal, Gnome, Honey, Insulation, Jodhpurs, Kitchen, Lipstick, Monocle, Nymph, Oyster, Prospector, Quartz, Reward, Spring, Trolley, Unanimous, Vulture, Writer, Xerophyte, Youngster, Zealot.

WORD SEEK 24 WORD LIST

"Autumn Leaves," "Baby Face," "Basie Blues," "Blue Room," "Boogie-Woogie," "Boo-Hoo," "Born Free," "Downtown," "Dream Lover," "Earth Angel," "Easter Parade," "Fiddle Faddle," "For You," "Glow Worm," "Heartaches," "Heat Wave," "High Noon," "Homesick," "It's You," "Java Jive," "Last Date," "Maria Elena," "Mary Anne," "Mona Lisa," "Moonglow," "Night Waltz," "Riff Song," "Rose O'Day," "Rose Room," "Russian Lullaby," "Santa Maria," "Simple Melody," "Star Dust," "Swan Lake."

WORD SEEK 26 WORD LIST

Alibi, Barnstorm, Cannibal, Dummy, Encore, Farthing, Garter, Hedgehog, Illusion, Javelin, Know-how, Liberty, Mackerel, Newcomer, Ocelot, Periscope, Quinine, Ransom, Steak, Throng, Underdog, Villain, Wanton, Xylem, Yarrow, Zephyr.

WORD SEEK 27 WORD LIST

Glove, Ermine, Earn, Normal, Leap, Pretend, Doom, Mirth, Halter, Ripen, Naval, Lope, Eked, Dampen, Noon, North, Hidden, Naphtha, Abound, Dream, Mast, Tend, Decant, Torment, Terror, Rout, Treat, Tried, Dormer, Repeat.

FRAMEWORK 2 REVELATION

A first-grade teacher knows how to make little things count.

FRAMEWORK 5 RELATED WORDS

Brushes, Crayons, Pencils, Markers.

FRAMEWORK 13 REVELATION

Words once spoken can never be recalled.

FRAMEWORK 15 WORD LIST

3: All, Duo, Era, Fin, Has, Hem, Ivy, Lam, Lea, Rue, Spa, Tea, Yen; 4: Auto, Char, Goer, Halo, Horn, Item, Mint, Oven; 5: Apron, Inert; 6: Agenda, Behave, Elicit, Entice, Icicle, Impose, Rustic, Untrue; 7: Algebra, Limited, Lozenge, Nursery, Paragon, Thermos; 8: Ambition, Monotony, Narrator, Protocol.

FRAMEWORK 25 WORD LIST

3 Letters: Den, Dew, Pay; 4 Letters: Amid, Arts, Dial, East, Hare, Late, Loot, Nest, Seam, Tend, Toga, Wean, Wets; 5 Letters: Acted, Attic, Dance, Dream, Hinge, Loyal, Maple, Medal, Peach, Plane, Ridge, State, Weird; 6 Letters: Darted, Dawdle, Donate, Edited, Hoarse, Median, Pierce, Retain.

FRAMEWORK 27 QUOTATION

Keep thy eyes wide open before marriage and half shut afterward.

ESCALATORS

1

SCRAPE	P	SCARE	C	EARS
HOARSE	A	SHORE	H	ROSE
REPAST	P	STARE	A	REST
DECALS	E	SCALD	S	CLAD
ARREST	R	ASTER	E	STAR

2

STAPLE	S	PLATE	P	TALE
ORIENT	I	TENOR	O	RENT
BALLET	L	TABLE	L	BEAT
INVEST	V	STEIN	I	SENT
SEARCH	E	CRASH	S	ARCH
RASHER	R	SHARE	H	SEAR

3

NESTER	S	ENTER	R	TEEN
WHALES	H	SWALE	A	SLEW
ACTION	O	ANTIC	I	CANT
WONDER	W	DRONE	N	RODE
REFINE	E	INFER	I	FERN
PERSON	R	OPENS	N	POSE
ANGERS	S	RANGE	G	NEAR

MASTERWORDS

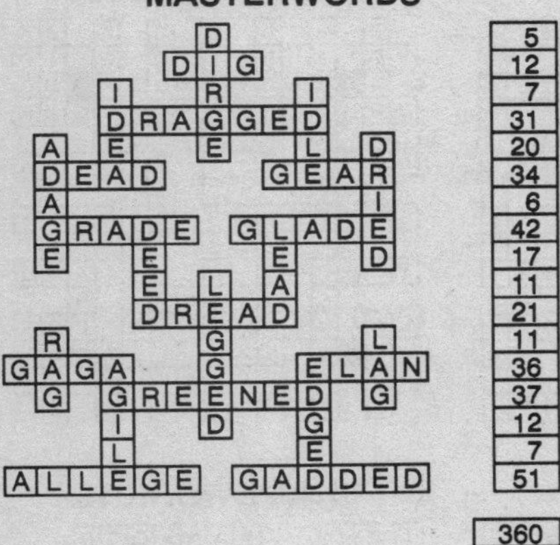

FILL-IN

MAZE

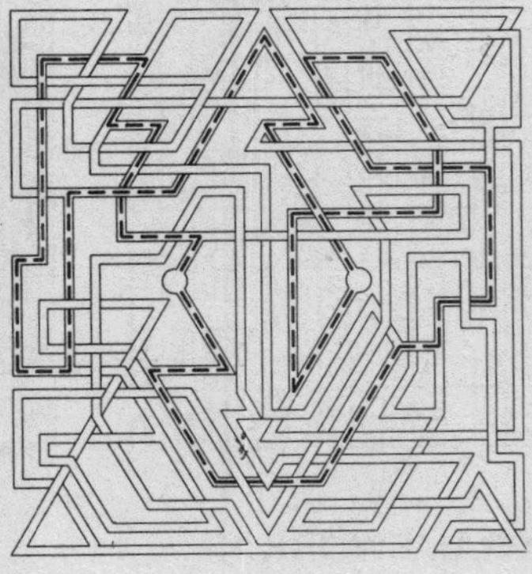

PATHFINDER

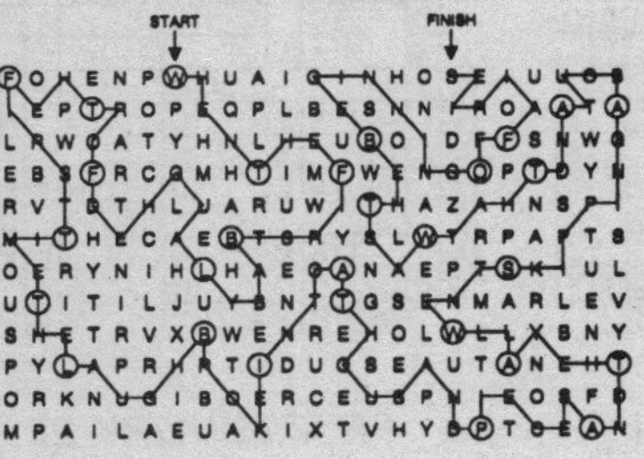

When the first baby laughed for the first time, the laugh broke into a thousand pieces and they all went skipping about and that was the beginning of fairies.

DOUBLE TROUBLE

	TER	SE		BE	T	A		BO	A	S
AC	R	E		T	E	SS		U	R	AL
T	A	D			AL	I		QU	IL	T
		S	PA	T		SI	T	E		
M	AD		N	AS	H		AN	T	L	ER
AD	A		CA	TER	I	N	G		EA	R
RE	M	AR	K		VE	I	L		N	OR
		RE	E	D		LE	E	K		
AL	M	S		AN	DES			NI	AG	ARA
COV	E	T		I	SER	E		F	A	BLE
E	AT	S		EL	T	ON		E	TE	

DOUBLE CROSSER

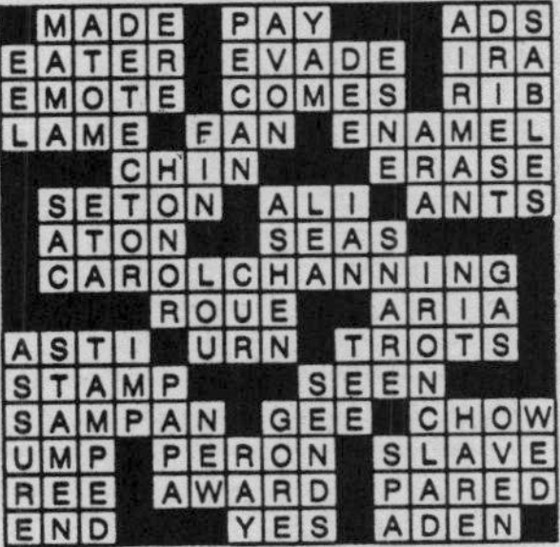

Spring is seldom as slushy as the poetry it inspires.

Author: Carol Channing

PUZZLER

TELECAST

WINDOW BOXES

1-d Hack, 2-e Yolk, 3-h Baby, 4-a Oust, 5-c Kale, 6-j Slim, 7-b Wage, 8-i Rove, 9-f Veal, 10-g Anew.

SYLLACROSTIC

(Baruch) Spinoza: We feel and know that we are eternal.

1. Sacramento, 2. Powwow, 3. Indistinct, 4. Nourish, 5. Ocarina, 6. Zealot, 7. Allow, 8. Windowpane, 9. Ethiopia, 10. Forefinger, 11. Elbe, 12. Exclusive, 13. Limpet, 14. Aptitude, 15. Navigator, 16. Divan, 17. Karma, 18. Normal.

FINISH THE FOURS

FICTIONAL CHARACTER: Captain Kirk

ANAGRAM MAGIC SQUARE

1. Antler, 2. Search, 3. Master, 4. Incase, 5. Lances, 6. Elapse, 7. Ingest, 8. Salver, 9. Melons, 10. Instep, 11. Glares, 12. Hawser, 13. Tracer, 14. Infest, 15. Entrap, 16. Reader, 17. Tinsel, 18. Hoarse, 19. Ardent, 20. Naples, 21. Aprons, 22. Grease, 23. Rebate, 24. Islets, 25. Nadirs.

SAYING: A smile is mightier than a grin.

BULL'S-EYE SPIRAL

OUTWARD: 1. Not, 4. Leek, 8. Aware, 13. Carrot, 19. Cadet, 24. Cider, 29. Presser, 36. Demote, 42. Tabor, 47. Pyle, 51. Villa, 56. Minarets, 64. Atlas, 69. Reveres, 76. Paler.

INWARD: 80. Relapse, 73. Reversal, 65. Taster, 59. Animal, 53. Lively, 47. Probate, 40. Tome, 36. Dresser, 29. Predicted, 20. Actor, 15. Racer, 10. Awake, 5. Elton.

FLOWER POWER

C: 1. Paves, 2. Dozen, 3. Color, 4. Doted, 5. Seder, 6. Sapor, 7. Nosed, 8. Linen, 9. Vowed, 10. Today, 11. Balsa, 12. Laird, 13. Sober, 14. Novel, 15. Cover, 16. Lived, 17. Relet, 18. Rated.

CC: 1. Paler, 2. Dated, 3. Covet, 4. Dozed, 5. Soles, 6. Seton, 7. Nader, 8. Loped, 9. Visor, 10. Toner, 11. Bowed, 12. Laden, 13. Salad, 14. Noisy, 15. Cobra, 16. Loved, 17. River, 18. Revel.

SCOREBOARD

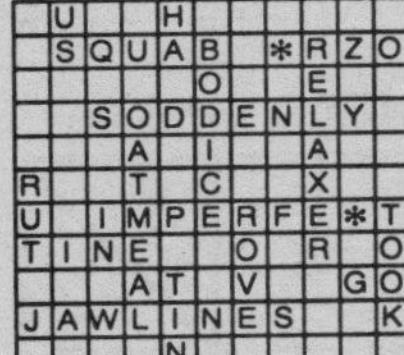

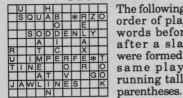

The following is our order of play. The words before and after a slash (/) were formed in the same play. Our running tally is in parentheses.

Dice (4), Per (10), Bodice (16), Squab (26), Perfect (46), Soddenly (84), Imperfect (120), Took (128), Laxer (133), Oatmeal (147), Line (155), Rove (162), Jawline (190), Jawlines (235), In (239), Relaxer (253), Ha (260), Us (264), At/Tin (272), Tine/In (278), Orzo (286), Go (292), Rut (295).

SECRET WORD

1. Vital, 2. Album, 3. Girls, 4. Knots, 5. Snarl, 6. Probe.

1. Nicer, Entry, Crews, Earls, Slice, Swear, Avert, Raven, Yearn.
2. Scrub, Corks, Roman, Amuse, Poems, Block, Ounce, Opals, Karen.
3. Longs, Atone, Sting, Scent, Inert, Eclat, Scare.
4. Maker, Ascot, Cream, Reams, Akron, Marts, Enact.
5. Towed, Adore, Notes, Gnaws, Lodge, Elton.
6. Shine, Epics, Abhor, Robin, Chins, Harps.

DIAL-A-GRAMS

A. A bullfrog's mating call can be heard for about half a mile.

B. Millions of years ago horses were no bigger than cats.

C. A beaver's flat tail is used in swimming and to warn others of danger.

D. The more a female duck quacks, the more her ducklings gather around her.

E. A mole can dig underground as fast as it can walk above ground.

F. Some moths can hear a bat's sonar.

G. A kitten cuts its baby teeth at three to six weeks of age.

H. The pea crab is about the size of the nail on a child's little finger.

I. Both squid and octopus are known as inkfish.

FRAMEWORK 2

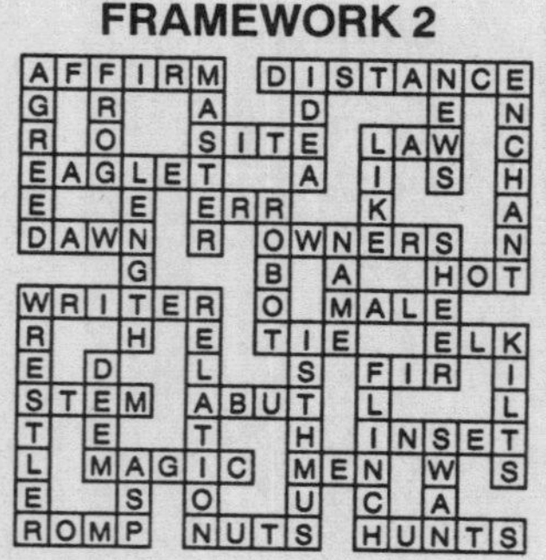

FRAMEWORK 3

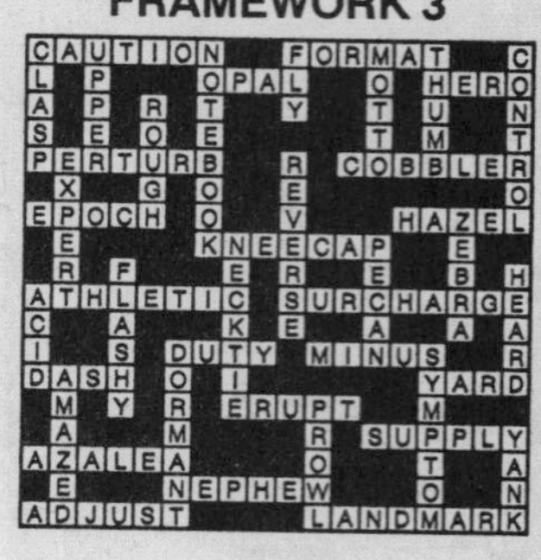

FRAMEWORK 4

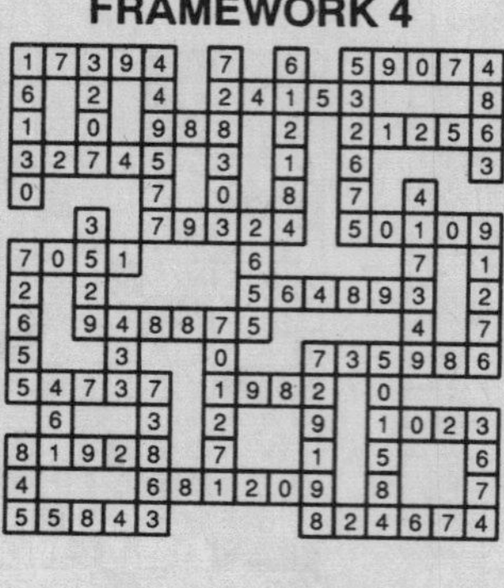

FRAMEWORK 5

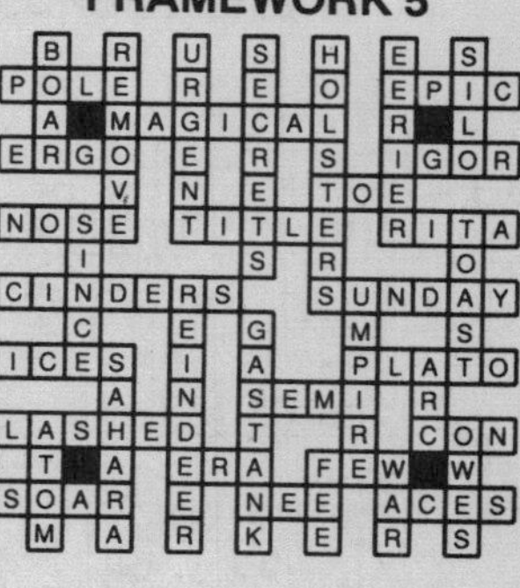

FRAMEWORK 12

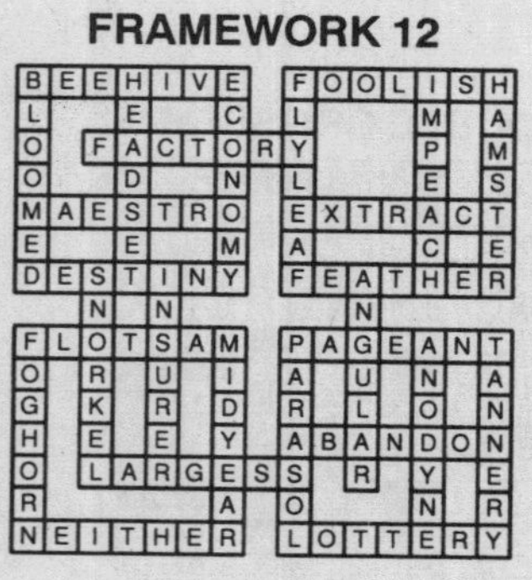

FRAMEWORK 13

FRAMEWORK 14

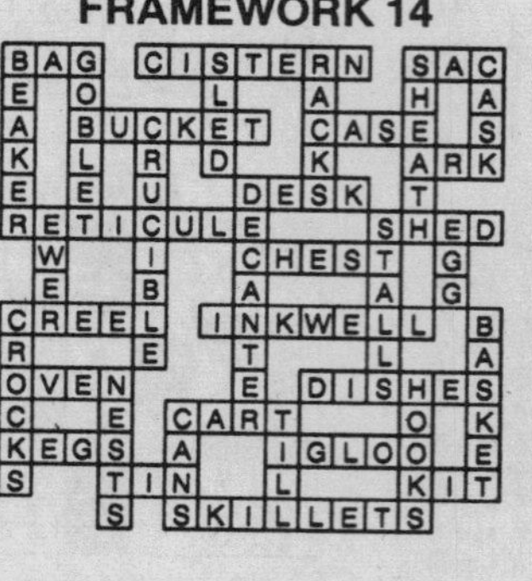

FRAMEWORK 15

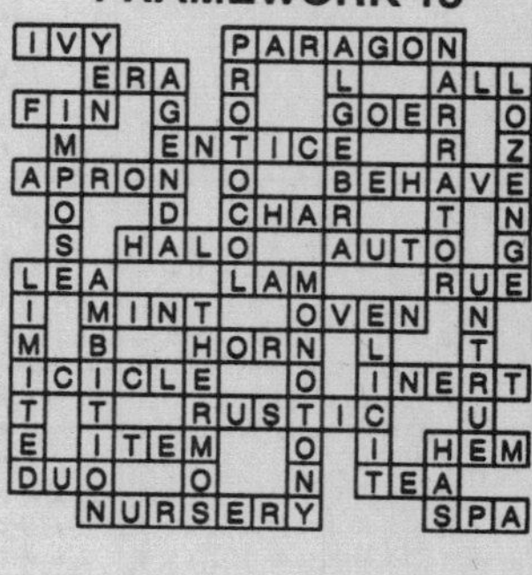

FRAMEWORK 19

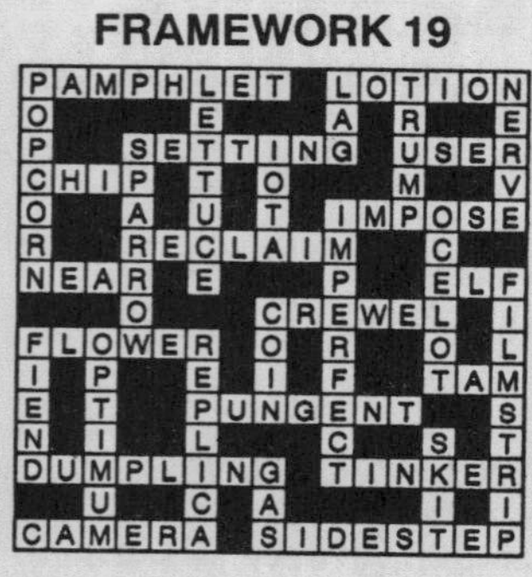

FRAMEWORK 20

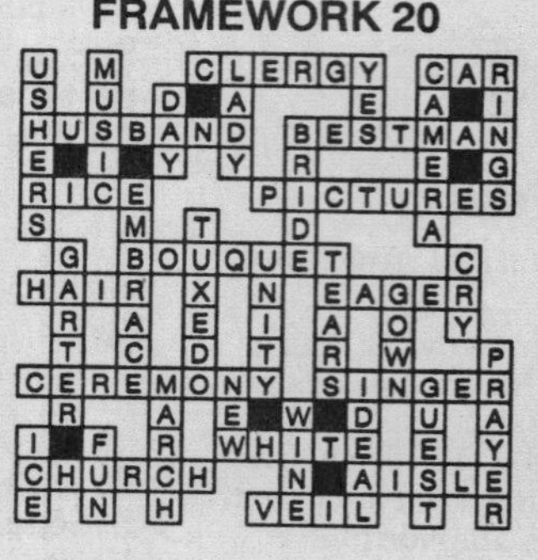

FRAMEWORK 21

FRAMEWORK 22

FRAMEWORK 24

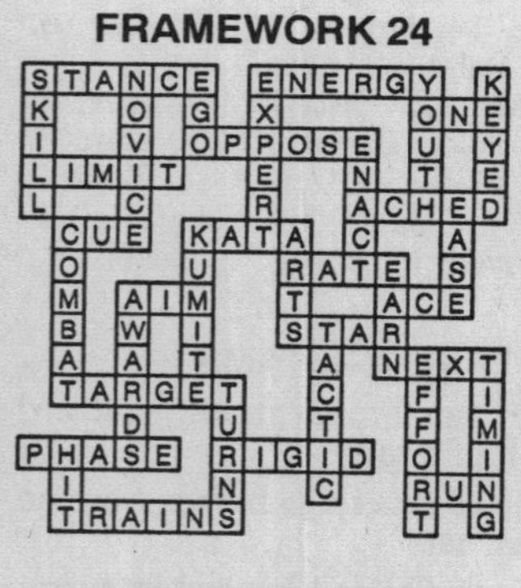

FRAMEWORK 25

FRAMEWORK 26

FRAMEWORK 27

FRAMEWORK 33

FRAMEWORK 34

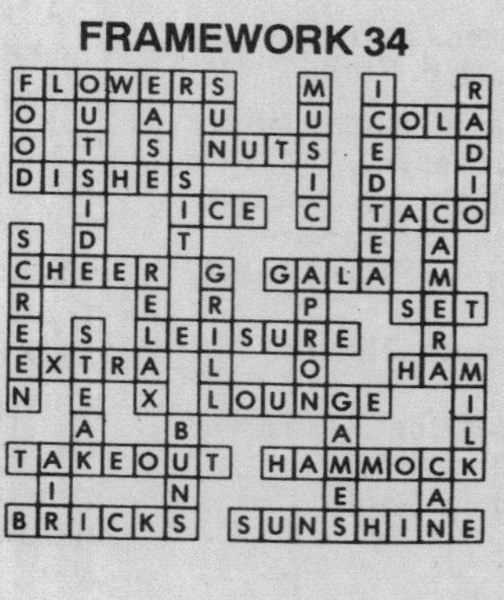

PICTURE THIS

TRIANGLE SUMS

1 9 3
4 2
2 4 2 5 4 1
9 6
5 8 3

FRAMEWORK 1
FRAMEWORK 6
FRAMEWORK 7
FRAMEWORK 8
FRAMEWORK 9
FRAMEWORK 10
FRAMEWORK 11
FRAMEWORK 16
FRAMEWORK 17
FRAMEWORK 18
FRAMEWORK 23
FRAMEWORK 28

FRAMEWORK 29

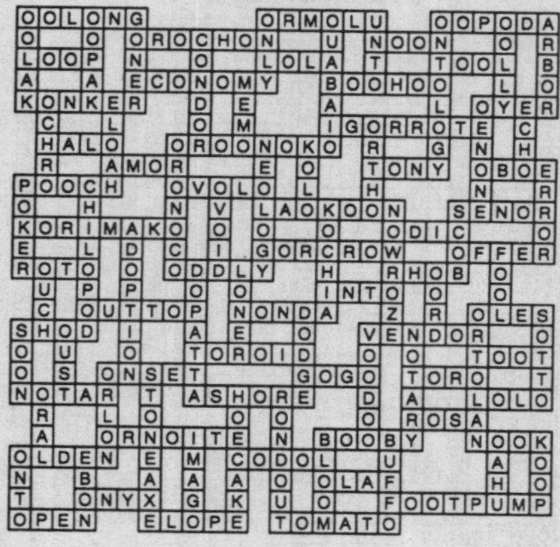

FRAMEWORK 30

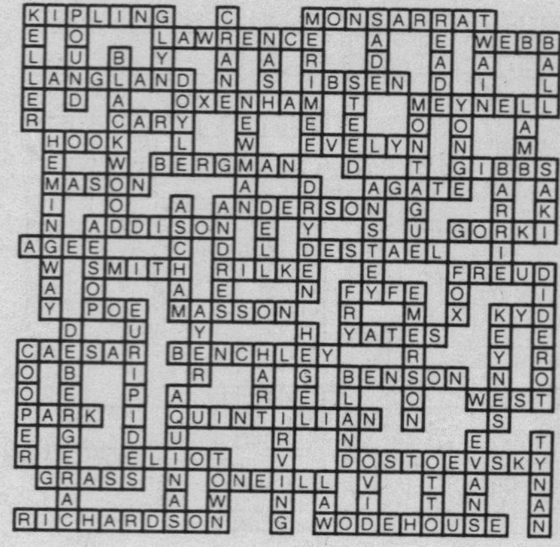

FRAMEWORK 31

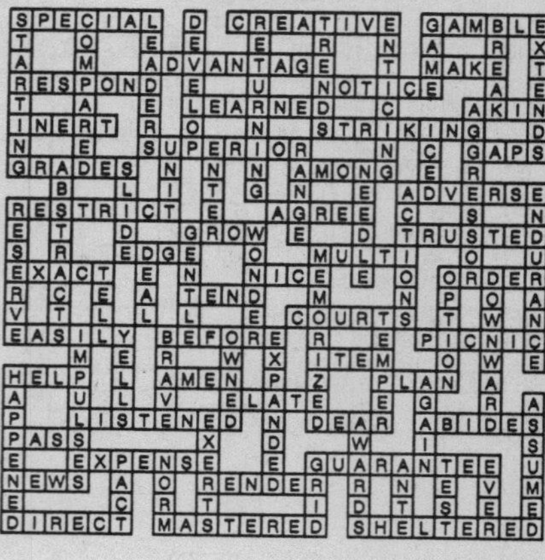

FRAMEWORK 32

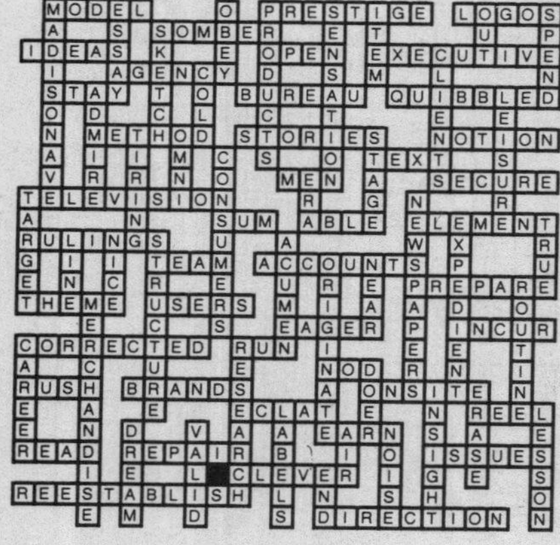

DIAGRAMLESS FILL-IN

STRETCH LETTERS

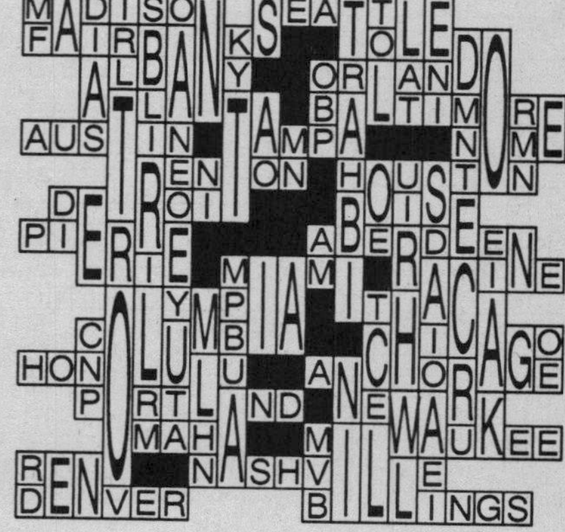

ALPHA QUOTES

1. Etiquette is learning to yawn with your mouth closed.
2. Show me a pharaoh who ate crackers in bed and I'll show you a crummy mummy.

CRYPTO-RIDDLE

QUESTION: What's the difference between a jeweler and a jailer?
ANSWER: One of them is selling watches, while the other one is watching cells.

TWO AT A TIME

1. Legal (E, Z); 2. Wanes (A, K); 3. Shack (I, J); 4. Reeds (V, W); 5. Shore (T, X); 6. Tails (H, Y); 7. Rakes (Q, U); 8. Salad (B, L); 9. Smear (C, P); 10. Riled (D, G); 11. Stain (F, N); 12. Prose (M, R); 13. Revel (O, S).

GIVE AND TAKE

1. Cowl, Scowl, Slow, Plows, Slop, Spoil; 2. Gear, Great, Rate, Heart, Heat, Lathe; 3. Have, Haven, Nave, Raven, Near, Range; 4. Mile, Smile, Lies, Tiles, Lets, Stale; 5. Pine, Spine, Spin, Pains, Span, Spank; 6. Teak, Stake, Sake, Asked, Desk, Decks; 7. Wear, Water, Wart, Straw, Star, Trays.

WHAT'S LEFT?

Hitch your wagon to a star. (Ralph Waldo Emerson)

LETTER SCORE

1. Lion, 2. Numb, 3. Frying, 4. Turtle, 5. Virtue, 6. Music, 7. Rustle, 8. Sugar, 9. Nectar, 10. Atlas.

THROWBACKS

1. Sate, Sale, Sled; 2. Lawn, Lane, Leer; 3. Stem, Seal, Teal; 4. Rent, Rant, Gnat; 5. Edit, Exit, Dirt; 6. Core, Idea, Dire; 7. Sore, Obey, Bray; 8. Yogi, Logo, Polo.

QUOTAGRAMS

A. Education will never become as expensive as ignorance.
B. You grow up the day you have your first real laugh—at yourself.
C. As the arts advance towards their perfection, the science of criticism advances with equal pace.
A: 1. Develop, 2. Beacon, 3. Cerise, 4. Axioms, 5. Winning, 6. Crease, 7. Eventual.
B: 1. Helpful, 2. Year, 3. Varsity, 4. Wharf, 5. Loose, 6. Uruguay, 7. Youth, 8. Toady, 9. Rogue.
C: 1. Coquette, 2. Sprit, 3. Cheetahs, 4. Tainted, 5. Showcase, 6. Miniver, 7. Wildfire, 8. France, 9. Vacation, 10. Chapter, 11. Cascades.

HEXAGRAMS

Largess, Lasagna, Abstain, Yardage, Pertain, Doorway, Wiretap, Petrify, Forward, Therapy, Theater.

HEADINGS

1. Sapphire, Ruby, Zircon, Diamond, Peridot, Jasper, Spinel.
2. Dealer, Price, Options, Warranty, Model, Lights, Shift.
3. Corset, Plume, Shawl, Tabard, Pinafore, Bustle, Oxfords.

SPELLBOUND

1. Lazy (4), Inquest (7), Avow (4), Pecking (7), Major (5), Helix (5), Brads (5), Often (5), Much (4), Windy (5), Ruches (6).
TOTAL: 57 + 10 = 67
2. Toxin (5), Mark (4), Plexus (6), Conga (5), Whiskey (7), Plumb (5), Wizen (5), Adjust (6), Wolf (4), Acquire (7), Vows (4).
TOTAL: 58 + 10 = 68

MATCHMAKER

Sunday-Tuesday, Upset-Irate, Penny-Candy, Easter-Eggs, Rice-Xavier, Cute-Pretty, Active-Inert, Los-Angeles, Iguana-Lizard, Free-Independent, Radio-Dial, Apparent-Obvious, Grade-Class, Illinois-Indiana, Lemon-Orange, Iota-Upsilon, Sweet-Sour.
SONG TITLE: Supercalifragilisticexpialidocious

ALPHABET SOUP

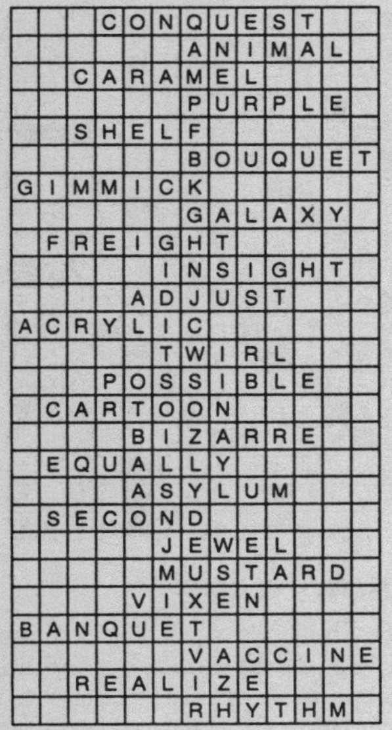

HOW MANY SQUARES?

28

CROSS NUMBERS

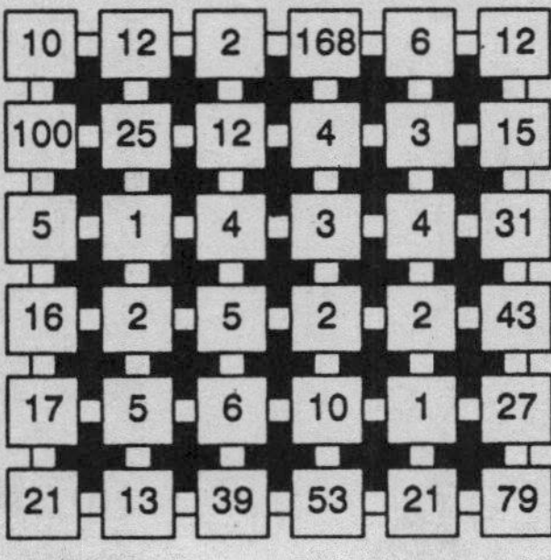

CRACKERJACKS

FORGER

RINGERS

1. Break, Slant, Probe, Flood; 2. Facet, Audio, Order, Dogma; 3. Grant, Unite, Ranch, Angle; 4. Sharp, Eagle, Brook, Dodge; 5. Ounce, Wharf, Hotel, Lucky.

PLACE YOUR NUMBER

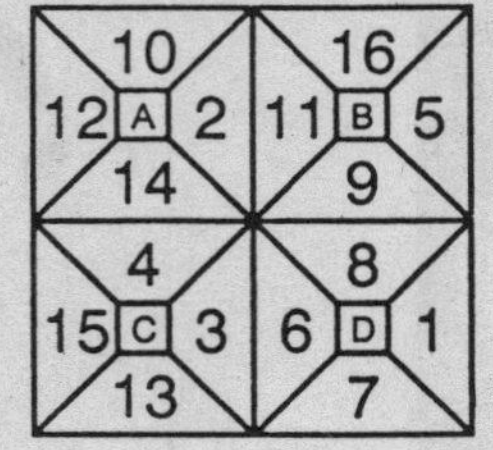

LETTER TILES

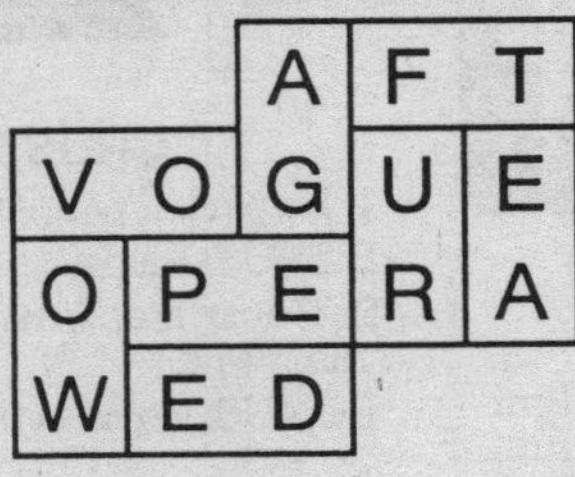

LINE 'EM UP

MADEMOISELLE

BRICK BY BRICK

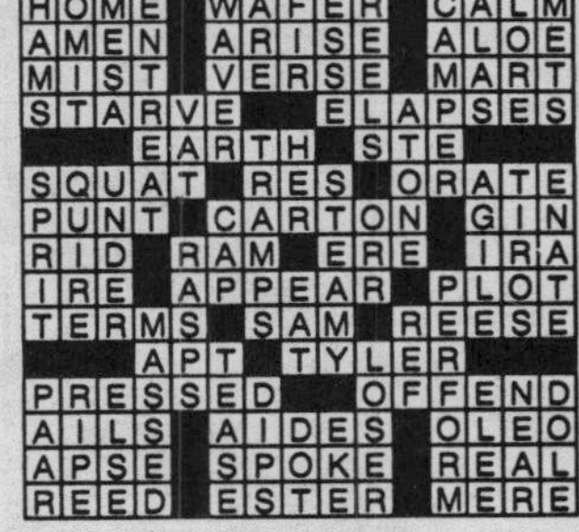

BUILD-A-PYRAMID

I
IN
NIL
NAIL
ALIEN
ENTAIL
RELIANT
TERMINAL

PYRAMID POWER

1. Allude, 2. Caller, 3. Camper, 4. Danced, 5. Depend, 6. Edgers, 7. Eludes, 8. Lender, 9. Lesser, 10. Orders, 11. Relish, 12. Repels, 13. Resort, 14. Rushed, 15. Silver, 16. Vessel.

CRYPTO-FAMILIES

1. WIZARD: Ruby slippers, Wicked witch, Munchkins, Emerald City, Cowardly Lion, Auntie Em, Scarecrow, Dorothy, Tin Man, Toto.
2. CHINESE: Fried rice, Peking duck, Sesame noodles, Wonton soup, Lo Mein, Lemon chicken, Happy family, Egg roll, Moo shu, Shrimp toast.
3. TRADEMARKED: Walkman, Thermos, Kleenex, Band-Aid, Pyrex, Velcro, Scotch Tape, Tylenol, Popsicle, Rolodex.
4. LEADERS: Patton, Montgomery, Mark Antony, Dayan, Napoleon, Eisenhower, Lee, Alexander, Genghis Khan, Washington.
5. CARTOONISTS: Trudeau, Breathed, Disney, Larson, Guisewite, Browne, Hart, Watterson, Addams, Groening.
6. "ION": Champ, Content, Recess, Divers, Obsess, Intent, Mans, Port, Accord, Tract.

DIAMOND RINGS

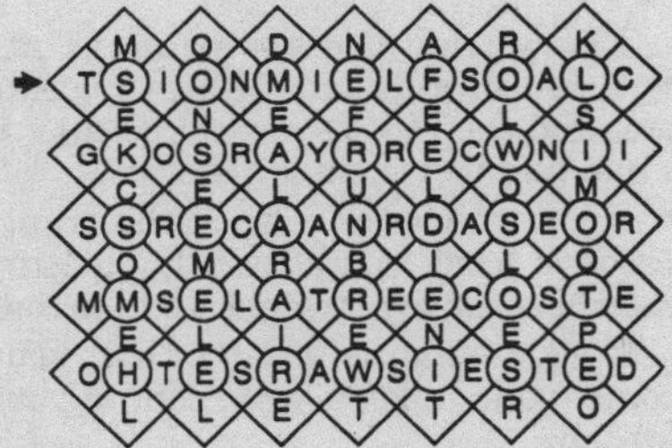

1. Smite, 2. Onion, 3. Mined, 4. Elfin, 5. False, 6. Orals, 7. Lacks, 8. Gecko, 9. Norse, 10. Relay, 11. Furry, 12. Creel, 13. Clown, 14. Minis, 15. Cross, 16. Creme, 17. Clara, 18. Urban, 19. Laird, 20. Aloes, 21. Romeo, 22. Memos, 23. Smell, 24. Trail, 25. Beret, 26. Niece, 27. Close, 28. Estop, 29. Thole, 30. Tells, 31. Aries, 32. Sweat, 33. Tines, 34. Ester, 35. Depot.
T(obias) G. Smollett, Roderick Random: Some folks are wise, and some are otherwise.

MATCH-UP

6 and 10 match. (Differences: 1. Napkin, 2. Tablecloth, 3. Chair seat, 4. No ring around chair legs, 5. No flower or wine glass, 7. No rope on wine bottle, 8. Missing chair leg, 9. Table legs, 11. Coffee pot and cup, 12. Chair back.)

WORD MATH

	0	1	2	3	4	5	6	7	8	9
1.	H	Y	P	O	C	R	I	T	E	S
2.	G	R	A	N	D/H	O	T	E	L	S
3.	T	H	U	M	B	N	A	I	L	S
4.	S	O/G	R	A	C	E	F	U	L	
5.	B	R	I	N	G	S/H	O	M	E	
6.	W	H	I	T	E/F	L	A	G	S	

CODEWORD

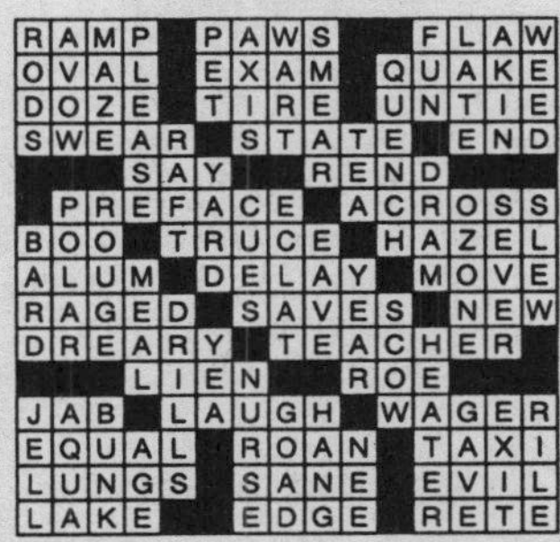

1-S, 2-A, 3-P, 4-O, 5-Q, 6-Y, 7-B, 8-Z, 9-X, 10-U, 11-L, 12-K, 13-C, 14-T, 15-E, 16-G, 17-D, 18-W, 19-I, 20-V, 21-N, 22-M, 23-F, 24-H, 25-R, 26-J.

ESCALATORS

1

GAMBLE	G	BLAME	M	BALE
SOLELY	O	YELLS	Y	SELL
AWHILE	I	WHALE	W	HEAL
ABSENT	N	BASTE	A	BETS
ARGYLE	G	RELAY	Y	EARL

2

REMISS	S	MISER	M	SIRE
CABALS	C	BALSA	A	SLAB
HONEST	H	SETON	S	NOTE
COATED	O	CADET	T	ACED
ASHORE	O	SHARE	E	RASH
CELLAR	L	CLEAR	R	LACE

3

STEAMS	S	MATES	M	TEAS
OUSTER	U	STORE	O	REST
RENTAL	N	ALTER	R	TEAL
RANSOM	R	MOANS	N	AMOS
INSIDE	I	DINES	I	ENDS
STONES	S	ONSET	N	TOES
EAGLES	E	GALES	G	LEAS

DIAGRAMLESS FILL-IN

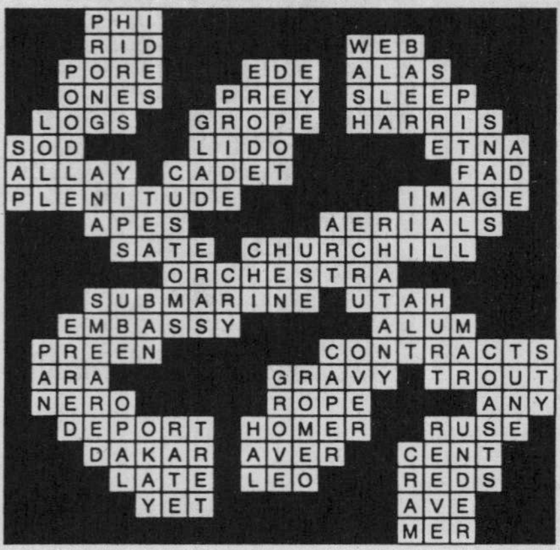

LETTER POWER

1. Missouri (10), 2. Martini (14), 3. Ignition (28), 4. Chromium (25), 5. Zucchini (34), 6. Hibiscus (42), 7. Macaroni (41), 8. Puccini (54), 9. Pizzeria (50), 10. Marzipan (55).

FLOWER POWER

C: 1. Toque, 2. Niter, 3. Pilot, 4. Sense, 5. Merry, 6. Torah, 7. Wedge, 8. Touch, 9. Torch, 10. Banty, 11. Funny, 12. Bonne, 13. Minot, 14. Value, 15. Chose, 16. Clash, 17. Fence, 18. Letup.

CC: 1. Tense, 2. Notch, 3. Pique, 4. Situp, 5. Melee, 6. Tenor, 7. Worst, 8. Terre, 9. Today, 10. Bough, 11. Farce, 12. Bunch, 13. Month, 14. Vinny, 15. Canny, 16. Chloe, 17. Flout, 18. Lease.

SECRET WORD

1. Scout, 2. Dares, 3. Smock,
4. Mount, 5. Gives, 6. Scrap.

1. Paint, Andes, Tiers, Hopes, Force, Infer, Nudge, Dutch, Eight, Rouge; 2. Cling, Hardy, Angel, Latch, Linda, Egypt, Niche, Grind, Epics, Style; 3. Carol, Omits, Vista, Evict, Ravel, Alike, Limes, Lakes; 4. Munch, Chile, Kilts, Inlet, Noise, Locks, Emily, Youth; 5. Doing, Ogled, Novel, Adorn, Trial, Evans, Stern; 6. Ripen, Emits, Media, Napes, Acrid, Nicer, Timed.

SCOREMASTER

J	U	S	T							M
I		Q						S		O
B		U					S	P	U	N
		I						A		E
		R						R		Y
	T	E	A	C	H			K		
D	O				E	L	F	I	N	
A			W		X			N		
Z			O					G		
E			R							
D	O	V	E	T	A	I	L			

The following is our order of play. The words before and after a slash (/) were formed in the same play. Scores are given in parentheses.

Each (12), Re (6), To/Teach (34), El/He (9), Ire (8), Do (7), Elf (6), Daze (16), Squire (32), Elfin (18), Dazed (54), Kin (18), Just (36), King (24), Jib (33), Parking (60), Dove (24), Spun (20), Hex (13), Ore (6), Dovetail (54), Money (57), Wore (10), Sparking (64).

PICTURE THIS

CROSSBLOCKS

1. Pa/p/a/l, S/p/inn/ing, St/r/e/am, Mi/rr/o/r.
BONUS: Pa/p/e/r

2. Co/ur/s/e, I/ns/tru/ct, Deb/a/ta/ble, Ta/ng/e/nt.
BONUS: Co/ns/ta/nt

CRYPTOGRAMS

1. To overcome writer's block, get something — anything — down on paper. Don't wait for perfection to issue forth. Since the key to good writing is re-writing, give yourself something to edit.

2. Every time the government attempts to handle our affairs it costs more, and the results are worse than if we had handled them ourselves.

3. If you think the way of the transgressor is hard, you should try getting somewhere on the straight and narrow.

4. If your outgo is greater than your income, your upkeep will soon be your downfall.

5. Men are more important than tools. If you don't believe it, put a good tool in the hands of a poor workman.

6. Autumn is the most beautiful time of the year to the person who has no leaves to rake.

7. When some men discharge an obligation, you can hear the report for miles around.

8. A lot of molehills become mountains when someone adds a little dirt.

9. Some people think that the U.S. Weather Bureau is a perfect example of a non-prophet organization.

10. A rich man is one who is never afraid to ask the clerk to show him something cheaper.

11. Destiny shapes our ends, but a reducing diet also helps.

12. Something that has been greatly cheapened by overproduction is legislation.

13. Quarrels would not last long if the fault were on one side only.

14. Fill your waterbed with beer and get a foam mattress.

15. They say bad news travels fast — unless you mail it.

16. The biggest fish are caught by the tale.

FILL-IN

C	H	I	P		B	E	E	S		S	L	I	P		P	E	L	F
L	O	D	E		E	A	R	N		T	O	N	E		O	D	O	R
A	V	E	R		G	R	E	A	T	A	U	N	T		L	I	N	E
P	E	A	S	O	U	P		P	O	R	T		U	N	I	T	E	D
			I	A	N		S	P	O	T		S	L	A	T			
T	R	E	A	T		P	O	E	T		S	H	A	M	E	F	U	L
W	O	R	N		P	U	R	R		P	L	A	N	E		A	P	E
I	D	A		G	A	P	E		H	E	A	R	T		R	I	O	T
T	E	D	I	O	U	S		L	E	A	S	E		H	O	R	N	S
		I	D	O	L		T	E	A	C	H		J	U	L	Y		
R	I	C	E	D		G	R	A	P	E		C	A	M	E	L	O	T
E	R	A	S		W	E	E	D	S		P	U	M	P		A	G	O
D	O	T		P	A	N	E	S		C	A	B	S		K	N	E	W
O	N	E	S	I	D	E	D		D	O	S	E		H	I	D	E	S
			E	N	D	S		P	O	U	T		M	E	N			
S	H	O	V	E	L		S	E	E	N		D	A	N	G	L	E	S
L	O	P	E		E	N	T	E	R	T	A	I	N		D	O	V	E
O	M	A	R		R	E	E	L		E	R	R	S		O	V	E	R
G	E	L	S		S	E	W	S		R	A	T	E		M	E	R	E

BOWL GAME

STRIKES: 1. Chessboard, 2. Jackknives, 3. Poinsettia, 4. Coordinate, 5. Butterball, 6. Kinematics, 7. Ingratiate, 8. Waitresses, 9. Licentious, 10. Retrospect.

SPARES: 1. Beach, Dross; 2. Jives, Knack; 3. Poise, Titan; 4. Antic, Rodeo; 5. Bleat, Blurt; 6. Kites, Manic; 7. Giant, Irate; 8. Sties, Swear; 9. Coils, Unite; 10. Erect, Sport.

LOGIC PROBLEM

(Clue numbers in parentheses)

Dates are June 4, 8, 15, 16, and 20 (intro.). Dr. Ambs [earlier than 2 others (3)] isn't June 20; he's June 4, and Dr. Carroll is June 20 (4). Ms. Allen is 4 days after Dr. Ambs [June 4] (3); she's June 8. Dr. Carroll [June 20] didn't go to Michigan (2), Harvard (4), Ohio [before 2 others (5)], or Kansas [before 2 others (6)]; she went to Columbia. Her fiance isn't Dr. Ambs [June 4], Mr. Black (1), Mr. Lambert (2), or Mr. Reed [before 1 other (6)]; he's Mr. Kline. Ms. Harvey [before Mr. Lambert and after Ohio couple (5)] isn't June 16 [Mr. Kline June 20] or June 4 (5); she's June 15, and Mr. Lambert is June 16. Ms. Garrison [after 2 others (6)] isn't June 4; she's June 16. Ms. Jackson is June 4. Mr. Lambert [June 16] didn't go to Michigan (2), Ohio [before 2 others (5)], or Kansas [before 2 others (6)]; he went to Harvard. The Michigan couple [just after Mr. Black (7)] isn't June 4 or June 8 [Dr. Ambs June 4]; they're June 15, and Mr. Black is June 8. Mr. Reed is June 15. Mr. Black didn't go to Kansas (1); Dr. Ambs did. Mr. Black went to Ohio.

In summary:

Ms. Allen, Mr. Black, Ohio, June 8

Dr. Carroll, Mr. Kline, Columbia, June 20

Ms. Garrison, Mr. Lambert, Harvard, June 16

Ms. Harvey, Mr. Reed, Michigan, June 15

Ms. Jackson, Dr. Ambs, Kansas, June 4

DOUBLE OCCUPANCY

BE	LI	EF		AL	LU	DE		CU	DG	EL
HE		FI	AS	CO		TO	MA	TO		DE
ST	IN	GY		VE	LO	UR		UT	TE	RS
	VA				CA				ET	
RE	DE	EM		CU	TE	ST		FI	ER	CE
BA		PI	KE	RS		AI	MI	NG		AS
TE	NU	RE		ED	GE	RS		ER	AS	ES
	AN				NE				CE	
AC	CE	DE		CA	RA	FE		BU	ND	LE
TI		MO	ME	NT		LI	NI	NG		AR
ON	IO	NS		ER	MI	NE		LE	MO	NS

HOW MANY TRIANGLES?

24 (ADF, AFG, BEH, BGH, CDG, CEG, CFG, CFH, CGH, CIJ, CIK, CIP, CJK, CKP, DFG, EGH, IJP, IKP, IOP, JKP, KPQ, LMP, LNP, MNP)

FILL 'ER UP

Snowy, Polite, Embark, Slender, Market, Utopia, Crunch, Definite, Shatter, Paper, Appoint, Scraggly, Element, Lasagna, Aghast, Parody, Thermos, Orator, Turnip, Spigot.

BOWL GAME

STRIKES: 1. Consecrate, 2. Determined, 3. Birthstone, 4. Transistor, 5. Mechanical, 6. Impersonal, 7. Tenderloin, 8. Outlandish, 9. Paintbrush, 10. Theatrical. SPARES: 1. Scone, Trace; 2. Ended, Merit; 3. Stein, Throb; 4. Snort, Stair; 5. Camel, Chain; 6. Prime, Salon; 7. Liner, Noted; 8. Hound, Tails; 9. Habit, Spurn; 10. Cheat, Trail.

CLASSIFIED ADDS

1. Tea, Alabama, Abel, Ladybug, Gum.
2. Brandy, Yes, Shem, Mosquito, Oak.
3. Water, Rush, Hiram, Mayfly, Yew.
4. Cola, Aerosmith, Hosea, Aphid, Dogwood.
5. Milk, Kansas, Saul, Louse, Elm.
6. Stout, Traffic, Caleb, Bumble bee, Eucalyptus.
7. Rum, Metallica, Abraham, Moth, Hemlock.
8. Root beer, R.E.M., Moses, Scarab, Bayberry.

SCOREBOARD

Q	U	I	T	S						
				W	A	G	*	S		
				A					*	
		B	O	N	E	R			N	
	T		Z			U			J	
F	A	V	O	R	E	D			O	
	X		N		R	E	L	A	Y	S
P	I	L	E				O			U
A							T	E	R	M
T	H	I	C	K	E	N	S		I	
									D	O

The following is our order of play. The words before and after a slash (/) were formed in the same play. Our running tally is in parentheses.

Favored (33), On (37), Zone (45), Ax (53), Tax (62), Taxi (72), Bone/Ozone (87), Boner (99), Wan (107), Swan (116), Its (119), Quits (129), Rude (143), Pat/Pi (155), Wag (163), Wage (172), Wages (192), Er/Re (199), Relay (207), Joy (210), Thick (234), Thicken (262), Sum/Relays (286), Lots/Thickens (339), Term (347), Enjoy (354), Rid (361), Pile (365), Do (367).

WEAVER WORDS

E	R	A	R	E	A	Y	E	S	C	A	R	P	S	E	E	P	H	A	R	A	O	H	O	V
E	K	R	A	V	D	R	A	A	T	R	O	A	I	R	E	M	A	E	R	E	Y	A	L	E
G	S	A	M	O	O	D	S	E	R	B	U	R	L	A	P	I	L	L	A	R	E	S	T	R
N	A	V	E	D	O	R	E	L	I	M	S	E	E	T	A	E	L	I	N	I	A	L	I	A
I	G	E	L	A	M	A	D	I	E	U	T	E	N	S	I	L	O	A	G	O	R	A	L	L
R	A	R	O	T	E	W	O	N	S	M	I	R	T	U	N	L	A	W	E	N	I	S	E	I
A	B	O	R	N	E	O	M	A	H	A	L	F	A	L	F	A	N	E	W	E	B	E	R	M
N	A	Y	R	A	T	C	E	N	I	H	T	R	O	P	U	T	E	S	E	R	I	M	A	I
S	N	E	E	L	S	I	P	A	N	S	I	E	S	A	L	A	D	E	R	E	K	I	T	S

LOOSE TILE

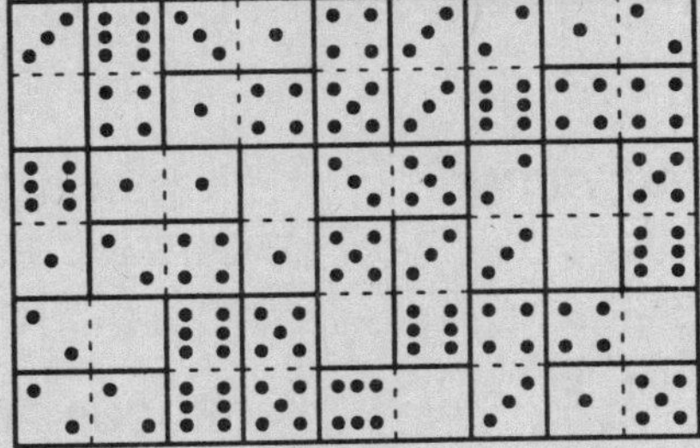

The 2-5 is the loose tile.

MIDDLE OF THE ROAD

A back seat driver never runs out of gas.

WORD MATH

1. Blacksmith, 2. Beauty shop, 3. Nightmares.

TAKE A LETTER

1. Artist, Farmer, Intern; 2. Editor, Notary, Parson; 3. Etcher, Marine, Waiter; 4. Critic, Doctor, Ensign; 5. Lawyer, Typist, Warden.

WORD MERGERS

1. Her, Tag; Gather.
2. Bin, Elm; Nimble.
3. Rich, She; Cherish.
4. Lore, Tub; Trouble.
5. Lay, Quit; Quality.
6. Cane, Glee; Elegance.
7. Pear, Seat; Separate.
8. China, Roam; Harmonica.

LOGIC PROBLEM

(Clue numbers in parentheses)

Floors are 1st, 3rd, 4th, 7th, and 10th (intro.). Robert [4th floor (6)] didn't plant wandering Jew [10th floor (3)], caladium [Maria (4)], English ivy [3rd floor (5)], or fern (6); he planted coleus. Grace [zinnia (2)] didn't plant wandering Jew (2) or English ivy [petunias (5)]; she planted fern. Sarah didn't plant English ivy (1); Ernest did. Sarah planted wandering Jew. Maria doesn't live on the 1st floor (4); Grace does. Maria lives on the 7th floor. Maria [7th floor] didn't plant begonias (4) or marigolds (7); she planted pansies. Sarah didn't plant begonias (1); Robert did. Sarah planted marigolds.

In summary:
Ernest, 3rd, petunia, English ivy
Grace, 1st, zinnia, fern
Maria, 7th, pansy, caladium
Robert, 4th, begonia, coleus
Sarah, 10th, marigold, wandering Jew

MATHBOXES

A.

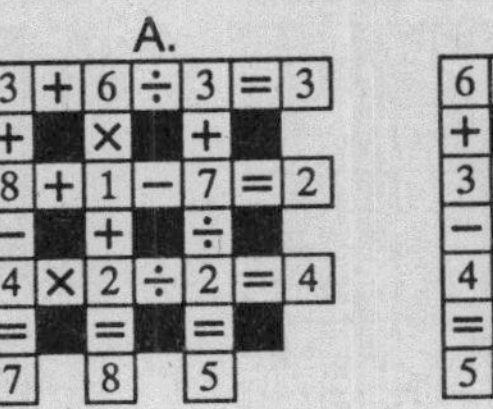

B.

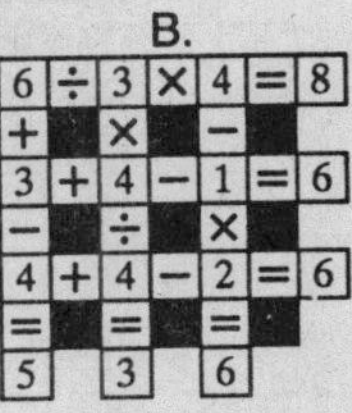

SCRAMBLED HEADWEAR

Beanie, Bowler, Cloche, Fedora, Helmet, Panama, Turban, Wimple.

BITS AND PIECES

1. Madrid, Spain; 2. Brussels, Belgium; 3. Copenhagen, Denmark; 4. Helsinki, Finland; 5. Vienna, Austria; 6. Paris, France.

FOUR-FIT

1. Linguist, 2. Expedite, 3. Culinary, 4. Unsteady, 5. Progress, 6. Adorable, 7. Interior, 8. Pleasant, 9. Simulate, 10. Pharmacy, 11. Employee, 12. Waitress, 13. Commence, 14. Escapade, 15. Ignorant.

GIVE AND TAKE

1. Open, Phone, Hone, Shone, Shoe, House; 2. Head, Shade, Dash, Hands, Sand, Stand; 3. Line, Alien, Lane, Clean, Cane, Dance; 4. Card, Chard, Hard, Shard, Rash, Sharp; 5. Name, Meant, Mate, Metal, Tale, Plate; 6. Race, Scare, Sear, Arose, Sore, Horse; 7. Land, Laden, Lead, Ideal, Idle, Slide; 8. Fast, Facts, Cast, Stack, Tack, Track; 9. Hard, Heard, Herd, Hired, Ride, Wired; 10. Time, Merit, Term, Tamer, Mare, Frame.

SYLLACROSTIC

(Eleanor) Roosevelt: No one can make you feel inferior without your consent. 1. Reciprocal, 2. Origami, 3. Ottoman, 4. Stroganoff, 5. Elucidate, 6. Vancouver, 7. Egadi, 8. Libretto, 9. Taylor, 10. Narrow, 11. Operandi, 12. Outfit, 13. Naismith, 14. Embargo, 15. Caribou, 16. Abolitionist, 17. Notoriety, 18. Mikado, 19. Aracaju, 20. Kindergartner, 21. Egocentric, 22. Yevtushenko, 23. Objection, 24. Umbrellas, 25. Felicitate, 26. Equestrian, 27. Exuberant.

QUOTAGRAMS

A. People like to praise those who praise them.
B. A professor is someone who talks in someone else's sleep.
C. The exact contrary of what is generally believed is often the truth.

A: 1. Sophia, 2. Keeper, 3. Mohair, 4. Tiptoe, 5. Theses, 6. Powell.
B: 1. Lesson, 2. Slope, 3. Seesaw, 4. Insane, 5. Simple, 6. Soothe, 7. Smoke, 8. Roofer.
C: 1. Wealth, 2. Alone, 3. Vanish, 4. Teeth, 5. Trudge, 6. Crafty, 7. Other, 8. Before, 9. Sixty, 10. Client.

ALPHABET SOUP

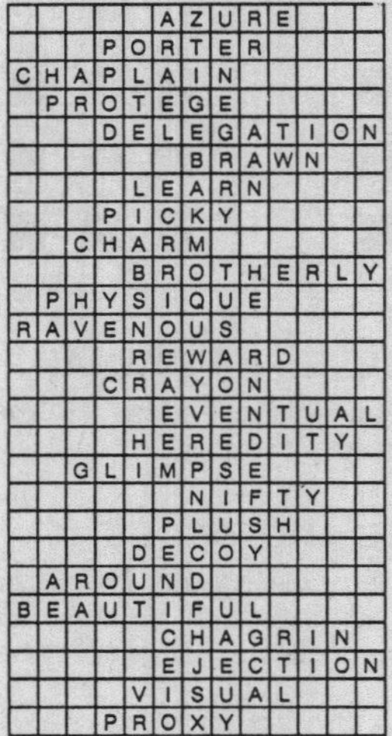

CRACKERJACKS

A G/RO/AN/ MAN

PLACE YOUR NUMBER

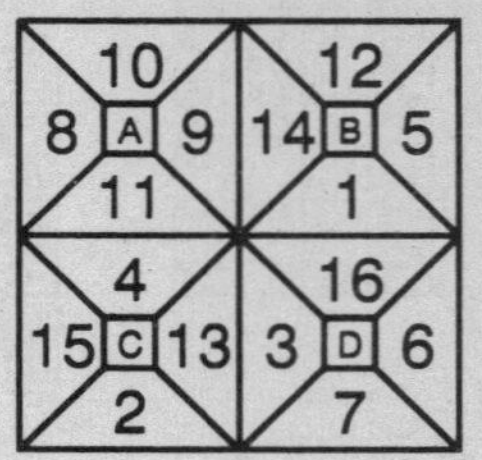

BUILD-A-PYRAMID

A
AN
VAN
VANE
NAIVE
NATIVE
VINTAGE
NEGATIVE

NUMBER SLEUTH

DART GAME

Habit, Havoc, Hello, Honey, Humid.

HOCUS-POCUS

1. Logic, 2. Apron, 3. Wrath, 4. Yodel, 5. Prune, 6. Flash, 7. Hotel, 8. Knead.
8-LETTER WORD: Graduate

SUM TOTALS

KEYWORD

OUTLANDISH

BORROW AND SCORE

1. Adopt, 2. Tardy, 3. Dainty, 4. Ration, 5. Pertain, 6. Chapter, 7. Particle, 8. Percolate.
SCORE: 89.

DOUBLE TROUBLE

WH	E	RE		TR	A	P	PER		CHU	TE
O	VE	N		E	LL	E	RY		R	AM
SE	N	T		A	S	TER		A	CH	ED
		S	HU	T		S	TO	VE		
PA	RIS		LA	MEN	T		TE	N	DE	R
ST	E	EL		T	HE	SE		GER	M	AN
ED	S	E	L		DA	N	TE		UR	GE
		C	ODE	S		TI	AR	A		
ST	A	TED		P	AN	NE		ST	I	LE
AB	BE		M	EN	TA	L		AI	SLE	S
LE	TS		AC	T	RES	S		RE	S	T

FLOWER POWER

C: 1. Scene, 2. Spice, 3. Olive, 4. Close, 5. Shane, 6. Shone, 7. Cloud, 8. Algae, 9. Crete, 10. Aroma, 11. Brink, 12. Wreck, 13. Peach, 14. Glass, 15. Snarl, 16. Small, 17. Soils, 18. Shunt.
CC: 1. Shill, 2. Scull, 3. Opens, 4. Clint, 5. Slice, 6. Shove, 7. Chase, 8. Alone, 9. Clone, 10. Argue, 11. Bread, 12. Wrote, 13. Prime, 14. Geena, 15. Slack, 16. Snack, 17. Smash, 18. Soars.

ESCALATORS

1

COWERS	W	SCORE	C	ROSE
BRAISE	I	SABER	R	BASE
COUNTS	N	SCOUT	U	COTS
TIRADE	T	AIRED	I	READ
ELAPSE	E	PEALS	S	LEAP
WONDER	R	ENDOW	E	DOWN

2

CARPET	A	CREPT	C	PERT
HOSTEL	L	THOSE	H	TOES
PLEASE	P	EASEL	A	ELSE
RETAIL	I	ALTER	L	TEAR
TINDER	N	TRIED	E	DIRT
LATHES	E	HALTS	T	LASH

3

CHARGE	H	GRACE	G	CARE
ORIOLE	O	OILER	O	RILE
CASTLE	C	STALE	A	LETS
ANKLES	K	LANES	L	SANE
DEFILE	E	FIELD	I	FLED
SURELY	Y	LURES	E	SLUR

CODEWORD

S	K	Y	L	I	G	H	T		J	U	M	P	E	R
Q		O		N		O		Z		N		R		E
U	S	U	A	L		W	R	E	S	T	L	I	N	G
I		N		E				A		O		Z		A
R	I	G	H	T	F	U	L	L	Y		C	E	L	L
R		S				N				S				E
E	N	T	R	A	N	C	E	D		K	E	P	T	
L		E		X		L		E		I		R		P
	F	R	E	E		E	X	T	E	N	S	I	V	E
B				S				E				V		R
U	P	O	N		J	O	U	R	N	A	L	I	S	M
B		C		S		U				L		L		E
B	A	C	K	W	A	R	D	S		A	R	E	N	A
L		U		A		S		I		R		G		T
E	N	R	A	G	E		S	T	A	M	P	E	D	E

1-O, 2-T, 3-M, 4-S, 5-P, 6-Z, 7-F, 8-L, 9-G, 10-A, 11-Q, 12-E, 13-R, 14-V, 15-D, 16-W, 17-N, 18-X, 19-H, 20-U, 21-B, 22-I, 23-K, 24-J, 25-C, 26-Y.

CHANGAWORD

1. Mars, Marl, Mall, Hall.
2. Best, Rest, Rust, Ruse, Rise, Ride.
3. Plum, Slum, Slam, Seam, Seat, Peat, Pest.
4. Spar, Sear, Seat, Sent, Pent, Pint, Ping, King.

CRYPTO-FAMILIES

1. SEWING: Zippers, Needles, Buttons, Thread, Scissors, Buckles, Elastic, Patterns, Snaps, Pins.
2. CAT WORDS: Catfish, Catacombs, Caterpillar, Catnap, Category, Cataclysm, Catchall, Catwalk, Catabolism, Caterwaul.
3. BLUE: Crab, Fox, Whale, Cheese, Goose, Pike, Flag, Point, Berry, Spruce.
4. PASS: Telegram, Memorandum, Dispatch, Bulletin, Communique, Missive, Speech, Commentary, Editorial, Message.
5. HEAT: Campfire, Broiler, Grill, Range, Hibachi, Gas burner, Toaster, Oven, Microwave, Fondue pot.
6. WHIPPERSNAPPER: Child, Small fry, Toddler, Moppet, Infant, Juvenile, Tyke, Baby, Newborn, Youngster.

DOUBLE OCCUPANCY

PA	ST	OR		AL	LU	RE		CL	UT	CH
LA		NE	ED	LE		PE	WT	ER		AS
CE	LE	RY		GE	NI	AL		GY	RA	TE
	NG				TW				KI	
WI	TH	IN		BL	IT	HE		DI	SH	ES
GG		TE	AP	OT		AR	RI	VE		CA
LE	GE	ND		CH	AT	TY		ST	RI	PE
	RB				TA				TU	
SA	IL	OR		FL	IN	CH		RE	AL	TY
TI		AN	CH	OR		AN	OI	NT		PI
RE	NE	GE		ID	IO	CY		AL	MO	ST

CROSSOUT QUOTE

The race may not be to the swift nor the victory to the strong, but that's how you bet.

CATEGORIES

TOOLS: Chisel, Lathe, Awl, Mattock, Pliers.
HORSES: Clydesdale, Lipizzaner, Arabian, Morgan, Percheron.
GEORGIA CITIES: Columbus, La Grange, Atlanta, Macon, Perry.
TREES: Cedar, Larch, Ash, Maple, Pine.
CAREERS: Commerce, Law, Architecture, Medicine, Plumbing.

QUOTATGRAMS

A. The man who is pulling his own weight never has any left over to throw around.
B. If you love yourself overmuch, nobody else will love you at all.
C. Remember when greeting cards wished you well instead of insulting you?

A: 1. Gentler, 2. Hothouse, 3. Whip hand, 4. Wishful, 5. New Haven, 6. Yearlong, 7. Tomorrow, 8. Visitant.
B: 1. Follow, 2. Every, 3. Lay by, 4. Riled, 5. Folio, 6. Hones, 7. Toulouse, 8. Lovely, 9. Vacuum.
C. 1. Aweigh, 2. Route, 3. Moisten, 4. Somber, 5. Wilting, 6. Shelley, 7. Rude, 8. Scare, 9. Funny, 10. Wedding.

DIAGRAMLESS FILL-IN

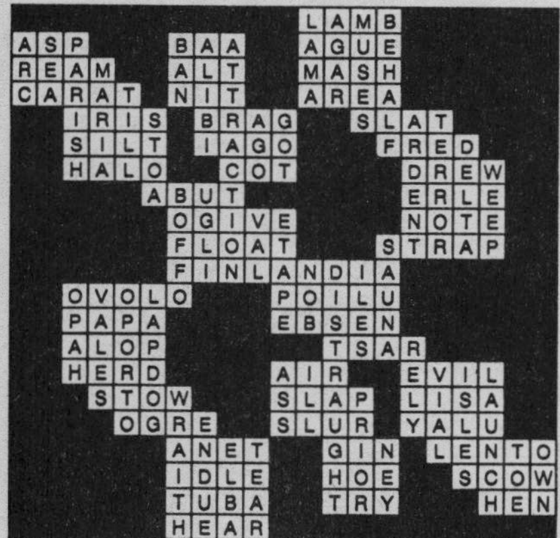

PICTURE THIS

BUILDING BLOCKS

Found, Fondue, Muffin, Uniform, Affluent.

ASSOCIATIONS

Flower, Tulip, Holland, Dutch, Treat, Dessert, Cake, Walk.

LINKWORDS

1. Pea, 2. Book, 3. Letter, 4. Plow, 5. Print, 6. Back, 7. Glass, 8. Switch, 9. Freeze, 10. Mark, 11. Flower, 12. Way.

SYLLACROSTIC

(Herbert V.) Prochnow: Ignorance is a voluntary condition.

1. Propaganda, 2. Romanov, 3. Oregano, 4. Colorful, 5. Haiku, 6. Nonpartisan, 7. Outlet, 8. Wisteria, 9. Improper, 10. Gravy, 11. Nordic, 12. Ohio, 13. Reputation, 14. Assimilated, 15. Nefertiti, 16. Carpet, 17. Ennui, 18. Indigo, 19. Shaman.

SECRET WORD

1. Scarf, 2. Husky, 3. Wives, 4. Mural, 5. Poets, 6. Minor.

1. Mouse, Ulcer, Flame, Flush, Lemon, Earns, Ranch.
2. Shrug, Lurks, Early, Drake, Duels, Older, Glory.
3. Hands, Urban, Straw, Brews, Avert, Naive, Drain, Shrub.
4. Prune, Argue, Impel, Nepal, Tines, Image, Nurse, Guest.
5. Maple, Inept, Noisy, Smile, Trial, Rainy, Empty, Learn, Simon.
6. Snore, Eying, Cages, Ocean, Nomad, Dregs, Amend, Rides, Yearn.

SQUARE DEAL

	M		D		D		S		N		S	
E	1	A	2	T	3	I	4	K	5	E	6	H
	Z		R		E		R		W		O	
Y	7	A	8	T	9	A	10	P	11	A	12	B
	L		P		M		E		R		T	
A	13	F	14	I	15	T	16	W	17	A	18	U
	G		L		S		S		E		B	
W	19	R	20	L	21	P	22	N	23	S	24	O
	O		O		I		A		T		S	
R	25	F	26	O	27	R	28	H	29	N	30	G
	D		H		T		D		I		U	
W	31	R	32	E	33	O	34	T	35	N	36	F
	A		A		M		R		K		D	

1. Maze, 2. Dart, 3. Diet, 4. Risk, 5. Knew, 6. Shoe, 7. Lazy, 8. Trap, 9. Team, 10. Pear, 11. Warp, 12. Boat, 13. Flag, 14. Flip, 15. Mist, 16. Stew, 17. Wear, 18. Tuba, 19. Grow, 20. Roll, 21. Slip, 22. Snap, 23. Nest, 24. Boss, 25. Ford, 26. Hoof, 27. Riot, 28. Hard, 29. Thin, 30. Snug, 31. Draw, 32. Hear, 33. Tome, 34. Trod, 35. Knit, 36. Fund.

BOWL GAME

STRIKES: 1. Depreciate, 2. Researcher, 3. Improvised, 4. Elementary, 5. Methodical, 6. Silhouette, 7. Candelabra, 8. Tripartite, 9. Genialness, 10. Abstemious.

SPARES: 1. Peace, Tried; 2. Cheer, Rears; 3. Prime, Voids; 4. Enter, Mealy; 5. Cloth, Media; 6. Louse, Tithe; 7. Banal, Cadre; 8. Tapir, Trite; 9. Genes, Slain; 10. Abuse, Moist.

LOGIC PROBLEM

(Clue numbers in parentheses)

The theaters were numbered 1 through 5 (intro.). The woman who watched *The Roman* in Theater 2 (4) wasn't Sheena, Valerie (4), Liz [*Psychic* (3)], or Madge [sat in a theater numbered 2 higher than another (5)]; she was Thelma. Trevor sat in Theater 1 (1). Madge didn't sit in Theater 1, 2, 3 [Trevor theater 1], or 5 (5); she sat in Theater 4, Albert sat in Theater 2, and *The Smiling* was shown in Theater 5 [only higher than Theater 4] (5). Madge didn't watch *The Glob* or *The Smiling* (5); she watched *Marian's Baby*. *Psychic* wasn't shown in Theater 3 (3); *The Glob* was. *Psychic* was shown in Theater 1. Sheena sat in a higher-numbered theater than the one in which *Marian's Baby* [Theater 4] was shown (2); she sat in Theater 5. Valerie sat in Theater 3. Cyril sat in a theater numbered 1 less than the one in which Fraser sat (6), so Cyril and Fraser sat in 3 and 4 or 4 and 5, respectively. Neville didn't sit in Theater 5 [Sheena] (2) or 4 [would put Cyril and Fraser in theaters 3 and 5]; he sat in Theater 3. Cyril sat in Theater 4 and Fraser sat in Theater 5 (6).

In summary:
Liz, Trevor, Psychic, Theater 1
Madge, Cyril, Marian's Baby, Theater 4
Sheena, Fraser, The Smiling, Theater 5
Thelma, Albert, The Roman, Theater 2
Valerie, Neville, The Glob, Theater 3

FILL-IN

PEST BULB SHOP RAPT
OVER ASEA TODO ERIE
MIRE REST APES GILA
PLEADED TIRE IDEALS
COD MERE ETON
STALE LARK GLITTERS
LORE HATE SLAVE MEL
ATE RAT DEMOTE PINE
MEASURES LOVE PETTY
END HEDGE TEE
SCENT LAVE STRANDED
TORT TAPERS AIR IDE
AMI HOMER TAMP PAIN
BANTERED WAVE RELET
ELMS TINE TAR
SCHEME HAND MINUTES
LOOT NEAR ABET SOLO
IDLE TRIO ROLL ELSA
PEER SALT DATE DEEP

CHAIN REACTION

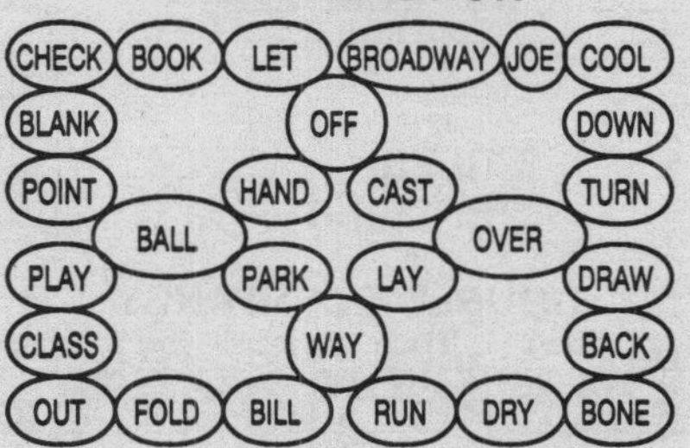

CIRCLE SUMS

A-2, B-7, C-8, D-4, E-5, F-3, G-9, H-6, I-1.

CHIPS

Our national flower is the concrete cloverleaf.

MATCH-UP

5 and 10 match.

(Differences: 1. Turned-up feather missing, 2. Black feather, 3. Short visor, 4. Studs missing, 6. Visor, 7. Turned-in feather missing, 8. Squirrel, 9. Bottom border black, 11. Black feather, 12. Black studs.)

SPIDER'S WEB

1-e Nose, Senor; 2-i Dole, Older; 3-b Dune, Under; 4-g Pita, Tapir; 5-l Heir, Hirer; 6-p Coat, Actor; 7-k Moan, Manor; 8-n Opal, Polar; 9-a Boat, Tabor; 10-m Rode, Order; 11-r Tine, Niter; 12-d Teen, Enter; 13-o Tone, Noter; 14-f Goat, Gator; 15-h Mule, Lemur; 16-q Boar, Arbor; 17-c Mean, Namer; 18-j Bead, Debar.

PORT: Southampton, England

FLOWER POWER

C: 1. Stage, 2. Slimy, 3. Peace, 4. Blimp, 5. Frisk, 6. Prine, 7. Grant, 8. Clint, 9. Brine, 10. Trick, 11. Place, 12. Grope, 13. Graph, 14. Chose, 15. Scaly, 16. Slice, 17. Smite, 18. Spate.

CC: 1. Spicy, 2. State, 3. Plate, 4. Beige, 5. Flame, 6. Pricy, 7. Grime, 8. Crisp, 9. Blank, 10. Trine, 11. Print, 12. Glint, 13. Grace, 14. Crock, 15. Shape, 16. Scope, 17. Slash, 18. Smile.

ALPHABET SOUP

FREQUENT
ELECTION
SYSTEM
EXAMPLE
SAUCE
IDEAL
ARRIVE
CHURCH
HONEST
ABJECT
JUSTIFY
DISTANCE
BRINK
PRIME
LAUGHTER
NINETY
TOURIST
TABLE
JACUZZI
SPIDER
PASTURE
AWFUL
DOLLAR
MAJESTY
OVERCOME
ACCENT

BRICK BY BRICK

ALBS SEGAL MIFF
PARE EVADE EMIL
EVAPORATES SPRY
AWARE ENSNARE
RANG ESE
AVATAR DOS SST
WROTE APORT SPA
RICE ADANO PIER
ISA ARENA FRONT
TET BED TALENT
IOU SLAP
GOATEES IRATE
LINT INCINERATE
IRAE ROONE ETAL
ELLS ESTES DATA

FOUR CORNERS

F	L	A	P
L	I	R	A
A	N	E	W
W	E	A	N

P	L	U	G
L	O	S	E
O	P	E	N
W	E	R	E

B	O	S	S
A	B	L	E
L	O	A	N
K	E	P	T

S	P	A	T
P	O	L	E
E	L	S	E
D	O	O	M

TILES

OSTENSIBLE

ABACUS

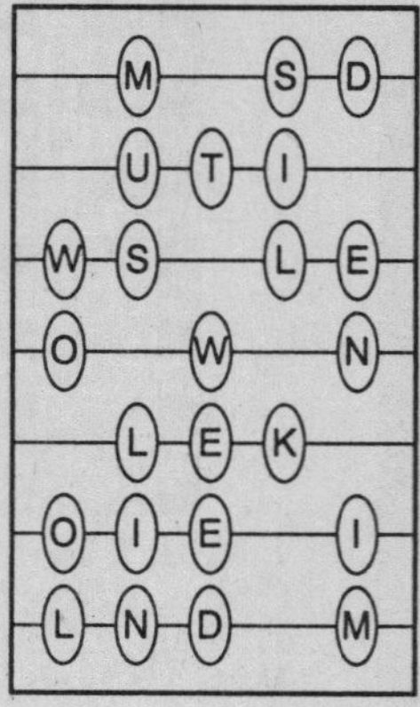

LINE 'EM UP

FLUORESCENCE

CHIPS

Life is too short to stuff a mushroom.

PUZZLE IN THE ROUND

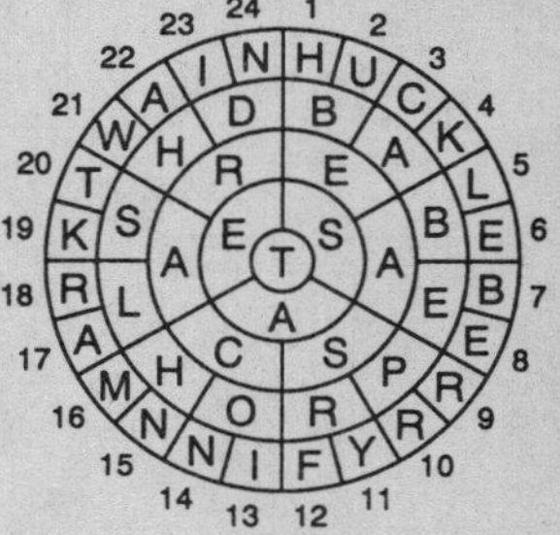

1. Beths, 2. Tubes, 3. Caste, 4. Skate, 5. Blast, 6. Beast, 7. Baste, 8. Tease, 9. Traps, 10. Strap, 11. Yeast, 12. Feast, 13. Coati, 14. Canto, 15. Chant, 16. Match, 17. Alate, 18. Later, 19. Steak, 20. Taste, 21. Threw, 22. Heart, 23. Tired, 24. Trend.
TITLE AND AUTHOR: Huckleberry Finn, Mark Twain.

DOUBLE OCCUPANCY

CA	PI	TA		CH	AI	SE		DI	OX	IN
NI	■	ME	NT	OR	■	RU	BI	ES	■	CI
NE	AR	LY		AL	BU	MS		EL	AP	SE
	RI				SI				PA	
IN	VE	ST		MA	NG	LE		FE	LL	OW
VI	■	AG	EN	DA	■	MU	SS	EL	■	NE
TE	AS	ES		ME	TE	RS		ER	RO	RS
	HO				EP				TU	
AR	RE	ST		BR	EE	CH		PU	ND	IT
CA	■	OR	IG	IN	■	ID	EA	LS	■	CH
DE	FI	ED		ES	PI	ED		ED	IT	ED

ASSOCIATIONS

Early, Bird, Chicken, Coward, Yellow, Jacket, Eton, School, Master.

ROUNDABOUT

1. Insect, 3. Aching, 5. Onrush, 7. Escape, 9. Spider, 11. Netted, 13. Cellar, 15. Parlor, 17. Hornet, 19. Beetle, 21. Fliers, 23. Frowns.
RIDDLE ANSWER: A shoestring.

ANAGRAM MAGIC SQUARE

1. Anvil, 2. Lacer, 3. Ideas, 4. Teach, 5. Those, 6. Lance, 7. Elgar, 8. Grace, 9. Odors, 10. Stair, 11. Shale, 12. Items, 13. Pines, 14. Grape, 15. Outer, 16. Exalt, 17. Scars, 18. Alden, 19. Least, 20. Otter, 21. Nails, 22. Grade, 23. Wrote, 24. Amble, 25. Yards.
SAYING: A little gossip goes a long way.

SECRET WORD

1. False, 2. Charm, 3. Write, 4. Packs, 5. Stain, 6. Broad.

1. Dozen, Ideas, Shift, Hoist, Often, Noise, Eliza, Snarl, Thorn; 2. Fresh, Aches, Smite, Chief, Incas, Nears, Amish, Tines, Emits; 3. Coast, Omars, Moans, Power, Owner, Saint, Epics; 4. Blend, Upset, Nepal, Ducks, Lurks, Ednas, Scrub; 5. Vague, Avert, Raven, North, Ingot, Shire, Hover; 6. Grant, Eland, Noble, Ergot, Ruled, Abler, Lunge.

CODEWORD

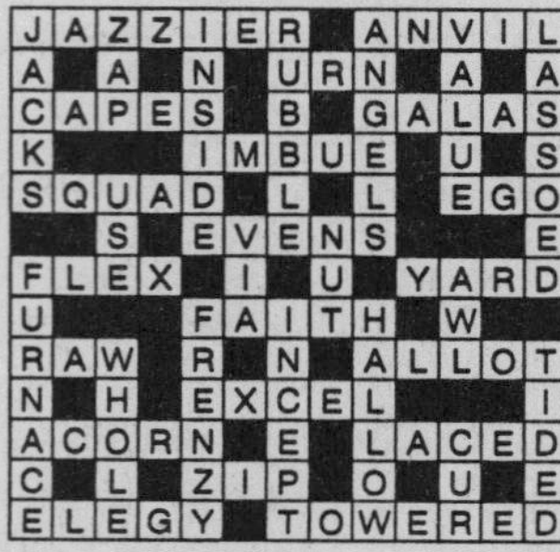

1-F, 2-E, 3-V, 4-Q, 5-N, 6-B, 7-K, 8-M, 9-G, 10-C, 11-W, 12-P, 13-Y, 14-U, 15-L, 16-J, 17-O, 18-S, 19-T, 20-Z, 21-H, 22-X, 23-R, 24-I, 25-A, 26-D.

PULLING STRINGS

1. Harsh, 2. Bathysphere, 3. Type, 4. Bee, 5. Pastry.

CHANGAWORD

1. Beef, Beep, Seep, Step, Stew.
2. Soup, Soul, Foul, Fowl, Bowl.
3. Hard, Hare, Hale, Hole, Role, Roll.
4. Cook, Coot, Coat, Moat, Meat, Meal.

HEXAGRAMS

Bagpipe, Embassy, Pageboy, Embargo, Besmear, Payment, Progeny, Grocery, Bawdier, Acronym, Crowbar, Uranium, Sawbuck.

SYLLACROSTIC

(Jonathan) Winters: I couldn't wait for success . . . so I went ahead without it.
1. Workaholic, 2. Iodine, 3. Nefarious, 4. Taurus, 5. Ecclesiastes, 6. Romeo, 7. Safari, 8. Interview, 9. Censure, 10. Orlon, 11. Upright, 12. Liberia, 13. Diminish, 14. Neptune, 15. Tarantula, 16. Wagered, 17. Andrew, 18. Illini, 19. Tacit, 20. Foolish, 21. Oregano, 22. Rousseau, 23. Scarlet, 24. Ubangi, 25. Cellist.

CHAIN REACTION

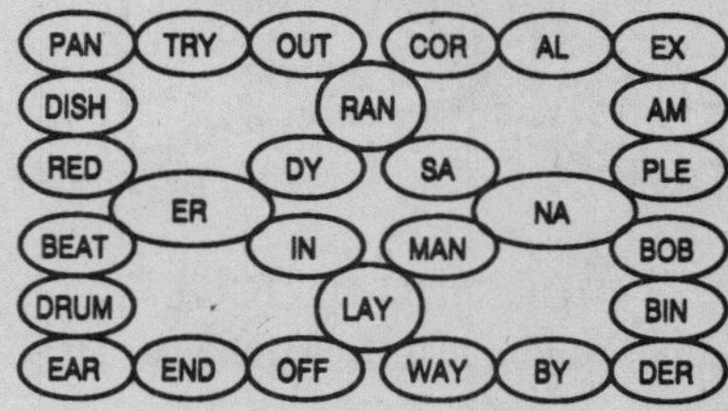

MIND TICKLER

Twenty-eight 25¢ stamps and twenty-four 29¢ stamps.

FAN WORDS

1. Times, 2. Smite, 3. Omits, 4. Moist, 5. Wrest, 6. Strew, 7. Lance, 8. Clean.
8-LETTER WORD: Immortal

DROP-INS

1. Manifold, 2. Straight, 3. Complete, 4. Painting, 5. Ejection, 6. Skirmish, 7. Breadbox, 8. Jodhpurs, 9. Energize, 10. Aqueduct.

CRYPTIC GEOGRAPHY

1. Montana
The name "Montana" comes from a Spanish word meaning "mountainous." The mountains contained a wealth of gold and silver, which gave the state its nickname, "The Treasure State."

2. Washington, D.C.
This city was designed and laid out before the first buildings were erected. George Washington chose the exact spot and hired Major Pierre L'Enfant to draw plans for the city. The streets form squares like a checkerboard. Major avenues diagonally crisscross this design, leading to the centers of government like spokes in a wheel.

PUZZLE IN THE ROUND

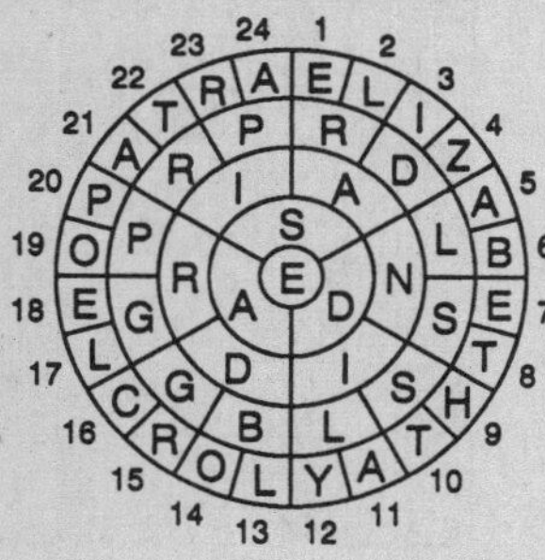

1. Erase, 2. Earls, 3. Ideas, 4. Dazes, 5. Eland, 6. Blend, 7. Dense, 8. Dents, 9. Hides, 10. Diets, 11. Ailed, 12. Yield, 13. Blade, 14. Adobe, 15. Grade, 16. Caged, 17. Regal, 18. Agree, 19. Opera, 20. Paper, 21. Raise, 22. Tries, 23. Spire, 24. Sepia.

ACTRESS & ROLE: Elizabeth Taylor, Cleopatra

LINKWORDS

1. Crow, 2. Cake, 3. Band, 4. Ball, 5. Shoe, 6. Apple, 7. Pot, 8. Stop, 9. Nut, 10. After.

HEADINGS

1. Deposit, Certificate, Balance, Loan, Checkbook, Interest, Savings, Money.
2. Treasure, Frigate, Buccaneer, Ship, Spyglass, Crossbones, Eyepatch, Hook.
3. Frock, Mackintosh, Cardigan, Pajamas, Jumper, Vest, Overalls, Shirt.

STARSPELL

5-letter words: Areal, Arson, Award, Aware, Delve, Eager, Eagle, Eared, Galea, Glare, Glede, Lager, Legal, Leper, Level, Lever, Never, Newel, Newer, Opera, Perse, Poser, Regal, Renew, Repel, Revel, Scene, Scone, Scope, Seven, Sever, Sewer, Velar, Verse, Verso, Wager.
6-letter words: Cereal, Depone, Depose, Drawer, Eleven, Garage, Garden, Genera, Larder, Opener, Pelage, People, Person, Plagal, Poplar, Recede, Regale, Regard, Renege, Reopen, Repose, Reseal, Reveal, Revere, Reward, Secede, Senega, Serene, Severe, Sewage, Versed, Warden, Warder.

SCOREBOARD

	L			S		F				
	I			O	V	E	*	T		
Z	O	N	E	D		R		O	A	T
	N		*			A		E		
			J	A	I	L				
	C	R	O	W	N					
	H		Y	E		S	Q	U	I	B
	U					T				E
	M					A		U		R
S	P	A	R	K	I	N	G	S		E
		X				D	O			T

The following is our order of play. The words before and after a slash (/) were formed in the same play. Our running tally is in parentheses.

Own (3), Crown (14), Chum (24), Joy (30), Spa/Chump (51), Ye/We (57), Jail/Awe/In (66), Spar (77), Spark (101), Ax (103), Sparking (148), Enjoy (158), Zone (162), And (165), Stand (173), Squib (189), Be (193), Beret (203), Feral (213), Over (222), Overt (242), So (249), Zoned/Sod (262), Ion (265), Lion (273), Us/Sparkings (323), Oat/To (332), Toe (338), Do/Go (344).

DOUBLE DELIGHT

GA	ZE	BO		CA	JO	LE		BO	UN	TY
LL	■	ST	RA	ND	■	GA	MB	LE	■	RA
OP	TI	ON		OR	NA	TE		RO	DE	NT
	GE				TI				FE	
BU	RS	AR		SE	VE	RE		CR	AT	ER
ND	■	MI	SS	AL	■	ST	AT	ED	■	RO
LE	VE	ES		ED	IT	ED		OS	CA	RS
	LV				SE				ES	
SE	ET	HE		PI	LF	ER		SE	AR	CH
AS	■	AL	MO	ST	■	OD	DE	ST	■	IM
ON	AG	ER		OL	DI	ES		ET	CH	ED

FLOWER POWER

C: 1. Fates, 2. Nasal, 3. Nares, 4. Bogey, 5. Handy, 6. Boner, 7. Paver, 8. Conan, 9. Coded, 10. Gazer, 11. Rotor, 12. Cater, 13. Hotel, 14. Mates, 15. Taper, 16. Paces, 17. Label, 18. Rival.

CC: 1. Fiber, 2. Naves, 3. Natal, 4. Basel, 5. Horas, 6. Bagel, 7. Pones, 8. Candy, 9. Covey, 10. Goner, 11. Radar, 12. Cozen, 13. Hated, 14. Motor, 15. Tater, 16. Pater, 17. Lapel, 18. Races.

CRYPTOGRAMS

1. The great man is too often all of a piece; it is the little man that is a bundle of contradictory elements. He is inexhaustable. You never come to the end of the surprises he has in store for you. (W. Somerset Maugham)

2. "It looks like a bad storm coming," said a hostess to a visiting neighbor. "You had better stay for dinner." "No thanks," the neighbor said absently. "I don't think it will be that bad."

3. Man looking at Christmas cards ready to mail: "This year it finally happened — the stamps cost more than the cards." (Goddard Sherman)

4. Into the space of one little hour sins enough may be conjured up by evil tongues to blast the fame of a whole life of virtue.

5. One cool judgment is worth a thousand hasty councils. The thing to do is to supply light and not heat. (Woodrow Wilson)

6. Earn with integrity and enthusiasm; invest with wisdom and restraint; spend with care and discretion; give with joy and generosity.

7. Before television and radio, the business of life itself consumed most of the waking hours of Americans.

8. The probability that we may fail in the struggle ought not to deter us from the support of a course we believe to be just. (Abraham Lincoln)

9. We spend our lives trying to accumulate money, then look back to the times when we had none and call them the "good old days."

10. Some people succeed because they are destined to, but most people succeed because they are determined to.

11. Many a businessman wanted his son to share in the business but the government beat him to it.

12. Philosophy is an orderly way of discussing subjects we don't know anything about.

CODEWORD

P	A	R	I	T	Y	■	A	■	E	■	M	■
L	■	E	■	H	■	Q	U	E	S	T	E	D
E	X	T	R	A	■	■	G	■	C	■	D	■
N	■	I	■	W	O	R	E	■	A	X	I	S
T	O	N	■	■	A	■	R	■	L	■	A	■
Y	■	A	C	U	T	E	■	J	A	U	N	T
■	■	■	A	■	H	■	P	■	T	■	■	■
J	O	U	S	T	■	K	O	P	E	K	■	D
■	C	■	H	■	A	■	T	■	■	I	C	E
M	E	S	A	■	B	E	S	T	■	B	■	V
■	A	■	B	■	O	■	■	A	L	I	B	I
E	N	S	L	A	V	E	■	X	■	T	■	C
■	S	■	E	■	E	■	F	I	Z	Z	L	E

1-L, 2-P, 3-A, 4-R, 5-D, 6-Q, 7-I, 8-E, 9-J, 10-G, 11-H, 12-W, 13-U, 14-X, 15-S, 16-Z, 17-Y, 18-F, 19-K, 20-O, 21-C, 22-M, 23-N, 24-T, 25-V, 26-B.

DART GAME

Motto, Mince, Media, Mural, Magic.

WORD MATH

	0	1	2	3	4	5	6	7	8	9
1.	C	A	I	R	O/E	G	Y	P	T	
2.	S	U	B	H	E	A	D	I	N	G
3.	S	C	A	R	Y/M	O	V	I	E	
4.	O	L	D/P	I	C	T	U	R	E	
5.	M	O	N	A	R	C	H	I	S	T
6.	T	E	N/O	F/C	L	U	B	S		

SYLLACROSTIC

J(osh) Billings: Genius learns from nature; talent from books.

1. Jingo, 2. Blossom, 3. Intern, 4. Libra, 5. Lenient, 6. Impromptu, 7. Number, 8. Genuine, 9. Select, 10. Gorilla, 11. Eternal, 12. Negative, 13. Ignition, 14. Unit, 15. Sheriff, 16. Litter, 17. Eskimo, 18. Aluminum, 19. Rhubarb, 20. Nuncio, 21. Seraglio, 22. Forsook, 23. Raucous.

LOGIC PROBLEM

(Clue numbers in parentheses)

Ages are 7, 8, 9, 10, and 11 (intro.). Rudi [8 or 10 yrs. old (4)] wasn't the Cheshire Cat [7 or 9 yrs. old (2)]; Norah was (2). Meharg [White Rabbit or Mad Hatter (1)] isn't 9 yrs. old [Cheshire Cat or Queen of Hearts (3)]; Cayne is (3), and the 8-yr.-old is Palmer (5). Malcolm [7 or 11 yrs. old (4)] isn't Cayne [9 yrs. old]; he's Bernier (4), and Cayne is Pearl (2). Meharg is Jason (1). Palmer, the 8-yr.-old [White Rabbit or Queen of Hearts (5)], isn't Norah [Cheshire Cat]; Palmer is Rudi. Norah is Kirkland. 9-yr.-old Pearl Cayne was the Queen of Hearts (3); 8-yr.-old Rudi was the White Rabbit (5), and Jason Meharg was the Mad Hatter (1). Malcolm was Tweedledum. The Cheshire Cat wasn't the 9-yr.-old [Queen of Hearts]; she was the 7-yr.-old (2), and Malcolm is 11 yrs. old (4). Jason is 10 yrs. old.

In summary:
Jason Meharg, Mad Hatter, 10
Malcolm Bernier, Tweedledum, 11
Norah Kirkland, Cheshire Cat, 7
Pearl Cayne, Queen of Hearts, 9
Rudi Palmer, White Rabbit, 8

ABACUS

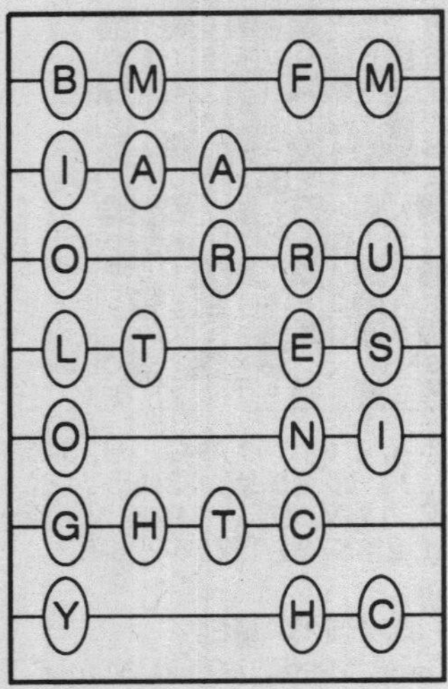

KEYWORD

WINDJAMMER

CIRCLE SUMS

A-7, B-9, C-2, D-6, E-3, F-8, G-5, H-4.

DIAL-A-GRAMS

A. The reward of a thing well done is to have done it.

B. We confess small faults, in order to insinuate that we have no great ones.

EXCHANGE BOARDS

6-LETTER WORDS: Monkey, Uphold, Comedy, Pronto, Answer, Sledge, Format, Pestle.

4-LETTER WORDS: Fold, Cope, Erst, Upon, Tome, Mole, Eddy, Prey, Germ, Honk, Swan, Slat.

WORD MERGERS

1. Ran, Vie; Ravine.
2. Camp, Cot; Compact.
3. Con, Oval; Volcano.
4. Core, Nut; Trounce.
5. Crest, You; Courtesy.
6. Grail, Man; Marginal.
7. Shape, Spin; Happiness.
8. Forty, Mail; Formality.

SCOREMASTER

S
QUALM INK
U IS I
A H L
BE FACET
N RUG E
ADJOIN R
O D V
Y EXPORT
ZEST WO

The following is our order of play. The words before and after a slash (/) were formed in the same play. Scores are given in parentheses.

Rug (6), Hag (9), Ace (14), Rid (5), Fun/In/Face (29), Shag (22), Join (22), Ride (12), Kilt/Facet (57), Joy (24), Mi/Is (13), Kilter (45), Qualm (57), Zest/Joys (67), Ex (16), Ink (27), Squab (48), Adjoin (28), Export (36), Enjoys/Be (38), Vow (17), To (9).

PICTURE THIS

TRY-ANGLES

S
P O
R U N
I R O N
N O I S E
G O B L E T

DIAGRAMLESS FILL-IN

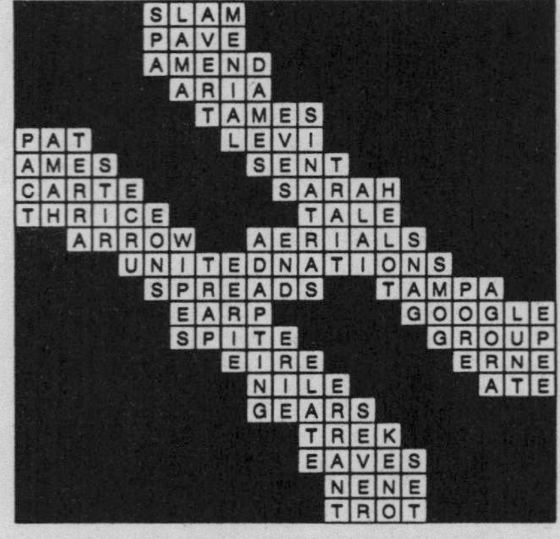

BUILDING BLOCKS

Petal, Depart, Pastel, Capital, Portrait.

ESCALATORS

1

PASTOR	P	ROAST	A	SORT
SPINET	I	SPENT	P	NEST
SOUGHT	G	SHOUT	O	THUS
STRIKE	I	TREKS	K	REST
ENRAGE	N	EAGER	E	GEAR

2

CARAFE	A	FARCE	F	RACE
DASHED	D	SHADE	A	SHED
DEMAND	D	MANED	M	DEAN
AUSTIN	A	UNITS	I	STUN
HELMET	M	ETHEL	L	THEE
STEAMY	S	MEATY	Y	TAME

3

BRACES	B	SCARE	C	SEAR
UNITES	U	STEIN	I	NETS
STELLA	L	LEAST	T	SALE
LAWYER	W	RELAY	A	LYRE
ARDENT	A	TREND	D	RENT
BARRED	R	BREAD	E	DRAB
FLAKES	K	FALSE	L	SAFE

NUMBER SLEUTH

WHEEL SUMS

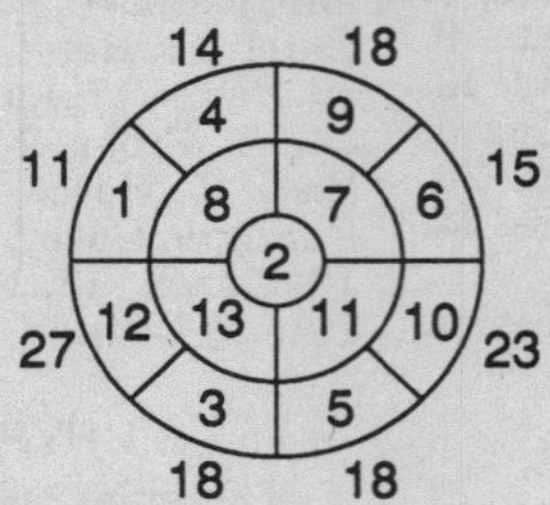

BRICK BY BRICK

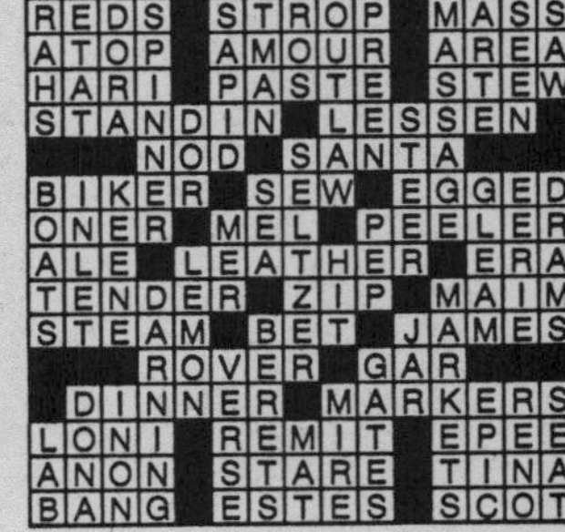

STEP BY STEP

1. Crown, Grown, Grows, Gross, Gloss, Glass.
2. Score, Shore, Chore, Chose, Chase, Chasm.
3. Favor, Savor, Saver, Sever, Sewer, Sewed.
4. Bluet, Blunt, Brunt, Grunt, Grant, Grand.

ANAGRAM QUOTE

A debate is the longest distance between two points of view.

BOWL GAME

STRIKES: 1. Tabernacle, 2. Generality, 3. Applesauce, 4. Lackluster, 5. Compliance, 6. Balderdash, 7. Parliament, 8. Ramshackle, 9. Tambourine, 10. Mineralogy.

SPARES: 1. Blare, Enact; 2. Enter, Gaily; 3. Pause, Place; 4. Cruel, Stalk; 5. Conic, Maple; 6. Addle, Brash; 7. Paint, Realm; 8. Camel, Shark; 9. About, Miner; 10. Ingle, Mayor.

SPIDER'S WEB

1-j Emir, Merit; 2-n Anne, Anent; 3-a Boor, Robot; 4-r Achy, Yacht; 5-f Rhea, Heart; 6-b Maid, Admit; 7-d Bide, Debit; 8-l Iamb, Ambit; 9-p Sale, Least; 10-h Line, Inlet; 11-c Cart, Tract; 12-o Teen, Tenet; 13-i Peal, Leapt; 14-q Dice, Edict; 15-e Role, Lerot; 16-g Seas, Asset; 17-k Name, Meant; 18-m Beer, Beret.

NURSERY RHYME: Mary Had a Little Lamb

QUOTAGRAMS

A. Our necessities are few but our wants are endless.

B. If you want to be respected, you must respect yourself.

C. The man of few words doesn't have to take so many of them back.

A: 1. Belief, 2. Twain, 3. Soot, 4. Reassure, 5. Secret, 6. Answer, 7. Unused.
B: 1. Peanuts, 2. Forest, 3. Yosemite, 4. Buttery, 5. Couples, 6. Fury, 7. Cowed.
C: 1. Wakened, 2. Vowed, 3. Meat hook, 4. Rhythm, 5. Fastest, 6. Moon, 7. Beacon, 8. Staff.

ALPHABET SOUP

TREFOIL
SQUASH
GRAZE
CIRCUS
REFEREE
GARDEN
AVERAGE
MAGNET
ISLAND
PICKLE
MECHANIC
PRAIRIE
LEMON
JEALOUS
FREIGHT
GOBLIN
EXCERPT
SHOWER
MAGNIFIED
TRANCE
VENUE
TYPHOON
ELECT
RHYTHM
GALAXY
LICENSE

SUM TOTALS

	6	5		5	1			2	8	1	5	
5	3	1	9	8	7	6		1	5	3	2	
8	1		8	1		9	1	6			7	9
	2	1		7	2		8	9			1	7
8	4	2		9	4	3	5		9	5	4	8
9	7	8	6		1	2		5	8	6		
	9	3	1	7				1	3	2	4	
		4	8	9		9	8		5	7	3	4
1	3	5	9		2	7	9	6		8	5	9
7	9			9	4		2	1		9	6	
6	8			7	1	2		4	1		9	2
	7	9	8	5		1	4	9	8	6	7	5
	5	3	6	8			1	5		1	8	

CAMOUFLAGE

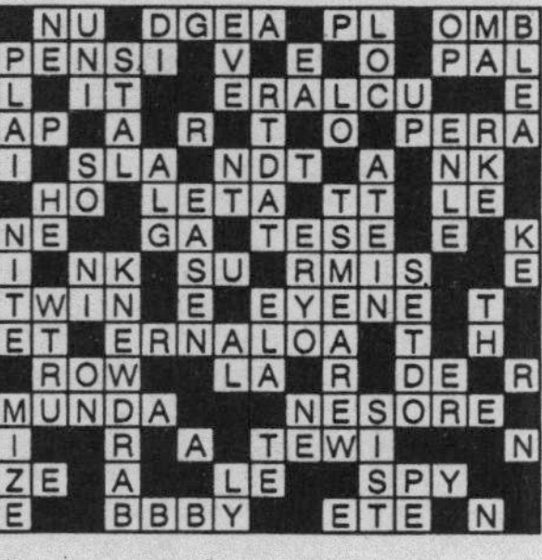

FOUR CORNERS

J	E	S	T
A	B	L	Y
C	O	O	P
K	N	E	E

C	H	I	N
L	A	N	E
U	R	N	S
B	E	S	T

C	L	I	P
R	A	R	E
I	D	O	L
B	E	N	T

C	U	B	E
A	G	E	D
S	L	A	G
T	Y	K	E

STARS AND ARROWS

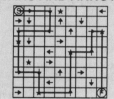

LITTLE PUZZLER

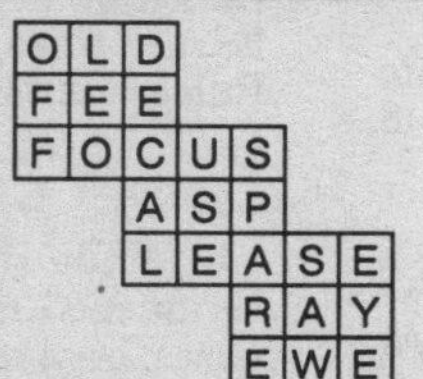

PICTURE THIS

MAZE

DOUBLE DELIGHT

HE	LE	NA		DE	BR	IS		CA	LI	CO
LI		TU	RT	LE		SU	PE	RB		WA
UM	PI	RE		TE	AS	ES		ON	WA	RD
	LL				SU				LR	
SH	OW	ER		ST	RE	ET		CO	US	IN
IF		RA	GL	AN		CH	OK	ER		FA
TY	RA	NT		CE	AS	ED		CE	ME	NT
	NC				CE				DI	
SC	OR	CH		CO	ND	OR		PE	AN	UT
AR		OR	IG	IN		AC	CU	SE		TE
AB	AC	US		ED	IB	LE		TA	PE	RS

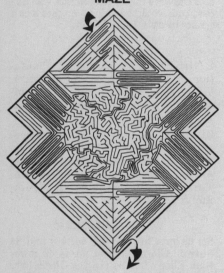

MIXED SIXES

The factory that produces the most important product is the home.

FLOWER POWER

C: 1. Awoke, 2. Alert, 3. Aries, 4. Torte, 5. Meats, 6. Brute, 7. Boars, 8. React, 9. Floss, 10. Glade, 11. Beets, 12. Flame, 13. Slope, 14. Erase, 15. Prior, 16. Donee, 17. Padre, 18. Clans.

CC: 1. Alder, 2. Aware, 3. Alone, 4. Treks, 5. Moire, 6. Beret, 7. Brats, 8. Route, 9. Feats, 10. Glare, 11. Blocs, 12. Feast, 13. Sleds, 14. Elate, 15. Proms, 16. Drape, 17. Poise, 18. Canoe.

CRYPTO-FAMILIES

1. BIRDS: Parrot, Goose, Oriole, Heron, Lark, Sparrow, Nutcracker, Hawk, Chicken, Eagle.
2. BIG: Immense, Gigantic, Colossal, Mammoth, Titanic, Leviathan, Gargantuan, Mountainous, Stupendous, Elephantine.
3. LIGHT: Year, Weight, House, Breeze, Cream, Ship, Hearted, Infantry, Footed, Artillery.
4. M's: Missile, Minesweeper, Machine gun, Marines, Mortar, Major, Munitions, March, Mission, Mess hall.
5. EATING: Bistro, Cafeteria, Coffee shop, Beanery, Luncheonette, Steakhouse, Tearoom, Pizzeria, Bar and grill, Diner.
6. HEAVENLY: Pluto, Neptune, Uranus, Asteroid, Jupiter, Mars, Comet, Evening star, Mercury, Moon.

DIAGRAMLESS FILL-IN

						G	U	M								
	F	O	R	D		A	T	O	M							
	O	M	A	R		P	A	V	E				G	O	S	H
	N	A	V	Y			H	E	R	E		K	E	N	Y	A
	T	H	E					S	E	N	T	I	M	E	N	T
		A	L	M	A					C	U	P		S	E	E
			S	U	L	K		W	O	R	N					
				D	E	E		O	H	O						
						N	O	R	M	A						
						T	A	D		C	H	I				
					B	U	R	Y		H	U	R	T			
H	A	S		T	I	C					T	A	R	T		
O	U	T	R	A	N	K	E	D					A	R	E	
G	R	E	E	N		Y	A	R	D			A	V	I	D	
S	A	N	D				S	A	I	D		D	E	A	N	
							T	I	N	Y		E	L	L	A	
								N	E	E						

SYLLABILITY

Physiopathological, Excommunicatory, Contemptibility, Mechanization, Luminescence, Pageantry, Giggle, Ring.

WORD MATH

	0	1	2	3	4	5	6	7	8	9
1.	L	O	N	G	E	S	T/D	A	Y	
2.	P	R	O	F	I	T	A	B	L	E
3.	C	O	U	N	T	E	R	S	P	Y
4.	H	A	R	M	O	N	I	Z	E	D
5.	C	H	I	V	A	L	R	O	U	S
6.	R	A	V	E	N	O	U	S	L	Y

SCRAMBLED GROUPS

Clique, Colony, Family, Flight, Galaxy, Legion, School, Senate, Throng, Troupe.

FOUR-FIT

1. Showcase, 2. Lacrosse, 3. Basement, 4. Ricochet, 5. Displace, 6. Customer, 7. Flotilla, 8. Sidestep, 9. Frequent, 10. Trousers, 11. Manicure, 12. Railroad, 13. Majority, 14. Poignant, 15. Culinary.

ANAGRAM QUOTES

1. Parents were invented to make children happy by giving them something to ignore.
2. Consider the postage stamp: its usefulness consists in the ability to stick to one thing till it gets there.
3. Misery loves company, but company does not reciprocate.
4. First love is only a little foolishness and a lot of curiosity.

QUOTAGRAMS

A: The vagabond, when rich, is called a tourist.

B: Writing comes more easily if you have something to say.

C: The nicest thing about new friends is that they haven't heard all your old stories yet.

A: 1. Habitual, 2. Ledger, 3. Cinch, 4. Strain, 5. Vote, 6. Shadow.
B: 1. Yogi, 2. Wister, 3. Moments, 4. Voyages, 5. Sincere, 6. Mouth, 7. Oily, 8. Haifa.
C: 1. Fusion, 2. Hothead, 3. Nobility, 4. Raunchy, 5. Stately, 6. Astonish, 7. Strength, 8. Deleted, 9. Review, 10. Threat.

RINGMASTER

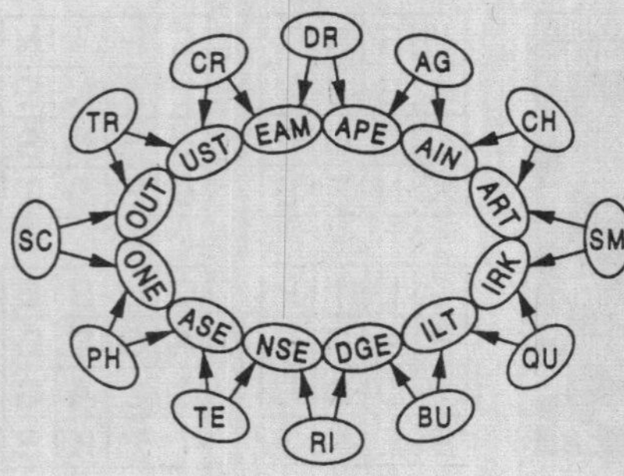

ABC'S

1. Vowels, 2. Glumly, 3. Coaxed, 4. Bustle, 5. Hamper, 6. Cozier, 7. Acquit, 8. Adjoin, 9. Forked, 10. Tunnel.

BUBBLES

1. Juneau, 2. Boston, 3. Denver, 4. Albany, 5. Helena, 6. Topeka.

BONUS: Dallas

THROWBACKS

1. Pare, Pawn, Pane; 2. Snug, Sure, Dreg; 3. Ewer, Tire, Tier; 4. Hurt, Turn, Tutu; 5. Deed, Drew, Redo; 6. Seen, Silk, Nice; 7. Carp, Idea, Dear; 8. Node, Wore, Word.

LIST-A-CROSTIC

THEME: Pulitzer Fiction Winners

James Gould Cozzens, John Updike, Margaret Mitchell, Saul Bellow, Norman Mailer, William Styron, John Steinbeck, Toni Morrison, Willa Cather, Pearl Buck, Edna Ferber, Ernest Hemingway, Eudora Welty.

READING DOWN: Upton Sinclair

A. Pajamas
B. Unlikely
C. Laches
D. Insurer
E. Town crier
F. Zimbalist
G. Emile Zola
H. Rematch
I. Fallen
J. Immutably
K. Coupled
L. Tumbler
M. Iron Man
N. On the job
O. New York
P. Whitewash
Q. Ignore
R. Narrows
S. Naked
T. Egg roll
U. Reject
V. Sodden

SCOREMASTER

									E	
	Z	O	O	M			J	O	L	T
	I			U	R	N		K		
	N			G		E		R		
I	C	E				S	L	A	B	
				F	I	T			Y	
	D	I	V	A					W	E
	E								O	
	P		A	N					R	
	T	U	X		S	Q	U	A	D	S
	H									

The following is our order of play. The words before and after a slash (/) were formed in the same play. Scores are given in parentheses.

It (3), Nest (14), Urn (10), Mug (7), Slab (16), By (11), Fit (6), Zoom (39), Fa (4), Zinc (48), Diva (16), Depth (45), Tux (30), Byword (60), We (10), Quad (39), Ice (14), Squad (51), Okra (20), Jolt (36), An/Ax (14), Squads (57), El (9).

THREESOMES

SECRET WORD

1. Lotus, 2. Fruit, 3. Coats, 4. Solve, 5. April, 6. Alien.

1. Waits, Alone, Tuner, Early, Route, Lairs, Irony, Lower, Yearn; 2. Prune, Infer, Nepal, Eliot, After, Price, Porch, Lunar, Ethan; 3. Joyce, Atone, Cafes, Knife, Enjoy, Token, Stein; 4. Ulcer, Norse, Curse, Other, Vault, Evans, Ranch; 5. Slope, Hones, Owner, While, Earns, Riles, Swipe; 6. Mural, Admit, Rules, Tours, Inert, Audio, Norma.

CRYPTOGRAMS

1. While the medical profession has conquered most of the childhood diseases, boys and girls seem to be afflicted as much as ever with whatever it is that prevents them from being sleepy at bedtime.

2. A very wealthy man said, "I never saw anything I could buy for a dollar that appealed to me as much as the dollar itself."

3. Adolescence is a period of rapid changes. When a young adult is between the ages of twelve and seventeen, for example, a parent ages as much as twenty years.

4. Our strength as humans is that we can laugh at ourselves for being ridiculous. Our weakness is that we have to do it so often.

5. An archaeologist is the best husband any woman can have; the older she gets, the more interested he is in her. (Agatha Christie)

6. Much of good manners is about knowing when to pretend that what's happening isn't happening.

7. The best way to learn how to do it yourself is to criticize the way the committee is going to do it.

8. When you become famous, you can't forget old friends. Oh, you can try, but they won't let you. (Rodney Dangerfield)

9. Temper is a quality that at a critical moment tends to elicit the best in steel and the worst in people.

10. The vision must be followed by the venture. It is not enough to stare up the steps — we must step up the stairs.

11. To live is so startling it leaves little time for anything else. (Emily Dickinson)

12. Solitude is fine, but you need someone to tell you that solitude is fine. (Honore de Balzac)

13. Natural talents are like natural plants; they need carefully planned pruning.

14. "Is it bad luck to have a black cat follow you?" "That depends, are you a man or mouse?"

DOUBLE TROUBLE

W	IN	CE	■	SPE	W	■	■	AN	N	EX
IN	VE	RT	■	C	AKE	■	PRE	T	EX	T
■	TE	A	■	TA	N	TRU	M	■	T	END
■	R	IN	GLE	T	■	ANT	I	C	■	■
LAV	A	■	AN	O	N	■	SE	R	P	ENT
I	T	CH	■	R	OM	P	■	AFT	E	R
SH	E	A	TH	■	AD	O	BE	■	R	ANT
■	■	SE	A	SON	■	LIC	E	N	SE	■
PA	N	■	N	AR	RAT	E	■	E	VE	■
R	E	MAR	KS	■	HE	M	■	ST	R	OVE
ROT	AT	E	■	■	R	AN	■	LE	E	R

CHANGAWORD

1. Farm, Harm, Hard, Hand, Land.
2. Corn, Torn, Tern, Teen, Seen, Seed.
3. Grow, Glow, Plow, Plot, Plat, Peat, Peas.
4. Barn, Bare, Bale, Sale, Salt, Silt, Silo.

QUOTEFALLS

1. You have to be with a child today to be in his memory tomorrow.
2. It isn't always easy to tell the difference between a real cliff and a bluff.
3. The hardest arithmetic to master is that which enables us to count our blessings.
4. If Darwin's theory of evolution was correct, cats would be able to operate a can opener by now. (Larry Wright)

BOWL GAME

STRIKES: 1. Conscience, 2. Plantation, 3. Deservedly, 4. Suggestion, 5. Wintertime, 6. Investment, 7. Principled, 8. Charitable, 9. Telescopic, 10. Minestrone.

SPARES: 1. Scenic, Cone; 2. Nation, Plat; 3. Revels, Eddy; 4. Gouges, Tins; 5. Mitten, Wire; 6. Event, Mints; 7. Pencil, Drip; 8. Breach, Tail; 9. Colic, Steep; 10. Miner, Stone.

LOGIC PROBLEM

Street nos. are 25, 32, 44, 50, and 84 (intro.). Gloria's street no. is 40 lower than Ellen's [no. 84 (1)] (1); Gloria lives at 44. Jack didn't call Star Cab [Ellen (1)], Arrow Cab [Burt (2)], Blue Cab, or City Cab (3); he called Quick Cab. The one who called City Cab [street no. 25 higher than one who lives at Paradise Condominiums (3)] doesn't live at no. 25, no. 32 [no no. 7], or no. 44 [no no. 19]; that one lives at no. 50, and the one who lives at Paradise Condominiums lives at no. 25. Gloria [no. 44] didn't call City Cab [no. 50]; Amos did. Gloria called Blue Cab. The one who lives in Paradise Condominiums [no. 25] isn't Amos [no. 50], Ellen [Valhalla House (1)], Gloria [Jubilee Village (2)], or Jack [Avalon Towers (3)]; that one is Burt. Jack lives at no. 32. Amos lives at Utopian Apartments.

In summary:

Amos, City Cab, Utopian Apartments, 50
Burt, Arrow Cab, Paradise Condominiums, 25
Ellen, Star Cab, Valhalla House, 84
Gloria, Blue Cab, Jubilee Village, 44
Jack, Quick Cab, Avalon Towers, 32

ALPHABET SOUP

VAPORIZED
THRILL
RANCH
SURGEON
DIAGONAL
GIMMICK
PUDDLE
MEMORY
LEARN
JUGGLE
INTERIM
DENSE
BEAUTIFY
EXCITED
DOUBLET
WINDOW
COUGH
CLOWN
BURDEN
ACCEPT
BAROQUE
BALLOONED
AUTHOR
APPROPRIATE
ANNUITY
ADVANCE

FILL-IN

U	S	E	■	C	L	I	M	B	■	M	O	A
P	O	D	■	H	O	V	E	L	■	O	W	N
S	P	I	G	O	T	■	W	A	N	T	E	D
■	■	T	A	R	■	A	S	S	E	T	■	■
W	A	I	T	E	R	S	■	T	O	O	T	H
A	L	O	E	■	A	S	P	E	N	■	O	E
G	I	N	■	S	T	E	E	D	■	S	P	A
O	N	■	S	T	E	R	E	■	S	H	I	P
N	E	V	E	R	■	T	R	O	P	I	C	S
■	■	A	R	E	A	S	■	D	U	N	■	■
B	E	S	E	T	S	■	M	O	D	E	S	T
O	R	E	■	C	I	D	E	R	■	R	I	O
Y	E	S	■	H	A	R	T	S	■	S	P	Y

SUM TOTALS

■	3	4	■	3	1	■	1	8	■	5	2	■
7	8	9	6	4	3	■	6	9	7	8	3	■
8	9	■	9	8	6	1	5	■	2	4	1	■
■	■	6	7	■	■	4	9	7	3	■	5	1
5	4	2	■	1	5	■	■	5	9	■	9	4
9	6	■	1	2	7	3	■	■	8	9	7	■
■	5	2	3	■	9	7	1	■	5	7	4	■
■	3	8	2	■	■	9	4	7	6	■	8	9
1	7	■	9	8	■	■	7	9	■	9	6	8
8	9	■	7	2	9	1	■	■	3	4	■	■
■	2	9	8	■	7	2	8	9	1	■	9	7
■	1	8	5	9	6	■	5	6	4	2	3	1
■	8	7	■	6	1	■	1	3	■	6	8	■

BRICK BY BRICK

LAIC SLEEP SELF
ODOR PARSE OMAR
RATE IRATE NINA
DRAWING PRATES
CREE SHOT
REVUES STOWAWAY
ABETS DEALS ILE
JOS SERGE NIL
ANT BABAS FOCAL
SYSTEMIC DURESS
REST CARD
ESCARP ARSENAL
CHIC APART ROMA
HATE DANTE EVEN
OWES ENDED DANK

LUCKY CLOVER

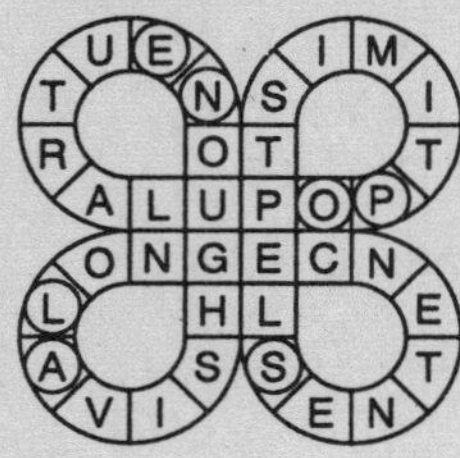

KEYWORD

VENTILATOR

NUMBER SLEUTH

WORD MERGERS

1. May, One; Yeoman.
2. Else, Hay; Eyelash.
3. Belt, Sum; Stumble.
4. Acre, Land; Calendar.
5. Reel, Tout; Roulette.
6. Stare, Vise; Assertive.
7. Drove, Pant; Davenport.
8. Cone, Drain; Ordinance.

THREE TO ONE

1. Knowledgeable, 2. Cabinet, 3. Runaround, 4. Pastorate, 5. Nightingale, 6. Sandpaper, 7. Paperback, 8. Snapdragon.

HOP, SKIP, AND JUMP

SERPENTINE

WORD CALCULATOR

1. Adrift, 2. Pocket, 3. Dahlia, 4. Island, 5. Beyond, 6. Fidget, 7. Poison, 8. Worthy.

DOUBLE TROUBLE

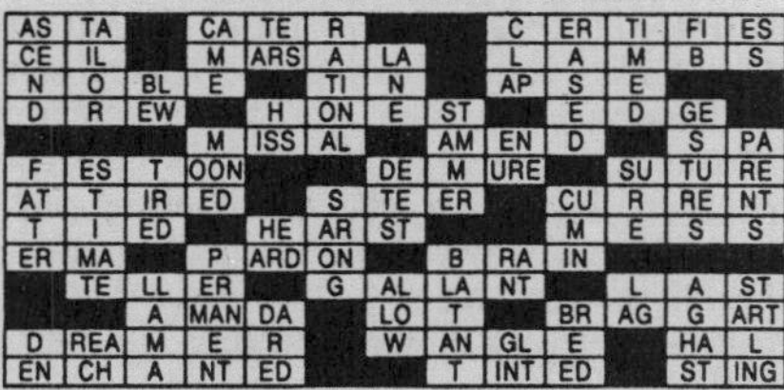

AS	TA	■	CA	TE	R	■	■	C	ER	TI	FI	ES
CE	IL	■	M	ARS	A	LA	■	L	A	M	B	S
N	O	BL	E	■	TI	N	■	AP	S	E	■	■
D	R	EW	■	H	ON	E	ST	■	E	D	GE	■
■	■	■	M	ISS	AL	■	AM	EN	D	■	S	PA
F	ES	T	OON	■	■	DE	M	URE	■	SU	TU	RE
AT	T	IR	ED	■	S	TE	ER	■	CU	R	RE	NT
T	I	ED	■	HE	AR	ST	■	■	M	E	S	S
ER	MA	■	P	ARD	ON	■	B	RA	IN	■	■	■
■	TE	LL	ER	■	G	AL	LA	NT	■	L	A	ST
■	■	A	MAN	DA	■	LO	T	■	BR	AG	G	ART
D	REA	M	E	R	■	W	AN	GL	E	■	HA	L
EN	CH	A	NT	ED	■	■	T	INT	ED	■	ST	ING

YOU KNOW THE ODDS

1. Beagle, 2. Cocker spaniel, 3. Spitz, 4. Chihuahua, 5. Skye terrier, 6. Dalmatian.

TRADE-OFF

1. Hornet, Cornet; 2. Refuge, Refuse; 3. Wonder, Wander; 4. Impact, Impart; 5. Waiver, Waiter; 6. Threat, Thread.

FLOWER POWER

C: 1. Jewel, 2. Deter, 3. Navel, 4. Saves, 5. Reese, 6. Frost, 7. Clink, 8. Grind, 9. Alien, 10. Greer, 11. Bread, 12. Trent, 13. Glass, 14. Crags, 15. Bogey, 16. Ritzy, 17. Razor, 18. Paced.

CC: 1. Jazzy, 2. Decoy, 3. Newer, 4. Sated, 5. Ravel, 6. Fever, 7. Creel, 8. Gloss, 9. Arise, 10. Glint, 11. Brink, 12. Treed, 13. Green, 14. Clear, 15. Brand, 16. Roast, 17. Riggs, 18. Pates.

THREE'S COMPANY

1. Sandbox, Slide, Swing; 2. Danson, Koppel, Turner; 3. Bunker, Fairway, Green; 4. Alder, Larch, Pine; 5. Base, Mound, Sacrifice; 6. American, Qantas, Southwest; 7. Bonanza, Cheers, M*A*S*H; 8. Delicious, Rome, Winesap; 9. Doyle, Stevenson, Twain; 10. Alter, Amend, Transform; 11. Orange, Prune, Tomato; 12. Sandburg, Shelley, Whitman; 13. Brown, Rainbow, Speckled; 14. Bowler, Fez, Tam-o'-shanter; 15. Franc, Pfennig, Shilling.

MIX AND MINGLE

1. Offspring, 2. Bandwagon, 3. Eye shadow, 4. Willpower, 5. Outskirts, 6. Red carpet, 7. Mousetrap, 8. Locksmith, 9. Overthrow.
BONUS: Elbowroom

BULL'S-EYE SPIRAL

OUT: 1. Nod, 4. Nab, 7. Aloofness, 16. Elated, 22. Rage, 26. Roots, 31. Pilot, 36. Even, 40. Ally, 44. Rebel, 49. Asp, 52. Ace, 55. Lucid, 60. Ire, 63. Well, 67. Aware, 72. Mace, 76. Diced.

IN: 80. Decide, 74. Camera, 68. Wall, 64. Ewe, 61. Ridicule, 53. Cap, 50. Sale, 46. Beryl, 41. Lane, 37. Veto, 33. Lips, 29. Too, 26. Regard, 20. Eta, 17. Lessen, 11. Fool, 7. Abandon.

ESCALATORS

1

SOLEMN	L	OMENS	S	NOME
EITHER	I	THERE	H	TREE
SOAKED	O	ASKED	A	DESK
NORMAL	N	MOLAR	R	LOAM
SPINET	S	INEPT	E	PINT

2

CARMEN	M	CRANE	R	ACNE
ORIENT	I	TENOR	O	RENT
COSTAR	C	ASTOR	O	ARTS
MAKING	K	GAMIN	N	MAGI
AGREED	E	RAGED	E	DRAG
SYDNEY	Y	DYNES	Y	SEND

3

FARMED	F	DREAM	M	DEAR
DONATE	O	DANTE	A	TEND
RETURN	R	TUNER	N	TRUE
ARGUES	E	SUGAR	A	RUGS
MANGLE	M	GLEAN	G	LANE
DIAPER	A	PRIDE	E	DRIP
ARDENT	N	TRADE	R	DATE

SECRET WORD

1. Drawl, 2. Quips, 3. Shaft, 4. Throb, 5. Strum, 6. Wager.

1. Swarm, Twine, Agile, Mints, Maine, Earns, Ridge, Ideas, Nails, Glide.
2. Wiper, Ideal, Strew, Equal, Cared, Rocks, Aesop, Cruet, Kilts, Squad.
3. Chafe, Hymns, Infer, Mince, Names, Entry, Yacht.
4. Place, Usher, Lutes, Saber, About, Trace, Epoch.
5. Guest, Unlit, Items, Trial, Angel, Realm.
6. Girls, Aglow, Miles, Brawl, Limbs, Elbow.

SYLLACROSTIC

C(harles) Haddon: By perseverance the snail reached the ark.

1. Compliment, 2. Hopscotch, 3. Anticipate, 4. Designates, 5. Decoration, 6. Opera, 7. Nairobi, 8. Bilingual, 9. Yesteryear, 10. Provolone, 11. Extravaganza, 12. Rustic, 13. Stopwatch, 14. Executive, 15. Validated, 16. Elegant, 17. Research, 18. Arrogance, 19. Novella, 20. Corridor, 21. Embark.

TURN A PHRASE

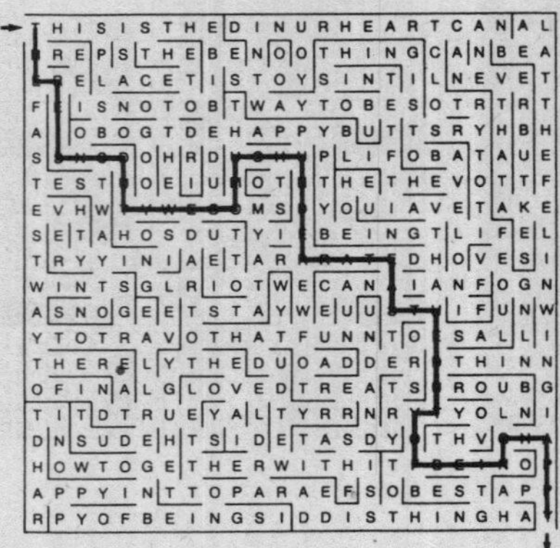

Quote: There is no duty we so much underrate as the duty of being happy.

MASTERWORDS

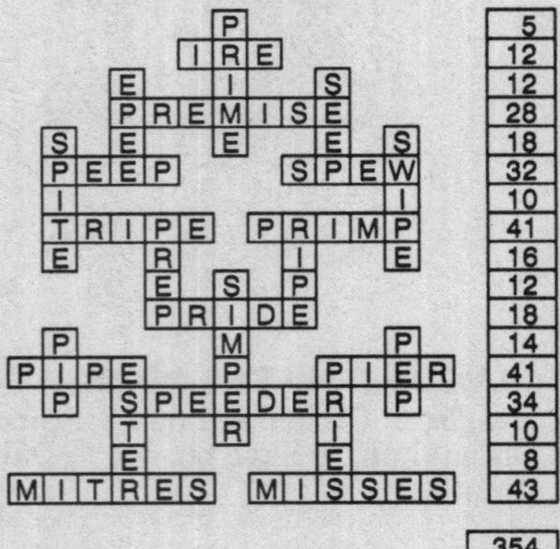

QUOTAGRAMS

A. Positive anything is better than negative nothing. (Elbert Hubbard)

B. Size is not grandeur, and territory does not make a nation. (Thomas Henry Huxley)

C. To speak ill of others is a dishonest way of praising ourselves. (Will and Ariel Durant)

A. 1. Vinegar, 2. Beehive, 3. Tight, 4. Sinning, 5. Snooty, 6. That, 7. Patient.
B. 1. Andirons, 2. Earmark, 3. Dainty, 4. Target, 5. Notorious, 6. Seize, 7. Tendon.
C. 1. Portia, 2. Lighthouse, 3. Defensive, 4. Follows, 5. Airiness, 6. Sassy, 7. Partook.

SCOREMASTER

The following is our order of play. The words before and after a slash (/) were formed in the same play. Scores are given in parentheses.

Kit (9), Ark (9), Ad (3), Skit (11), Ton (10), Adz (19), Evil/Tone (36), Weskit (16), Tube (14), Hark (14), Quiz (27), Do/Devil (41), Shark (32), Toner/Or (19), All (15), Itch (18), Quag (42), Alley (30), Snitch (66), Grope (36), Major (28), Ox (22), Soften (33).

DOUBLE TROUBLE

WORD WAYS

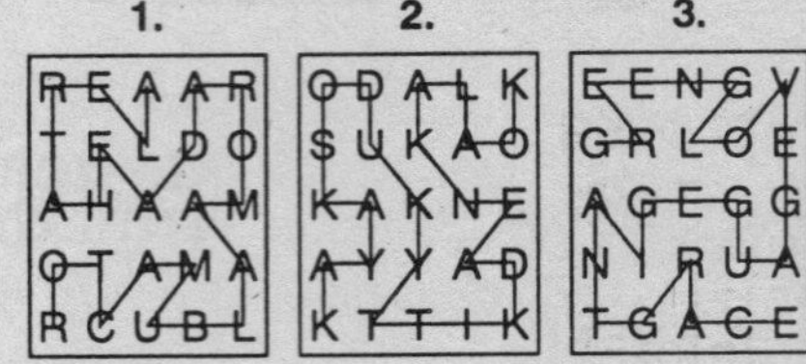

1. Alert, Ahead, Aroma, Album, Actor.
2. Koala, Knead, Kitty, Kudos, Kayak.
3. Green, Glove, Gauge, Giant, Grace.

LOGIC PROBLEM

Mos. were May, June, July, Aug., and Sept. (intro.). The piece found in Sept. [last] doesn't have the American Sweetheart (1), Victory (2), Laurel (4), or Cherry Blossom pattern (5); it has the Windsor pattern. The piece found in May [1st] doesn't have the American Sweetheart (1), Victory (2), or Cherry Blossom pattern (5); it has the Laurel pattern. The piece with the Victory pattern [found before the platter (2)] wasn't found at the antique shop [found after the platter (4)]; it was found at the yard sale (2). The piece with the Victory pattern [yard sale] was found before the platter (2), which was found before the piece discovered in the antique shop (4), so it wasn't found in Aug. or June (2,5); it was found in July, the platter was found in Aug., the piece discovered in the antique shop was found in Sept. (2,4), the piece with the Cherry Blossom pattern was found in June, and the saucer was found in May (5). The piece with the American Sweetheart pattern was found in Aug.; the creamer was found in Sept. (1). The piece discovered in the attic wasn't found in Aug., Sept., or May (1); it was found in June. The piece with the Laurel pattern wasn't discovered at the estate sale (3); it was discovered at the auction. The piece with the American Sweetheart pattern was found at the estate sale. The dinner plate doesn't have the Victory pattern (2); it has the Cherry Blossom pattern. The bowl has the Victory pattern.

In summary:
May, saucer, Laurel, auction
June, dinner plate, Cherry Blossom, friend's attic
July, bowl, Victory, yard sale
August, platter, American Sweetheart, estate sale
September, creamer, Windsor, antique shop

WORDBENDERS

CODEWORD

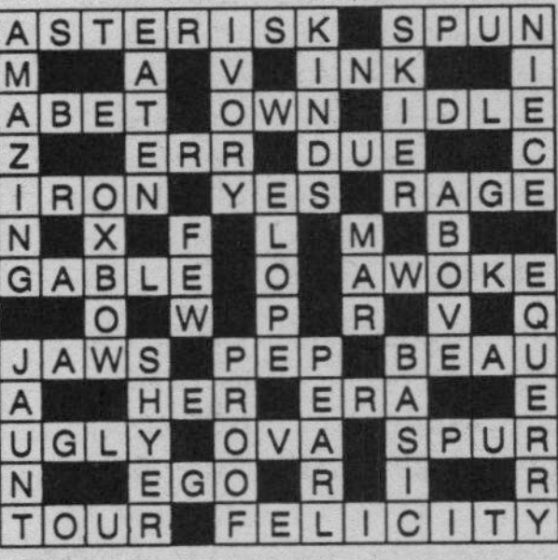

1-J, 2-D, 3-H, 4-M, 5-I, 6-P, 7-T, 8-Y, 9-A, 10-B, 11-N, 12-Q, 13-L, 14-R, 15-E, 16-S, 17-W, 18-U, 19-C, 20-K, 21-O, 22-F, 23-X, 24-G, 25-Z, 26-V.

BOWL GAME

STRIKES: 1. Prosperity, 2. Ultimately, 3. Elasticity, 4. Numerology, 5. Telecaster, 6. Watercress, 7. Conspiracy, 8. Allegiance, 9. Systematic, 10. Delightful.

SPARES: 1. Piper, Story; 2. Amity, Tulle; 3. Laity, Cites; 4. Morel, Young; 5. Crate, Sleet; 6. Scare, Strew; 7. Acorn, Spicy; 8. Canal, Liege; 9. Caste, Misty; 10. Filth, Glued.

CRYPTO-FAMILIES

1. HANG UPS: Calendar, Wallpaper, Photograph, Wind chimes, Telephone, Painting, Clothing, Pennant, Mirror, Mobile.

2. VOCALISTS: Balladeer, Crooner, Serenader, Songbird, Opera singer, Diva, Improvisator, Cantor, Caroler, Minstrel.

3. THINGS TO CUT: Prices, Bangs, Cards, Fingernails, Pie crust, Corners, Budget, Flowers, Paper dolls, Grass.

4. NOT REAL: Make-believe, Fraudulent, Simulation, Fabrication, Counterfeit, Man-made, Bogus, False, Fictitious, Imitation.

5. CITIES: Yokohama, Oshkosh, Topeka, Yonkers, Helsinki, Spokane, Jackson, Frankfurt, Tokyo, Jakarta.

6. JUST DUCKY: Eider, Mallard, Merganser, Pintail, Teal, Widgeon, Bufflehead, Harlequin, Oldsquaw, Scoter.

ALPHABET SOUP

AFTER
OBEDIENCE
MURAL
INSURANCE
LUXURIOUS
THROW
GULLIBLE
FORGET
STOUT
DYNAMITE
LUCKY
WAIVER
TABLE
TEMPO
GRAVITY
BLAZER
SQUAT
RENOVATE
ESCORT
CONDUCT
SMIRK
GROOVE
QUITE
APPREHEND
FROTH
PROJECT

BRICK BY BRICK

STARE INTO DAME
ORDER NEAR ELAN
WEASELSOUT BIND
SER COIN SATES
STUD ABET
HALO EAGLEEYED
PAPERS REAP OVA
ENID PRIED EKED
EON TEES ELDERS
PIGHEADED EASY
ASKS ELAM
OMENS AMOR LAD
WALK PIGEONHOLE
ELSE ARAN EERIE
STAR MART DREAD

SUM TOTALS

349 421 47
2183 42135 16
97 2987 7398
53 5721 12
85 18 2796
92 8496 97
4819 891 2741
16 8197 97
8324 78 89
97 7291 31
4831 9486 57
13 64921 5923
96 371 362

PLACES, PLEASE

SATEDSNSECONDSE
KOOOATIITOBORTH
YNLLLIPSCANIART
HGIELSANERNRDER
TIPLALIGJDEDADO
NWORBANLBPMARUT
DETAGILBOLDEEOS
NERYNLLRFMESALB
ODEROICLFDIDLAU
MDADDHAEEWDTIMH
EEUUETAGROWLTPE
LESSNNREIAUGYER
IETTEIHNNRATRAD
ERAAPTKTGSLOEIS
AREPOUTBOARDRUM

FILL-IN

ECHO TACT NAP
THAW ECRU ERA
NAVIGATOR AFT
ARENA INNER
GUNNY ANNA
ELI GAG STEEL
LINNET FOSSIL
LOVED PIN SLY
ANEW CIGAR
STARE TULIP
HUT MARMALADE
ORE INCA EKES
END DEED SEAT

WHIRLY WORDS

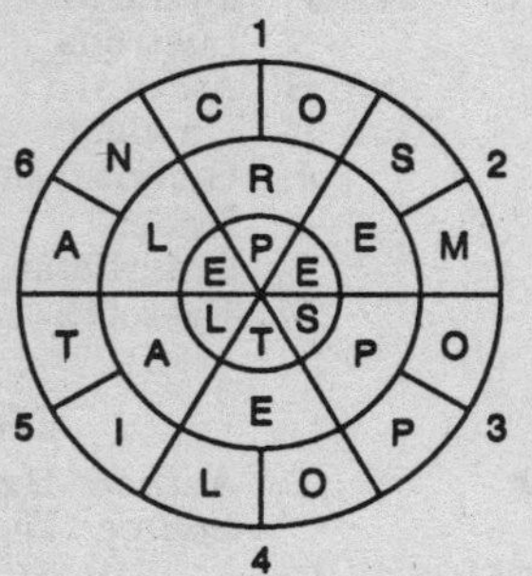

PERFECT FIT

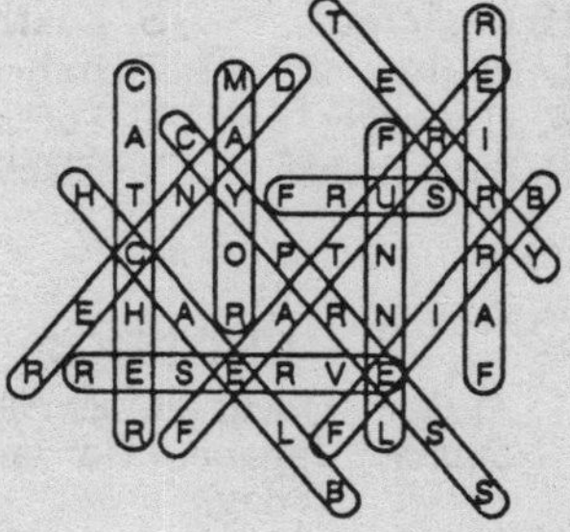

WORD MERGERS

1. Dregs, Tour; Drugstore.
2. Moat, Print; Important.
3. Inlet, Nave; Valentine.
4. Chart, Sore; Orchestra.
5. Blast, Cone; Constable.
6. Nail, Tamed; Laminated.
7. Babe, Roads; Baseboard.
8. Boar, Elate; Elaborate.

TRIANGLE SUMS

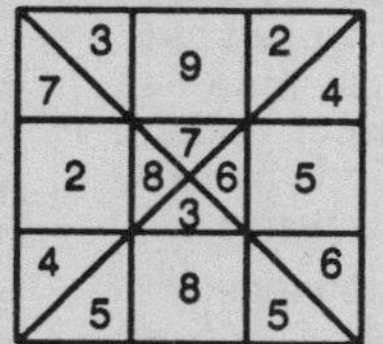

CRISSCROSS

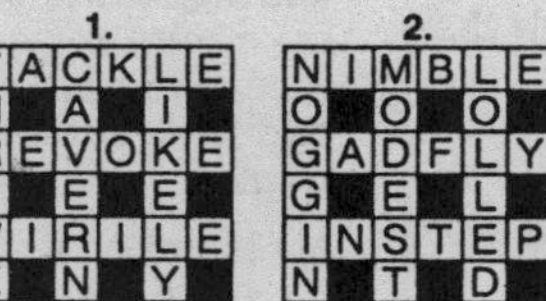

PUZZLER

LEMONADE

DAISY

Leopard, Attempt, Concept, Empathy, Nuptial, Insipid
BONUS WORD: Pelican

FRAMEWORK FIRST WORDS ACROSS

Framework 2: Affirm
Framework 3: Caution
Framework 4: 17394
Framework 5: Pole
Framework 6: Washing
Framework 7: Colony
Framework 8: Inca Maiden
Framework 9: Filter
Framework 10: Original
Framework 13: Swamp
Framework 14: Bag
Framework 15: Ivy
Framework 16: Upswing
Framework 17: Secrets
Framework 18: Popular
Framework 19: Pamphlet
Framework 20: Clergy
Framework 21: Lipstick
Framework 24: Stance
Framework 26: 4623
Framework 28: Ground
Framework 29: Oolong
Framework 30: Kipling
Framework 31: Special
Framework 32: Model
Framework 33: Yacht
Framework 34: Flowers

CODEWORD

1-U, 2-Q, 3-P, 4-V, 5-A, 6-O, 7-R, 8-Z, 9-K, 10-X, 11-L, 12-T, 13-N, 14-S, 15-H, 16-I, 17-C, 18-D, 19-J, 20-W, 21-F, 22-B, 23-E, 24-Y, 25-G, 26-M.

SECRET WORD

1. Twain, 2. Lapse, 3. Wanes, 4. Twigs, 5. Lofts, 6. Rough.

1. Timer, Orate, Morse, Swarm, Arose, Wyman, Yeast, Earns, Riots.
2. Brick, Abide, Cribs, Kilns, Slick, Larks, Incas, Drips, Epics.
3. Dials, Wield, Iowan, Norse, Drift, Lifts, Eland, Snide.
4. Bring, Right, Abets, Niche, Crane, Hinge, Ewing, Swear.
5. After, Talon, Tires, Infer, Cared, Scold.
6. Clout, Other, Argue, Riles, Sight, Eclat.

LOGIC PROBLEM

(Clue numbers in parentheses)

"Food Feasts" isn't at 12 ["Kitchen Topics" (1)], 1, or 3 p.m. [last and 2nd to last (intro.)] (6); it's at 9 or 11 a.m. It doesn't feature Antone (2), Franco ["Culinary Delights" (4)], Pierre (5), or Charles (6); it features Henri. It's not on channel 9 (6); it's on 14 [only channel left 2 more than another (intro.)] (2). It isn't aired at 11 a.m. [no channel 11 (intro.)] (3); it's aired at 9 a.m. (above). Antone's show is on channel 12 (2). The 11 a.m. show isn't on channel 7 [airs either 1 or 3 p.m. show (intro., 5)]; it's on channel 12 [only channel left 3 more than another (intro.)] (3). "Eating Healthy" is on channel 9 (3). "Kitchen Topics" [12 p.m.] isn't on channel 7 (5) or 12 [11 a.m.]; it's on 4. "Culinary Delights" [Franco] isn't on channel 12 [Antone]; it's on 7. "Smart Cooking" is on channel 12. Charles isn't on channel 9 (6); he's on 4. Pierre is on channel 9. "Eating Healthy" doesn't air at 3 p.m. [last] (4); it airs at 1 p.m. "Culinary Delights" airs at 3 p.m.

In summary, chef, show, channel, time:
Antone, "Smart Cooking," 12, 11 a.m.
Charles, "Kitchen Topics," 4, 12 p.m.
Franco, "Culinary Delights," 7, 3 p.m.
Henri, "Food Feasts," 14, 9 a.m.
Pierre, "Eating Healthy," 9, 1 p.m.

CROSTIC 1

Author: (Mark) Twain
Source: The Business of Life

Of all God's creatures there is only one that cannot be made the slave of the lash. That one is the cat. If man could be crossed with the cat, it would improve man, but it would deteriorate the cat.

A. Toccata
B. Wadsworth
C. Aviator
D. Immature
E. Needles
F. Thatch
G. Haifa
H. England
I. Brute
J. Utmost
K. Sweetheart
L. Intention
M. Naturally
N. Ebbed
O. Shepherd
P. Scotch
Q. Ovid
R. Futile
S. Loathsome
T. Itch
U. Footloose
V. Elected

CROSTIC 2

Author: David (H.) Engel
Source: Japanese Gardens (for Today)

Living close to nature is the very essence of life in Japan . . . House and garden represent the happy marriage of art and nature, and one can barely distinguish a dividing line at which the house ends and the garden begins.

A. Dachshund
B. Apiarist
C. Vainglory
D. Inlaid
E. Dependence
F. Eyesight
G. Narrate
H. Gravel
I. Edifice
J. Loose
K. Josh White
L. Andante
M. Pheasant
N. Andiron
O. Neutron
P. Emphatic
Q. Sheath
R. Effusive
S. Gander
T. Argyle
U. Reins
V. Danish
W. Entente
X. Noggin
Y. Suburb

CRYPTO-FAMILIES

1. NOTIONS: Thimble, Seam ripper, Thread, Patterns, Scissors, Bias tape, Elastic, Needles, Button, Snaps.

2. SOAK IT: Douse, Quench, Inundate, Souse, Swamp, Drown, Flood, Immerse, Drench, Submerge.

3. SUPERBOWL MVP'S: Phil Simms, Terry Bradshaw, Jim Plunkett, Ottis Anderson, Bart Starr, Doug Williams, Lynn Swann, Larry Csonka, Joe Namath, Len Dawson.

4. ANGRY WORDS: Tiff, Argument, Spat, Quarrel, Squabble, Debate, Disagreement, Altercation, Dispute, Bickering.

5. YELLOW ____: Poplar, Streak, Warbler, Light, Journalism, Perch, Jacket, Pages, Ribbon, Pine.

6. ORANGES: Hamlin, Temple, Navel, Seville, Homosossa, Valencia, Parson, St. Michael, Pineapple, Enterprise.

CROSTIC 3

Author: (Reader's) Digest
Source: Laughter (the) Best Medicine

At a party in New York, violinist Isaac Stern was introduced to Muhammad Ali. "You might say we're in the same business," said Stern, "we both earn a living with our hands." Ali eyed Stern with admiration. "You must be pretty good," he said, "there isn't a mark on you."

A. Dirigible
B. Insistent
C. Gratuity
D. Everywhere
E. Skittish
F. To the teeth
G. Lustrous
H. Awkward
I. Unwieldy
J. Gymnasium
K. Hades
L. Traditions
M. Eyetooth
N. Reasons
O. Bacon
P. Estuary
Q. Savannah
R. Trinidad
S. Marianas
T. Eyewash
U. Donne
V. Isaiah
W. Community
X. Impromptu
Y. Naiad
Z. Elbowroom

CROSTIC 4

Author: Harry Waugh
Source: Diary of a Winetaster

Every collector has to start somewhere, whatever his interest may be —china, books, wine or pictures. He usually finds one or two things that take his fancy; from time to time he sees something else he cannot resist, and then suddenly . . . he finds he has a small collection already in being.

A. Holiday
B. About-face
C. Rhinestone
D. Right whale
E. Yosemite
F. Withholds
G. Acumen
H. Unattached
I. Grass roots
J. Hyacinth
K. Docket
L. Intense
M. Artichoke
N. Red ribbon
O. Yellowlegs
P. Oodles
Q. Flivver
R. Assesses
S. Wholesaler
T. In the hole
U. Nanny
V. Enact
W. The Misfits
X. Anthracite
Y. System
Z. Tensor
a. Euphemism
b. Refinement

ROULETTE

1. Herald, 2. Robots, 3. Adonis, 4. Wallop, 5. Uppish, 6. Tulips, 7. Escrow, 8. Assign, 9. Nymphs, 10. Motion, 11. Tsetse, 12. Nutmeg, 13. Oxlip, 14. Laces, 15. Matte, 16. Throb, 17. Own, 18. Ici, 19. Imp, 20. Tam, 21. Eclat, 22. Idols, 23. Prong, 24. Hoops. OUTER RING: Herman Wouk, "The Caine Mutiny"

QUOTEFALLS

1. Fashion is that by which the fantastic becomes for a moment universal.
2. A man cannot leave a better legacy to the world than a well-educated family.
3. Blessed are those who can give without remembering and take without forgetting.
4. An efficient employee is one who keeps on his toes but never steps on the other fellow's.

CROSTIC 5

Author: D.H. Lawrence
Source: The Plumed Serpent

Life makes, and moulds, and changes the problem. The problem will always be there, and will always be different. So nothing can be solved, even by life and living, for life dissolves and resolves, solving it leaves alone.

A. Donnybrook
B. Halfway
C. Lawns
D. Addled
E. Well-nigh
F. Rhos
G. Evensong
H. Norms
I. Cabbages
J. Evade
K. Tablet
L. Hoofbeats
M. Evils
N. Philistine
O. Lively
P. Universal
Q. Mills
R. Engine
S. Damsels
T. Sniff
U. Elided
V. Revolve
W. Pillow
X. Effete
Y. Nomads
Z. Tabernacle

CROSTIC 6

Author: Tom Landry
Source: (Tom Landry:) An Autobiography

I believe most of a person's character is developed as a child. It's the result of values learned from family and other significant people early in life — which is what makes our role as parents and the role of those who coach kids so important.

A. Theatrical
B. Offshore
C. Mishmash
D. Loser
E. Assistance
F. Newsman
G. Dollop
H. Reelect
I. Yokohama
J. Affidavit
K. Nowhere
L. Allows
M. Undercover
N. Television
O. Opportune
P. Bathhouse
Q. Italic
R. Officers
S. Glimpse
T. Released
U. Aphrodite
V. Pathfinder
W. Hailstone
X. Yardstick

TOP TO BOTTOM

1. Told, Tole, Tore, Tort, Tare, Tart, Tact, Tack.
2. Chin, Chip, Chap, Chaw, Clap, Claw, Clew, Clef.

CHANGAWORD

1. Hunt, Punt, Punk, Puck, Peck.
2. Make, Take, Tape, Type, Typo.
3. Type, Tope, Tore, Wore, Word.
4. Send, Bend, Bond, Bone, None, Note.

FLOWER POWER

C: 1. Parry, 2. Paint, 3. Munch, 4. Quack, 5. Brand, 6. Tears, 7. Prado, 8. Fears, 9. Hurry, 10. Quake, 11. Boned, 12. Sunny, 13. Found, 14. Donne, 15. Saucy, 16. North, 17. Porch, 18. Farce.

CC: 1. Party, 2. Parch, 3. March, 4. Quire, 5. Bunny, 6. Tract, 7. Peach, 8. Frank, 9. Heard, 10. Quads, 11. Burro, 12. Soars, 13. Funky, 14. Donee, 15. Sound, 16. Nanny, 17. Pound, 18. Force.

CROSTIC 7

Author: (Walt) Whitman
Source: Slang in America

Language is not an abstract construction of the learned, or of dictionary makers, but is something arising out of the work, needs, ties, joys, affections, tastes of long generations of humanity.

A. Wanton
B. Hoes
C. Informal
D. Thickset
E. Misfits
F. Affright
G. Nuggets
H. Soften
I. Loan
J. Austere
K. Nourished
L. Goody Goody
M. Instigate
N. Narration
O. Attain
P. Mockery
Q. Effortless
R. Robe
S. Innocuous
T. Castanets
U. Abjection

CROSTIC 8

Author: Pierre Daninos
Source: Apres Vous

Usually when a Frenchman passes a pretty woman in the street, he first looks at her legs to see if she is really all she seemed at first glance; then he turns around to have a better view, and eventually realizes he is going in the same direction she is.

A. Powhatan
B. Inveterate
C. Enchainers
D. Refreshes
E. Runnymede
F. Eulogizing
G. Dilettante
H. Affability
I. Narcissism
J. In the money
K. Night latch
L. Osseous
M. Sweetheart
N. All the same
O. Perks
P. Rehearsed
Q. Easy street
R. Sewers
S. Villanella
T. Out of sight
U. Unleashed
V. Shovel hat

SYLLACROSTIC

June Smith: Few wishes come true by themselves.

1. Jumbo, 2. Uniform, 3. Nibble, 4. Efficient, 5. Snicker, 6. Marabou, 7. Imagine, 8. Taxicab, 9. Hardy, 10. Flagrant, 11. Embellish, 12. Wrangle, 13. Wolfram, 14. Ingenious, 15. Stampede, 16. Historical, 17. Eruv, 18. Stymie, 19. Crocus.

SCOREMASTER

									S	
					F	L	A	N	K	
			D		O				I	
H	O	W	E	V	E	R			R	
			N			A	N		T	
	B			T	U	G			E	
	I			O					D	
	S			X						T
	Q			I				J	O	Y
M	U	S	I	C	A	L				P
	E					A	Z	U	R	E

The following is our order of play. The words before and after a slash (/) were formed in the same play. Scores are given in parentheses.

Tug (6), To (6), Rag (12), Toxic (32), Ever (16), Sic (8), Foe (11), Flan (14), Music (36), Flank (60), However (36), Ski (27), Musical (51), Skirt (39), La (3), Skirted (54), Azure (39), Type (36), En (6), Joy (26), Bisque (69), Den (10), An (6).

CROSTIC 9

Author: H(enry) Kissinger
Source: White House Years

Former Secretary of State Dean Acheson, invited by then-President Nixon to participate in a council of past and present Presidential advisers, was asked afterward why the meeting had taken so long. He replied: "We are all old and we are all eloquent."

A. Handstand
B. Kid gloves
C. Infallible
D. Stiffen
E. Spoon
F. Irish stew
G. Narwhal
H. Green Acres
I. Equinox
J. Rapid-fire
K. White paper
L. Happy Days
M. Ice cream
N. Toasted
O. Entertain
P. Hearst
Q. Overawed
R. Up-to-date
S. Sea lane
T. Ennead
U. Yellow card
V. Edmonton
W. Alternate
X. Rocket
Y. Settled in

CROSTIC 10

Author: S(am) Levenson
Source: Everything but Money

I learned from experience that if there was something lacking it might turn up if I went after it, saved up for it, worked for it, but never if I just waited for it. Of course you had to be lucky, too, but I discovered . . . the more I hustled the luckier I seemed to get.

A. Suggestion
B. Limbo
C. Exact
D. Verdure
E. Ethiopia
F. Neediest
G. Staff
H. Outwitted
I. Necktie
J. Effective
K. Voodoo
L. Empire
M. Racetrack
N. Yiddish
O. Truthful
P. Humidified
Q. Injurious
R. Northwest
S. Grackle
T. Bitterroot
U. Uther
V. Tholepin
W. Mafia
X. Otherwise
Y. Network
Z. Effulged
a. Ytterbium

CHANGAWORD

1. Slip, Snip, Snit, Knit, Knot.
2. Fire, Hire, Hare, Hale, Sale.
3. East, Past, Pant, Want, Wand, Wind.
4. Tail, Tall, Ball, Bale, Bane, Bone.

SECRET WORD

1. Spray, 2. Braid, 3. Trade, 4. Tramp, 5. China, 6. Blond.

1. Diets, Rapid, Irony, Zones, Zesty, Leaps, Elton; 2. Earns, Nobel, Table, Welts, Ideas, Norse, Endow; 3. Crude, Oscar, Music, Miser, Emits, Roams, Comet, Edict; 4. Venom, Apron, Gable, Among, Bland, Oater, Novel, Depot; 5. Draws, Irons, Noise, Nader, Enact, Rowed, Witch, Aster, Roast, Earth; 6. Fable, Abhor, Infer, Robin, Heart, Abide, Ideal, Radio, Edith, Dealt.

CROSTIC 11

Author: (Lucy) Montgomery
Source: Anne of Green Gables

Isn't it splendid to think of all the things there are to find out about? It just makes me feel glad to be alive—such an interesting world. It wouldn't be half so interesting if we knew all about everything, would it? There'd be no scope for imagination, then, would there?

A. Mite
B. Outlandish
C. Nightshade
D. Twinkle
E. Golden Girl
F. Oblivious
G. Meerschaum
H. Entitle
I. Ratite
J. Yeti
K. Affidavit
L. No-hitter
M. Nikita
N. Earth Angel
O. Outflow
P. Flubbed
Q. Gowen
R. Rites
S. Elton John
T. Enthusiast
U. New Bedford
V. Good Sports
W. Authentic
X. Button-down
Y. Like new
Z. Elle
a. Stepfather

CROSTIC 12

Author: A(braham) A. Davidson
Source: (The Story of) American Painting

Paul Revere . . . best remembered for his famous ride from Boston to Lexington . . . was a metalsmith and engraver; he designed the first seal for the United Colonies and later designed and printed the first Continental bond issue.

A. Afterward
B. Agree
C. Do-si-do
D. Assemble
E. Varnish
F. In stitches
G. Desert
H. Shoo-in
I. Off-limits
J. Number
K. At long last
L. Moment
M. Evergreen
N. Redden
O. Interlude
P. Chiffon
Q. Alphabet
R. Nodded
S. Prods
T. Abate
U. Interest
V. Nation
W. Textile
X. Infer
Y. Nursed
Z. Gumshoe

WORD MATH

	0	1	2	3	4	5	6	7	8	9
1.	F	L	A	S	H	P	O	I	N	T
2.	L	A	M	B	R	E	Q	U	I	N
3.	J	O	C	U	L	A	R	I	T	Y
4.	C	H	E	V	R	O	T	A	I	N
5.	S	U	Z	E	R	A	I	N	T	Y
6.	C	O	E	Q	U	A	L	I	T	Y

BOWL GAME

STRIKES: 1. Headmaster, 2. Noticeable, 3. Pedestrian, 4. Tournament, 5. Specialist, 6. Competitor, 7. Liberation, 8. Decorative, 9. Importance, 10. Forecaster.

SPARES: 1. Dream, Haste; 2. Bacon, Elite; 3. Drain, Steep; 4. Otter, Unman; 5. Aspic, Islet; 6. Motto, Price; 7. Alien, Orbit; 8. Trace, Video; 9. Cream, Point; 10. Farce, Store.

CROSTIC 13

Author: D(ebby) Wood
Source: (For Fathers, It Really Is) The Thought That Counts (Shopper, 6/90)

As Father's Day fast approaches, I've come to realize that my husband is no longer hard to buy for . . . He's impossible! There's nothing he needs. And what he doesn't need, he doesn't want. I'd rather shop for Donald Trump!

A. Dabbed
B. Warns
C. Offshoot
D. Obeyed
E. Dovetail
F. Thinned
G. Hens
H. Erase
I. Tarzan
J. Hillary
K. Ostend
L. Upholds
M. Giraffe
N. Hammered
O. Through
P. Thirsty
Q. Honored
R. Athos
S. Transoms
T. Chopped
U. Operatic
V. Unwanted
W. Names
X. Thespians
Y. Seethe

CROSTIC 14

Author: Velma Sykes
Source: Why Ridicule Him?

We laugh at Ponce de Leon—
That fountain which he sought
Was but a myth, yet we must own
Though his search came to naught,
Most of us seek the self-same thing
And for the self-same reason,
To put off Age, endeavoring
To keep Youth beyond its season.

A. Vendetta
B. Egghead
C. Laugh track
D. Mammoth
E. Awesome
F. Shipshape
G. Yachtsman
H. Know about
I. Establish
J. Show-off
K. Whodunit
L. Hottentot
M. Yoo-hoo
N. Repentant
O. Iowa State
P. Doughnut
Q. Ingress
R. Chauffeur
S. Usefulness
T. Lenses
U. Eyeteeth
V. Haughty
W. In effect
X. Mongoose

SUM WORDS

1. Conestoga, 2. Serenade, 3. Punctual, 4. Monastery.

SCOREBOARD

	W	H	O	M						
		A		A	C	T	I	O	*	S
		T			O			N	U	
		S	E	Q	U	I	*		T	
			P		N					
	A	L	O	F	T			V		
	Z	A	X			B	R	I	D	E
J	U	R	Y			A		N		
	R					L		E	K	E
D	E	S	I	G	N	E	R	S		
O										

The following is our order of play. The words before and after a slash (/) were formed in the same play. Our running tally is in parentheses.

Oft (3), Loft (7), Aloft (18), Azure (29), Zax/La/Ox (41), Design (67), Designer (112), Pox (118), Epoxy (128), Count (133), Sequin (147), Hats (152), Jury/Lar (159), Vines/Designers (212), Who (218), Act (226), Whom/Ma (241), Eke (248), Action (270), Ride (278), Bale/Bride (301), Nut (306), On/Nu (314), Do (323), Actions (347).

CROSTIC 15

Author: Charles L. Adams
Source: All in a Day's Work (Reader's Digest June 1990)

Reading water meters in an unfamiliar part of town, I came upon a house with no number. Then I noticed an elderly man gardening at the first house on that block. "Excuse me," I said to him. "Are you Number One?" He smiled and replied, "My wife thinks so!"

A. Chauffeur
B. Hibernian
C. Affable
D. Reemerge
E. Lied
F. Excitement
G. Sharpen
H. Lime
I. Answer
J. Dishwasher
K. Author
L. Modem
M. Shine
N. Annotate
O. Lugubrious
P. Loman
Q. Inaptitude
R. Noone
S. Amendment
T. Diminution
U. Arch
V. Yardstick
W. Showman
X. Wits
Y. Ontology
Z. Riptide
a. Keynote

CROSTIC 16

Author: (Bennett) Cerf
Source: (Bennett Cerf's) Treasury of Atrocious Puns

A magician and his wife whom he was wont to saw in half as the climax of the act, retired after a full twenty years on the vaudeville circuit, and opened a dairy outside Los Angeles. The sign over the doorway reads, "Milk sold . . . by the half gal."

A. Chow chow
B. Estimate
C. Rhone
D. Flashy
E. Toots
F. Rotates
G. Exhalation
H. Amish
I. Sweetened
J. Unabridged
K. Ready
L. Yachting
M. Official
N. Flawless
O. Awards
P. Thief
Q. Roan
R. Overview
S. Changed
T. Illegal
U. Overheated
V. Ultimatum
W. Swathed
X. Polly
Y. Ukrainian
Z. Nifty
a. Saddle

SPLIT PERSONALITIES

1. Hyacinth, 2. Zinnia, 3. Violet, 4. Geranium, 5. Dahlia, 6. Morning glory, 7. Orchid, 8. Marigold, 9. Snapdragon, 10. Periwinkle.

QUOTAGRAMS

A. Most of us hate to see a poor loser—or a rich winner. (Harold Coffin)
B. The wheel was man's greatest invention until he got behind it. (Bill Ireland)
C. A pessimist is a person who is always building dungeons in the air.

A. 1. Moonshine, 2. Teacher, 3. Proof, 4. Swear, 5. Tour, 6. Sailor, 7. Toes.
B. 1. Tremendous, 2. Investigate, 3. Whitewash, 4. Notable, 5. Linen, 6. Tent, 7. High.
C. 1. Eyelids, 2. Proposition, 3. Washing, 4. Business, 5. Hawaiian, 6. Mustard, 7. Single.

CROSTIC 17

Author: (Mark) Van Doren
Source: Liberal Education

We like a great memory. Memory performs the impossible for man; holds together past and present, gives continuity and dignity to human life. This is the companion, this is the tutor, the poet, the library, with which you travel.

A. Vaudeville
B. Aright
C. Newspaper
D. Dhoti
E. Oftentimes
F. Rhyme
G. Emissary
H. Now and then
I. Lithesome
J. Imprimatur
K. Broth
L. Etiology
M. Ratio
N. Attorney
O. Lowest
P. Esteem
Q. Dimes
R. Umpteenth
S. Choppy
T. Airtight
U. Thrifty
V. Infrasonic
W. Oshkosh
X. Nightclub

CROSTIC 18

Author: R(obert) A(rthur) Cutter
Source: (The) New Guide to Motorcycling

There is a definite mystique to owning a motorcycle. It is something that puts you apart from the crowd, even in cycle-crazy areas like California. It is a mystique that should remain no matter how many machines take to the roads and hills, no matter how many people end up as riders.

A. Ramshackle
B. Anonymous
C. Cat's cradle
D. Up in the air
E. Thermostat
F. Tartan
G. Epitomize
H. Require
I. Noised
J. Eyewitness
K. White water
L. Gifts
M. Unfamiliar
N. Infinity
O. Dishcloth
P. Enhance
Q. Tosca
R. Overwhelm
S. Moneymaker
T. Oddity
U. Toddy
V. Oomph
W. Roast
X. Choosy
Y. Yarmouth
Z. Caique
a. Latent
b. Impartial
c. Naples
d. Gents

LETTER POWER

1. Colorado (11), 2. Oolong (19), 3. Mongoose (31), 4. Leonora (33), 5. London (40), 6. Monopoly (60), 7. Woodwind (53), 8. Solomon (79), 9. Bronco (60), 10. Dogwood (92).

QUOTEFALLS

1. Parent to teen-aged children: Don't go to a lot of trouble on my account.
2. If you can't say anything nice about someone, you're probably a lot of fun to talk to.
3. Research shows that tall men are just as short at the end of the month as anybody else.
4. Poise is the presence of mind to continue talking while the other person picks up the check.